Addison-Wesley

Geometry

Stanley R. Clemens
Phares G. O'Daffer
Thomas J. Cooney
John A. Dossey

ADDISON-WESLEY PUBLISHING COMPANY

Menlo Park, California · Reading, Massachusetts · New York
Don Mills, Ontario · Wokingham, England · Amsterdam · Bonn
Sydney · Singapore · Tokyo · Madrid · San Juan

ISBN 0-201-29022-7

4 5 6 7 8 9 10-VH-95 94 93

Authors

Stanley R. Clemens is Professor of Mathematics at Bluffton College. He received a B.A. from Bluffton College, an M.A. from Indiana University, and a Ph.D. in Mathematics from the University of North Carolina. Dr. Clemens has written several journal articles and co-authored *Laboratory Investigations in Geometry* and *Geometry: An Investigative Approach*, both published by Addison-Wesley.

Phares G. O'Daffer is Professor Emeritus of Mathematics at Illinois State University. He received a B.A. and an M.A. in mathematics from Illinois State University, and a Ph.D. in Mathematics Education from the University of Illinois. Formerly a high school teacher, Dr. O'Daffer is the author or co-author of numerous articles and textbooks, including *Experiences With Geometry, Laboratory Investigations in Geometry,* and *Geometry: An Investigative Approach,* all published by Addison-Wesley. He has also served as president of the Illinois Council of Teachers of Mathematics.

Thomas J. Cooney is Professor of Mathematics Education at the University of Georgia. A former high school mathematics teacher who taught geometry for six years, he received a B.A. and an M.A. from the University of Toledo and a Ph.D. in Mathematics Education from the University of Illinois. Dr. Cooney is a member of the Evaluation Working Group for the development of the Curriculum and Evaluation Standards for the National Council of Mathematics Teachers, and is Issue Editor for the 1990 NCTM yearbook. He has numerous publications on teaching mathematics and is a frequent speaker at national and international meetings.

John A. Dossey is Professor of Mathematics at Illinois State University, where he received a B.A. and an M.A.; he received a Ph.D. from the University of Illinois. He has taught at every level from grade 7 through graduate school and has been a K–12 supervisor of mathematics. During 1986–88, Dr. Dossey served as President of NCTM. He has also served on the Mathematics Science Education Board, the National Research Council, and the Mathematical Association of America's Board of Governors. He is co-author of *Addison-Wesley Essentials of Mathematics*.

Contents

1   Basic Ideas of Geometry

2   Introduction to Proof

3   Parallel Lines and Planes

4   Congruent Triangles

5   Using Congruent Triangles and Parallel Lines

6   Similarity

7 Right Triangles

8 Circles

9 Constructions and Loci

10 Area and Perimeter of Polygons

11 Surface Area and Volume

12 Coordinate Geometry

13 Transformations

Basic Ideas of Geometry

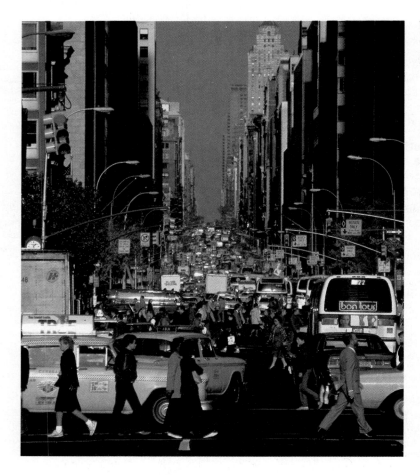

What concepts of geometry can you find in this street scene?

DEFINITIONS AND POSTULATES

OBJECTIVE: *Name, describe, and draw models for points, lines, and planes and use these terms to define some basic relationships.*

1-1 Points, Lines, Planes, and Space

As you learn about geometry, you will see that it is useful in many occupations and can help you develop your ability to discover, organize, and reason carefully. To begin your study of geometry, you need to understand the meaning of three basic terms—point, line, and plane.

Think of a **point** as a location, such as a dot on a map or on a computer. A point has no size but can be represented by a dot labeled with a capital letter. Point A, point B, point C are shown below.

Some computers use a string of very small dots, or "bits," to show lines. This suggests the idea that a line is a set of points.

A •

   • C

   • B

A **line,** like all geometric figures, is an infinite set of points. This idea is understood by thinking of straightness as suggested by the string of very small dots on the computer screen. A line has no thickness. A line is named by a lower-case letter or by any two points on the line. The double arrow indicates that the line continues without end in both directions.

line ℓ, $\overleftrightarrow{AB}$, or $\overleftrightarrow{BA}$

A **plane** is also an infinite set of points. This idea is understood by thinking of flatness as suggested by a table top extending in all directions without bound. A plane has no thickness and is named by a capital letter or three points not in a straight line. *Point, line,* and *plane* are called undefined terms in geometry. Some relationships between points, lines, and planes are also described using terms that are not defined, such as those in italics below.

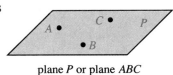

plane P or plane ABC

Point A is *on* line ℓ.
A, B, and C, are *in* line ℓ.
ℓ *contains* A, B, and C.
ℓ *passes through* A, B, and C.
B is *between* A and C.

Point C and line n are *in* plane R.
Plane R *contains* C and n.

It is important to understand that for a point to be *between* two other points as described above, all three points must be on the same line.

Definitions use undefined terms, previously defined terms, and ordinary words to give clear meaning to terms used in geometry. For example, the undefined term "point" is used to define space: **space** is the set of all points.

The following definitions describe other relationships with points, lines, and planes.

Collinear points are points all in one line. Points that are not in one line are called **noncollinear points.**

Coplanar points are points all in one plane. Points that are not in the same plane are called **noncoplanar points.** Similarly, **coplanar lines** are lines all in one plane. These ideas are illustrated in this figure.

The **intersection** of two figures is the set of points both figures have in common.

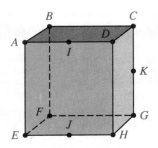

A, I, and D are collinear.
A, B, and C are noncollinear.
E, F, G, and H are coplanar.
A, B, D, and E are noncoplanar.
$\overleftrightarrow{AB}$ and $\overleftrightarrow{AD}$ are coplanar.

Example

Use symbols to describe the intersection of planes P and Q.

Solution

The intersection of planes P and Q is $\overleftrightarrow{CD}$.

Try This

Use symbols to describe the intersection of $\overleftrightarrow{AB}$ and $\overleftrightarrow{CD}$.

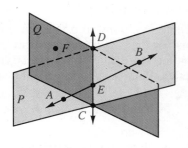

A **postulate** is a statement that is accepted as true without proof. The following postulates give some basic relationships among points, lines, planes, and space. Note that "two points (lines, planes)" means "two *different* points (lines, planes)."

● **POSTULATE 1**

A line, a plane, and space each contain an infinite number of points. Some points in a plane are noncollinear. Some points in space are noncoplanar.

● **POSTULATE 2**

For any two points, there is exactly one line containing them.

● **POSTULATE 3**

For any three noncollinear points, there is exactly one plane containing them.

● **POSTULATE 4**

If two points are in a plane, then the line containing them is in the plane.

● **POSTULATE 5**

If two planes intersect, then they intersect in exactly one line.

The following is a **convincing argument** that two lines cannot intersect in more than one point.

Two lines, ℓ and m, cannot intersect in two or more points. If they could, you would have two points that have more than one line containing them. This contradicts Postulate 2.

Class Exercises

Short Answer

1. Name real-world objects that suggest points, lines, and planes.
2. Give five different names for this line.
3. Two lines that have a point in common are called __?__ lines.
4. Three points that are all on a line are __?__ points.
5. Four points that are not in the same plane are __?__ points.

Sample Exercises

6. Name four sets of three collinear points.
7. Name two sets of three noncollinear points.
8. Name three pairs of intersecting lines. Give the points of intersection.
9. Name two points between *K* and *P*. Why is point *L* not between points *K* and *P*?

10. Name three sets of four points that are coplanar.
11. Name two coplanar lines.
12. Use three points in each plane to name a pair of intersecting planes. Name the line of intersection.

13. Draw and label a diagram showing four coplanar points, *G*, *H*, *I*, and *J*.
14. State the postulate that asserts that this statement is true. You can name as many points as you wish on a line.

Discussion

15. Think of this formation of geese flying south in the winter as a set of points. Use the words collinear, noncollinear, coplanar, and noncoplanar to describe the situation.
16. Use the postulates to give a convincing argument that the existence of a line and a point not on the line is enough to establish the existence of an infinite number of lines.

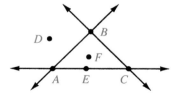

Exercises

A

Write each of the following using symbols.

1. the line containing points *A* and *B*
2. a point not on $\overleftrightarrow{AC}$
3. a pair of lines that intersect at point *A*
4. a point on $\overrightarrow{AC}$ but not on $\overrightarrow{BC}$
5. a point between *A* and *C*

Draw and label each figure.

6. two points, *J* and *K*
7. three noncollinear points: *R*, *S*, and *T*
8. $\overleftrightarrow{GH}$
9. line ℓ containing points *M*, *N*, and *Q*
10. plane *R* containing points *A* and *B*
11. $\overleftrightarrow{CD}$ and $\overleftrightarrow{EF}$, intersecting at point *Z*
12. three collinear points: *C*, *D*, and *E*
13. point *L* between points *S* and *T*

Determine whether each statement is true or false.

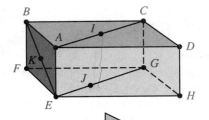

14. Points E, J, and G are collinear.
15. Points A, F, and H are coplanar.
16. Plane ABC intersects plane AIJ in $\overleftrightarrow{AC}$.
17. $\overleftrightarrow{IJ}$ intersects $\overleftrightarrow{EG}$ at point I.

Complete each statement.

18. The intersection of $\overleftrightarrow{MK}$ and $\overleftrightarrow{NP}$ is ___.
19. The intersection of plane R and plane S is ___.
20. Line ___ intersects plane S in only one point.

State the postulate that asserts that each statement is true.

21. Point A and B are on $\overleftrightarrow{AB}$ and are not both on any other line.
22. When planes P and Q have line ℓ in common, they have no other line in common.
23. When points A and B are in plane R, $\overleftrightarrow{AB}$ is also in plane R.
24. When three noncollinear points A, B, and C are in plane P, all three are in no other plane.
25. A carpenter often needs to make a straight line. To do this, he stretches a taut chalkline from point A to point B and snaps the string to form a straight line. Which postulate does this suggest?

B

Determine whether each statement is true or false. If false, explain why.

26. Three collinear points are always coplanar.
27. Three coplanar points are always collinear.
28. Any three points are coplanar.
29. When A is between C and D, the three points are collinear.
30. It is possible to have four coplanar points, no three of which are collinear.
31. Space may contain more, but not less, than four noncoplanar points.

Given the first statement, state the postulate that allows you to conclude that the second statement is true.

32. Two planes, M and N, both contain line ℓ. Therefore it is impossible for planes M and N both to contain another line, m.
33. Two lines, ℓ and m, both contain point A. Therefore it is impossible for lines ℓ and m both to contain another point, B.
34. Three noncollinear points A, B, and C are contained in plane M. Therefore points A, B, and C cannot all be contained in another plane, N.
35. A and B are points in plane M. Therefore, every point of $\overleftrightarrow{AB}$ is in plane M.

36. A photographer uses a tripod to hold a camera. Explain why a tripod has three legs instead of four. Which postulate applies to this situation?

C

37. Make drawings, when possible, to show that four coplanar lines can be drawn to intersect in only

    a. 1 point   **b.** 2 points   **c.** 3 points   **d.** 4 points   **e.** 5 points   **f.** 6 points

38. List 12 different sets of four coplanar points for this cube. List the letters in each set alphabetically.

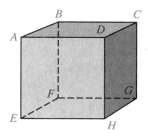

Critical Thinking

39. Points U, V, W, X, and Y are collinear. How many line segments are determined?

40. When one line is drawn through each pair of points, three points determine at most three lines. Give a convincing argument that n points determine at most $\dfrac{n(n-1)}{2}$ lines.

Algebra Review

Simplify.

1. $|3|$ **2.** $|-6|$ **3.** $|7.5|$ **4.** $|-10|$

5. $|0|$ **6.** $|7-3|$ **7.** $|4-9|$ **8.** $|-3-4|$

9. $|5-(-2)|$ **10.** $|-1-1|$ **11.** $|-2-(-4)|$ **12.** $|6-6|$

Study Skills

Every math subject in high school has its own special language. Geometry is no different. During your study of geometry, you will need to understand the meaning of many unfamiliar words used throughout this text. The more you understand the language of geometry, the more you will be able to develop skills in critical thinking, logical reasoning, and problem solving.

A good way to learn new terms and symbols is to keep track of them in a notebook or on flashcards. Then, you can always refer to your notebook or flashcards if necessary. Writing down a term and its symbol can also help you remember what the symbol means.

Here is a helpful format to use.

Term	Definition	Example/Figure	Symbol
angle	a figure consisting of two noncollinear rays with a common endpoint		$\angle A$ $\angle BAC$ $\angle CAB$
congruent segments	segments that have the same length		$\overline{AB} \cong \overline{BC}$

A format similar to the one above can be used for keeping track of geometric formulas.

1-2 Distance and Segment Measure

EXPLORE

Mark a pair of points on a sheet of paper. Find the distance between the points without laying one end of the ruler on a point. Try this with several pairs of points.

Can you state a generalization for finding the distance?

In algebra, you learned that the points on a line can be matched one-to-one with real numbers. A number that corresponds to a point on the line is the **coordinate** of that point. For example, the coordinate of point C below is -3.

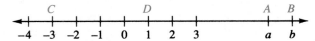

In geometry, you can use these ideas to understand distance. As you may have discovered in the Explore, the **distance** AB between any two points A and B with coordinates a and b on a number line is found as follows.

$$AB = |a - b| \quad \text{or} \quad AB = |b - a|$$

For example, on the number line above,

$$CD = |-3 - 1| = |-4| = 4 \quad \text{or} \quad CD = |1 - (-3)| = |4| = 4$$

The following postulate summarizes these ideas about distance.

● **POSTULATE 6** Ruler Postulate

The points on a line can be matched one-to-one with real-number coordinates so that

a. for any two points there corresponds a unique positive number, called the distance between the two points;

b. the distance between any two points is the absolute value of the difference of their coordinates.

Example 1

Find the distance between R and S.

Solution

$$RS = |-1.5 - 2| = |-3.5| = 3.5$$

Try This

Find the distance between T and U.

A **segment** is a set of points consisting of two points, called **endpoints,** and all the points between these points.

A segment is named by its endpoints. Write $\overline{AB}$ or $\overline{BA}$ to name the segment with endpoints A and B. The **length of a segment** is the positive real number that is the distance between its endpoints. The length of $\overline{AB}$ is written as AB.

The following postulate ensures that the lengths of parts of a segment can be added to give the length of the whole segment.

● POSTULATE 7 Segment Addition Postulate

If Q is between P and R, then $PQ + QR = PR$.

Example 2

Q is between P and R.   Find PQ.

Solution

$2x + (x + 9) = 30$ *Use the Segment Addition Postulate*
$3x + 9 = 30$ *($PQ + QR = PR$) to write the equation.*
$3x = 21$
$x = 7$
$PQ = 2x = 2(7) = 14$

Try This

Find QR and check to see if $PQ + QR = PR$.

You have used a single real-number coordinate to describe the location of a point on a line. An ordered pair (x, y) of numbers, called **coordinates,** can be used to describe the location of a point in the plane. For example, a horizontal **x-axis** and a vertical **y-axis** have been used here to graph $\overline{AB}$. The coordinates of the endpoints of $\overline{AB}$ are $(2, 1)$ and $(4, 3)$.

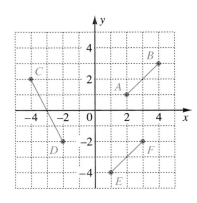

Example 3

Give the coordinates of the endpoints of $\overline{CD}$ and the coordinates of a point between C and D.

Solution

The coordinates of C are $(-4, 2)$; the coordinates of D are $(-2, -2)$; the point with coordinates $(-3, 0)$ is between C and D.

Try This

Give the coordinates of the endpoints of $\overline{EF}$ and the coordinates of a point between E and F.

Class Exercises

Short Answer

(Ex. 1–10, 13)

Give the coordinate of each of the following.

1. point G 2. point F 3. point A

Name the point with the given coordinate.

4. -1 5. 6   6. $-4\frac{1}{2}$
7. Complete the following to find AE. $|-6 - ?| = ?$
8. The distance between points D and H is ___ .
9. Between which two points is the point with coordinate -1.73?
10. Give three numbers that are coordinates for points between G and H.

11. A segment is a set of __?__ . The length of a segment is a __?__ .
12. Which postulate allows us to say that $DF = 9$?

Sample Exercises

13. Find BG on the number line used in Exercises 1–10.

Find the distance between each pair of points with the given coordinates.

14. 17, 32   15. $-9, 13$ 16. $-6.2, -8.7$ 17. $7\frac{3}{4}, -4\frac{1}{2}$

18. F is between T and R. $TF = 3x$, $FR = 4x - 2$, $TR = 54$
    Find TF and FR.

19. If $PQ + QR = PR$, which of the points P, Q, or R is between the other two?
20. Use the Segment Addition Postulate to give an addition equation and two subtraction equations that are true about the lengths x, y, and z of segments in this figure.

Discussion

21. Describe the difference in meaning between $\overline{AB}$, $\overleftrightarrow{AB}$, and AB.
22. A student claimed that the Ruler Postulate makes every line in the plane a "number line ruler." Do you think this is true? If so, give a convincing argument why or why not.
23. Find the lengths of the four segments shown. Can you give a rule for finding the length of a horizontal segment with endpoint coordinates (a, c) and (b, c)? a vertical segment with endpoint coordinates (w, s) and (w, t)?

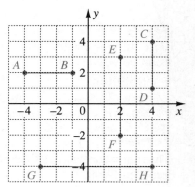

Exercises

A

Find each distance on the number line.

A B C D E F G H I J K L M N P
-21 -18 -15 -12 -9 -6 -3 0 3 6 9 12 15 18 21

1. KN **2.** PH **3.** FJ **4.** DI **5.** DA
6. AF **7.** BN **8.** IC **9.** CP **10.** DK

Find the distance between each pair of points with the given coordinates.

11. 15, 12 **12.** 14, 28 **13.** 33, 12 **14.** 17, 0 **15.** 13, 21
16. -15, 13 **17.** 19, -12 **18.** -13, -17 **19.** $-5\frac{1}{2}$, $8\frac{3}{4}$ **20.** 7.26, -8.7

Write and solve an equation to find the length of each segment.

21. $AB = x$, $BC = 2x$, $AC = 18$ Find AB and BC.
22. $AB = y - 2$, $BC = y$, $AC = 22$ Find AB and BC.
23. $EB = x$, $BD = 30$, $ED = 4x + 6$ Find EB and ED.
24. $BD = t + 9$, $EB = t$, $ED = 31$ Find BD and EB.

25. B is between A and C. $AB = 2x$, $BC = 3x - 1$, $AC = 14$
Find AB and BC.
26. T is between R and S. $RT = 2x$, $TS = 4$, $RS = 3x - 1$
Find RS and RT.
27. A basketball coach is interested in measuring a player's vertical jumping
ability. While standing and reaching up, the player's hand reaches the
4-in. mark on the scale. When jumping, the player can reach the 19-in.
mark. What is the player's vertical jumping ability?

B

Use the segment lengths in the figure to evaluate each expression.

28. $AC + BD$ **29.** $AD - AB$
30. $(AD - CD) + AC$ **31.** $(AC - BD) + BC$

A   B   C D
  6   13   4

**Points A, B, and C are collinear. The lengths of certain segments
are given. Which point is between the other two?**

32. $AC = 4$, $CB = 8$, $AB = 12$ **33.** $BA = 9$, $BC = 12$, $AC = 3$
34. $AC = 26$, $BC = 19$ Find the coordinates a and b.

A   B   C
a   b   54

35. $DE = EF$ Find e.

D   E   F
-7   e   13

A, B, and C are collinear points with coordinates a, b, and c.

36. If $b = -10$, $c = 4$, and $BA = 287$, find BC and CA. Give two possible
answers. How many answers are possible?
37. C is between A and B. $AC = CB$, $CB = 10$, $c = 14$
Give two possible coordinates for A.
38. B is between A and C. $AB = \frac{1}{5}BC$, $AC = 18$ Find AB and BC.
39. A is between B and C. $AB = \frac{1}{6}BC$, $AC = 25$ Find AB and BC.

C

Find the value of the variable.

40. $AB = 3x - 4$, $AC = 40$, $AB = BC$
41. $BC = 2x^2$, $AC = 64$, $AB = BC$
42. $FE = 2x$, $EC = x^2$, $FC = 24$

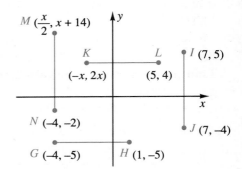

43. Find the length of $\overline{GH}$, $\overline{IJ}$, $\overline{KL}$, and $\overline{MN}$.

44. Points B and C divide $\overline{AD}$ in the ratio 8:5:3. $AD = 48$
Show that $AB = BD$. (HINT: Let $AB = 8x$.)

Critical Thinking

45. Draw two different figures, each of which satisfies all these
conditions. How are the figures related?
a. There are five points A, B, C, D, and E all collinear.
b. $CA = AD$.   **c.** $AB = BC$ **d.** $AD = DE$
e. E is not between C and D.

46. Give the coordinates, a and b, of two points that are close together on
the number line. A student claimed that no matter how close together a
pair of points are chosen, the point with coordinate $\frac{(a + b)}{2}$ would be
between them. Try some examples. Do you think the student's claim is
true? Give a convincing argument to support your conclusion.

Algebra Review

Solve for x.

1. $5x + 2x = 49$ **2.** $3x - 2 + x = 14$
3. $12x - (7x - 1) = 66$ **4.** $8x + 1 - (4x + 2) = 3x$

Computer Activity

This BASIC program finds the length of a segment on the number line given
the coordinates of its endpoints.

```
10 REM FIND SEGMENT LENGTH ON A NUMBER LINE
20 INPUT "ENTER TWO COORDINATES  "; A,B
30 PRINT " THE LENGTH OF THE SEGMENT IS  "; ABS(A−B)
40 END
```

1. Run the program to find the length of the segment with endpoint
   coordinates -6 and 11.
2. Change the program so that the user can find the lengths of as many
   segments as desired without rerunning the program.
3. Why is the ABS function used in line 30?
4. Rewrite the program without using the ABS function.

1-3 Rays, Angles, and Angle Measure

You can use what you have learned about lines to understand rays. Then the definition of a ray can be used to define an angle. Looking at the golf iron suggests that it is useful to be able to measure angles.

A **ray**, $\overrightarrow{AB}$, is the part of $\overleftrightarrow{AB}$ that contains the point A and all the points on the same side of A as B. The single arrowhead indicates that the ray continues without end in one direction. Point A is the endpoint of $\overrightarrow{AB}$.

Ray *AB* or $\overrightarrow{AB}$

5 iron

Angles are measured in many everyday situations, including sports. For example, the angles of golf irons vary from 18° to 58°.

When the points of two rays all lie on the same line, the rays are **collinear rays.** Otherwise, they are **noncollinear rays.**

An **angle** is a figure consisting of two noncollinear rays with a common endpoint. $\overrightarrow{AB}$ and $\overrightarrow{AC}$ are **sides** of the angle. Point A is the **vertex** of the angle.

The angle can be named using three letters, either $\angle BAC$ or $\angle CAB$. Notice that the vertex is always written in the middle. Sometimes an angle is named using only the vertex letter or a number, as long as no confusion results. For example, the angle above could be named $\angle A$ or $\angle 1$.

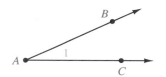

In geometry, you will usually measure angles using a unit called a **degree(°)**. The figure below shows a 1° angle.

A protractor marked in degree units can be used as follows to find the measure of an angle.

Read the outer scale.
The degree measure of $\angle DEF$ is 30.
Write: $m\angle DEF = 30$

Read the inner scale.
$m\angle JKL = 65$

This procedure for measuring angles is justified by the following postulate.

● **POSTULATE 8** Protractor Postulate

Given any line AB in a plane with point O between A and B; $\overrightarrow{OA}$, $\overrightarrow{OB}$, and all the rays from point O on one side of $\overleftrightarrow{AB}$ can be matched one-to-one with the real numbers from 0 through 180 so that

a. $\overrightarrow{OA}$ is matched with 0
b. $\overrightarrow{OB}$ is matched with 180
c. if $\overrightarrow{OR}$ is matched with r and $\overrightarrow{OS}$ is matched with s, then
$m \angle ROS = |r - s| = |s - r|$

The Protractor Postulate ensures that every angle has a unique number between 0 and 180 called its measure. This picture will help you understand the postulate.

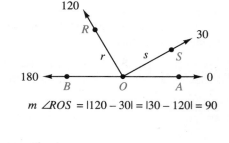

$m \angle ROS = |120 - 30| = |30 - 120| = 90$

Angles are classified according to their measures as shown below.

This mark is often used to indicate a right angle.

Acute angle

Measure between 0 and 90 degrees

Right angle

Measure 90 degrees

Obtuse angle

Measure between 90 and 180 degrees

Example 1

Find the measure of $\angle JFI$.
Classify it as an acute, right, or obtuse angle.

Solution

$m \angle JFI = |160 - 110| = |50| = 50$

Since $m \angle JFI$ is less than 90, it is acute.

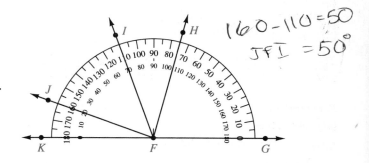

160-110=50
JFI = 50°

Try This

Find the measure of $\angle JFH$. Classify it as an acute, right, or obtuse angle.

An angle in the plane separates the plane into three parts—the points in the **interior** of the angle, the points of the angle, and the points in the **exterior** of the angle.

Point F is in the interior of $\angle D$.
Point P is in the exterior of $\angle D$.
Point C is on $\angle D$.

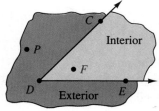

The following postulate, like the Segment Addition Postulate, describes an important property of angles.

● POSTULATE 9   Angle Addition Postulate

If F is in the interior of $\angle CDE$, then
$m \angle CDF + m \angle FDE = m \angle CDE$.

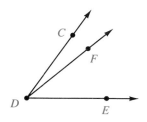

Example 2 shows how the Angle Addition Postulate may be used to find the measure of angles.

Example 2

$m \angle BOD = 45$, $m \angle BOC = 132$
Find $m \angle DOC$.

Solution

$$m \angle BOD + m \angle DOC = m \angle BOC \quad \textit{Angle Addition Postulate}$$
$$45 + m \angle DOC = 132$$
$$m \angle DOC = 132 - 45$$
$$m \angle DOC = 87$$

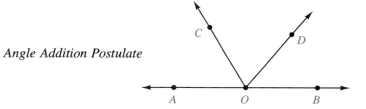

Try This

$m \angle BOD = 37$, $m \angle DOC = 54$
Find $m \angle BOC$.

The Angle Addition Postulate also applies when algebraic expressions represent angle measures. This idea is illustrated in the following example.

Example 3

$m \angle BAC = 46$
Find $m \angle BAD$ and $m \angle DAC$.

Solution

$$m \angle BAD + m \angle DAC = m \angle BAC$$
$$(4x - 3) + 3x = 46 \quad \textit{Angle Addition Postulate}$$
$$7x - 3 = 46$$
$$7x = 49$$
$$x = 7$$

$m \angle BAD = 4x - 3 = 4(7) - 3 = 25$
$m \angle DAC = 3x = 3(7) = 21$

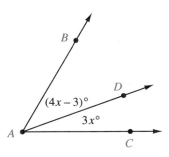

Try This

Suppose $m \angle BAC = 9x$, $m \angle DAC = 2x + 16$, and $m \angle BAD = 40$.
Find $m \angle BAC$ and $m \angle DAC$.

Class Exercises

Short Answer

Complete each statement.

1. Point Q is called the ⎯ of $\overrightarrow{QD}$.
2. The vertex of $\angle BQC$ is point ⎯ .
3. Two other names for $\angle BQC$ are ⎯ and ⎯ .
4. The unit of angle measure is called a ⎯ .
5. $m \angle BQD = $ ⎯
6. $m \angle 1 + m \angle 2 = $ ⎯

7. Use symbols to name four acute angles.
8. Use symbols to name four obtuse angles.
9. Name a point in the interior and a point in the exterior of $\angle BQE$.

Sample Exercises

Find the measure of each angle.

10. $\angle BQC$ 11. $\angle BQE$ 12. $\angle AQF$
13. $\angle AQC$ 14. $\angle CQD$ 15. $\angle EQD$

Find each angle measure.

16. $m \angle 4 + m \angle 3$ 17. $m \angle AQE - m \angle 4$ 18. $m \angle BQE - m \angle BQC$
19. Use a protractor to draw a 35° angle.

First estimate each angle. Then measure to check your estimate.

20.

21.

Discussion

22. Does the order in which the letters are written matter when naming a segment? Does it matter when naming a ray? an angle? Explain.
23. A student claimed that the Protractor Postulate "places a protractor" along side of every line in the plane. Is this a good description? Give a convincing argument to support your conclusion.

Exercises

A

Find the measure of each angle.

1. $m\angle QAP$ 2. $m\angle WAS$
3. $m\angle PAT$ 4. $m\angle PAV$
5. $m\angle SAU$ 6. $m\angle VAR$

7. Write four different names for the angle below.   165   30

For each angle below, (a) visually classify as acute, right, or obtuse, (b) estimate the actual measure, and (c) use a protractor to find the actual measure.

8. $\angle CBD$ 9. $\angle EBC$
10. $\angle FBC$ 11. $\angle GBD$
12. $\angle FBD$ 13. $\angle GBF$

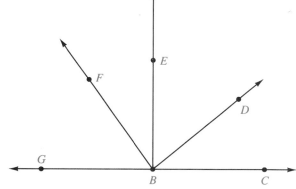

14. Use a protractor to draw a 125° angle.

Write and solve an equation to find the measure of each angle.

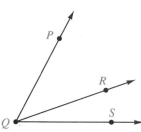

15. $m\angle PQS = 45$, $m\angle SQR = 26$
    Find $m\angle PQR$.
16. $m\angle PQS = 80$, $m\angle RQP = 37$
    Find $m\angle SQR$.
17. $m\angle PQS = 4x$, $m\angle SQR = 2x$, $m\angle RQP = 24$
    Find $m\angle SQR$ and $m\angle PQS$.
18. $m\angle SQR = 3x - 2$, $m\angle SQP = 5x$, $m\angle PQR = 34$
    Find $m\angle SQR$ and $m\angle PQS$.

45 · 2

19. $m\angle PQS = 6x$, $m\angle PQR = 3x + 2$, $m\angle SQR = 22$
    Find $m\angle PQS$ and $m\angle PQR$.

20. A source of light, such as a flashlight, is said to emit rays. Give another example of rays.

Determine whether each statement is true or false. If false, draw a figure to justify your answer.

21. $\overrightarrow{AB}$ is the same ray as $\overrightarrow{BA}$.
22. Any figure made up of two rays is an angle.
23. $\angle JKL$ is the same angle as $\angle LKJ$.
24. Every angle is either acute, right, or obtuse.
25. A point in the plane that is not in the interior of an angle must be in the exterior of the angle.
26. When D is in the interior of $\angle ABC$, the Angle Addition Postulate allows you to conclude that $m\angle ABC + m\angle DBC = m\angle ABD$.

B

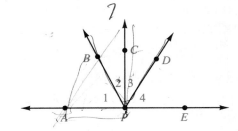

$\angle IKF$ **is a right angle.** $m\angle HKI = 20$, $m\angle HKG = m\angle FKG$, $m\angle DKE = m\angle HKI$ **Find the measure of each angle.**

27. $m\angle HKF$ 28. $m\angle HKG$ 29. $m\angle DKE$
30. $m\angle EKF$ 31. $m\angle IKE$ 32. $m\angle EKH$

$m\angle BPD = m\angle DPE$ **Find the measure of each angle.**

33. $m\angle APC = 90$, $m\angle 1 = 3x + 5$, $m\angle 2 = 2x$ Find $m\angle 1$.
34. $m\angle 4 = 4x + 12$, $m\angle BPE = 10x$ Find $m\angle 4$.
35. $m\angle 4 = x + 30$, $m\angle BPD = 3x - 10$ Find $m\angle 4$.
36. $m\angle 2 = 3x$, $m\angle 3 = 3x + 9$, $m\angle BPD = 7x$ Find $m\angle 3$.
37. $m\angle 4 = 72$, $m\angle 2 = m\angle 3$ Find $m\angle 2$.
38. $m\angle LMN = 37$, $m\angle LMQ = 48$
    Find $m\angle NMQ$. (Find two possible answers.)

Draw each figure. Use a protractor if needed.

39. two angles with equal measures that each have $\overrightarrow{AB}$ as a side
40. two angles in which the vertex of each is in the interior of the other
41. two angles that intersect in exactly one point
42. two rays that intersect in a segment
43. three rays that form an obtuse angle, a right angle, and an acute angle

44. Two sides of a picture frame are glued together to form a corner. Each side is cut at a 45° angle. What is the measure of the corner of the frame? Which postulate or definition is being used?

C

Determine whether each statement is always, sometimes, or never true. Give a reason for your answer.

45. $m\angle ABC + m\angle CBD = m\angle ABD$
46. $\overrightarrow{RS}$ and $\overrightarrow{RT}$ are the same ray.
47. $\angle ABC$ and $\angle CAB$ are the same angle.
48. $\angle ABC$ and $\angle EBF$ are the same angle.
49. If E is between D and F, then $\overrightarrow{ED}$ and $\overrightarrow{EF}$ make up $\overrightarrow{DF}$.
50. The sum of two acute angles is an obtuse angle.

51. Without using a protractor, find the measure of the angle formed by the hands of a clock when it is 8:00 and when it is 8:20.

Critical Thinking

52. How many different angles are formed when ten distinct rays are drawn in the interior of the angle?

When *one* ray is drawn, *three* angles are formed.
When *two* rays are drawn, *six* angles are formed.

Complete this table and discover a pattern to help you predict the number of angles formed when ten rays are drawn.

Number of rays	1	2	3	4	5	· · ·
Number of angles	3	6				· · ·

Mixed Review

Complete each statement.

1. $\overleftrightarrow{CE}$ and $\overleftrightarrow{AF}$ intersect at point ___ .
2. $AD +$ ___ $= AF$
3. Points C, D, and E are ___ .
4. If $AF = 28$ and $DF = 15$, then $AD =$ ___ .
5. If $CD = 4x + 1$, $DE = 2x - 5$, and $CE = 14$, then $CD =$ ___ .
6. If $m \angle CDF = 65$, then it is a(n) ___ angle.

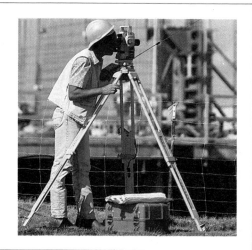

1-4 Congruent Segments and Angles

How could you use these tools to construct
a. a segment $\overline{CD}$ so that $CD = AB$?
b. an angle $\angle F$, so that $m\angle F = m\angle E$?

straightedge
(no marks)

compass

In the Explore, you may have been able to construct an "exact" copy of a segment and an angle. This suggests the idea of congruence as defined below.

■ DEFINITION

Congruent segments are segments that have the same length.

You write $\overline{CD} \cong \overline{EF}$ and say, "$\overline{CD}$ is congruent to $\overline{EF}$."
Statements such as $\overline{CD} \cong \overline{EF}$ are equivalent to statements such as
$CD = EF$, so you will see these types of statements used interchangeably.

■ DEFINITION

The **midpoint of a segment** is the point that divides the segment into two congruent segments.

M is the midpoint of $\overline{RS}$, since $\overline{RM} \cong \overline{MS}$ (or $RM = MS$). The two segments are marked to show that they are congruent.

■ DEFINITION

The **bisector of a segment** is any point, line, part of a line, or plane that divides the segment into two congruent segments. Since $\overline{GM} \cong \overline{MH}$, point M, line ℓ, $\overline{FM}$, and plane S are all bisectors of $\overline{GH}$.

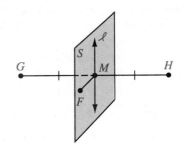

● **POSTULATE 10** Midpoint Postulate

A segment has exactly one midpoint.

Example 1

V is the midpoint of $\overline{UW}$.
Find *UW*.

Solution

$$UV = VW$$
$$3a + 5 = 5a - 7$$
$$2a = 12$$
$$a = 6$$

Since V is the midpoint of segment $\overline{UW}$, the lengths of $\overline{UV}$ and $\overline{VW}$ are equal.

$UV = 3a + 5 = 3(6) + 5 = 23$ $UW = 2UV = 46$

Try This

Suppose that $UV = \frac{x}{4} + 3$ and $VW = \frac{2x}{5}$.   Find *UW*.

■ **DEFINITION**

Congruent angles are angles that have the same measure.

You write $\angle GHI \cong \angle JKL$. Note the marks that are used to show that $\angle GHI$ is congruent to $\angle JKL$.

Statements such as $\angle GHI \cong \angle JKL$ are equivalent to statements such as $m\angle GHI = m\angle JKL$, so these two types of statements will be used interchangeably from now on. The idea of congruent angles is used in the following important definition.

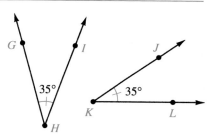

■ **DEFINITION**

The **bisector of an angle** is a ray in the interior of the angle that divides the angle into two congruent angles.

$\overrightarrow{BD}$ is the bisector of $\angle ABC$, since $\angle ABD \cong \angle DBC$.

It is natural to think that an angle could not have two or more bisectors. The following postulate states that this is true.

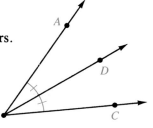

● **POSTULATE 11** Angle Bisector Postulate

An angle has exactly one bisector.

Example 2

$\overrightarrow{YP}$ bisects $\angle XYZ$. $m\angle XYP = 4n - 9$, $m\angle PYZ = 2n + 25$ Find $m\angle PYZ$.

Solution

$m\angle XYP = m\angle PYZ$ Since $\overrightarrow{YP}$ bisects $\angle XYZ$, we know that the
$4n - 9 = 2n + 25$ measures of the two angles formed are equal.
$2n = 34$
$n = 17$
$m\angle PYZ = 2n + 25 = 2(17) + 25 = 59$

Try This

$\overrightarrow{YP}$ bisects $\angle XYZ$. $m\angle PYZ = 4x$, $m\angle XYZ = 9x - 8$ Find $m\angle XYZ$.

Class Exercises

Short Answer

Complete each statement.

1. Two segments are congruent if they have the same ____ .
2. The statement $\overline{EF} \cong \overline{GH}$ is equivalent to the statement ____ .
3. Two angles that have the same measure are ____ .
4. H is the midpoint of $\overline{CD}$ and $HD = 9$ cm. $CH =$ ____
5. $CE = 8$ cm and $EF = 8$ cm, so ____ .
6. $\overrightarrow{CF}$ is the bisector of $\angle DCG$ and $m\angle FCG = 32$. $m\angle FCD =$ ____
7. $\overline{EF}$ is a bisector of $\overline{CG}$. $CG = 12$, $EG =$ ____

Sample Exercises

8. $\overrightarrow{PR}$ bisects $\angle QPS$. $\overrightarrow{PV}$ bisects $\angle QPU$. Name two pairs of congruent angles.
9. $\overrightarrow{UR}$ bisects $\overline{VS}$. $VP = 2x + 5$, $VS = 5x$ Find PS.
10. $\overrightarrow{PR}$ bisects $\angle QPS$. $m\angle QPR = 3p + 10$, $m\angle QPS = 7p$ Find $m\angle RPS$.

Discussion

11. Does it make sense to say that a line or a ray has a midpoint? Explain why or why not.
12. Given that $FG = GH$, why is G not the midpoint of $\overline{FH}$?
13. Given that $\angle 1 \cong \angle 2$, why is $\overrightarrow{GE}$ not the bisector of $\angle FGH$?
14. How could you find the midpoint of each segment on the graph?
Complete a table like the following.

Endpoint 1	Endpoint 2	Midpoint
$A(1, 5)$	$B(3, 1)$	$M(2, 3)$

Can you discover a rule for finding the coordinates of the midpoint of a segment with endpoints (a, b) and (c, d)?

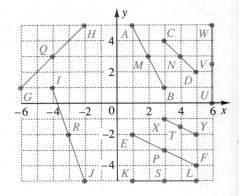

Exercises

A

1. H is the midpoint of $\overline{GI}$. $\overline{GI}$ bisects $\overline{EJ}$. $DE = EF$
   Name the congruent segments formed.
2. The midpoint of $\overline{ST}$ is R. Name the congruent segments formed.
3. Line ℓ bisects $\overline{GH}$ at point S. Name the congruent segments formed.
4. $\overline{JK}$ and $\overline{AB}$ bisect each other. What other true statements can you make about this situation?
5. Name two pairs of segments on the number line that have the same length. Use the symbol $\cong$ to write a statement about each pair of segments.

Give the coordinate of the midpoint for each segment.

6. $\overline{DE}$ 7. $\overline{AD}$

M is the midpoint of $\overline{AB}$. Find AM, MB, and AB.

8. $AM = 2x + 9$, $MB = 4x - 5$ 9. $AM = 2z + 6$, $MB = \frac{5z}{2}$
10. $AM = 2x^2 + 16$, $AB = 6x^2$ 11. $AM = \frac{x + 8}{3}$, $MB = \frac{x - 1}{2}$

12. $\overrightarrow{YT}$ is the bisector of $\angle XYZ$. Name the congruent angles that are formed.

$\angle TRV$ is a right angle. $\angle URS$ is a right angle.
$\overrightarrow{RU}$ bisects $\angle TRV$.
$\overrightarrow{TR}$ bisects $\angle QRU$.
$\overrightarrow{RV}$ bisects $\angle SRU$.
Find the measure of each angle.

13. $m\angle TRU$ 14. $m\angle URV$ 15. $m\angle VRS$
16. $m\angle TRQ$ 17. $m\angle URS$ 18. $m\angle TRS$

$\overrightarrow{BD}$ is the bisector of $\angle ABC$. For each exercise, find $m\angle ABC$, $m\angle CBD$, and $m\angle DBA$.

19. $m\angle ABD = 2y - 3$, $m\angle DBC = y + 12$
20. $m\angle ABD = 5(x - 8)$, $m\angle DBC = \frac{5x}{3}$
21. $m\angle ABD = 7x + 2$, $m\angle DBC = 2(46 - x)$
22. $m\angle ABD = 2x^2$, $m\angle ABC = 64$

23. Assuming there is an equal amount of weight on each end, a lever will balance when the fulcrum is located at the midpoint. How long is the lever $\overline{AC}$ if $AB = 5$ ft and the lever is balanced?

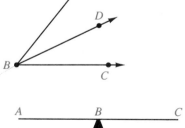

Determine whether each statement is true or false. Give a definition or a postulate to support your answer.

24. A segment can have more than one midpoint.
25. Any pair of segments that are congruent have the same length and any pair of segments that have the same length are congruent.
26. The bisector of an angle is sometimes in the exterior of the angle.
27. An angle cannot have two or more bisectors.
28. The bisector of an obtuse angle forms two obtuse angles.

B

29. $PS = 3x + 2$, $SQ = 4x - 5$, $PQ = 39$ Is S the midpoint of $\overline{PQ}$?
30. $PQ = 36$, $PS = 4b + 2$, $SQ = 6b - 6$ Does ℓ bisect $\overline{PQ}$ at S?
31. $PQ = 72$, $PS = 5h + 3$, $SQ = 8h - 9$ Is S the midpoint of $\overline{PQ}$?

32. $\angle WXY$ is a right angle.
    $m\angle WXZ = 5t + 5$
    $m\angle YXZ = 6t - 3$
    Is $\overrightarrow{XZ}$ the bisector of
    $\angle WXY$?

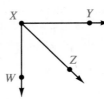

33. $m\angle ABC = 130$
    $m\angle ABD = 3x + 4$
    $m\angle CBD = 4x - 14$
    Is $\overrightarrow{BD}$ the bisector of
    $\angle ABC$?

R is the midpoint of $\overline{ST}$. $\overline{PQ}$ bisects $\overline{RT}$.
$\overline{ST} \cong \overline{SQ}$, $\overline{PV} \cong \overline{VQ}$, $\overline{SQ} \cong \overline{PQ}$
Write *true*, *false*, or *no conclusion* for each statement.

34. $\overline{SR} \cong \overline{RT}$
35. $\overline{RU} \cong \overline{UT}$
36. $\overline{PU} \cong \overline{UQ}$
37. $\overleftrightarrow{ST}$ is a bisector of $\overline{PQ}$.
38. $\overline{PQ}$ intersects $\overline{ST}$.
39. V is the midpoint of $\overline{PQ}$.

40. When a beam of light reflects off a mirror,
    the angle of incidence is equal to the angle
    of the reflection. If the angle of incidence
    is 35°, find $m\angle ABC$.

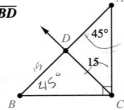

C

41. The numbers r, s, and t are coordinates of points R, S, and T on a
    number line. If $r = -12$, $s = 10$, and S is the midpoint of $\overline{RT}$, find t.
42. F is the midpoint of $\overline{EG}$. The coordinate of F is $f = 5.3$. The coordinate
    of G is $g = 7.9$. Find the coordinate of E.

$\overrightarrow{CD}$ bisects $\angle C$ and $\overline{AB}$. $\angle A \cong \angle B$, $\overline{CD} \cong \overline{BD}$
Find each of the following.

43. $m\angle ACD$
44. $m\angle CBD$
45. AD
46. AB

47. Find the coordinates of the midpoints D and E. How do the lengths
    of $\overline{DE}$ and $\overline{AB}$ compare? Draw a different triangle on a coordinate
    grid and find these midpoints and segment lengths. Do the segments
    compare in the same way?
48. Points A and B divide $\overline{CD}$ into the ratio 7:4:3. $CD = 56$ and A is
    between C and B. Draw a figure for the situation, find the length of each
    segment shown, and determine which point is the midpoint of $\overline{CD}$.

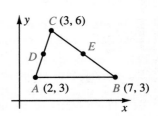

Critical Thinking

49. Write a formula for finding the midpoint of $\overline{AB}$ on the number line, where the coordinates of A and B are a and b.
(HINT: Draw a number line and try some specific segments.)

50. The figure shows the compass marks (red) and the lines (dotted red) that were made to construct the bisector of a segment and the bisector of an angle. Study the diagrams. Then draw and bisect a segment and an angle.

Bisect a segment   Bisect an angle

 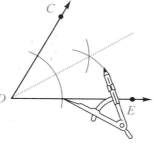

51. Collect the needed data, make a scale drawing of a baseball diamond, and use the words "midpoint" and "angle bisector" to describe the location of the pitcher's mound as accurately as possible.

Algebra Review

Simplify.

1. $\sqrt{4^2 + 3^2}$

2. $\sqrt{6^2 + 8^2}$

3. $\sqrt{5^2 + (-2)^2}$

4. $\sqrt{(6-2)^2 + (4-1)^2}$

5. $\sqrt{(7-1)^2 + (2-3)^2}$

6. $\sqrt{(5-8)^2 + (7-12)^2}$

Calculator Investigation

A calculator can help you find the coordinate of the midpoint of a segment when you know the coordinates of its endpoints.

If A and B have coordinates a and b respectively, then the coordinate of the midpoint of $\overline{AB}$ is $\frac{a+b}{2}$.

Example

Find the coordinate of the midpoint of $\overline{AB}$ if $a = 6$ and $b = 24$.

Enter: 6 ⊞ 24 ⊟ ⊡ 2 ⊟   Display: 15   The coordinate of the midpoint of $\overline{AB}$ is 15.

Use a calculator to find the coordinate of the midpoint of $\overline{AB}$.

1. $a = 7, b = 9$

2. $a = 8, b = 17$

3. $a = 0, b = -1$

4. $a = -3, b = 3$

5. $a = -5, b = 15$

6. $a = 107, b = 249$

7. $a = -5, b = -40$

8. $a = 1.5, b = 2.7$

1-5 Triangles

Since triangles are used so often in geometry and its applications, it is important to be able to define triangles and to classify the different types of triangles.

■ DEFINITION

A **triangle** is a figure formed by three segments joining three noncollinear points.

We can name triangle ABC by writing $\triangle ABC$, $\triangle BCA$, $\triangle ACB$, $\triangle CBA$, $\triangle CAB$, or $\triangle BAC$. In the figure, A, B, and C are the **vertices**; $\overline{AB}$, $\overline{BC}$, and $\overline{AC}$ are the **sides**; and $\angle A$, $\angle B$, and $\angle C$ are the **angles of the triangle.** Every triangle has *three* vertices, *three* sides, and *three* angles.

The words *opposite* and *included* are used to talk about relationships between sides and angles of a triangle. In $\triangle ABC$, for example,
$\overline{AB}$ is *opposite* $\angle C$ and $\angle C$ is *opposite* $\overline{AB}$;
$\angle C$ is *included* between side $\overline{BC}$ and side $\overline{AC}$;
$\overline{AB}$ is *included* between $\angle A$ and $\angle B$.

Triangles can be classified according to the types of angles they have, as shown in the figures below.

Acute triangle	**Right** triangle	**Obtuse** triangle	**Equiangular** triangle

All acute angles— $\angle A$, $\angle B$, and $\angle C$ are all acute.	One right angle $\angle G$ is a right angle.	One obtuse angle $\angle D$ is obtuse.	All angles congruent $\angle J \cong \angle K \cong \angle L$

In a right triangle, the side opposite the right angle is called the **hypotenuse.** The other two sides are called the **legs.**

Example 1

Name an equiangular triangle.

> #### Solution
> $\triangle PQS$

Try This

Name two right triangles.

Another way of classifying triangles is by the number of congruent sides they have as shown in the figures below.

Scalene triangle	Isosceles triangle	Equilateral triangle
No sides congruent	At least 2 sides congruent $\overline{EF} \cong \overline{FG}$	All sides congruent $\overline{HI} \cong \overline{IJ} \cong \overline{JH}$

Example 2

Name an isosceles triangle and give its congruent sides.

Solution

$\triangle STV$ is isosceles.
$\overline{ST} \cong \overline{SV}$

Try This

Name an equilateral triangle and give its congruent sides.

A coordinate grid is useful for exploring side length relationships in triangles and other figures.

In algebra, you learned that the length of $\overline{AB}$ on a coordinate grid—where A has coordinates (x_1, y_1) and B has coordinates (x_2, y_2)—can be found using the following.

Distance Formula $\quad AB = \sqrt{(x_2 - x_1)^2 + (y_2 - y_1)^2}$

This formula will be used to explore relationships and solve problems throughout the book and will be proved in Chapter 12. The following example illustrates its use.

Example 3

Find the length of $\overline{AB}$ in $\triangle ABC$ on the coordinate grid above.

Solution

$AB = \sqrt{(x_2 - x_1)^2 + (y_2 - y_1)^2}$ *Use the Distance Formula with*
$AB = \sqrt{(5 - 2)^2 + (3 - 1)^2}$ *$A(2, 1)$ and $B(5, 3)$.*
$AB = \sqrt{3^2 + 2^2}$ *$x_2 = 5$, $x_1 = 2$, $y_2 = 3$, and*
$AB = \sqrt{9 + 4}$ *$y_1 = 1$*
$AB = \sqrt{13} \approx 3.6$

Try This

Find the length of $\overline{AC}$ in $\triangle ABC$ on the coordinate grid above and decide if $\triangle ABC$ is an isosceles triangle.

Class Exercises

Short Answer

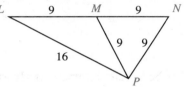

1. Name the vertices of △KLM.
2. Name the sides of △KLM.
3. Give five other names for △KLM.
4. Does △KLM appear to be scalene, isosceles, or equilateral?
5. Does △KLM appear to be acute, right, obtuse, or equiangular?
6. If ∠L is a right angle, name the hypotenuse and legs of △KLM.

Sample Exercises

7. $\overline{US} \cong \overline{UT}$, $\overline{US} \cong \overline{TS}$ Other congruences are marked. Use the labeled points to name an isosceles, an equilateral, and a scalene triangle.

Classify these triangles as acute, obtuse, right, or equiangular.

8.   9.   10.   11.

The lengths of the segments are given in the figure. Name each of the following.

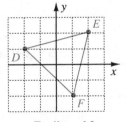

12. an isosceles triangle that is not equilateral
13. an equilateral triangle
14. a scalene triangle

15. Use the Distance Formula to find the length of the shortest side of a triangle with vertex coordinates $(2, 6)$, $(6, 3)$, and $(-6, -5)$.

Discussion

16. Can a triangle be both equilateral and isosceles? Explain.
17. Is it possible to find three points with integer coordinates that can be graphed and connected to form an equilateral triangle? Test some examples using the Distance Formula. Then form a hypothesis.

Equilateral ?

Exercises

A

Name each of the following.

1. four triangles
2. five other names for △AEC
3. the sides of △BED
4. the angles of △BED
5. an equilateral triangle
6. an isosceles triangle
7. a scalene triangle
8. an obtuse triangle
9. an acute triangle
10. the vertices of △BEA

Classify each triangle as equilateral, isosceles, or scalene.

11.
8
8   8

12.
10
12
7

13.
11
11
6

14.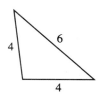
4   6
4

Classify each triangle as acute, obtuse, right, or equiangular.

15.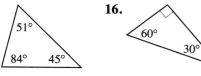
51°
84°   45°

16.
60°
30°

17.
115°   30°
35°

18.
60°
60°
60°

Classify each triangle.

19. $\triangle ABC$ with $AB = BC$
20. $\triangle DEF$ with $m\angle E = 90$
21. $\triangle JKL$ with $JK = KL = LJ$
22. $\triangle MNP$ with $MN \neq NP \neq PM$
23. $\triangle QRS$ with $m\angle Q = 145$, $m\angle R = 15$, and $m\angle S = 20$
24. Find the length of a segment with endpoint coordinates $(2, 3)$ and $(8, 11)$.
25. A triangle has vertex coordinates $(1, 1)$, $(1, 5)$, and $(5, 3)$. Find the length of each side and decide what type of triangle it is.
26. A typical type of rig for a sailboat consists of two sails—a jib and a mainsail. Classify each triangle as one or more of the following: acute, obtuse, right, isosceles, equiangular.

B

Determine whether each statement is always, sometimes, or never true.

27. A right triangle is an isosceles triangle.
28. A right triangle is an acute triangle.
29. An equilateral triangle is an isosceles triangle.
30. An isosceles triangle is an equilateral triangle.
31. A scalene triangle is an obtuse triangle.

Write and solve an equation to find each of the following.

32. Find RT.

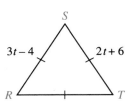
S
$3t - 4$ $2t + 6$
R   T

33. Find UW.

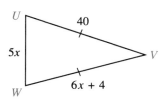
U   40
$5x$ V
W $6x + 4$

34. Find GI.

H
54   $5s + 9$
G $7s$ I

35. Find $m\angle T$ and $m\angle Z$.

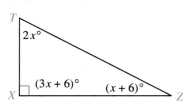
T
$2x°$
$(3x + 6)°$ $(x + 6)°$
X   Z

36. Find CE and DE.

$3x - 4$ E
C
$2x$
D
$CE + ED + DC = 88$

37. Find $m\angle A$.

B
$3n + 8$
$9n°$
A $2n + 4$ C
perimeter = 84

C

38. The playground equipment pictured to the right is built by forming equilateral triangles with several pieces of metal. Assume each piece of metal is 2 ft long (e.g., $AB = 2$ ft). What is the greatest number of equilateral triangles in the structure that can be made with 24 ft of metal? the fewest number?

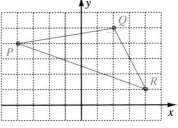

39. Graph the coordinates $(2, -3)$, $(5, 1)$, and $(8, -3)$ and connect them to form a triangle. Find the length of each side and decide what type of triangle it is.

40. Find the length of each side of $\triangle PQR$ having vertices with the coordinates $(4, 1)$, $(2, 5)$ and $(-4, 4)$. What type of triangle is it? Multiply each number in the coordinates by -1 and do the exercise again.

41. Choose a segment and construct an equilateral triangle that has sides congruent to the chosen segment.

42. Use a compass and straightedge to construct a triangle that has sides congruent to $\overline{AB}$, $\overline{CD}$, and $\overline{EF}$.

A ———————— B

C ———— D

E ———————— F

Critical Thinking

43. How could you glue six toothpicks together to form four triangles? (HINT: Regardless of the size of the toothpicks, you will need to use plenty of space!)

44. There are 27 different equilateral triangles in the figure to the right. How many of them can you name?

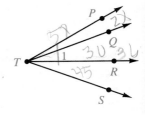

Mixed Review

Complete each statement.

1. $m\angle RTS = 45$, $m\angle QTR = 30$, $m\angle QTS =$ ___
2. If $m\angle PTR = 5x$, $m\angle PTQ = 2x$, and $m\angle QTR = 36$, then $m\angle PTQ =$ ___.
3. $\overrightarrow{TQ}$ bisects $\angle PTR$. If $m\angle PTR = 62$ and $m\angle QTR = x + 1$, then $x =$ ___.
4. Two other names for $\angle QTR$ are ___ and ___.

Quiz

1. Find the distance between the pair of points with coordinates -8 and 14.
2. Name two sets of three collinear points.
3. $AC = 25$, $AB = 2x + 2$, $BC = 6x - 9$ Find AB.
4. B is the midpoint of $\overline{ED}$. $EB = 2y + 1$, $BD = 3y - 6$ Find BD.
5. $m\angle DAC = 43$, $m\angle EAD = 75$ Find $m\angle EAC$.
6. $\overrightarrow{AC}$ bisects $\angle EAD$. Name a pair of congruent angles.
7. $\overline{AB} \cong \overline{BD} \cong \overline{AD}$ What type of triangle is $\triangle ABD$?
8. $m\angle EBA = 90$ What type of triangle is $\triangle BAE$?

COMPARING APPROACHES IN GEOMETRY

Three Basic Transformations

Three basic transformations used in Euclidean Geometry are the **translation, reflection,** and **rotation.**

A translation slides a figure in one direction.

translation direction

For a reflection there is a line that acts like a mirror. A figure is reflected across this mirror line.

reflection line

A rotation turns a figure through some angle about a fixed center point.

rotation center

One of the important properties of these transformations is that they preserve segment lengths and angle measures as illustrated in the figures below.

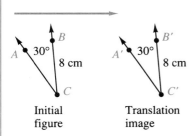

Initial figure   Translation image

An angle and its translation image have the same measure. A segment and its translation image have the same length.

Initial figure   reflection line   Reflection image

An angle and its reflection image have the same measure. A segment and its reflection image have the same length.

rotation center   Rotation image

An angle and its rotation image have the same measure. A segment and its rotation image have the same length.

Exercises

1. $\overline{CD}$ is the reflection image of $\overline{AB}$ in the y-axis. Use the distance formula to show that these segments are congruent.

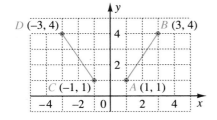

2. $\overline{CD}$ is the 90° rotation image of $\overline{AB}$ with rotation center $(0, 0)$. Use the distance formula to show these segments congruent.

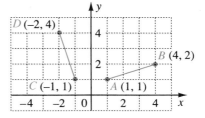

REASONING

1-6 Conditional Statements

This advertisement uses an **if-then statement** to encourage you to draw a positive conclusion about the product. The *if* part is called the **hypothesis** and the *then* part is called the **conclusion.** This type of statement is also very important in geometry. Here are some other examples.

If you want economy, then drive a Gazelle.

hypothesis	conclusion
If you want economy,	*then* drive a Gazelle.
If $x = 5$,	*then* $x^2 = 25$.
If $\triangle ABC$ is equilateral,	*then* $\triangle ABC$ is isosceles.

You can use symbols to express an if-then statement by writing "if p, then q" or "$p \rightarrow q$" where p represents the hypothesis and q represents the conclusion. "$p \rightarrow q$" is read "p implies q."

An if-then statement can be called a **conditional statement,** or simply a conditional. Example 1 presents some skills you will need in order to understand and use conditionals.

Example 1

State the hypothesis and conclusion of this conditional.
If it rains before noon, then we will not play tennis.

> #### Solution
> Hypothesis: It rains before noon.
> Conclusion: We will not play tennis.

Try This

Give a conditional with the following hypothesis and conclusion.
Hypothesis: All angles of $\triangle KLM$ have measure less than 90.
Conclusion: $\triangle KLM$ is acute.

Some statements do not contain *if* and *then* but can be written as an if-then statement. For example, each of these statements has the same meaning.

If a number is even, *then* it has a factor.	(*if* p, *then* q)
A number has a factor *if* it is even.	(q, *if* p)
A number is even *implies* it has a factor.	(p *implies* q)
A number is even *only if* it has a factor.	(p *only if* q)
All even numbers *are* numbers that have a factor.	(*all* p *are* q)

A conditional may be true, or it may be false. Suppose, for example, that your teacher stated this conditional.

$$p \qquad\qquad\qquad\qquad q$$

If you get an A on every geometry test, *then* you will get an A in the course.

The only time when you would be treated unfairly and the conditional would be false is if you received an A on every test (p is true) but did not get an A in the course (q is false). This **truth table** shows that a conditional is false only when an example can be found where the hypothesis is true, but the conclusion is false.

Truth Table

p	q	$p \rightarrow q$
T	T	T
T	F	F
F	T	T
F	F	T

Example 2

State as a conditional. Show that the conditional is false.
All right triangles are isosceles.

Solution

Conditional: If a triangle is a right triangle, then it is isosceles.

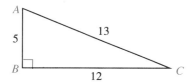

The hypothesis is true: $\triangle ABC$ is a right triangle.
The conclusion is false: $\triangle ABC$ is *not* isosceles.
Therefore the conditional is false.

Try This

State as a conditional. Show that the conditional is false.
Two lines form right angles if they intersect.

A single example, such as the one in Example 2, that shows a general conditional statement to be false is called a **counterexample.**

The **converse** of a conditional is formed by interchanging the hypothesis and the conclusion. For example,

Conditional ($p \rightarrow q$): If you live in Dallas, then you live in Texas.
Converse ($q \rightarrow p$): If you live in Texas, then you live in Dallas.

In this case, the conditional is true but the converse is false. On the other hand, the following conditional is true and so is its converse.

Conditional: If you are a native Texan, then you were born in Texas.
Converse: If you were born in Texas, then you are a native Texan.

Remember, *a true statement may or may not have a true converse*.

When a conditional and its converse are both true, we can combine the two statements into one statement, called a **biconditional,** by using the phrase *if and only if*. For example, you are a native Texan *if and only if* you were born in Texas. A definition should always be interpreted as a biconditional even though it may not be stated in the *if and only if* form.

Example 3

State the converse of the given statement. If both the statement and the converse are true, state them as a biconditional.
If a triangle has at least two congruent sides, then it is isosceles.

Solution

Converse: If a triangle is isosceles, then it has at least two congruent sides.
Biconditional: A triangle is isosceles if and only if it has at least two congruent sides.

Try This

State the converse of the given statement. If both statements are true, state them as a biconditional.
If M is the midpoint of $\overline{AB}$, then M is between A and B.

If you begin with a conditional, such as "If you live in Dallas, then you live in Texas," you can form two other types of statements.

The **inverse** is formed by negating both the hypothesis and the conclusion.

Inverse (not $p \rightarrow$ not q): If you do not live in Dallas, then you do not live in Texas.

The **contrapositive** is formed by interchanging the hypothesis and the conclusion and negating both.

Contrapositive (not $q \rightarrow$ not p): If you do not live in Texas, then you do not live in Dallas.

Example 4

State the inverse and contrapositive of the statement.
If two segments have the same length, then they are congruent.

Solution

Inverse: If two segments do not have the same length, then they are not congruent.
Contrapositive: If two segments are not congruent, then they do not have the same length.

Try This

State the inverse and contrapositive of the given statement.
If $\triangle EFG$ is an obtuse triangle, then it contains an obtuse angle.

Class Exercises

Short Answer

Complete each statement.

1. The *if* part of a conditional is called the ___ .
2. The *then* part of a conditional is called the ___ .

3. When the hypothesis and the conclusion of a conditional are interchanged, the resulting statement is the ___ of the conditional.
4. If a statement and its converse are true, they can be combined to form a ___ .
5. When the hypothesis and conclusion of a conditional are negated, the resulting statement is the ___ of the conditional.
6. When the hypothesis and conclusion of a conditional are interchanged and negated, the resulting statement is the ___ of the conditional.
7. Is the converse of a true conditional always true?

Sample Exercises

Give the hypothesis and the conclusion of each statement.

8. If a triangle has all sides congruent, then the triangle must be equilateral.
9. If two distinct lines intersect, then their intersection is a point.
10. If a line and a plane intersect and the line does not lie in the plane, then their intersection is a point.
11. If a nonzero whole number has exactly two factors, then the number is prime.

State a conditional with the given hypothesis and conclusion.

12. Hypothesis: A line is the bisector of a segment.
    Conclusion: The line contains the midpoint of the segment.
13. Hypothesis: A triangle has no sides congruent.
    Conclusion: The triangle is scalene.

State as a conditional.

14. A line bisects a segment if it divides the segment into two congruent segments.
15. m ending in 0, 2, 4, 6, or 8 implies that m is an even number.
16. You will fail the course only if you get an F on the final exam.

Give a counterexample to show that the given conditional is false.

17. If three points are coplanar, then they are collinear.
18. If a triangle is isosceles, then it is equilateral.
19. If two angles are acute, then they are congruent.
20. State as a conditional. Then state the converse, inverse, and contrapositive of the conditional.
    All hard workers improve.
21. Give an example of a true conditional that has a true converse and state it as a biconditional.

Discussion

22. When asked how she decided if a conditional was true or false, Mary said, "I assume that the hypothesis is true and ask myself if the conclusion could possibly be false. If it can, I say that the conditional is false." Does Mary's method work? Explain, using an example.
23. Give a convincing argument that the contrapositive of a conditional is the same as the converse of the inverse of the conditional.

Exercises

A

State the hypothesis and conclusion for each statement.

1. If you are funny, then you will make people laugh.
2. If point A is the midpoint of $\overline{EF}$, then A divides $\overline{EF}$ into two congruent segments.
3. If a point is in the interior of an angle, then it cannot be in its exterior.
4. If Michele's age is 15, then she is too young to vote.
5. If $\angle A \cong \angle B$, then $m \angle A = m \angle B$.
6. If A is between B and C, then A, B, and C are collinear.
7. If $\triangle JKL$ has three acute angles, then $\triangle JKL$ is acute.

Write a conditional with the given hypothesis and conclusion.

8. Hypothesis: A number is prime.
   Conclusion: The number has exactly two divisors.
9. Hypothesis: A man lives in Houston.
   Conclusion: He lives in Texas.
10. Hypothesis: The angles of a triangle are congruent to each other.
    Conclusion: The triangle is equiangular.
11. Hypothesis: Four points are all in one plane.
    Conclusion: The points are coplanar.
12. Hypothesis: B is between A and C.
    Conclusion: $AB + BC = AC$
13. Hypothesis: R is between S and U, and T is between R and U.
    Conclusion: T is between S and U.

Write each statement as a conditional. Then determine whether it is true or false.

14. A number ends in five if it is even.
15. A line which bisects a segment contains the midpoint of the segment.
16. An angle is obtuse only if it has measure less than 90.
17. Collinear points are points that lie on the same line.
18. All left-handed people are male.
19. Go to law school and you will become a judge.
20. All acute angles are congruent.
21. Every equilateral triangle is also an isosceles triangle.

Write the converse of each statement.

22. If a person is swimming, then that person is wet.
23. If two angles have the same measure, then they are congruent.
24. If $ab = 0$, then $a = 0$ or $b = 0$.
25. If two angles each measure 30, then they are congruent.
26. If you are 21 years old or older, then you can legally vote.
27. If two lines have a common point, then they are intersecting lines.
28. If an angle is an acute angle, then its measure is less than 90.
29. If $\triangle ABC$ is equilateral, then $\triangle ABC$ is isosceles.

30. The statements in Exercises 22–29 are all true. For those that also have true converses, write the statement and its converse as a biconditional.
31. Write the inverse and contrapositive of the statements in Exercises 25–26.

B

Write two conditionals that are equivalent to the given biconditional.

32. An angle is a right angle if and only if its measure is 90.
33. Two angles are congruent if and only if they have the same measure.
34. M is the midpoint of $\overline{AB}$ if and only if M is between A and B and $\overline{AM} \cong \overline{MB}$.
35. $\overrightarrow{BD}$ is the bisector of $\angle ABC$ if and only if D is in the interior of the angle and $\angle ABD \cong \angle DBC$.
36. A triangle is a right triangle if and only if it has one right angle.

Give the hypothesis and conclusion of each statement.

37. Jim may vote if and only if he is at least 18 years old.
38. A, B, and C are collinear provided A, B, and C are all on one line.
39. A number is odd whenever it ends in five.
40. A person can be president if and only if the person is at least 35 years old.
41. Angles with the same measure are congruent.
42. All lines with a common point are intersecting lines.

Write a conditional for each figure. Is the converse of each statement true?

43.
44.
45.

C

46. Using biconditionals, write complete definitions of the following types of triangles:
    scalene, isosceles, equilateral.
47. Using biconditionals, write complete definitions of the following types of triangles:
    acute, obtuse, right, equiangular.
48. Write the converse, inverse, and contrapositive of the following statement. Determine whether each is true or false.
    If a figure is a triangle, then it has three segments.
49. Use the conditional to show that the contrapositive of the inverse of a conditional is the same as the converse of the conditional.
    If a triangle is an equilateral triangle, then it is an isosceles triangle.

Critical Thinking

50. Write as many conditionals as you can that have the same meaning as the statements in this advertisement from the Nowork Company.

    Join the Nowork Company and make a fast buck. Work for Nowork and get promoted fast. We hire only smart people who are too dumb to know they are smart. Nowork assures you excellent training at no pay. You will like working for the Nowork Company. We hire any human. We fire any human.

51. In this truth table, the symbol $\sim p$ is used for "not p." When p is true, $\sim p$ is false; when p is false, $\sim p$ is true. $\sim q$ has the same meaning. Use this idea and the Truth Table on page 33 to complete this table.

If two statements involving p and q have the same truth values for all truth values of p and all truth values of q, then the statements are **equivalent.** Are a conditional and its contrapositive equivalent?
Make truth tables to answer this question for the converse and for the inverse.

		Conditional		Contrapositive	
p	q	$p \rightarrow q$	$\sim q$	$\sim p$	$\sim q \rightarrow \sim p$
T	T	T	F	F	T
T	F				
F	T				
F	F				

52. Write a true conditional (if a, then b), and then rewrite it in each of the following forms. Which of these statements do you think are true?

　a. b if a　　**b.** a only if b　　**c.** a is all that is needed to ensure b
　d. b must be true in order for a to be true　　**e.** a implies b.

Mixed Review

Classify each triangle.

1. $\triangle ABC$ with $m \angle C = 90$
2. $\triangle KLM$ with $\overline{KL} \cong \overline{LM}$
3. $\triangle XYZ$ with $\angle X \cong \angle Y \cong \angle Z$
4. $\triangle DEF$ with $m \angle D = 50$, $m \angle E = 60$, $m \angle F = 70$

CONNECTIONS ⟨⟩

Reasoning and Venn Diagrams

Venn diagrams can be used to represent statements. For example, the statement "All lizards are reptiles" can be represented by the Venn diagram to the right. We can see that if an animal is a lizard, then it is also a reptile; but the converse is not necessarily true.

Venn diagrams are also useful in showing the relationship between groups of objects or people. The relationship between people who jog and people who swim is shown in the Venn diagram at the right. The green region represents people who both swim and jog.

Draw a Venn diagram to represent each statement.

1. All apples are fruits.
2. If a woman is a doctor, then she is a college graduate.

Use a Venn diagram to solve.

3. At Cortez High School 32 students take biology, 30 students take history, and 26 students take geometry. Ten students take both geometry and biology, 14 students take geometry and history, and 16 students take history and biology. Six students take all three subjects. How many students take geometry but not history or biology?

1-7 Drawing and Supporting Conclusions

In Lesson 1-6, you analyzed both real-world and geometric conditional statements. In this section, you will see how true conditionals can be used to help you draw conclusions in geometry. This process is described here and analyzed below.

Drawing a Conclusion in Geometry

You know this conditional is true:
> If at least two sides of a triangle are congruent, then the triangle is isosceles.

You are given: $\triangle ABC$ with $\overline{AC} \cong \overline{AB}$
You conclude: $\triangle ABC$ is isosceles.

Notice the following about the situation above.

- The conditional is a true general statement.
  (a definition, a postulate, or a statement that has been proved to be true)
- The *given* information establishes the truth of the *hypothesis* of the conditional.
- The *specific conclusion* about $\triangle ABC$ follows from the *conclusion* of the conditional.

The reasoning process described above is called **affirming the hypothesis.** It is a pattern of inference often used in geometric proofs and is logically represented as shown to the right.

Affirming the Hypothesis

$p \rightarrow q$ is true.
p is given.
_____
Conclude that q is true.

Example 1

Use the conditional and the given information to draw a conclusion.

Conditional (true): If a point is the midpoint of a segment, then it divides the segment into two congruent segments.
Given: M is the midpoint of $\overline{CD}$.
Conclusion: ?

Solution
$\overline{CM} \cong \overline{MD}$

Try This

Does the following conditional support the conclusion?
If not, restate the conditional so that it will.
Conditional: If the measure of an angle is greater than 90, then it is obtuse.
Given: $\angle 1$ is obtuse.
Conclusion: $m\angle 1 > 90$

A conclusion drawn from given information can be supported by citing a definition, a postulate, or another conditional known to be true. A complete knowledge of the definitions, postulates, and true statements studied so far will help you do this. Also, paying careful attention to the key words and symbols in the given information often suggests the correct supporting statement.

Example 2

State a conditional that supports the given conclusion.

Given: $\overrightarrow{GH}$ bisects $\angle FGI$.
Conclusion: $\angle 1 \cong \angle 2$
Conditional: ?

Solution

If a ray bisects an angle, then it divides the angle into two congruent angles.

Try This

Draw a conclusion from the given information. State a conditional to support the conclusion.

Given: Line ℓ bisects $\overline{ST}$ at W.
Conclusion: ?
Conditional: ?

Class Exercises

Short Answer

Determine whether each statement is true or false.

1. Conditionals are used in geometry to draw conclusions.
2. A false conditional cannot be used to support a conclusion.
3. A postulate can be used to support a conclusion.
4. A definition cannot be used to support a conclusion.
5. In order to draw a conclusion, the specific given information must meet the conditions of the hypothesis of a true conditional.

Sample Exercises

Use the given definition or postulate to draw a conclusion

6. Definition: If three points are all on one line, then the points are collinear.
   Given: Points I, J, and K are all on line ℓ.
   Conclusion: ?

7. Definition: If three points are collinear, then the points are all on one line.
   Given: E, F, and G are collinear.
   Conclusion: ?

8. Postulate: If point Q is between P and R, then $PQ + QR = PR$.
   Given: Point C is between B and D.
   Conclusion: ?

9. Postulate: If two planes intersect, then they intersect in exactly one line.
   Given: Planes P and Q intersect.
   Conclusion: ?

Discussion

10. Give an example of the reasoning described by the following.
    "If $p \rightarrow q$ is true and p is true, then q is true,"
    where p and q are replaced by real-world statements.

Exercises

A

Use the conditional and given information to draw a conclusion.

1. Conditional: If a triangle is equiangular, then all sides of the triangle are congruent.
   Given: $\triangle LMN$ is equiangular.

2. Conditional: If a ray bisects an angle, then it divides the angle into two congruent angles.
   Given: $\overrightarrow{JK}$ bisects $\angle TJR$.

3. Conditional: If a triangle contains a right angle, then it is a right triangle.
   Given: $\triangle GEF$, with right angle, $\angle E$

4. Conditional: If a and b are the coordinates of points A and B on the number line, then the distance between A and B is $|a - b|$.
   Given: The coordinate of point A is -7. The coordinate of point B is 9.5.

Change the conditional so that it will be true and will support the conclusion.

5. Conditional: (to be changed) If an angle measures 90, then it is a right angle.
   Given: $\angle 6$ is a right angle.
   Conclusion: $m \angle 6 = 90$

6. Conditional: (to be changed) If a point is the midpoint of a segment, then it divides the segment into two segments.
   Given: T is the midpoint of $\overline{PQ}$.
   Conclusion: $\overline{PT} \cong \overline{TQ}$

7. Conditional: (to be changed) If a triangle has at least two congruent sides, then it is equilateral.
   Given: $\triangle DEF$ with $\overline{DE} \cong \overline{DF} \cong \overline{EF}$
   Conclusion: $\triangle DEF$ is isosceles.

8. Conditional: (to be changed) If two angles have the same measure, then the angles are congruent.
   Given: $\angle A \cong \angle B$
   Conclusion: $m \angle A = m \angle B$

State a true conditional that supports the conclusion.

9. Given: $\angle QCN \cong \angle NCK$
   Conclusion: $\overrightarrow{CN}$ bisects $\angle QCK$.

10. Given: $\overrightarrow{CN}$ bisects $\angle QCK$.
    Conclusion: $\angle QCN \cong \angle NCK$

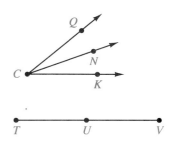

11. Given: $\overline{TU} \cong \overline{UV}$
    Conclusion: U is the midpoint of $\overline{TV}$.

12. Given: U is the midpoint of $\overline{TV}$.
    Conclusion: $\overline{TU} \cong \overline{UV}$

13. Explain why the conditional "If a triangle is equilateral, then all of its sides are congruent" does not support the conclusion that has been drawn from the given information below.
    Given: $\triangle MNP$ with $\overline{MN} \cong \overline{MP} \cong \overline{NP}$
    Conclusion: $\triangle MNP$ is equilateral.

14. Explain why the conditional "If M is between A and B, then A, B, and M are collinear" does not support the conclusion that has been drawn from the given information below.
    Given: M is between A and B.
    Conclusion: $AM = MB$

Draw a conclusion from the given information and state a true conditional to support it.

15. Conditional: ?
    Given: $\overrightarrow{EF}$ bisects $\angle GEH$.
    Conclusion: ?

16. Conditional: ?
    Given: $\angle GEF \cong \angle FEH$
    Conclusion: ?

17. Conditional: ?
    Given: $\triangle ABC$ is scalene.
    Conclusion: ?

18. Conditional: ?
    Given: No sides of $\triangle ABC$ are
    congruent.
    Conclusion: ?

19. Conditional: ?
    Given: $m\angle PQR = m\angle STW$
    Conclusion: ?

20. Conditional: ?
    Given: $\angle PQR \cong \angle STW$
    Conclusion: ?

21. Conditional: ?
    Given: $m\angle 1 = 30$, $m\angle 2 = 60$
    Conclusion: ?

22. Conditional: ?
    Given: $\overrightarrow{LN}$ bisects $\angle KLM$
    Conclusion: ?

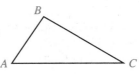

B

For each given, write two different conditionals that lead to two different conclusions.

23. Line ℓ bisects $\overline{GH}$ at point M.
24. $\triangle ABC$ with $\overline{AB} \cong \overline{BC} \cong \overline{AC}$
25. Point N is between points S and T.

Draw a conclusion from each figure. Name a definition that supports your conclusion.

26.

27.

28.

29.

Draw a conclusion from the true statement and the given information. You may need to rewrite the statement as a conditional.

30. True statement: The bisector of an angle divides it into two congruent angles.
    Given: $\overrightarrow{BD}$ bisects $\angle ABC$.

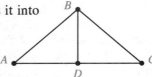

31. True statement: A midpoint divides a segment into two congruent segments.
Given: T is the midpoint of $\overline{GH}$.

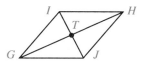

32. True statement: Congruent angles have the same measure.
Given: $\angle 3 \cong \angle PQR$
$\angle 2 \cong \angle PQR$

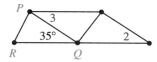

33. True statement: An average of 90% or more will earn an A.
Given: Jerome had an average of 93%.

C

Another useful pattern of reasoning, denying the conclusion, is described to the right—p and q represent the hypothesis and conclusion of a conditional. Use this pattern to draw conclusions from the given information.

34. If a triangle is isosceles, then it has at least two congruent sides. $\triangle JKL$ has no congruent sides.
35. If $\overrightarrow{AB}$ is the bisector of $\angle CAD$, then $\angle CAB \cong \angle BAD$.
$m\angle CAB \neq m\angle BAD$.

A third important pattern of reasoning, the chain rule, is described to the right. Use it to draw a conclusion from the given information.

36. If it rains today, then we will not have a picnic. If we do not have a picnic, then we will not see our friends.
37. If a line is a bisector of a segment, then it divides the segment into two congruent segments. If a line divides a segment into two congruent segments, then it contains the midpoint of the segment.

Denying the Conclusion
Conditional: $p \to q$
Given: q is false.
Conclusion: p is false.

The Chain Rule
Conditional 1: $p \to q$
Conditional 2: $q \to r$
Conclusion: $p \to r$

Critical Thinking

38. Three people named Glynn, Harding, and MacFeely fill the positions of accountant, clerk, and cashier in a department store. If MacFeely is the cashier, Harding is the clerk. If MacFeely is the clerk, Harding is the accountant. If Harding is not the cashier, Glynn is the clerk. If Glynn is the accountant, MacFeely is the clerk. What is each person's job?

Algebra Review

State a property that asserts that each of the following is true.
1. $a + b = b + a$
2. $6(x + y) = 6x + 6y$
3. $(m + n) + 1 = m + (n + 1)$
4. If $c = d$ and $d = e$, then $c = e$.

Enrichment
Symbolic Logic

You have already seen that letters and symbols can be used to represent statements. For example, if p represents the statement "William lives in Houston" and q represents the statement "William lives in Texas," then $p \rightarrow q$ represents the conditional "If William lives in Houston, then William lives in Texas."

Other symbols are often used to modify or connect statements.
The symbol $\sim$ is used to represent the word "not."
The symbol $\wedge$ is used to represent the word "and."
The symbol $\vee$ is used to represent the word "or."

Example

p	We will go to a movie.
q	We will play basketball.
$\sim p$	We will *not* go to a movie.
$p \wedge q$	We will go to a movie *and* we will play basketball.
$p \vee q$	We will go to a movie *or* we will play basketball.

These symbols can also be used to represent more complicated statements as in the following examples.

$\sim p \wedge \sim q$	We will *not* go to a movie *and* we will *not* play basketball.
$\sim(p \wedge q)$	We will *not* go to a movie *and* play basketball.

Notice the difference between these statements and how this difference is reflected in their symbolic equivalents.

Exercises

Suppose p represents the statement "Alice will buy a car" and q represents the statement "Alice will visit Hawaii."

Write each statement in words.

1. $\sim q$ 2. $p \wedge q$
3. $\sim p \vee \sim q$ 4. $\sim p \vee q$

Write each statement using symbols.

5. Alice will not buy a car.
6. Alice will buy a car or Alice will visit Hawaii.
7. Alice will not buy a car and Alice will not visit Hawaii.
8. Alice will buy a car or Alice will not visit Hawaii.

Let p represent the statement "This idea is good" to help answer each of the following.

9. Explain why $\sim(\sim p)$ is equivalent to p.
10. Explain why $p \vee \sim p$ always represents a true statement.
11. Explain why $p \wedge \sim p$ always represents a false statement.

1-8 Deductive Reasoning—Using Algebraic Properties

Charlie's dog was born the same time as Patty's dog. While talking with Sally, Patty learned that her dog was the same age as Sally's dog. What can you conclude from this information?

When you conclude that Charlie's dog is the same age as Sally's dog, you are using **deductive reasoning,** a process in which conclusions are drawn logically from given information. This conclusion is true because of the transitive property of equality reviewed in the table below.

PEANUTS

OWOOOo

DOGS HAVE BEEN HOWLING AT THE MOON NOW FOR OVER FIVE THOUSAND YEARS..

THE MOON HASN'T MOVED, AND DOGS ARE STILL DOGS..

THAT PROVES SOMETHING, BUT I DON'T KNOW WHAT!

11-28   SCHULZ

© 1958 United Feature Syndicate, Inc.

The measures of segments and angles are real numbers, so the properties you used in algebra are also important in geometry.

Properties of Equality

For all real numbers a, b, c, and d the following are true.

Reflexive Property	$a = a$
Symmetric Property	If $a = b$, then $b = a$
Transitive Property	If $a = b$ and $b = c$, then $a = c$
Addition Property	If $a = b$ and $c = d$, then $a + c = b + d$
Subtraction Property	If $a = b$ and $c = d$, then $a - c = b - d$
Multiplication Property	If $a = b$ and $c = d$ then $ac = bd$
Division Property	If $a = b$ and $c \neq 0$, then $\frac{a}{c} = \frac{b}{c}$
Substitution Property	If $a = b$, then a and b may be substituted for each other in any equation or inequality.

Properties of Real Numbers

Commutative Property	$a + b = b + a$, $ab = ba$
Associative Property	$a + (b + c) = (a + b) + c$, $a(bc) = (ab)c$
Distributive Property	$a(b + c) = ab + ac$

Example 1

Which property allows you to conclude that the following is true?
If $m \angle J = m \angle K$ and $m \angle K = m \angle L$,
then $m \angle J = m \angle L$.

Solution

Transitive Property

Try This

Which property allows you to conclude that the following is true?
If $CD = EF$ and $GH = IK$,
then $CD + GH = EF + IK$.

In algebra, deductive reasoning and the above properties can be used to **prove** that the procedure used for solving an equation is correct. The following example illustrates the idea of a **paragraph proof.**

Example 2

Give a paragraph proof that the following is true.
If $4(x + 7) = 52$, then $x = 6$.

Proof Since $4(x + 7) = 52$, it follows from the Distributive Property that $4x + 28 = 52$. Also, using the Subtraction Property, $4x = 24$. Then, applying the Division Property, it can be concluded that $x = 6$.

Try This

Give a paragraph proof that the following is true.
If $3(x - 2) = 9$, then $x = 5$.

The following describes the deductive reasoning process used in the above proof. It should be distinguished from the **inductive reasoning** process in which a conjecture is made by looking at several specific examples. (See page 429 for an example of this type of reasoning.)

Deductive Reasoning

- Start with the *given* conditions (the hypothesis).
- Present a series of statements, with reasons, that lead logically to the desired conclusion.
  (The reasons can be definitions, accepted properties or postulates, or statements that have been proved.)
- Assert the result you wanted to *prove* (the conclusion).

When the deductive reasoning process is used correctly, a proof results. This proof provides a valid argument that a mathematical statement, called a **theorem,** is true. Consider the following geometry theorem.

◆ **THEOREM 1.1** �

Congruence of segments and angles is reflexive, symmetric, and transitive.

The definitions of congruent segments and angles allow you to interchange congruence statements with statements about measures or real numbers. These ideas and the properties of equality and real numbers can be used to write a paragraph proof that the above theorem is true as illustrated in the following example.

Example 3

Write a paragraph proof that congruence of segments is symmetric, that is, if $\overline{AB} \cong \overline{CD}$, then $\overline{CD} \cong \overline{AB}$.

Proof Since $\overline{AB} \cong \overline{CD}$, $AB = CD$. But then, from the Symmetric Property of Equality, $CD = AB$. It follows, from the definition of congruent segments, that $\overline{CD} \cong \overline{AB}$.

Try This

Complete the following paragraph proof that congruence of angles is reflexive, that is, $\angle E \cong \angle E$.

Proof Since ____ is a real number, $m \angle E = m \angle E$ by the ____ Property of Equality. But then, $\angle E \cong \angle E$ by the definition of ____ .

You will be asked to give a paragraph proof for other parts of Theorem 1.1 in Exercises 32–34.

Theorem 1.2 will be useful in later proofs. It ties together the symmetric and transitive parts of Theorem 1.1.

◆ THEOREM 1.2 ✳

If two segments are congruent to the same segment, then they are congruent to each other.

Example 4

Write a paragraph proof that Theorem 1.2 is true. Indicate where you used Theorem 1.1.

Proof Suppose $\overline{AB} \cong \overline{EF}$ and $\overline{CD} \cong \overline{EF}$. From symmetry of congruence (Theorem 1.1), $\overline{EF} \cong \overline{CD}$. But then $\overline{AB} \cong \overline{EF}$ and $\overline{EF} \cong \overline{CD}$, so transitivity of congruence (Theorem 1.1) allows the conclusion that $\overline{AB} \cong \overline{CD}$.

Try This

Give a paragraph proof for Theorem 1.3 below. Indicate where you used Theorem 1.1.

◆ THEOREM 1.3 ✶

If two angles are congruent to the same angle, then they are congruent to each other.

Class Exercises

Short Answer

Which property asserts that

1. a number is equal to itself?
2. the sides of an equality can be interchanged?
3. if a first number equals a second and the second number equals a third, then the first number equals the third number?
4. you can add the same number to each side of an equation and the equality is preserved?

Sample Exercises

Name the property of equality (reflexive, symmetric, or transitive) that allows you to conclude that each statement is true.

5. If $JK = LM$, then $LM = JK$.
6. If $m \angle R = m \angle S$, then $m \angle S = m \angle R$.
7. $MN = MN$
8. If $AB = CD$ and $CD = EF$, then $AB = EF$.
9. If $x = 3$, then $3 = x$.
10. $m \angle C = m \angle C$

Give the part of Theorem 1.1 that allows you to conclude that each statement is true.

11. If $\angle R \cong \angle S$, then $\angle S \cong \angle R$.
12. If $\overline{EF} \cong \overline{GH}$ and $\overline{GH} \cong \overline{CD}$, then $\overline{EF} \cong \overline{CD}$.
13. $\angle PQR \cong \angle PQR$
14. If $\angle GHI \cong \angle JKL$ and $\angle JKL \cong \angle PQR$, then $\angle GHI \cong \angle PQR$.
15. If $\overline{LM} \cong \overline{PQ}$, then $\overline{PQ} \cong \overline{LM}$.

Discussion

16. Plan and give a paragraph proof that congruence of angles is transitive.
17. Which property supports each of the following?
    a. If 12 in. = 1 ft, then 1 ft = 12 in.
    b. If Sue is Deborah's sister and Deborah is Jane's sister, then Sue is Jane's sister.
    Give some other real-world situations that illustrate the Reflexive, Symmetric, and Transitive Properties.

Exercises

A

Use the given property of equality to draw a conclusion.

1. Symmetric Property: If $a = b$, then $b = a$.
   Given: $PQ = RS$

2. Reflexive Property: If a is a real number, then $a = a$.
   Given: CD is a real number.

3. Transitive Property: If $a = b$ and $b = c$, then $a = c$.
Given: $JK = LM$, $LM = PQ$

4. Symmetric Property: If $a = b$, then $b = a$.
Given: $m \angle W = m \angle X$

5. Reflexive Property: If a is a real number, then $a = a$.
Given: $m \angle T$ is a real number.

6. Transitive Property: If $a = b$ and $b = c$, then $a = c$.
Given: $m \angle 1 = m \angle 2$, $m \angle 2 = m \angle 3$

Use the given property to draw a conclusion.

7. Addition Property: If $a = b$ and $c = d$, then $a + c = b + d$.
Given: $AB = CD$, $EF = GH$

8. Subtraction Property: If $a = b$ and $c = d$, then $a - c = b - d$.
Given: $m \angle A = m \angle B$, $m \angle R = m \angle S$

9. Multiplication Property: If $a = b$ and $c = d$, then $ac = bd$.
Given: $PQ = RS$, $TU = VW$

10. Division Property: If $a = b$ and $c \neq 0$, then $\frac{a}{c} = \frac{b}{c}$.
Given: $m \angle A = m \angle B$, $m \angle C = 30$

11. Substitution Property: If $a = b$, then a and b can replace each other in any equation or inequality.
Given: $ST = XY + 60$, $XY = 90$

State a part of Theorem 1.1 as a reason for each statement.

12. $\overline{GH}$ is congruent to itself. ___

13. If $\overline{AB} \cong \overline{EF}$, then $\overline{EF} \cong \overline{AB}$.

write out what u do

14. If $\angle R \cong \angle S$ and $\angle S \cong \angle T$, then $\angle R \cong \angle T$.

15. If $\angle CDE \cong \angle FGH$, then $\angle FGH \cong \angle CDE$.

16. Any angle is congruent to itself.

17. If $\overline{GH} \cong \overline{CD}$ and $\overline{CD} \cong \overline{EF}$, then $\overline{GH} \cong \overline{EF}$.

B

Write a paragraph proof to prove that each conditional is true.

18. If $\frac{x}{4} - 7 = 16$, then $x = 92$.

19. If $15p + 4 = 64$, then $p = 4$.

20. If $5x - 4 = 24 + (-2x)$, then $x = 4$.

21. If $3(n + 1) = 99$, then $n = 32$.

Use the given property to complete each statement.

22. Symmetric Property: If $\angle DEF \cong \angle GHI$, then ___ .

23. Transitive Property: If $AB + CD = EF$ and $EF = GH$, then ___ .

24. Substitution Property: If $m \angle 1 - m \angle 2 = 90$ and $m \angle 2 = m \angle 4$, then ___ .

25. Reflexive Property: $m \angle RST = $ ___

26. Addition Property: If $MN = RS$ and $AB = CD$, then ___ .

27. Subtraction Property: If $m \angle 1 + 45 = m \angle 2 + 45$, then ___ .

28. Multiplication Property: If $\frac{1}{5}CD = 15$, then ___ .

29. Division Property: If $3m \angle JKL = 111$, then ___ .

30. $\angle APB \cong \angle DPE$, $\angle CPD \cong \angle DPE$, $\angle DPE \cong \angle BPF$
Which other angles are congruent?

31. $\overline{AB} \cong \overline{CD}$, $\overline{EF} \cong \overline{CD}$, $\overline{AC} \cong \overline{DF}$, $\overline{DF} \cong \overline{CE}$
Which other segments are congruent?

C

32. Write a paragraph proof that congruence of segments is transitive.
33. Write a paragraph proof that congruence of segments is reflexive.
34. Write a paragraph proof that congruence of angles is symmetric.

Critical Thinking

35. A relation that is reflexive, symmetric, and transitive is called an **equivalence relation.** For example, all three of these properties hold for "is congruent to," and so it is an equivalence relation. Which of the following are equivalence relations? If a relation is not an equivalence relation, give a counterexample.

a. is younger than
b. is in the same class in school as
c. is the same type of angle as
d. is greater than (for segment lengths)

Mixed Review

1. Name three collinear points.
2. $BD = 15$, $CD = 8$ Find BC.
3. Name the vertex of $\angle ABD$.
4. Name the point in the interior of $\angle EBD$.
5. $m\angle EBC = 125$, $m\angle ABD = 70$ Find $m\angle ABE$.
6. $m\angle EBA = 3x + 10$, $m\angle ABC = 7x - 10$,
$m\angle EBC = 100$ Find $m\angle EBA$.
7. $\overrightarrow{BA}$ bisects $\angle EBC$. C is the midpoint of $\overline{BD}$.
Name two congruent angles and two congruent segments.

Quiz

Use the statement "If an angle is ~~not~~ a right angle, then it ~~does not~~ measures 90."

1. Write the hypothesis and conclusion of the statement.
2. Write the converse of the statement. Flip ~~the~~ measures 90 then right angle
3. Write the inverse of the statement. not
4. Write the contrapositive of the statement. not
5. Write the statement as a biconditional. if + only if
6. Given that $\angle RST$ is a right angle, use the statement to draw a conclusion.

7. Which property allows you to conclude that the following is true?
If $ST = UV$, then $UV = ST$.
8. Use the addition property (if $a = b$ and $c = d$, then $a + c = b + d$) to draw a conclusion.
Given: $EF = FG$, $AB = BC$ EF + AB = FG + BC
9. State a part of Theorem 1.1 as a reason for the following statement.
If $\angle B \cong \angle C$, then $\angle C \cong \angle B$.

CRITICAL THINKING

Common Errors in Everyday Reasoning

These situations will help you discover or review some common reasoning errors.

Situation 1

Jason saw an advertisement on television that stated, "If you want top power and control, then buy a Smasher tennis racket." He assumed that, "If I buy a Smasher, then I'll have top power and control."

1. If the statement in the advertisement is represented by $p \rightarrow q$, how would you represent Jason's assumption?
2. Do you think Jason's reasoning was logically correct? Explain why or why not.

Situation 2

Martina's teacher said, "If you don't get an A on this test, then you won't get an A in the course." Martina assumed that, "If I do get an A on this test, then I will get an A in the course."

1. If Martina's teacher's statement is represented by $p \rightarrow q$, how would you represent Martina's assumption?
2. Do you think Martina's reasoning was logically correct? Explain why or why not.

You learned earlier that when the statement is true, the converse and inverse are not necessarily true. In the situation above, Jason was making a very common error in reasoning called *assuming the converse*. Martina was making a common error in reasoning called *assuming the inverse*.

Try These Situations

Is there a reasoning error in each situation? If so, explain what error was made.

1. Isaac's little brother Ted knew that if a vehicle was a car, then it had four wheels. When given a toy wagon with four wheels, he concluded that it was a car.
2. Jose's coach said, "If you win the most tryout games, then you will make the tennis team." Jose did not make the team, so he concluded that he did not win the most games.
3. Tanya read that if a dog is show quality, then it has registration papers. She told her friend Marta that a dog that has no registration papers is not show quality.
4. Mr. Wilson read an advertisement that said, "If you take one ABC tablet each day, then you will keep your good health." He began to feel uneasy thinking, "If I don't take an ABC tablet each day, then I won't keep my good health."

If you take one ABC tablet each day, then you will keep your good health.

5. Cathy's mother told her, "If you don't keep your room clean, then you won't get new wallpaper next spring." Cathy kept her room clean and was angry when she did not get new wallpaper. She felt her mother had broken her promise.
6. Copy a television or magazine advertisement that you think wants the viewer to assume the converse or inverse. Explain your interpretation.

CHAPTER SUMMARY

Vocabulary

acute (1-3)
angle (1-3)
biconditional (1-6)
bisector (1-4)
collinear (1-1)
conclusion (1-6)
conditional (1-6)
congruent (1-4)
contrapositive (1-6)
converse (1-6)
coordinate(s) (1-2)
coplanar (1-1)
counterexample (1-6)
deductive reasoning (1-8)
degree (1-3)

distance (1-2)
equiangular (1-5)
equilateral (1-5)
exterior (1-3)
hypotenuse (1-5)
hypothesis (1-6)
interior (1-3)
intersection (1-1)
inverse (1-6)
isosceles (1-5)
leg (1-5)
line (1-1)
midpoint (1-4)
noncollinear (1-1)
noncoplanar (1-1)

obtuse (1-3)
plane (1-1)
point (1-1)
postulate (1-1)
proof (1-8)
protractor (1-3)
ray (1-3)
right (1-3)
scalene (1-5)
segment (1-2)
side (1-3)
space (1-1)
theorem (1-8)
triangle (1-5)
vertex (1-3)

Key Ideas

1. Three basic undefined terms in geometry are *point*, *line*, and *plane*. These are used to define other terms.

2. A postulate is a statement accepted as true without proof. We have studied the Ruler Postulate, the Segment and Angle Addition Postulates, the Protractor Postulate, the Midpoint Postulate, and the Angle Bisector Postulate.

3. Lines are denoted $\overleftrightarrow{AB}$, rays $\overrightarrow{AB}$, and segments $\overline{AB}$. The length of $\overline{AB}$ is denoted AB.

4. An angle consists of two rays with a common endpoint and is denoted $\angle ABC$, with the letter in the middle representing the vertex. Angles are classified as acute, right, or obtuse depending upon their measure.

5. Congruent segments are segments that have the same length. Congruent angles are angles that have the same measure.

6. The midpoint of a segment is the point that divides the segment into two congruent segments. The bisector of an angle is a ray in the interior of the angle that divides the angle into two congruent angles.

7. A triangle is a figure formed by three segments joining three noncollinear points and is denoted $\triangle ABC$. Triangles are classified by the number of congruent sides they have or by the type of angles they have.

8. An if-then statement is called a conditional. The *if* part is the hypothesis, the *then* part is the conclusion. The converse is formed by interchanging the hypothesis and the conclusion.

9. A conclusion drawn from given information can be supported by citing a definition, a postulate, or a conditional known to be true.

10. Deductive reasoning is a process in which conclusions are drawn logically from given information. A theorem is a mathematical statement that can be proved to be true using deductive reasoning.

CHAPTER REVIEW

1-1

Determine whether each statement is true or false.

1. The intersection of $\overleftrightarrow{RT}$ and $\overleftrightarrow{UV}$ is point S.
2. Points R, S, and T are coplanar.
3. V is between R and T.

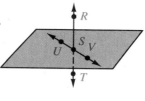

1-2

4. Find the distance betweeen the pair of points with coordinates -10 and 7.
5. B is betwen A and C. $AB = 3x - 4$, $BC = x - 5$, $AC = 19$
   Find AB.

1-3

Complete each statement.

6. The vertex of $\angle DCE$ is point ___ .
7. $m\angle DCA = 37$, $m\angle ACF = 20$, $m\angle DCF =$ ___

1-4

8. $\overrightarrow{CF}$ bisects $\angle ACB$. Name two congruent angles.
9. $\overleftrightarrow{BD}$ bisects $\overline{AE}$. $AC = 4x - 3$, $CE = 3x + 5$ Find x.

1-5

10. Name an isosceles triangle in the figure to the right.
11. Name an obtuse triangle in the figure to the right.
12. Find the distance between the points with coordinates $(1, -4)$ and $(9, -10)$.

1-6

13. State the hypothesis and conclusion.
    If a number is positive, then it is greater than zero.
14. Write a conditional using the following.
    Hypothesis: Mr. Wong lives in Ohio.
    Conclusion: He lives in the United States.
15. Write the converse.
    If a triangle is equilateral, then its sides are congruent.

$$d = \sqrt{(x_2 - x_1)^2 + (y_2 - y_1)^2}$$

$$d = \sqrt{64 + 36}$$
$$d = \sqrt{100}$$

$$d = 10$$

1-7

16. Use the conditional "If two segments are congruent, then they have the
    same length" to draw a conclusion.
    Given: $\overline{EF} \cong \overline{GH}$
17. State a conditional that supports the conclusion:
    Given: $m\angle A = 90$ Conclusion: $\angle A$ is a right angle.

1-8

18. Use the transitive property (if $a = b$ and $b = c$, then $a = c$) to draw a conclusion.
    Given: $AB = BC$, $BC = CD$
19. Which property of equality allows you to conclude that if $RS = TU$, then
    $TU = RS$?

CHAPTER TEST

1. Name three collinear points.
2. Name the intersection of $\overline{CD}$ and $\overline{ED}$.
3. Name the intersection of the plane containing
   G, F, H and the plane containing B, C, H.
4. Find the distance between the points with
   coordinates 4 and -7.
5. Find JL.
6. The distance between which pair of points is 2?

Complete each statement.

7. The Segment Addition Postulate states that if V is between U and W,
   then $UV +$ ___ $= UW$.
8. Q is between P and R. $PQ = t + 7$, $QR = 8t - 4$, $PR = 12$, $QR =$ ___
9. If $MP = 5$, $NP = 17$, and $NM = 12$, then point ___ is between the other two.

10. The vertex of $\angle WXY$ is point ___ .
11. $m\angle WXY = 40$, $m\angle YXZ = 45$, $m\angle WXZ =$ ___
12. $m\angle WXZ = 74$, $m\angle WXY = 2x + 10$, $m\angle YXZ = x - 26$, $x =$ ___
13. X is the midpoint of $\overline{VY}$. Name two congruent segments.
14. $\overrightarrow{XY}$ bisects $\angle WXZ$. $m\angle WXY = 56$ Find $m\angle WXZ$.
15. $\angle WXZ$ is a right angle. $\overrightarrow{XY}$ bisects $\angle WXZ$.   Find $m\angle YXZ$.

Complete each statement.

16. A triangle with no sides congruent is called ___ .
17. An isosceles triangle has ___ congruent sides.
18. If $m\angle J = 30$, $m\angle K = 140$, and $m\angle L = 10$, then $\triangle JKL$ is a(n) ___ triangle.
19. The distance between the points with coordinates $(0, 0)$ and $(6, 8)$ is ___ .
20. The distance between the points with coordinates $(2, 1)$ and $(5, 5)$ is ___ .
21. The distance between the points with coordinates $(-2, -1)$ and $(5, -5)$ is ___ .

Use the statement "If it is raining, then we will play chess."

22. Write the hypothesis and the conclusion of the statement.
23. Write the converse of the statement.
24. Write the contrapositive of the statement. − use not

25. True or false? A postulate cannot be used to support a conclusion.
26. Use the conditional "If an angle is less than 90°, then it is acute" to draw
    a conclusion. Given: $m\angle BCD = 79$
27. State a conditional that supports the conclusion.
    Given: $\triangle MNP$ is isosceles. Conclusion: Two sides of $\triangle MNP$ are congruent.
28. True or false? Deductive reasoning is a process in which hypotheses are
    drawn logically from given information.
29. Use the symmetric property to draw a conclusion. Given: $m\angle A = m\angle Z$
30. Which property or theorem allows you to conclude that the following statement is
    true? If $\overline{AB} \cong \overline{CD}$ and $\overline{CD} \cong \overline{EF}$, then $\overline{AB} \cong \overline{EF}$.

PROBLEM SOLVING

Draw a Diagram

Problems can be fun to solve if you know different ways to tackle them. There are several techniques for solving mathematical problems. One of these is to Draw a Diagram.

Example

The manager of a shopping mall was asked to rope off a rectangular section of the parking lot for an automobile show. The area roped off was 200 ft by 300 ft. Posts were to be placed every 25 ft around the lot. How many posts were needed?

UNDERSTAND the problem.
Question: How many posts were needed?
Data: The area was 200 ft by 300 ft. Posts were placed every 25 ft around the lot.

Develop and carry out a PLAN.
Draw a diagram.

Find the ANSWER and CHECK.
From the diagram we see that 40 posts were needed.
The answer is reasonable.

Problems

Draw a diagram to help solve each problem.

1. How many spokes does a wheel have if there are 16 spaces between the spokes?

2. What is the greatest number of pieces into which a pie can be cut with four straight cuts? (The pieces may not be stacked.)

3. Four cars are parked in a row. The white car is 25 ft to the right of the blue car and 15 ft to the right of the grey car. The grey car is 35 ft to the left of the red car. What is the distance between the blue car and the red car?

4. A bug crawls up a pole 2 in. in 2 minutes, then slips down 1 in. in one minute, then crawls up 2 in. in 2 minutes, and so on. At this rate, how long will it take the bug to reach a height of 10 inches?

5. Roberto can hang wallpaper on a square wall with 12-ft sides in 40 minutes. Assuming the wallpaper is hung at the same rate, how long will it take him to cover a square section of wall with 6-ft sides?

6. Mapleton is midway between Elmville and Jefferson. Hoover City is midway between Elmville and Mapleton. Plymouth is midway between Elmville and Hoover City. If the distance between Elmville and Plymouth is 12 mi, what is the distance between Elmville and Jefferson?

Introduction to Proof

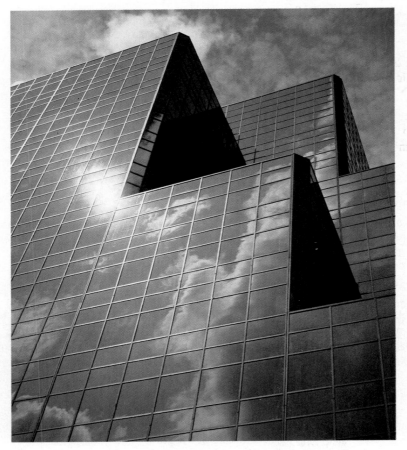

The horizontal and vertical lines on this building are perpendicular. Give a convincing argument that they form congruent vertical angles.

PROOF: SEGMENTS, LINES, AND ANGLES

OBJECTIVE: *Complete two-column proofs.*

2-1 Two-Column Proofs

In Chapter 1, you learned that the proof of a theorem can be written in paragraph form. In this chapter, you will learn how to organize your reasoning to write a proof in two-column form.

In a **two-column proof,** such as the one shown below, statements that lead to the desired conclusion are listed in the left column and a reason for each statement is listed in the right column.

Given: $\triangle ABC$ with $\overline{AB} \cong \overline{AC}$

Prove: $\triangle ABC$ is isosceles.

Proof

Statements	Reasons
1. $\triangle ABC$ with $\overline{AB} \cong \overline{AC}$	1. Given
2. $\triangle ABC$ is isosceles.	2. Definition of isosceles triangle (If at least two sides of a triangle are congruent, then the triangle is isosceles.)

These reasons can be any of the following: given information, definitions, postulates (including algebraic properties), or previously proven theorems.

In the left column, Statement 1 is the given information. Statement 2 is the conclusion. In the right column, Reason 1, "Given," tells why Statement 1 is true. Reason 2 is a definition that, coupled with the given information, supports the conclusion. In this proof, an abbreviated statement of a definition is given in parentheses, but in the proofs that follow it is sufficient to state only the name of the definition. This example shows a two-column proof that has more than two steps.

Example

Complete the proof by supplying the missing reasons.

Given: B is the midpoint of $\overline{AC}$. C is the midpoint of $\overline{BD}$.

Prove: $\overline{AB} \cong \overline{CD}$

Proof

Statements	Reasons
1. B is the midpoint of $\overline{AC}$.	1. Given
2. C is the midpoint of $\overline{BD}$.	2. Given
3. $\overline{AB} \cong \overline{BC}$	3. Definition of midpoint
4. $\overline{BC} \cong \overline{CD}$	4. Def of midpoint
5. $\overline{AB} \cong \overline{CD}$	5. Segment congruence is transitive. (Theorem 1.1)

Solution

2. Given

4. Definition of midpoint

The summary below describes the parts of a two-column proof. The steps for constructing a two-column proof to prove a theorem will be given in Lesson 2-5.

Key Elements of a Two-Column Proof

1. *Given:* a statement of the facts given to be true
2. *Diagram:* a figure that shows the given information
3. *Prove:* a statement of the conclusion to be established
4. *Statements:* numbered statements in the left column that must be shown to be true in order to prove the conclusion
5. *Reasons:* numbered reasons in the right column that support the statements in the left column—can be given information, definitions, postulates (including properties of algebra), or previously proven theorems

Class Exercises

Short Answer

1. What are five main parts of a two-column proof?
2. What four types of reasons can be used to support statements in a two-column proof?

Sample Exercises

3. Complete the proof by choosing a reason for each statement.

   Given: $\overrightarrow{AC}$ bisects $\angle BAD$. $\overrightarrow{AD}$ bisects $\angle CAE$.

   Prove: $\angle BAC \cong \angle DAE$

Proof Statements | Reasons

Statements	Reasons	Choose from these reasons:
1. $\overrightarrow{AC}$ bisects $\angle BAD$.	1.	a. Congruence of angles is transitive (Theorem 1.1).
2. $\overrightarrow{AD}$ bisects $\angle CAE$.	2. D	b. Given
3. $\angle BAC \cong \angle CAD$	3. C	c. Definition of angle bisector
4. $\angle CAD \cong \angle DAE$	4. C	
5. $\angle BAC \cong \angle DAE$	5. A	

4. In the proof in Class Exercise 3, which two statements were used, together with Theorem 1.1, to establish the truth of Statement 5?

Discussion

5. Explain how the following reasoning process is used in the proof in Class Exercise 3.

   "Whenever $p \rightarrow q$ is true and p is true, then q is true." (See Ch. 1, p. 39.)

6. A research scientist claimed he had found a compound which would prevent the common cold. Suppose he gave this compound to 20 people for a period of two months. If none of these people had gotten a cold in these two months, would the scientist have proven that the compound is a preventive? Why or why not? Discuss the meaning of "proof."

Exercises

A

Complete each proof by choosing a reason for each statement.

1. Given: $\overrightarrow{RV}$ bisects $\angle SRT$.

$\angle 3 \cong \angle 1$

Prove: $\angle 3 \cong \angle 2$

Proof Statements | Reasons

1. $\overrightarrow{RV}$ bisects $\angle SRT$.	1. ___ *Choose from these reasons:*
2. $\angle 3 \cong \angle 1$	2. ___ **a.** Definition of angle bisector
3. $\angle 1 \cong \angle 2$	3. ___ **b.** Angle congruence is transitive.
4. $\angle 3 \cong \angle 2$	4. ___ **c.** Given

2. Given: $BD = AD$

D is between A and C.

Prove: $BD + DC = AC$

Proof Statements | Reasons

1. $BD = AD$	1. ___ *Choose from these reasons:*
2. D is between A and C.	2. ___ **a.** Substitution Property
3. $AD + DC = AC$	3. ___ **b.** Given
4. $BD + DC = AC$	4. ___ **c.** Segment Addition Postulate

Choose reasons from the following list for each proof.

a. Substitution Property	**f.** Two angles $\cong$ to the same angle
b. Angle Addition Postulate	are $\cong$. (Theorem 1.3)
c. Definition of midpoint	**g.** Given
d. Congruence of segments is	**h.** Segment Addition Postulate
transitive (Theorem 1.1).	**i.** Addition of real numbers
e. Definition of angle bisector	

3. Given: $\overrightarrow{AH}$ is the bisector of $\angle GAI$.

Prove: $\angle GAH \cong \angle HAI$

Proof Statements | Reasons

1. $\overrightarrow{AH}$ is the bisector of $\angle GAI$.	1. ___
2. $\angle GAH \cong \angle HAI$	2. ___

4. Given: $\angle 1 \cong \angle 3$, $\angle 5 \cong \angle 3$

Prove: $\angle 1 \cong \angle 5$

Proof Statements | Reasons

1. $\angle 1 \cong \angle 3$	1. ___
2. $\angle 5 \cong \angle 3$	2. ___
3. $\angle 1 \cong \angle 5$	3. ___

5. Given: N is in the interior of $\angle GAB$.

Prove: $m\angle GAN + m\angle NAB = m\angle GAB$

Proof Statements   Reasons

    1. N is in the interior of $\angle GAB$.   1. ___

    2. $\angle GAN + m\angle NAB = m\angle GAB$ 2. ___

6. Given: B is between A and C.

    $AB = 9$

    $BC = 7$

Prove: $16 = AC$

Proof Statements   Reasons

    1. B is between A and C.   1. ___

    2. $AB = 9$, $BC = 7$ 2. ___

    3. $AB + BC = AC$ 3. ___

    4. $9 + 7 = AC$ 4. ___

    5. $16 = AC$ 5. ___

7. Given: $\overline{NA} \cong \overline{AM}$

    M is the midpoint of $\overline{AB}$.

Prove: $\overline{NA} \cong \overline{MB}$

Proof Statements   Reasons

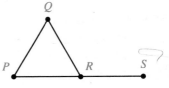

    1. $\overline{NA} \cong \overline{AM}$ 1. ___

    2. M is the midpoint of $\overline{AB}$.   2. ___

    3. $\overline{AM} \cong \overline{MB}$ 3. ___

    4. $\overline{NA} \cong \overline{MB}$ 4. ___

Complete each proof by supplying the missing reasons.

8. Given: $\overline{PQ} \cong \overline{RS}$

    $\overline{QR} \cong \overline{RS}$

Prove: $\triangle PQR$ is isosceles.

Proof Statements   Reasons

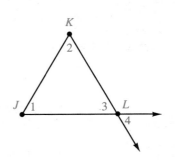

    1. $\overline{PQ} \cong \overline{RS}$ 1. ___

    2. $\overline{QR} \cong \overline{RS}$ 2. ___

    3. $\overline{PQ} \cong \overline{QR}$ 3. ___

    4. $\triangle PQR$ is isosceles.   4. ___

9. Given: $\triangle JKL$ is equiangular.

    $\angle 4 \cong \angle 3$

Prove: $\angle 4 \cong \angle 1$

Proof Statements   Reasons

    1. $\angle 4 \cong \angle 3$ 1. ___

    2. $\triangle JKL$ is equiangular.   2. ___

    3. $\angle 1 \cong \angle 3$ 3. ___

    4. $\angle 4 \cong \angle 1$ 4. ___

10. Given: H is the midpoint of $\overline{GI}$. $\overline{JH} \cong \overline{HI}$

Prove: $\triangle GHJ$ is isosceles.

Proof

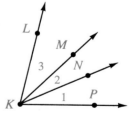

Statements	Reasons
1. $\overline{JH} \cong \overline{HI}$	1. ___
2. H is the midpoint of $\overline{GI}$.	2. ___
3. $\overline{GH} \cong \overline{HI}$	3. ___
4. $\overline{GH} \cong \overline{HJ}$	4. ___
5. $\triangle GHJ$ is isosceles.	5. ___

B

Complete each proof by supplying the missing statements or reasons.

11. Given: Q is between P and R.

Prove: $PQ = PR - QR$

Proof

Statements	Reasons
1. ___	1. ___
2. $PQ + QR = PR$	2. ___
3. $QR = QR$	3. Reflexive Property
4. $PQ + QR - QR = PR - QR$	4. ___
5. ___	5. Subtraction of real numbers

12. Given: $\triangle ABD$ is equilateral. $\overline{BD} \cong \overline{BC}$

Prove: $\triangle CBA$ is isosceles.

Proof

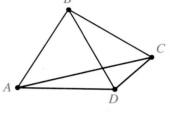

Statements	Reasons
1. $\triangle ABD$ is equilateral.	1. ___
2. ___	2. Given
3. $\overline{AB} \cong \overline{BD}$	3. ___
4. ___	4. Congruence of segments is transitive.
5. $\triangle CBA$ is isosceles.	5. ___

13. Given: $\overrightarrow{KM}$ is in the interior of $\angle LKN$ and $\angle LKP$. $\overrightarrow{KN}$ is in the interior of $\angle PKM$.

Prove: $m\angle LKP = m\angle 1 + m\angle 2 + m\angle 3$

Proof

Statements	Reasons
1. $\overrightarrow{KM}$ is in the interior of $\angle LKN$ and $\angle LKP$. $\overrightarrow{KN}$ is in the interior of $\angle PKM$.	1. ___
2. $m\angle PKM = m\angle 1 + m\angle 2$	2. ___
3. $m\angle LKP = m\angle PKM + m\angle 3$	3. ___
4. ___	4. Substitution Property

C

14. Write a two-column proof.

Given: $\overline{TU}$ bisects $\overline{RS}$. $\overline{UM} \cong \overline{MS}$

Prove: $\overline{RM} \cong \overline{UM}$

15. Draw a conclusion from the given data. Then write a two-column proof to show that your conclusion follows from the given data.

Given: G, H, I and J are collinear.
$GH + HI = IJ$

Critical Thinking

16. A car mechanic often uses "theorems" to "prove" things. Suppose it was given that (a) the car will not start and (b) the starter grinds very slowly. Choose reasons from the following "theorems" and write a two-column proof that the battery needs recharging.

Theorem 1: If the battery is dead, then the car will not start.
Theorem 2: If the starter grinds very slowly, then the battery voltage is low.
Theorem 3: If the battery voltage is low, then the battery needs recharging.

Mixed Review

1. $\overrightarrow{GB}$ bisects $\overline{DF}$. Name the congruent segments formed.
2. $GF = 12$, $GC = 17$, $\overline{FC} \cong \overline{EB}$
   Find EB.
3. $m\angle AGC = 10x$, $m\angle AGB = 5x + 3$, $m\angle BGC = 22$
   Find $m\angle AGC$.
4. $\overrightarrow{GB}$ bisects $\angle AGC$. $m\angle AGB = 2x$, $m\angle AGC = 3x + 9$
   Find $m\angle BGC$.

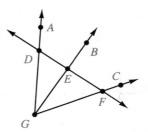

Historical Note

The Beginning of Geometry

Geometry is derived from two Greek words—*ge*, meaning earth, and *metrein*, meaning to measure. Geometry was used by Egyptians as long ago as 3000 B.C., when annual flooding and channel changes of the Nile River required officials to establish new boundaries and to calculate the areas of lands to be taxed. Their calculations were based on observation and measurement.

The uncertainty of the rules that were arrived at by Egyptians through "trial and error" was a major concern of many Greek scholars. Around 300 B.C., Greek scholars began developing a geometry based upon logical deduction. The most famous among the Greek scholars was Euclid, a mathematician and teacher who combined the geometric knowledge of his time with a more logical system. His famous book, *The Elements*, presents geometry in an organized fashion. It is this logical pattern of thinking, commonly called Euclidean Geometry, that you will study in this book.

2-2 Complementary, Supplementary, and Vertical Angles

The ideas about angles you learned in Chapter 1 will be used in this section to help you see that pairs of angles are often related in special ways. You will see how some of these relationships can be proved using a two-column proof. Consider the following definitions.

■ **DEFINITION**

Complementary angles are two angles whose measures have a sum of 90.

Each angle is called the complement of the other. $\angle P$ and $\angle Q$ are complementary since $m\angle P + m\angle Q = 90$.

■ **DEFINITION**

Supplementary angles are two angles whose measures have a sum of 180.

Each angle is called the supplement of the other. $\angle E$ and $\angle F$ are supplementary since $m\angle E + m\angle F = 180$.

Example 1

$\angle ABD$ is complementary to $\angle DBC$. Find $m\angle DBC$ and $m\angle ABD$.

Solution

$x + 5x = 90$ *The sum of the measures of complementary angles is 90.*
$6x = 90$
$x = 15, m\angle DBC = 15$
$5x = 75, m\angle ABD = 75$

Try This

$\angle EFH$ is supplementary to $\angle HFG$. Find $m\angle HFG$ and $m\angle EFH$.

Two angles that have the same vertex and a common side, but which have no common interior points, are called **adjacent angles.** Angles 1 and 2 are adjacent. They each have vertex B and common side $\overrightarrow{BD}$.

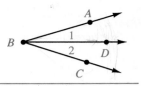

■ DEFINITION

A **linear pair** of angles is a pair of adjacent angles with the two noncommon sides on the same line.

Angles 3 and 4 form a linear pair. They are adjacent and their noncommon sides, $\overrightarrow{HK}$ and $\overrightarrow{HG}$, are on a line.

The following postulate describes an important property of a linear pair of angles.

● POSTULATE 12   Linear Pair Postulate

Two angles that form a linear pair are supplementary.

Postulate 12 can be used to prove Theorem 2.1.

◆ THEOREM 2.1

The sum of the measures of the angles in a linear pair is 180.

Proof Since the two angles of a linear pair are supplementary (Postulate 12), it follows from the definition of supplementary angles that the sum of the measures of the two angles is 180.

Example 2

$\angle 1$ and $\angle 2$ form a linear pair. $m\angle 2$ is three times $m\angle 1$. Find $m\angle 1$ and $m\angle 2$.

Solution

Let $x = m\angle 1$. Then $3x = m\angle 2$.

So, $x + 3x = 180$ *The sum of the measures of the angles in a*
       $4x = 180$ *linear pair is 180.*
         $x = 45, 3x = 135$ $m\angle 1 = 45, m\angle 2 = 135$

Try This

$\angle 3$ and $\angle 4$ form a linear pair. $m\angle 4$ is 30 more than double $m\angle 3$. Find $m\angle 3$ and $m\angle 4$.

Vertical angles are two nonadjacent angles formed by a pair of intersecting lines. $\angle 1$ and $\angle 3$ are vertical angles, as are $\angle 2$ and $\angle 4$.

The following is a useful theorem about vertical angles.

◆ **THEOREM 2.2** Vertical Angle Theorem
If two angles are vertical angles, then they are congruent.

Given: $\angle 1$ and $\angle 3$ are vertical angles.
Prove: $\angle 1 \cong \angle 3$

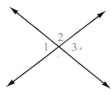

Proof Statements

1. $\angle 1$ and $\angle 3$ are vertical angles.	**1.** Given
2. $m\angle 1 + m\angle 2 = 180$ $m\angle 3 + m\angle 2 = 180$	**2.** The sum of the measures of the angles in a linear pair is 180 (Theorem 2.1).
3. $m\angle 1 + m\angle 2 = m\angle 3 + m\angle 2$	**3.** Substitution Property of Equality
4. $m\angle 1 = m\angle 3$	**4.** Subtraction Property of Equality
5. $\angle 1 \cong \angle 3$	**5.** Definition of congruent angles

Class Exercises

Short Answer

1. Name an angle that is supplementary to $\angle QMS$.
2. Name an angle that is complementary to $\angle QMS$.
3. Name a pair of adjacent angles with noncommon sides not on a line.
4. Name a pair of adjacent angles with noncommon sides on a line.
5. Which angle forms a linear pair with $\angle QMS$? with $\angle PMR$?
6. Name a pair of vertical angles.
7. Name an angle that is complementary but not adjacent to $\angle TMQ$.

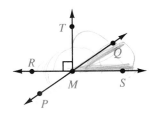

Sample Exercises

Assume that $m\angle QMS = 40$ and give the measure of each angle.

8. $m\angle TMQ$ 9. $m\angle RMP$ 10. $m\angle PMS$ 11. $m\angle RMQ$

12. If $m\angle RMP = 2x + 6$ and $m\angle QMS = 5x - 24$, find $m\angle RMP$ and $m\angle QMS$.

Give the measure of the complement and supplement of each angle.

13. $m\angle A = 40$ 14. $m\angle B = 65$ 15. $m\angle D = 87$
16. $m\angle M = x$ 17. $m\angle Q = 20 - x$ 18. $m\angle J = x^2$

19. Find the measure of an angle that is half the measure of its complement.

Discussion

Determine whether each statement is true or false. If true, give a convincing argument to support the statement. If false, give a counterexample.

20. The supplement of an acute angle is an obtuse angle.
21. The supplement of the complement of $\angle A$ always measures 90 more than $m\angle A$.

Exercises

A

1. Name a pair of angles that are both congruent and supplementary.
2. Name a pair of angles that are not congruent.
3. Name a pair of vertical angles.
4. Name a pair of adjacent angles that do not form a linear pair.
5. Name a pair of nonadjacent complementary angles.

Assume that $m \angle GXF = 40$ and $m \angle FXE = 30$. Find each measure.

6. $m \angle AXG$ 7. $m \angle CXB$ 8. $m \angle AXC$
9. $m \angle BXF$ 10. $m \angle AXD$ 11. $m \angle BXD$

12. If $m \angle BXD = 4x - 50$ and $m \angle GXE = 2x + 10$, find $m \angle BXD$ and $m \angle GXE$.
13. If $m \angle AXG = 3x$ and $m \angle GXF = 2x - 10$, find $m \angle AXG$ and $m \angle GXF$.
14. If $m \angle GXF = 2x + 15$ and $m \angle GXC = 3x + 5$, find $m \angle GXF$ and $m \angle GXC$.

15. If two angles are congruent and complementary, what are their measures?

Complete each proof.

16. **Given:** $m \angle 1 = 35$, $m \angle 2 = 55$

    Prove: $\angle 1$ and $\angle 2$ are complementary.

Proof Statements	Reasons
1. $m \angle 1 = 35$, $m \angle 2 = 55$	1. ___
2. $m \angle 1 + m \angle 2 = 35 + 55$	2. ___
3. $m \angle 1 + m \angle 2 = 90$	3. Addition of real numbers
4. $\angle 1$ and $\angle 2$ are complementary.	4. ___

17. **Given:** $\angle 1$ and $\angle 2$ are vertical angles. $\angle 3 \cong \angle 2$

    Prove: $\angle 3 \cong \angle 1$

Proof Statements	Reasons
1. $\angle 3 \cong \angle 2$	1. ___
2. $\angle 1$ and $\angle 2$ are vertical angles.	2. ___
3. $\angle 1 \cong \angle 2$	3. ___
4. $\angle 3 \cong \angle 1$	4. ___

18. **Given:** $\angle 1$ and $\angle 2$ form a linear pair. $m \angle 3 = m \angle 1$

    Prove: $\angle 2$ and $\angle 3$ are supplementary.

Proof Statements	Reasons
1. $m \angle 3 = m \angle 1$	1. ___
2. $\angle 1 + \angle 2$ form a linear pair.	2. ___
3. $m \angle 1 + m \angle 2 = 180$	3. ___
4. $m \angle 3 + m \angle 2 = 180$	4. ___
5. $\angle 2$ and $\angle 3$ are supplementary.	5. ___

19. The measure of one angle is twice the measure of its complement. Find the measures of the angles.
20. The measure of one angle is eight times the measure of its supplement. Find the measures of the angles.
21. In order to gain maximum distance, an Olympic ski jumper is interested in the measure of the angle formed by his or her body and skis. If $m\angle 1 = 155$, find $m\angle 2$.

B

Determine whether each statement is always, sometimes, or never true. Draw a figure to show your answer.

22. Two complementary angles are also adjacent angles.
23. Two angles in a linear pair are adjacent angles.
24. Vertical angles are adjacent angles.
25. An acute and an obtuse angle are complementary.
26. An angle and its supplement are congruent.

Find the measure of the complement and supplement of $\angle A$.

27. $m\angle A = 67.5$ 28. $m\angle A = 2y - 10$ 29. $m\angle A = 30 - 2x$

30. $m\angle AEC = 2x + 30$, $m\angle DEB = 3x + 10$.   Find $m\angle FED$ and $m\angle CEB$.
31. $m\angle AEC = 2x + 7$, $m\angle BEC = 5x - 2$.   Find $m\angle DEB$ and $m\angle FED$.
32. $m\angle AEC = 12x + 4$, $m\angle GEC = 6x + 14$.   Find $m\angle DEB$ and $m\angle FED$.
33. $m\angle AEC = 3x + 5$ and $m\angle DEF = 2x - 10$.   Find $m\angle DEF$ and $m\angle DEB$.

34. The difference in the measures of two supplementary angles is 38. Find the measures of the two angles.
35. The measure of the supplement of an angle is 30 more than twice the measure of the angle. Find the measures of the angles.
36. The difference in the measures of two complementary angles is 39. Find the measures of the two angles.
37. The ratio of the measure of an angle to its complement is $3:2$. Find the measure of the angles.

38. Complete the proof.
    Given: $\angle 1$ and $\angle 2$ form a linear pair.
    $\angle 1$ and $\angle 4$ are supplementary.

    Prove: $m\angle 4 = m\angle 2$

    Proof

Statements	Reasons
1. $\angle 1$ and $\angle 2$ form a linear pair.	1. ___
2. ___	2. Given
3. $m\angle 1 + m\angle 2 = 180$	3. ___
4. ___	4. Definition of supplementary angles
5. $m\angle 1 + m\angle 4 = m\angle 1 + m\angle 2$	5. ___
6. $m\angle 4 = m\angle 2$	6. ___

C

39. The measure of $\angle A$ is twice the measure of $\angle B$ and the measure of $\angle B$ is twice the measure of $\angle C$. If $\angle A$ and $\angle C$ are supplementary, find the measure of $\angle B$.

40. $\angle ABC$ and $\angle CBD$ form a linear pair. If $\overrightarrow{BE}$ bisects $\angle ABC$ and $\overrightarrow{BF}$ bisects $\angle CBD$, find the measure of $\angle EBF$.

41. Write a two-column proof.

    Given: $\angle 1$ is supplementary to $\angle 2$. $\angle 2 \cong \angle 3$
          $\angle 4$ is supplementary to $\angle 3$.

    Prove: $\angle 1 \cong \angle 4$

Critical Thinking

42. Part of a mathematician's work involves forming generalizations that describe useful relationships among mathematical ideas, such as the following. For any acute angle, what is the difference between its supplement and its complement? Form a generalization and use algebraic expressions to prove that the generalization is true.

Write a convincing argument to support each statement.

43. If two congruent angles form a linear pair, then each is a right angle.

44. The supplement of an obtuse angle is an acute angle.

45. The measure of an angle added to twice the measure of its complement equals the measure of its supplement.

Algebra Review

Solve for x.

1. $3(x - 20) = 5(28 - x)$ **2.** $2(x + 1) + 3 = 3(x - 1)$

3. $3x - 4(x + 2) = x - 8$ **4.** $-2(x - 4) = -1(x - 11)$

Computer Activity

This program finds the supplement of an angle.

```
10 REM FIND THE SUPPLEMENT OF AN ANGLE
20 INPUT "ENTER THE ANGLE MEASURE IN WHOLE
   DEGREES ";M
30 PRINT "THE SUPPLEMENT OF "M" DEGREES IS
   "180-M" DEGREES."
40 END
```

1. Change the program to output the complement of an angle.

2. Change the program so that the user is reprompted for the angle measure if the angle input is of measure less than 1 or of measure greater than 179.

3. Change the program so that the output will also state whether the input angle is obtuse, right, or acute.

2-3 Perpendicular Lines

 EXPLORE Draw a point P on a line q on a piece of wax paper. Figure out how to fold the wax paper so that the fold line r goes through P and forms right angles with line q. Notice that the reflection image of line q in line r is the line q again.

As you may have discovered in Exercise 43 on page 68, when the angles in a linear pair are congruent, they are right angles. This idea will be used to describe special pairs of intersecting lines that play an important role in geometry and its practical applications.

Consider the following definition.

■ DEFINITION

Perpendicular lines are two lines that intersect at right angles.

To indicate that l is perpendicular to m, you can write $l \perp m$.

This definition may be used in proofs as follows.

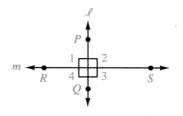

- When you know that $l \perp m$, the definition allows you to conclude that each angle ($\angle 1$, $\angle 2$, $\angle 3$, or $\angle 4$) is a right angle.
- When you know that any of these angles is a right angle, you may conclude that $l \perp m$.

Intersecting segments or rays on perpendicular lines are also considered perpendicular. In the figure, $\overline{PQ} \perp \overline{RS}$ and $\overrightarrow{PQ} \perp \overrightarrow{RS}$.

Example 1

$\overline{BC} \perp \overline{AD}$, $m\angle ABC = \frac{1}{2}x$, $m\angle ACB = 5x - 10$
Find $m\angle ABC$.

Solution

$5x - 10 = 90$ *Since $\overline{BC} \perp \overline{AD}$, $\angle ACB$ is a right angle*
$5x = 100$ *and has measure 90.*
$x = 20$
$m\angle ABC = \frac{1}{2}x = \frac{1}{2}(20) = 10$

Try This

Suppose $\overline{BC} \perp \overline{AD}$, $m\angle BDC = 3x$ and $m\angle ACB = 4x - 6$.   Find $m\angle BDC$.

Even though there are many lines perpendicular to a given line and many lines through a given point, it is natural to feel that there could not be more than one perpendicular to a line through a given point on the line. The following is a convincing argument that this is true.

It would be impossible for both *l* and *k* to be perpendicular to *m* through point *P* because this would produce a situation in which $m \angle QPR = 90$ and $m \angle QPS = 90$. Since *l* and *k* are different lines, $m \angle 1$ is a positive number. From the Angle Addition Postulate, $m \angle QPR + m \angle 1 = m \angle QPS$. But 90 plus a positive number cannot equal 90.

This leads to the following theorem.

◆ **THEOREM 2.3**

Through a given point on a line, there is exactly one line in the plane perpendicular to the given line.

A **line perpendicular to a plane** at *P* is a line through *P* that is perpendicular to *every* line in the plane that passes through *P*. For example, in this figure, line *l* is perpendicular to plane *M*, so it is also perpendicular to $\overleftrightarrow{AB}$ and $\overleftrightarrow{CD}$. The concept of a line being perpendicular to a plane is sometimes used in proofs.

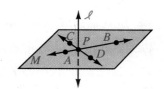

The following definition combines the ideas of perpendicular lines and the bisector of a segment.

■ **DEFINITION**

A **perpendicular bisector** of a segment is a line, segment, ray, or plane that is perpendicular to the segment and bisects it.

In the figure, $l \perp \overline{RS}$ at the midpoint *M* and so *l* is the perpendicular bisector of $\overline{RS}$.

Example 2

$\overline{AB}$ is the perpendicular bisector of $\overline{XY}$.
Draw four conclusions from this information.

Solution

$\overline{AB} \perp \overline{XY}$
$\angle ABX$ and $\angle ABY$ are right angles.
B is the midpoint of $\overline{XY}$.
$\overline{XB} \cong \overline{BY}$

Try This

$\triangle PQR$ is a right triangle and $\overline{RS}$ bisects $\overline{PQ}$.
Draw three conclusions.

PS≅SQ
S=midpoint
PRQ=90°

Class Exercises

Short Answer

1. When you know that two intersecting lines forming angles 1, 2, 3, and 4 are perpendicular, what can you conclude?
2. When you know that any one of the angles 1, 2, 3, or 4 formed by intersecting lines is a right angle, what can you conclude?
3. Describe two characteristics of a perpendicular bisector.

Give three real-world situations that illustrates each idea.

4. perpendicular lines   5. the perpendicular bisector of a segment

Sample Exercises

6. Which line is a perpendicular bisector?
7. Which line is a bisector but not perpendicular?
8. Name four right angles.
9. Find $m \angle DEF$.

10. If $\overline{MN} \perp \overline{ST}$ at X and X is the midpoint of $\overline{ST}$, state two conclusions.

Discussion

Use the figure to determine whether each statement is always, sometimes, or never true. Redraw the figure to support your answer.

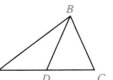

11. If $\overline{BD}$ is the perpendicular bisector of $\overline{AC}$, then $\overline{AC}$ is the perpendicular bisector of $\overline{BD}$.
12. If D is the midpoint of $\overline{AC}$, then $\overline{BD} \perp \overline{AC}$.
13. If $\overline{BD} \perp \overline{AC}$, then D is the midpoint of $\overline{AC}$.
14. Are the reflexive, symmetric, and transitive properties true for the relation "is perpendicular to"?

Exercises

A

Use these figures.

a.   b.   c.   d.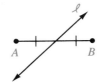

1. Which figure shows a perpendicular bisector?
2. Which figure shows a perpendicular but no bisector?
3. Which figure shows a bisector but no perpendicular?
4. Which figure shows no perpendicular and no bisector?

5. Line l is perpendicular to line m forming $\angle 1$, $\angle 2$, $\angle 3$, and $\angle 4$. What can you conclude about these angles?

6. $\overline{MN} \perp \overline{FG}$ at B Name four right angles.

7. $\overline{SX} \perp \overline{TR}$ in $\triangle RST$ Name a pair of congruent adjacent angles.

8. $\angle TSR$ and $\angle TXS$ are right angles in $\triangle RST$.   Name two pairs of perpendicular lines.

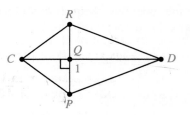

Find the measure of $\angle ABC$.

9.

$\overline{AB} \perp \overline{BD}$
$m\angle 1 = 27$

10.

$\overrightarrow{BC}$ bisects $\angle ABE$.
$\overline{AB} \perp \overline{BE}$

11.

$\overline{AB} \perp \overline{BE}$
$m\angle ABC = 2\,m\,\angle CBD$

12.

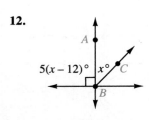

$5(x - 12)°$ $x°$

13.

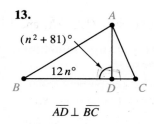

$(n^2 + 81)°$
$12\,n°$
$\overline{AD} \perp \overline{BC}$

14.

$2t°$ $\left(\dfrac{10t}{3}\right)°$
$\overline{CD} \perp \overline{AB}$

15. Complete the proof.

Given: $\angle 1$ is a right angle.
Q is the midpoint of $\overline{PR}$.

Prove: $\overline{CD}$ is the $\perp$ bisector of $\overline{PR}$.

Proof Statements	Reasons
1. Q is the midpoint of $\overline{PR}$.	1. ___
2. $\angle 1$ is a right angle.	2. ___
3. $\overline{CD} \perp \overline{PR}$	3. ___
4. $\overline{CD}$ is the $\perp$ bisector of $\overline{PR}$.	4. ___

B

Complete each proof.

16. **Given:** $m\angle 2 = 90$
$\angle 1$ and $\angle 2$ form a linear pair.

Prove: $m\angle 1 = 90$

Proof Statements	Reasons
1. $m\angle 2 = 90$	1. ___
2. ___	2. Given
3. $m\angle 1 + m\angle 2 = 180$	3. ___
4. $m\angle 1 + 90 = 180$	4. Substitution
5. ___	5. ___

17. Given: $\angle 1$ is complementary to $\angle 2$.
Prove: $\overline{PQ} \perp \overline{PR}$

Proof

Statements	Reasons
1. $\angle 1$ is complementary to $\angle 2$.	1. ___
2. $m\angle 1 + m\angle 2 = 90$	2. ___
3. $m\angle 1 + m\angle 2 = m\angle QPR$	3. ___
4. ___	4. Substitution
5. $\angle QPR$ is a right angle.	5. ___
6. ___	6. ___

18. To avoid slipping, mountain climbers try to keep their legs perpendicular to the side of the ledge. If the ledge is 60° off the vertical, find the climber's angle.

19. Draw two intersecting lines that contain line segments that do not intersect.

20. Draw a segment and use a compass and straightedge to construct its perpendicular bisector.

21. Draw a figure in which $\overline{AB}$ is the perpendicular bisector of $\overline{CD}$, but $\overline{CD}$ is not the perpendicular bisector of $\overline{AB}$.

22. Draw a figure in which $\overline{ST}$ is the perpendicular bisector of $\overline{UV}$, $\overline{WX}$, and $\overline{YZ}$.

23. $\overline{BD}$ is the perpendicular bisector of $\overline{AC}$ at X.
$\overline{EF}$ is the perpendicular bisector of $\overline{XC}$ at Y.
What is the ratio $\frac{YC}{AC}$? $\frac{YC}{XC}$? $\frac{AX}{YC}$?

Determine whether each statement is always, sometimes, or never true.

24. If $\overline{AB}$ is the perpendicular bisector of $\overline{GH}$, then $\overline{GH}$ is the perpendicular bisector of $\overline{AB}$.

25. If $\overline{JK}$ is the perpendicular bisector of $\overline{LM}$, then $\overline{LM}$ contains the midpoint of $\overline{JK}$.

26. If $\overline{EF} \perp \overline{GH}$, then $\overline{GH} \perp \overline{EF}$.

27. Line l and line m are both perpendicular to line t at point P on t.

Write an algebraic expression for each of the following, given that $\overline{CD}$ is the perpendicular bisector of $\overline{AB}$.

28. Express $m\angle DCE$ in terms of x.

29. Express $m\angle ACE$ in terms of x.

30. Express AB in terms of y.

31. Consider points $A(3, 0)$, $B(0, 2)$, $C(-1, 0)$, $D(0, -1)$ and $O(0, 0)$. Find $m\angle AOB$ and $m\angle COD$.

C

Write a two-column proof for each exercise.

32. Given: $\overline{AB} \perp \overline{BC}$, $\overline{BC} \perp \overline{CD}$
Prove: $\angle ABC \cong \angle BCD$

33. Given: $\angle 1$ is complementary to $\angle 2$.
Prove: $\overline{JK} \perp \overline{KL}$

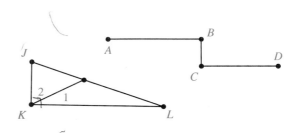

Critical Thinking

Determine whether each statement is true or false. If false, give a counterexample.

34. Given any triangle ABC, the perpendicular bisector of $\overline{AB}$ intersects the perpendicular bisector of $\overline{BC}$ at a point inside the triangle.

35. Given any triangle ABC, the line through A perpendicular to $\overline{BC}$ and the line through B perpendicular to $\overline{AC}$ intersect at a point inside the triangle.

36. Given any equilateral triangle, the line which is a perpendicular bisector of a side contains a vertex.

37. Figure out how to use a compass and unmarked straightedge to construct a perpendicular to a line l through a point P not on l. (HINT: Start by putting the compass tip on the point and making an arc that forms a segment on the line.)

Mixed Review

Use the statement "If a triangle is isosceles, then it has two congruent sides."

1. Write the hypothesis and the conclusion of the statement.

2. Write the contrapositive of the statement.

3. Write the converse of the statement.

4. Determine whether the converse is true or false.

5. Use the transitive property to draw a conclusion.
Given: $m \angle B = m \angle C$, $m \angle C = m \angle D$

Quiz

$\overrightarrow{AD}$ **is perpendicular to** $\overleftrightarrow{BE}$. **Complete each statement.**

1. $m \angle EGA =$ ___

2. $\angle BGC$ is complementary to ___ .

3. If $m \angle FGD = 105$, then $m \angle AGF =$ ___ .

4. $\angle EGF \cong$ ___

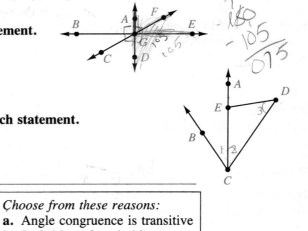

Complete the proof by choosing a reason for each statement.

5. Given: $\overrightarrow{CA}$ bisects $\angle BCD$. $\angle 2 \cong \angle 3$

Prove: $\angle 1 \cong \angle 3$

Proof

Statements	Reasons	
1. $\overrightarrow{CA}$ bisects $\angle BCD$.	1. ___	*Choose from these reasons:*
2. $\angle 1 \cong \angle 2$	2. ___	**a.** Angle congruence is transitive
3. $\angle 2 \cong \angle 3$	3. ___	**b.** Definition of angle bisector
4. $\angle 1 \cong \angle 3$	4. ___	**c.** Given

OBJECTIVE: *Draw and use appropriate diagrams for a proof.*

2-4 Drawing and Using Diagrams

A diagram in a two-column proof often helps supply given information. The guidelines below help you decide what information you can and cannot assume as given from a diagram when writing a two-column proof.

Information That May Be Assumed To Be Given From a Diagram

1. Straightness of lines
2. Betweenness of points
3. Collinearity of points on a line, coplanarity of points
4. Intersection of lines
5. Relative locations (interior, exterior, opposite)
6. Adjacency, nonadjacency of angles
7. Existence of the figures shown

Information That May *Not* Be Assumed From a Diagram

1. Congruence of segments or angles
2. Measures of segments or angles
3. Relative sizes of segments and angles
4. Midpoint of a segment or bisector of an angle
5. Perpendicular lines or right angles
6. Nonintersecting lines
7. Special types of figures (isosceles triangle, square, etc.)

Example 1

Which of the following may be assumed from the figure to be given?

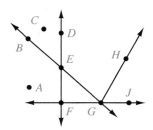

1. $\overleftrightarrow{BG}$ is a straight line.
2. $\overline{EF} \cong \overline{FG}$
3. Point E is between D and F.
4. $\angle DEB \cong \angle EFG$
5. $\angle EFG$ is a right angle.
6. $\angle BEF$ is obtuse.
7. C is in the interior of $\angle DEB$.
8. E is the midpoint of $\overline{DF}$.
9. $\angle EGH$ is adjacent to $\angle HGJ$.
10. $\overrightarrow{GH}$ is the bisector of $\angle EGJ$.
11. The figure formed by $\overline{EF}$, $\overline{FG}$, and $\overline{EG}$ is a triangle.

Solution

1, 3, 7, 9, 11

Try This

Give another statement that may be assumed from the diagram.

It is often necessary to draw a reasonably accurate diagram to represent given data when writing a proof. Such diagrams should contain all the information in the *Given* plus the type of assumed information in the chart above, but should not suggest any other additional information. For example, if the given information refers to a *triangle*, the diagram should not show what appears to be a *right triangle*.

Also, diagrams are sometimes marked to emphasize given data as shown in Example 2.

Example 2

Draw a diagram to show the given information. Mark it for emphasis.
Given: $\triangle EFG$ with $\angle EFH \cong \angle FGH$, $\overline{EF} \cong \overline{EH}$, $\overline{FH} \cong \overline{HG}$
$\angle EFG$ is a right angle. $m\angle FEH = 60$

Solution

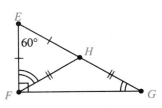

Note that the sides of $\triangle EFG$ are drawn to appear of different lengths since nothing was given to indicate otherwise.

Try This

Given: $\triangle ABC$ with $\overline{AB} \cong \overline{AC}$, $BC = 6$, $m\angle A = 35$
Draw and mark a diagram.

Class Exercises

Short Answer

State whether or not you can assume the information from the figure. Give a guideline from the charts on page 75 to justify your answer.

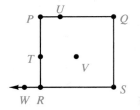

1. $\angle P$ and $\angle S$ are right angles.
2. V is inside the square.
3. $\overline{PQ} \cong \overline{RP}$
4. T is between P and R.
5. $\overline{PU}$ is shorter than $\overline{UQ}$.
6. P, Q, and R are noncollinear.
7. $\overleftrightarrow{PQ}$ and $\overleftrightarrow{RS}$ do not intersect.
8. $\overrightarrow{PQ}$ and $\overrightarrow{PR}$ intersect.
9. $\angle WRT$ and $\angle TRS$ are adjacent.
10. T is the midpoint of $\overleftrightarrow{PR}$.

Sample Exercises

11. Choose the best diagram for the given data. Justify your choice.
    Given: $\triangle DEF$, with $\overrightarrow{EG}$ bisecting $\angle DEF$

a.   b.   c.

Determine whether each of the following can be assumed from a diagram.

12. Two lines are perpendicular.
13. A ray is in the interior of an angle.
14. Two points are on opposite sides of a line.
15. One angle is smaller than another.

Discussion

16. Give as many statements as possible that a) can be assumed from this diagram and b) appear to be true but cannot be assumed.

Exercises

A

Indicate whether or not the information can be assumed from the diagram.

1. $\overrightarrow{NQ} \perp \overleftrightarrow{LQ}$
2. N, P, and Q are collinear.
3. M is the midpoint of $\overline{LN}$.
4. $\overline{NP} \cong \overline{PQ}$
5. $\angle MLP$ and $\angle PLQ$ are adjacent angles.
6. LP is greater than MN.
7. $\angle RMN$ and $\angle NMP$ form a linear pair.
8. The figure formed by $\overline{MN}$, $\overline{NP}$, and $\overline{PM}$ is a triangle.
9. $\angle NLQ \cong \angle QNL$
10. Point M is between L and N.
11. $\angle RML$ and $\angle NMP$ are vertical angles.
12. $\angle NQL$ is a right angle.
13. $\overrightarrow{LP}$ bisects $\angle MLQ$.
14. $\overleftrightarrow{RP}$ intersects $\overleftrightarrow{LM}$.
15. R and Q are on opposite sides of $\overleftrightarrow{LN}$.

16. Choose the best diagram for the given data. Justify your choice.
    Given: $\overline{RS}$ is the perpendicular bisector of $\overline{TU}$.

a.

b.

c.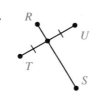

Draw a diagram to show the given information.

17. Given: $\overline{AB} \perp \overline{CD}$ intersecting at B, $\overrightarrow{BF}$ bisects $\angle ABD$.
18. Given: M is the midpoint of $\overline{RS}$. $\overleftrightarrow{JK}$ is the perpendicular bisector of $\overline{MS}$.
19. Given: $\triangle XYZ$ with $\angle Y \cong \angle Z$, T is between Y and Z.
    U is between T and Z.
20. Given: $\angle 1$ is supplementary and adjacent to $\angle 2$. $\angle 3$ is complementary
    and adjacent to $\angle 2$.
21. Given: $\angle 4$ and $\angle 5$ are vertical angles. $\angle 5$ is a right angle.

Draw a diagram and mark it to indicate the given information.

22. Given: $\triangle ABC$ with $\overline{AB} \cong \overline{AC}$, $m\angle A = 30$
23. Given: $\triangle SAT$ with $\angle A$ a right angle, $AT = 5$
24. Given: $\overline{FP}$ is the perpendicular bisector of $\overline{GY}$ and $\overline{GY}$ is the
    perpendicular bisector of $\overline{FP}$. $\overline{FY} \cong \overline{PG}$, $\overline{GF} \cong \overline{PY}$
25. Given: $\triangle JKL$ and $\triangle RST$, with $\overline{JK} \cong \overline{RS}$, $\overline{KL} \cong \overline{ST}$, and $\angle K \cong \angle S$

Draw a diagram and mark it as needed.

26. G, H, I are collinear. G, J, and K are collinear. H, J, and K are noncollinear.
27. $\triangle ABC$ is a right triangle. $\overrightarrow{BH}$ bisects the right angle. H, A, and C are collinear.

28. A surveyor often gathers field data at a work site and does computations later in the office. Set up and label a diagram that would illustrate the following data.

- A, B, and C are three noncollinear locations.
- The distance from location A to B is 174 ft.
- The distance from location B to C is 153 ft.
- $m\angle B$ is 23 degrees.
- C is to the north of A and B.

B

Draw a diagram and complete each proof.

29. Given: $l \perp m$ forming a linear pair of angles, $\angle 1$ and $\angle 2$

Prove: $m\angle 1 = m\angle 2$

Proof

Statements	Reasons
1. $l \perp m$	1. ___
2. $\angle 1$ and $\angle 2$ are right angles.	2. ___
3. ___	3. Definition of right angles
4. ___	4. Substitution

30. Given: $m\angle JKL = m\angle RST$
$\overrightarrow{ST}$ bisects $\angle RSU$.

Prove: $m\angle JKL = m\angle TSU$

Proof

Statements	Reasons
1. $m\angle JKL = m\angle RST$	1. ___
2. ___	2. Given
3. ___	3. Definition of angle bisector
4. $m\angle RST = m\angle TSU$	4. ___
5. $m\angle JKL = m\angle TSU$	5. ___

31. Draw and label a diagram for the given information.
Given: $\overleftrightarrow{AB}$ is the perpendicular bisector of $\overline{CD}$, intersecting at B.
$\overleftrightarrow{EF}$ is the perpendicular bisector of $\overline{BD}$, intersecting at F.
$\overleftrightarrow{GH}$ is the perpendicular bisector of $\overline{AB}$, intersecting at H.

32. Draw and label a right triangle with 30° and 60° angles, shortest side 1, next longest side approximately 1.7, and longest side 2.

C

33. Draw and label a diagram for the given information. Then write some other statements that are true about the figure.
Given: Point A is between C and D. A is also between G and H. $\overline{CH} \cong \overline{CG}$ and $\overline{HD} \cong \overline{GD}$, but $CH < HD$. $\angle HAC$ is a right angle.

34. Draw and label a diagram for the given information. Then find the measure of each angle.
Given: $\overrightarrow{QP} \perp \overrightarrow{QR}$ Three other rays with endpoint Q are in the interior of $\angle PQR$. These rays form nonoverlapping angles which have measures in the ratio $1:2:3:4$.

Critical Thinking

When you answer the question "What seems to be true about a situation?" you have formed a *hypothesis* about the situation. Consider Exercise 35.

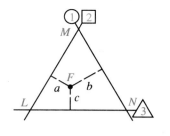

35. Highways 1, 2, and 3 intersect to enclose an equilateral triangle. Where should a factory be built inside this triangle so that the sum of the perpendicular distances from the factory to the highways (a + b + c) is the least? Form a hypothesis. How could you test your hypothesis?

36. A machinist is to make a metal plate like the one shown in this diagram. Interpret and analyze the diagram to find the missing dimensions indicated by A, B, C, D, and E.

Algebra Review

Factor.

1. $x^2 + 3x + 2$ 2. $y^2 + 8y + 12$ 3. $m^2 - 5m + 6$
4. $x^2 + 10x + 25$ 5. $n^2 - 4n - 21$ 6. $m^2 - 4$
7. $2y^2 - 3y - 2$ 8. $3s^2 + 2s - 1$ 9. $6x^2 + 7x - 3$

Enrichment

Optical Illusions

The optical illusions below help show why you should rely more on logical reasoning and less on visual information. Answer the questions. Then check with a ruler.

1. Which is longer, $\overline{AB}$ or $\overline{CD}$?

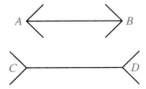

2. Will line k, when extended, meet point A, point B, or point C?

3. Which is longer, $\overline{AB}$ or $\overline{CD}$?

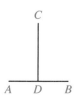

2-5 Planning and Writing a Proof

In proofs so far, you have started with the *Given* statement and used deductive reasoning to establish the truth of the *Prove* statement. In this section you will look more carefully at what it means to prove a theorem. To prove a theorem follow these five steps.

Proving a Theorem

Step 1: Write the theorem in IF-THEN form.
Step 2: Write the GIVEN from the hypothesis and the PROVE from the conclusion.
Step 3: Draw and label a DIAGRAM to show the given information.
Step 4: Analyze the situation and devise a PLAN.
Step 5: Write STATEMENTS leading from the *Given* to the *Prove* and give REASONS to support these statements.

In Step 2, keep in mind that the hypothesis is the *if* part of the if-then statement and the conclusion is the *then* part. The guidelines described in Lesson 2-4 may be helpful when drawing the diagram in Step 3. In Step 5, recall that you must use given information, definitions, postulates (including algebraic properties), or previously proven theorems as reasons for your statements.

Example 1 illustrates how to use Steps 1, 2, and 3 to begin the proof of Theorem 2.4.

◆ **THEOREM 2.4**

All right angles are congruent.

Example 1

Rewrite Theorem 2.4 in if-then form, write the *Given* and *Prove,* and draw a diagram showing the given information.

Solution

If two angles are right angles, then the angles are congruent.

Given: $\angle 1$ is a right angle.
$\angle 2$ is a right angle.

Prove: $\angle 1 \cong \angle 2$

The next example illustrates how Steps 4 and 5 are used to complete the proof of Theorem 2.4. Notice that to analyze the situation, you first look at what is to be proved and work backwards from there.

Example 2

Analyze the situation to devise a plan and prove Theorem 2.4.

Solution

Analysis I want to prove that $\angle 1 \cong \angle 2$. I can do this if I can show that they have the same measure. I can show they have the same measure since they are both right angles.

(This analysis shows how someone might work backwards to figure out how to prove Theorem 2.4. It is a mental process that is not usually written.)

Plan Since $\angle 1$ and $\angle 2$ are right angles, they each have measure 90. Since the measures of the angles are equal, they are congruent. (This proof shows how someone might carry out the plan to write the two-column proof.)

(This plan shows how someone might organize the proof of Theorem 2.4 after having analyzed the situation.)

Proof

Statements	Reasons
1. $\angle 1$ and $\angle 2$ are right angles.	1. Given
2. $m\angle 1 = 90$, $m\angle 2 = 90$	2. Definition of right angles
3. $m\angle 1 = m\angle 2$	3. Substitution Property
4. $\angle 1 \cong \angle 2$	4. Definition of congruent angles

◆ **THEOREM 2.5** Midpoint Theorem
The midpoint M of $\overline{AB}$ divides $\overline{AB}$ so that $AM = \frac{1}{2} AB$.

Example 3

Prove the Midpoint Theorem.

Solution

Theorem: If M is the midpoint of $\overline{AB}$, then $AM = \frac{1}{2} AB$.

Given: M is the midpoint of $\overline{AB}$.

Prove: $AM = \frac{1}{2} AB$.

Analysis I can prove $AM = \frac{1}{2} AB$ if I can show that $2AM = AB$ or $AM + AM = AB$. I can show that $AM + AM = AB$ if I can show that $AM + MB = AB$, since $AM = MB$. But I know that $AM + MB = AB$ because of the Segment Addition Postulate.

Plan $AM + MB = AB$ from the Segment Addition Postulate. Since $AM = MB$, it follows that $AM + AM = AB$, $2AM = AB$, and $AM = \frac{1}{2} AB$.

Proof

Statements	Reasons
1. M is the midpoint of $\overline{AB}$.	1. Given
2. $AM = MB$	2. Definition of midpoint
3. $AM + MB = AB$	3. Segment Addition Postulate
4. $AM + AM = AB$	4. Substitution Property
5. $2AM = AB$	5. Distributive Property
6. $AM = \frac{1}{2} AB$	6. Division Property of Equality

You will be asked to prove Theorem 2.5 in Exercise 26.

◆ **THEOREM 2.6** Angle Bisector Theorem

If $\overrightarrow{BD}$ is the bisector of $\angle ABC$, then $m \angle ABD = \frac{1}{2} m \angle ABC$.

Class Exercises

Short Answer

1. Arrange the steps for proving a theorem in the correct order.

   a. Analyze and plan.   **b.** Draw a diagram   **c.** Write the statements and reasons.
   d. Write the theorem in if-then form.   **e.** Write the *Given* and *Prove*.

State the theorem as a conditional.

2. Two intersecting lines are contained in exactly one plane.
3. A segment has exactly one midpoint.
4. Two intersecting lines have exactly one point in common.

Sample Exercises

State the *Given* and the *Prove* for each conditional.

5. If one angle of a linear pair is a right angle, then the other is also a right angle.
6. If a figure is a segment, then it has only one perpendicular bisector.
7. If $\overrightarrow{BD}$ is the bisector of $\angle ABC$, then $m \angle ABD = \frac{1}{2} m \angle ABC$.
8. Draw a diagram that shows the given information in this theorem. Every equilateral triangle is also an isosceles triangle.
9. Complete the following analysis of a proof.

   Given: $\angle 1$ and $\angle 2$ are vertical angles. $\angle 2 \cong \angle 3$

   Prove: $\angle 1 \cong \angle 3$

   I can prove $\angle 1 \cong \angle 3$ if I can prove that ____ and ____ .

Discussion

10. The definition a local police force used for speeding is, "Being clocked by correctly operating radar as traveling at least 3 mph over a posted speed limit." If a police officer wanted to convince a judge that a person was speeding, what would he need to prove? Suppose you were given that (a) Kim was clocked at 40 mph in a posted 35 mph zone and (b) Officer Sharpeye had a receipt showing that her radar had recently passed the operating check.
    How would you write a convincing informal argument that Kim was speeding? How would you write a two-column proof?

11. How would you use the steps for proving a theorem to prove that the following statement is true? An angle divided by a ray into two complementary angles is a right angle.

Exercises

A

1. Write this theorem as a conditional. Two intersecting lines that form congruent adjacent angles are perpendicular.
2. Write the *Given* and *Prove* for this theorem. Two angles supplementary to the same angle are congruent.
3. Draw a diagram to show the given information for this theorem. If one angle of a linear pair is a right angle, then the other angle is also a right angle.

Rewrite the theorem as a conditional, write the *Given* and *Prove*, and draw a diagram showing the given information.

4. Two perpendicular lines form congruent adjacent angles.
5. Two angles are right angles if they are congruent and supplementary.
6. An equilateral triangle is also an equiangular triangle.
7. Vertical angles are congruent.
8. Every equilateral triangle is also an isosceles triangle.

Complete the first line in the analysis of each proof.

9. **Given:** $m\angle 1 = 30$, $m\angle 2 = 13$, $m\angle 3 = 17$
   Prove: $\overrightarrow{BD}$ bisects $\angle ABC$.

   I can prove that $\overrightarrow{BD}$ bisects $\angle ABC$ if I can first prove that ___ .

10. **Given:** $\angle 1 \cong \angle 2$, $\angle 3 \cong \angle 4$
    Prove: $\angle 1 \cong \angle 4$

    I can prove that $\angle 1 \cong \angle 4$ if I can first prove that ___ .

11. **Given:** $\angle 1$ is complementary to $\angle 2$.
    Prove: $\overline{JK} \perp \overline{KL}$

    I can prove that $\overline{JK} \perp \overline{KL}$ if I can first prove that ___ .

12. **Given:** $\overline{RT} \perp \overline{SX}$, $\overline{WY} \perp \overline{SX}$
    Prove: $\angle 1 \cong \angle 3$
    I can prove that $\angle 1 \cong \angle 3$ if I can first prove that $\angle 1$ and $\angle 3$ are both ___ .

13. **Given:** $\overline{WX} \cong \overline{XY}$, $\angle SXW$ is a right angle.
    Prove: $\overline{SX}$ is the perpendicular bisector of $\overline{WY}$.
    I can prove that $\overline{SX}$ is the perpendicular bisector of $\overline{WY}$ if I can first prove that ___ .

The statements provided for each proof are correct but in the wrong order. Order them correctly and supply reasons as you write the proof.

14. Given: $m \angle DPW = 90$

Prove: $\overleftrightarrow{DP} \perp \overleftrightarrow{WP}$

    a. $\angle DPW$ is a right angle.   **b.** $\overline{DP} \perp \overline{WP}$ **c.** $m \angle DPW = 90$

15. Given: $\angle 1 \cong \angle 2,\ \angle 3 \cong \angle 4$

Prove: $\angle 1 \cong \angle 4$

    a. $\angle 1 \cong \angle 3$ **b.** $\angle 1 \cong \angle 2, \angle 3, \cong \angle 4$ **c.** $\angle 1 \cong \angle 4$ **d.** $\angle 2 \cong \angle 3$

16. Given: $\angle 1$ is complementary to $\angle 2$.

Prove: $\overline{JS} \perp \overline{XS}$

    a. $\angle JSX$ is a right angle.   **b.** $m \angle 1 + m \angle 2 = 90$ **c.** $m \angle 1 + m \angle 2 = m \angle JSX$
    d. $\angle 1$ is complementary to $\angle 2$ **e.** $\overline{JS} \perp \overline{XS}$ **f.** $m \angle JSX = 90$

17. Given: $\overline{RT} \perp \overline{PQ},\ \overline{WY} \perp \overline{PQ}$

Prove: $\angle 1 \cong \angle 3$

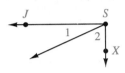

    a. $\overline{RT} \perp \overline{PQ}, \overline{WY} \perp \overline{PQ}$ **b.** $\angle 1 \cong \angle 3$ **c.** $\angle 1$ and $\angle 3$ are right angles.

18. Given: $CD = DE,\ \angle ADE$ is a right angle.

Prove: $\overline{AD}$ is the perpendicular bisector of $\overline{CE}$.

    a. $CD = DE$ **b.** $\angle ADE$ is a right angle.   **c.** D is the midpoint of $\overline{CE}$.
    d. $\overline{AD} \perp \overline{CE}$ **e.** $\overline{AD}$ is the perpendicular bisector of $\overline{CE}$.

B

Draw a diagram for the given information and write a two-column proof.

19. Given: $\overline{LM} \perp \overline{SM}$

    Prove: $m \angle LMS = 90$

20. Given: $GH = HJ$, H is between G and J.

    Prove: $GH = \frac{1}{2} GJ$

21. Given: $m \angle KLM = 90$

    Prove: $\overline{KL} \perp \overline{LM}$

22. Given: D is between vertices A and B of $\triangle ABC$. $\overline{CD} \perp \overline{AB}$

    Prove: $m \angle CDA = 90$

23. Given: $\overline{AB} \perp \overline{BC}$
             $\overline{DC} \perp \overline{BC}$

    Prove: $\angle ABC \cong \angle DCB$

24. Given: M is the midpoint of $\overline{AB}$. N is the midpoint of $\overline{CD}$. $CD = AB$

    Prove: $AM = CN$

25. Write a two-column proof.

Given: O is the midpoint of $\overline{BC}$.
$\triangle AOB$ is isosceles with $\overline{OA} \cong \overline{OB}$.

Prove: $\triangle AOC$ is isosceles.

C

26. Prove Theorem 2.6.

27. Prove the following theorem. If B is between A and C on one line, E is between D and F on another line, $AC = DF$, $BC = EF$, then $AB = DE$.

Critical Thinking

28. New hypotheses which lead to theorems are sometimes formed by asking, "What if . . . ?" This exercise comes from the question, "What if you think about angles instead of segments in the theorem in Exercise 27?". Write and prove a theorem about angles that is similar to the theorem in Exercise 27.

Mixed Review

Complete each statement.

1. $\triangle GCE$ is a(n) ____ triangle.
2. ____ is an isosceles triangle.
3. ____ is a right triangle.

4. Find the distance between the pair of points with coordinates $(7, 10)$ and $(1, 2)$.
5. Find the distance between the pair of points with coordinates $(1, -2)$ and $(-2, -3)$.

Study Skills

Preparing for a Geometry Test

A math test can seem threatening if you have not taken the necessary steps to prepare for it. The following guidelines are especially useful in preparing for a geometry test.

1. Since most concepts in geometry build upon previous ones, there is too much to learn the night before the test. Therefore, it is a good idea to keep up with daily assignments and to begin studying a few days before the test.

2. Review your notes and flashcards with definitions, postulates, and theorems. Concentrate on the points you found the most difficult.

3. If possible, find out about the type of questions that will be on the test, i.e., multiple choice, true or false, proofs, etc.

4. Skim the sections of the text you will be tested on, paying particular attention to the examples.

2-6 Theorems: Segments and Lines

Given three collinear points, A, B, and C, three segments ($\overline{AB}$, $\overline{BC}$, and $\overline{AC}$) are determined. Can you complete this table?

Number of Collinear Points	Number of Segments
3	3
4	?
⋮	⋮
n	?

In Lessons 1-8 and 2-3 you learned some methods for proving that two segments are congruent and two lines perpendicular. Other useful methods are presented and summarized in this lesson.

In the Explore, you developed skill in visualizing segments that overlap other segments. In the figure below, $\overline{AC}$ and $\overline{BD}$ share the common segment $\overline{BC}$. If you know that $\overline{AB} \cong \overline{CD}$, you should be able to prove that $\overline{AC} \cong \overline{BD}$.

This is the conclusion of the Common Segment Theorem, stated and proved below.

◆ **THEOREM 2.7**   Common Segment Theorem
  1. If $\overline{AB} \cong \overline{CD}$, then $\overline{AC} \cong \overline{BD}$.
  2. If $\overline{AC} \cong \overline{BD}$, then $\overline{AB} \cong \overline{CD}$.

Part 1

Given: $\overline{AB} \cong \overline{CD}$

Prove: $\overline{AC} \cong \overline{BD}$

Proof Statements	Reasons
1. $\overline{AB} \cong \overline{CD}$	1. Given
2. $AB = CD$	2. Definition of congruent segments
3. $BC = BC$	3. Reflexive Property
4. $AB + BC = CD + BC$	4. Addition Property
5. $AC = BD$	5. Segment Addition Postulate
6. $\overline{AC} \cong \overline{BD}$	6. Definition of congruent segments

The proof of Part 2 of Theorem 2.7 is similar to that of Part 1 and will be called for in Exercise 29.

Example 1

$\overline{PR} \cong \overline{QS}$ What can you conclude? Why?

Solution
$\overline{PQ} \cong \overline{RS}$ *Common Segment Theorem*

Try This
$\overline{GH} \cong \overline{IJ}$ What can you conclude? Why?

The following list summarizes the ways you have studied to prove that two segments are congruent.

Methods of Proving Two Segments Congruent

1. Prove that their measures are equal using the Segment Addition Postulate or properties of equality.
2. Prove that each segment is congruent to a third segment.
3. Prove that they are the two parts of a bisected segment.
4. Prove that they are sides of a triangle given to be isosceles or equilateral.
5. Prove that they are formed by adding or subtracting a common segment.

One way to prove that two lines are perpendicular is to first prove that the lines meet to form a right angle. The following theorem provides another way.

◆ THEOREM 2.8

If two lines form congruent adjacent angles, then they are perpendicular.

Given: $\angle 1 \cong \angle 2$
Prove: $\overline{BC} \perp \overline{AD}$

Analysis   I can prove $\overline{BC} \perp \overline{AD}$ if I can prove that $\angle 1$ and $\angle 2$ are right angles. I can prove they are right angles if I can prove that the measure of each is 90. I can prove this if I can prove that they have the same measure and the sum of their measures is 180. They are a linear pair and are congruent, so I can do this.

Plan   Start at the end of the analysis and work backwards.

You will be asked to prove Theorem 2.8 in Exercise 36.

Example 2

$\angle 3 \cong \angle 4$ What can you conclude about $\triangle ABC$?

Solution
$\angle 4$ is a right angle, so $\triangle ABC$ is a right triangle.   *Since $\angle 3$ and $\angle 4$ are congruent adjacent angles, $\overline{AC} \perp \overline{BC}$.*

Try This
If $\angle 3 \cong \angle 4$ and $\overline{DC} \cong \overline{BC}$, what can you conclude about $\overleftrightarrow{AC}$?

The following summarizes the ways you have studied to prove two lines perpendicular.

Methods of Proving Two Lines Perpendicular

1. Prove that the lines intersect to form a right angle.
2. Prove that the lines intersect to form congruent adjacent angles.

Theorem 2.9 will be proved in Lesson 5-6.

◆ **THEOREM 2.9**

Only one perpendicular can be drawn from a point to a line.

Class Exercises

Short Answer

Identify the common segment and tell whether you used addition or subtraction to arrive at the conclusion.

1. Given: $PR = QS$
   Conclusion: $PQ = RS$

   sub.

2. Given: $JK = LM$
   Conclusion: $JL = KM$

3. $\overline{JL} \cong \overline{KM}$ in the figure in Class Exercise 2. What can you conclude?
4. Lines j and k intersect to form congruent adjacent angles. What can you conclude?

Sample Exercises

Find the length of each segment.

5. $\overline{PQ} \cong \overline{ST}$, $RT = 9$,
   $RS = 5$ Find PQ.

6. $\overline{PR} \cong \overline{QS}$, $RS = 6$,
   $QR = 4$ Find PR.

Use the Common Segment Theorem to draw a conclusion.

7. $\overline{JK} \cong \overline{LM}$

8. $\overline{PQ} \cong \overline{RS}$

9. $\overline{WX} \cong \overline{YZ}$

Discussion

10. Complete the following in three different ways.
    If I know that ___, then I can conclude that $l \perp m$.
11. Give a convincing informal argument that when two adjacent angles are complementary their noncommon sides are perpendicular.

Exercises

A

Use the Common Segment Theorem to draw a conclusion.

1. $\overline{MN} \cong \overline{PQ}$

2. $\overline{KB} \cong \overline{PN}$

3. $\overline{IK} \cong \overline{EA}$

4. $\overline{EX} \cong \overline{WG}$

Find the length of each segment.

5.

$\overline{AB} \cong \overline{CD}$, $BD = 12$, $BC = 4$ Find AB

6.

$\overline{EG} \cong \overline{FH}$, $GH = 6$, $FG = 24$ Find EG

7.

$\overline{PQ} \cong \overline{RS}$, $QR = 8$, $RS = 2x$,
$QS = 4x - 2$ Find PR

8.

$\overline{WY} \cong \overline{XZ}$, $WY = 3x + 6$
$XY = 12$, $WX = x + 2$ Find YZ

Draw a conclusion stating that two segments are congruent.

9. $\triangle QRS$ is equilateral.
10. $\overline{PR}$ bisects $\overline{QS}$.
11. $\overline{QR} \cong \overline{QS}$, $\overline{RS} \cong \overline{QS}$
12. $\overline{PV} \cong \overline{RT}$

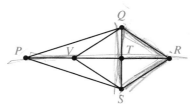

Draw a conclusion.

13. $\angle 3 \cong \angle 4$
14. $\angle 5$ and $\angle 6$ are complementary.

Determine whether each statement is true or false.

15. It is impossible for two different lines to be perpendicular to a given line.
16. If two lines are perpendicular, then they form congruent adjacent angles.
17. There is only one way to prove two segments congruent.
18. The Common Segment Theorem, as stated in this section, contains a statement and its converse.

Write a two-column proof for each exercise.

19. Given: $\angle 1$ and $\angle 2$ are complementary.
   Prove: $\triangle UTW$ is a right triangle.

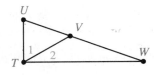

20. Given: $\angle 3 \cong \angle ABC$, $\angle 4 \cong \angle ABC$
   3 steps **Prove:** $\overline{BD} \perp \overline{AC}$

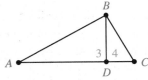

21. Given: $\overline{AB} \cong \overline{BD}$, $\overline{BC} \cong \overline{DE}$
   Prove: $\overline{AB} \cong \overline{CE}$

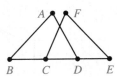

Complete each statement. Refer to the chart on page 87 as needed.

22. If I knew that ____,
   then I could conclude that $\overline{DC} \cong \overline{DE}$.

23. If I knew that ____,
   then I could conclude that $\overline{RS} \cong \overline{TU}$.

24. If I knew that ____,
   then I could conclude that $\overline{GH} \cong \overline{JI}$.

25. An architect was checking plans his assistant had made for a bowling alley. The information that $AC = BD$ was included, but he wondered if the gutters were the same width. Does he have enough information to tell? Explain.

B

Write a two-column proof for each exercise.

26. Given: $\overline{AB} \cong \overline{CD}$, $\overline{BC} \cong \overline{DE}$
   Prove: $\overline{AC} \cong \overline{CE}$

27. Given: $\overline{GI} \cong \overline{HJ}$, $\overline{IK} \cong \overline{JL}$
   Prove: $\overline{GH} \cong \overline{KL}$

28. Given: $\overline{PR}$ bisects $\overline{ST}$. $\overline{UY} \cong \overline{SU}$
   $\triangle UYX$ is equilateral.
   Prove: $\overline{TU} \cong \overline{UX}$

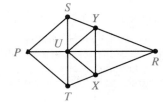

29. Write a two-column proof for Part 2 of Theorem 2.7.

30. Elevator *A* is just as far below the top floor as elevator *B* is above the ground floor. Elevator *A* is traveling down at the same rate elevator *B* is traveling up. If the elevators do not stop, will *A* reach the ground at the same time that *B* reaches the top? What theorem supports your answer? Explain.

Determine whether each statement is always, sometimes, or never true.

31. If two lines form at least one right angle, then they are perpendicular.

32. If two segments overlap in a common segment, then the noncommon parts of the two segments are congruent.

33. Two lines can be drawn through a point perpendicular to a given line.

34. Use the Distance Formula to show that $\overline{AC} \cong \overline{BD}$. What other segments do you know to be congruent? Verify this using the Distance Formula.

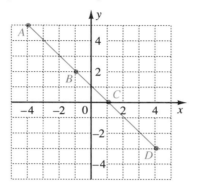

C

35. Given: ∠1 and ∠3 are complementary.
Prove: $\overline{AD} \perp \overline{DB}$

36. Complete a two-column proof for Theorem 2.8.

Critical Thinking

37. Given that $\overline{AB} \cong \overline{DE}$ and $\overline{AC} \cong \overline{DF}$, a geometry student concluded that $\overline{BC} \cong \overline{EF}$. She gave the Common Segment Theorem as a reason. Do you think she reasoned correctly? Give a convincing argument to support your position. If the reasoning is not correct, write a proof that $\overline{BC} \cong \overline{EF}$ using the correct reasoning.

Algebra Review

Solve each inequality.

1. $3x > 21$
2. $6 + 5y \geq 36$
3. $2x + 4 < 4$
4. $8y \leq 3y - 25$
5. $-2x < x + 9$
6. $x + 7 \geq 2 - x$

Math Contest Problem

At what exact times between 12 and 1 o'clock are the hands of a clock perpendicular to each other?

2-7 Proving Theorems: Angles

In the building of houses and other structures, many boards need to be cut at congruent angles. To prove a theorem, you often need to show that two angles are congruent. Some useful methods for doing this are presented or reviewed in this lesson. One method, the Common Angle Theorem, is similar to the Common Segment Theorem and is stated and proved below.

Notice that the *common angle*, ∠BOC, is *added* in Part 1 and *subtracted* in Part 2.

◆ **THEOREM 2.10**   Common Angle Theorem
  1. If ∠AOB ≅ ∠COD, then ∠AOC ≅ ∠BOD.
  2. If ∠AOC ≅ ∠BOD, then ∠AOB ≅ ∠COD.

Part 1

Given: ∠AOB ≅ ∠COD

Prove: ∠AOC ≅ ∠BOD

Proof Statements

Statements	Reasons
1. ∠AOB ≅ ∠COD	1. Given
2. m∠AOB = m∠COD	2. Definition of congruent angles
3. m∠BOC = m∠BOC	3. Reflexive Property
4. m∠AOB + m∠BOC = m∠COD + m∠BOC	4. Addition property
5. m∠AOC = m∠BOD	5. Angle Addition Postulate
6. ∠AOC ≅ ∠BOD	6. Definition of congruent angles

You will be asked to prove Part 2 in Exercise 30.

Example 1

∠VTU ≅ ∠WTX
What can you conclude about other angles?

Solution

∠WTU ≅ ∠VTX

Try This

∠XTV ≅ ∠UTW
What can you conclude about other angles?

The following theorem is the converse of Theorem 2.8.

◆ **THEOREM 2.11**

   If two lines are perpendicular, then they form congruent adjacent angles.

Given: $\overline{RS} \perp \overline{XY}$

Prove: $\angle RSX \cong \angle RSY$

Analysis I can prove $\angle RSX \cong \angle RSY$ if I can prove that each is a right angle.
I can prove that each is a right angle by the definition of perpendicular lines.

Plan Start at the end of the analysis and work backwards.

You will be asked to prove this theorem in Exercise 31.

Example 2

If $\overline{MN}$ is the perpendicular bisector of $\overline{PQ}$, what angles must be congruent?

   Solution

   $\angle PNM \cong \angle QNM$

Try This

If $\overline{RT} \perp \overline{MQ}$, what angles must be congruent?

The following two theorems show how complementary and supplementary angles can sometimes be used to prove that two angles are congruent.

◆ **THEOREM 2.12**   Congruent Complements Theorem

   Two angles that are complementary to the same angle (or to congruent angles) are congruent.

Given: $\angle A$ is complementary to $\angle C$. $\angle B$ is complementary to $\angle C$.

Prove: $\angle A \cong \angle B$

Plan Use the definition of complementary angles and algebraic properties to prove that $m\angle A + m\angle C = 90$, $m\angle B + m\angle C = 90$, and $\angle A \cong \angle B$.

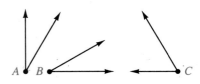

◆ **THEOREM 2.13**   Congruent Supplements Theorem

   Two angles that are supplementary to the same angle (or to congruent angles) are congruent.

Given: $\angle A$ and $\angle C$ are supplementary. $\angle B$ and $\angle C$ are supplementary.

Prove: $\angle A \cong \angle B$

Plan The plan is similar to that of Theorem 2.12.

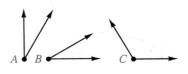

You will be asked to prove Theorems 2.12 and 2.13 in Exercises 32–33.

Example 3

Given: $\angle 2 \cong \angle 3$, $\angle 2$ is complementary to $\angle 3$.
$\angle 5$ is complementary to $\angle 3$.
What can you conclude?

Solution

$\angle 2 \cong \angle 5$ *Since $\angle 2$ and $\angle 5$ are complementary to $\angle 3$, they are congruent. (Theorem 2.12)*

$\angle 1 \cong \angle 4$ *Since $\angle 1$ and $\angle 4$ are supplementary to congruent angles ($\angle 2$ and $\angle 3$), they are congruent. (Theorem 2.13)*

Try This

Suppose $\angle 5$ is supplementary to $\angle 4$. What can you conclude? Why?

The following chart summarizes the ways you can prove that two angles are congruent. It will provide a helpful reference when writing proofs.

Methods of Proving Two Angles Congruent

1. Prove that their measures are equal using the Angle Addition Postulate and the properties of equality.
2. Prove that each angle is congruent to a third angle.
3. Prove that they are formed by a bisected angle.
4. Prove that they are vertical angles.
5. Prove that they are right angles.
6. Prove that they are formed by perpendicular lines.
7. Prove that they are formed by adding or subtracting a common angle.
8. Prove that they are supplements or complements of the same or congruent angles.

You have learned some ways to prove that an angle is a right angle. The following theorem provides another method that you will find useful in later proofs.

◆ THEOREM 2.14

If one angle of a linear pair is a right angle, then the other angle is also a right angle.

Given: $\angle 1$ is a right angle. $\angle 1$ and $\angle 2$ form a linear pair.

Prove: $\angle 2$ is right angle.

Plan $\angle 1$ and $\angle 2$ form a linear pair, so $m\angle 1 + m\angle 2 = 180$. $m\angle 1 = 90$ so, by using algebra, $m\angle 2 = 90$ and $\angle 2$ is a right angle.

You will be asked to prove this theorem in Exercise 34. The following chart summarizes the methods you have now studied for proving that an angle is a right angle.

Methods of Proving an Angle a Right Angle

1. Prove that it has a measure of 90.
2. Prove that it is formed by perpendicular lines.
3. Prove that it forms a linear pair with a right angle.

Class Exercises

Short Answer

Identify the common angle and tell whether you used addition or subtraction to arrive at the conclusion.

1.

Given: $m \angle AEB = m \angle CED$
Conclusion: $m \angle AEC = m \angle BED$

2.

Given: $m \angle QPS = m \angle TPR$
Conclusion: $m \angle QPR = m \angle SPT$

3. $\angle 4$ and $\angle 2$ are both complementary to $\angle 5$. What can you conclude?
4. $\angle 1$ and $\angle 3$ are both supplementary to $\angle 6$. What can you conclude?
5. $\angle 7$ and $\angle 8$ form a linear pair. $\angle 7$ is a right angle. What can you conclude?

Sample Exercises

What conclusions can you draw? State a reason to support each conclusion.

6. Given: $\angle 1 \cong \angle 3$
7. Given: $\angle KON \cong \angle FOM$
8. Given: $\angle 3 \cong \angle 5$, $\angle 1 \cong \angle 5$
9. Given: $\overline{JE} \perp \overline{DH}$
10. Given: $\angle 4 \cong \angle 7$
11. Given: $\overline{OK}$ bisects $\angle DOM$.

Complete each statement.

12. If I knew that ____ , then I could conclude that $\angle 3 \cong \angle 4$.
13. If I knew that ____ , then I could conclude that $\angle WXV \cong \angle ZXY$.
14. If I knew that ____ , then I could conclude that $\angle WXZ \cong \angle VXZ$.

15. Complete the following in three different ways. If I can prove that ____ , then I can prove that $\angle A$ is a right angle.

Discussion

Determine whether each statement is always, sometimes, or never true. Give reasons for your decisions.

16. If two lines intersect, then they form congruent adjacent angles.
17. If one angle of a linear pair is acute, then the other angle is also acute.
18. Two angles that are each supplementary to $\angle A$ are congruent.

Exercises

A

Use the Common Angle Theorem to draw a conclusion.

1.
Given: $\angle STQ \cong \angle PTR$

2.
Given: $\angle GKI \cong \angle HKJ$

3.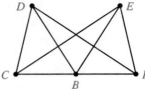
Given: $\angle CBD \cong \angle FBE$

4. What angle is "subtracted" from $\angle GKI$ and $\angle HKJ$ in Exercise 2?

Draw a conclusion stating that two angles are congruent. State a postulate, definition, or theorem that supports your conclusion.

5. $\angle 7 \cong \angle 9$

6. $\angle 8$ is complementary to $\angle 9$.
   $\angle 5$ is complementary to $\angle 9$.

7. $\angle EBC$ is supplementary to $\angle 1$.
   $\angle 2$ is supplementary to $\angle 1$.

8. $\angle 7 \cong \angle 2$, $\angle 9 \cong \angle 2$

9. $\overline{BF} \perp \overline{EG}$

10. $\overrightarrow{BF}$ bisects $\angle EBG$.

11. $\angle EBG$ and $\angle BFG$ are right angles.

12. $\angle 3$ is supplementary to $\angle 4$.
   $\angle 2$ is supplementary to $\angle 4$.
   If $m\angle 3 = 125$, find $m\angle 2$. Why?

13. $\angle 5$ is supplementary to $\angle 6$.
   $\angle 4$ is supplementary to $\angle 6$.
   If $m\angle 5 = 55$, find $m\angle 4$.
   Give two theorems that support your answer.

14. Use the data from Exercises 12 and 13 to give the measures of angles 1–8.

15. $\angle 5$ and $\angle 8$ are both supplementary to $\angle 7$. If $m\angle 7 = 104$, find $m\angle 5$.

16. When installing a windowpane, a carpenter must make sure the pane forms a right angle with the window ledge. If she finds that $\angle 1$ is a right angle, must she also measure $\angle 2$? What theorem supports your decision?

Determine whether each statement is true or false.

17. Two angles that are complementary and adjacent are congruent.

18. When two lines intersect, at least two pairs of congruent angles are formed.

19. An angle congruent to its supplement has measure 90.

20. An angle that forms a linear pair with an acute angle is obtuse.

Write a two-column proof for each exercise.

21.) **Given:** $\angle LMQ \cong \angle PMN$

   Prove: $\angle LMP \cong \angle QMN$

22.) **Given:** $\angle 2 \cong \angle 3$

   Prove: $\angle 1 \cong \angle 4$

23.) **Given:** $\angle 2 \cong \angle 3$, $\overline{HP} \perp \overline{PQ}$, $\overline{JQ} \perp \overline{PQ}$

   Prove: $\angle 1 \cong \angle 4$

B

Write a two-column proof for each exercise.

24.) **Given:** $\angle 1$ is complementary to $\angle 4$. $\angle 2$ is complementary to $\angle 3$. $\overrightarrow{BD}$ bisects $\angle ABC$.

   Prove: $\angle 4 \cong \angle 3$

25.) **Given:** $\overrightarrow{QT}$ bisects $\angle SQU$. $\overline{TQ} \perp \overline{PR}$

   Prove: $\angle 5 \cong \angle 8$

26.) **Given:** $\angle LMJ$ is a right angle. $\angle 5$ is complementary to $\angle 1$.

   Prove: $\angle 1 \cong \angle 6$

27.) **Given:** $\angle 1 \cong \angle 2$, $\angle 3 \cong \angle 4$

   Prove: $\angle 1 \cong \angle 3$

28.) **Given:** $\angle ABD$ is complementary to $\angle BAD$. $\angle EBC$ is complementary to $\angle BAD$.

   Prove: $\angle ABE \cong \angle CBD$

29.) **Given:** $\angle BFE \cong \angle ECA$, $\angle CFD \cong \angle ECA$

   Prove: $\angle BFD \cong \angle CFE$

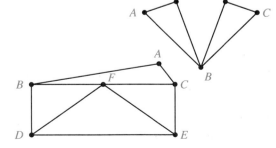

30. Prove Part 2 of the Common Angle Theorem (Theorem 2.10).

C

31. Prove Theorem 2.11.   **32.** Prove Theorem 2.12.
33. Prove Theorem 2.13.   **34.** Prove Theorem 2.14.

Critical Thinking

35. A student wrote the following formula to describe a relationship that is true for a certain set of angles. $A = S - 2C$, where A = measure of the angle, S = measure of the supplement of the angle, and C = measure of the complement of the angle. For what set of angles does the above formula hold?

Mixed Review

Complete each statement.

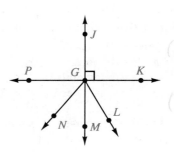

1. $\angle MGL$ is complementary to ___ .
2. $\angle PGN$ is supplementary to ___ .
3. $\angle PGM$ and ___ are vertical angles.
4. If $m\angle KGL = 56$, then $m\angle MGL =$ ___ .
5. If $m\angle MGN = 3x + 6$ and $m\angle NGP = 4x$, then $m\angle NGP =$ ___ .
6. $\angle MGN$ and ___ are a linear pair of angles.
7. $m\angle PGN +$ ___ $= 90$

Quiz

Indicate whether the information can be assumed from the diagram.

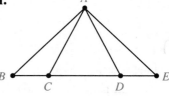

1. Points B, D, and E are collinear.
2. $\angle ABC \cong \angle AED$

3. Use the Common Segment Theorem to draw a conclusion.
   Given: $\overline{BC} \cong \overline{DE}$
4. If $\angle BAD \cong \angle CAE$, $m\angle CAD = 35$, and $m\angle CAE = 85$, find $m\angle BAC$.
5. If $\angle ACD$ is supplementary to $\angle ADE$, then $\angle ADC \cong$ _?_ .

Complete the first line in the analysis of the proof.

6. Given: $\overleftrightarrow{XY} \perp \overleftrightarrow{YZ}$
      $\overleftrightarrow{YZ} \perp \overleftrightarrow{ZW}$

   Prove: $\angle 1 \cong \angle 2$

   I can prove $\angle 1 \cong \angle 2$ if I can first prove that ___ .

Rewrite the theorem as a conditional, write the *Given* and *Prove*, and draw a diagram showing the given information.

7. The legs of a right triangle are perpendicular.

CRITICAL THINKING

Recognizing and Analyzing Assumptions

A statement of opinion, a discussion, an argument, and a proof are all based on assumptions. Sometimes these assumptions are not stated. You must figure out that assumptions are being made and identify what they are. Consider the following examples.

Example 1

Jeff's teacher said, "Proving theorems in geometry helps you develop more general reasoning abilities."
State several assumptions that Jeff's teacher may be making.

Solution

a. It is important to develop general reasoning abilities.
b. There is a need to justify proving theorems in geometry.
c. The logic used in geometric proof relates to the logic used in everyday reasoning.
d. This statement will motivate students to work harder when proving theorems.

Example 2

Lauren saw a television advertisement showing a marathon runner drinking Sunnyside orange juice. She said, "I'm going to drink that juice before my next aerobics class."
State an assumption she may be making.

Solution

Lauren might be assuming that the juice increased the marathon runner's energy level.

Example 3

Ah-hode said, "An altitude from any vertex of a triangle divides it into two triangles, each with an area smaller than the original."
State an assumption that Ah-hode is making.

Solution

Ah-hode was making the assumption that the original triangle was an acute triangle.

Exercises

1. Accept this story as an accurate depiction of an event that actually happened.

   Little Jack Horner sat in a corner
   eating his Christmas pie.
   He put in his thumb, pulled out a plum
   and said, "What a good boy am I."

   Which of these assumptions have you accepted as true?
   a. Jack was eating a plum pie.
   b. Jack felt he was a good boy because he pulled out a plum.
   c. It was Christmas day.
   d. Jack was sitting in the corner because he was being punished.
   e. Jack was a child.
   f. Jack was small.

2. Now reread the story. Which of these assumptions are valid, based only on the information in the story?

State an assumption that each speaker is making.

3. "I can't wait until I'm 16 years old!"
4. "I've enjoyed all of this author's other books, so this new one should be good."
5. "Extend the sides of a quadrilateral until they intersect. Call the point of intersection A."
6. "Let line m intersect line n at a point between A and B."
7. "Since $\angle RSV$ is the result of bisecting $\angle RST$ its measure is less than 45."
8. "The product of two positive numbers is always greater than either of the factors."
9. "Since n is a prime number, I know that n is odd."
10. "When evaluated, $-x$ is negative."
11. "I can construct an isosceles triangle with sides congruent to $\overline{AB}$, $\overline{CD}$, and $\overline{EF}$."
12. "I can find the square root of x."
13. Describe a situation that you have recently observed where unstated assumptions were involved.

CHAPTER SUMMARY

Vocabulary

adjacent angles (2-2)   perpendicular (2-3)   two-column proof (2-1)
complementary angles (2-2)   perpendicular bisector (2-3)   vertical angles (2-2)
linear pair (2-2)   supplementary angles (2-2)

Key Ideas

1. In a two-column proof, the left column contains statements that lead to the desired conclusion. The right column gives reasons why the statements are true.
2. The reasons in a two-column proof can be any of the following: given information, definitions, postulates (including algebraic properties), or previously proven theorems.
3. Two angles are complementary if the sum of their measures is 90. Two angles are supplementary if the sum of their measures is 180.
4. Two angles that form a linear pair are supplementary. The sum of the measures of a linear pair of angles is 180.
5. Perpendicular lines are two lines that intersect to form right angles.
6. Through a given point on a line there is exactly one line in the plane perpendicular to the given line.
7. Only certain information may be assumed from a diagram. This is listed in the chart on page 75.
8. The five steps in proving a theorem are listed on page 80.
9. Methods of proving two segments congruent are listed on page 87. Methods of proving two lines perpendicular are listed on page 88. Methods of proving two angles congruent and methods of proving that an angle is a right angle are listed on pages 94 and 95.
10. Only one perpendicular can be drawn from a point to a line.

CHAPTER REVIEW

2-1

Complete the proof by choosing a reason for each statement.

1. **Given:** $\overline{DE} \cong \overline{BE}$
   E is the midpoint of $\overline{BC}$.

   Prove: $\overline{DE} \cong \overline{EC}$

Proof Statements	Reasons
1. $\overline{DE} \cong \overline{BE}$	1. ___ *Choose from these reasons:*
2. E is the midpoint of $\overline{BC}$.	2. ___ **a.** Definition of midpoint
3. $\overline{BE} \cong \overline{EC}$	3. ___ **b.** Given
4. $\overline{DE} \cong \overline{EC}$	4. ___ **c.** Congruence of segments is transitive.

2-2

2. If $m\angle AFB = 3x + 10$ and $m\angle BFC = 5x$, find $m\angle AFB$.
3. Name two angles supplementary to $\angle BFD$.
4. If $m\angle EFD = x$ and $m\angle AFB = 3x - 40$, find x.

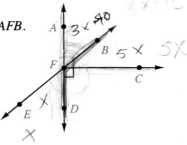

2-3

Suppose $\overline{CF}$ is the perpendicular bisector of $\overline{AD}$. Complete the following.

5. $m\angle CFD = $ _____
6. $\overline{AF} \cong $ _____

2-4

Which of the following may be assumed from the figure to be given information?

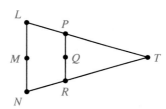

7. Point Q is between P and R.
8. Points M, Q, and T are collinear.
9. $\overrightarrow{LT}$ is a straight line.

2-5

10. Rewrite the theorem as a conditional, write the *Given* and *Prove*, and draw a diagram showing the given information.

    All equilateral triangles are also isosceles triangles.

11. The statements provided for the proof are correct, but in the wrong order. Order them correctly and supply reasons as you write the proof.

    Given: $\angle 2 \cong \angle 3$
    Prove: $\angle 1 \cong \angle 4$
    a. $\angle 2 \cong \angle 3$ b. $\angle 3 \cong \angle 4$ c. $\angle 1 \cong \angle 4$
    d. $\angle 1 \cong \angle 2$ e. $\angle 1 \cong \angle 3$

2-6

12. Use the Common Segment Theorem to draw a conclusion.
    Given: $\overline{PQ} \cong \overline{RS}$
13. If $\overline{PQ} \cong \overline{RS}$, $PR = 8$, and $QR = 3$, find RS.

2-7

14. Use the Common Angle Theorem to draw a conclusion.
    Given: $\angle QTS \cong \angle PTR$
15. Write a two-column proof.

    Given: $\angle 3$ is supplementary to $\angle 1$. $m\angle 1 + m\angle 2 = 180$
    Prove: $\angle 2 \cong \angle 3$

CHAPTER TEST

1. Complete the proof by choosing a reason for each statement.

   Given: U is between T and V. $WU = TU$

   Prove: $WU + UV = TV$

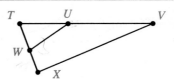

Proof Statements	Reasons	
1. $WU = TU$	1. ___	*Choose from these reasons:*
2. U is between T and V.	2. ___	**a.** Given
3. $TU + UV = TV$	3. ___	**b.** Substitution Property
4. $WU + UV = TV$	4. ___	**c.** Segment Addition Postulate

2. Name a pair of complementary angles.
3. $m\angle NRS$ is eight times $m\angle QRS$.   Find $m\angle NRS$.
4. If $m\angle NRP = 50$, find $m\angle QRS$.
5. Name a pair of perpendicular segments.
6. If $m\angle MRP = 11x + 2$ and $m\angle MRQ = 12x$, find $m\angle MRQ$.
7. If $\overleftrightarrow{RP}$ is the perpendicular bisector of $\overline{MS}$ and $MS = 17$, find RS.

Indicate which of the following may be assumed from the figure to be given information.

8. Points M, R, and S are collinear.   9. $\overline{RN} \cong \overline{RQ}$

10. Draw a diagram to show the given information.
    $\overleftrightarrow{LM} \perp \overrightarrow{PR}$ intersecting at M, $\overrightarrow{MN}$ bisects $\angle PML$.
11. Complete the first line in the analysis of this proof.

    Given: $\overline{TX} \cong \overline{XU}$, $\overline{XU} \cong \overline{XS}$

    Prove: X is the midpoint of $\overline{TS}$.

    I can prove X is the midpoint of $\overline{TS}$ if I can first prove that ___.
12. The statements provided for the proof in Problem 11 are correct, but in the wrong order. Order them correctly and supply reasons as you write the proof.

    a. $\overline{TX} \cong \overline{XS}$ **b.** $\overline{XU} \cong \overline{XS}$ **c.** X is the midpoint of $\overline{TS}$.   **d.** $\overline{TX} \cong \overline{XU}$

13. $\overline{BC} \cong \overline{DE}$ Name another pair of congruent segments.
    Give a reason to support your conclusion.
14. Write a two-column proof.

    Given: $\overline{AB} \cong \overline{BD}$, $\overline{BC} \cong \overline{DE}$

    Prove: $\overline{AB} \cong \overline{CE}$
15. $\angle BAD = \angle CAE$ Name another pair of congruent angles.
    Give a reason to support your conclusion.
16. Draw a conclusion that two angles are congruent. State a postulate, definition, or theorem that supports your conclusion.
    $\angle BDA$ is supplementary to $\angle ADE$. $\angle FAD$ is supplementary to $\angle ADE$.

17. Write a two-column proof.

    Given: $\angle DAF \cong \angle CAE$, $\angle BAC \cong \angle DAE$

    Prove: $\angle DAF \cong \angle BAD$

PREPARING FOR COLLEGE ENTRANCE EXAMS

Give the one correct answer for each question.

1. If $x - y = 7$, then $9 + y - x =$

(A) 16   (B) 2   (C) -2
(D) 0   (E) -16

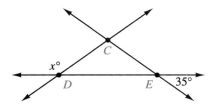

2. In the figure above, if $\angle CDE \cong \angle CED$, then $x =$

(A) 35   (B) 155   (C) 55
(D) 70   (E) 145

3. Which of the following is not evenly divisible by $3x^2$?

(A) $9x^3$ (B) $12x^4y$ (C) $3x^3 + 6x$
(D) $6(x^3 + x^2)$ (E) $3x(x + xy)$

4. Which of the following must be less than M if $M > 0$?

(A) $2M$ (B) M^2 (C) $\frac{2M}{3}$
(D) $\sqrt{M}$ (E) $\frac{1}{M}$

5. Which of the following is the graph of all x values such that $-x \geq -2$ and $x \geq -1$?

(A) ![number line from -1 to 2, filled -1 to 2] -1 0 1 2

(B) ![number line] -1 0 1 2

(C) ![number line] -1 0 1 2

(D) ![number line] -1 0 1 2

(E) ![number line] -1 0 1 2

6. The fraction $\frac{18}{24}$ equals all of the following EXCEPT

(A) $\frac{9}{12}$ (B) $\frac{36}{48}$ (C) $\frac{12}{16}$
(D) $\frac{20}{30}$ (E) $\frac{15}{20}$

7. In the figure above, if $\overrightarrow{EB}$ bisects $\angle AEC$, then $x =$

(A) 140   (B) 40   (C) 120
(D) 80   (E) 50

8. R years ago, Juan was three times as old as Ellen was. If Ellen is now 31 years old, how old is Juan now in terms of R?

(A) $31 + 3R$ (B) $93 + 4R$ (C) $3R - 93$
(D) $93 - 2R$ (E) $31 - 3R$

9. If $y < 0$, which of the following must be true?

(A) $-y < y$ (B) $-y > 0$ (C) $|y| < 0$
(D) $y - y > 0$ (E) $y^2 < 0$

10. If N is an even number, which of the following must be true?

   I. $\frac{N}{2}$ is odd.

   II. $2N - 1$ is odd.

   III. $2N - 2$ is even.

(A) II only   (B) III only   (C) I and II
(D) I and III   (E) II and III

![figure of grid with B at top left and H at bottom right]

11. A bear located at point B wants to eat some honey located at point H. If the bear can only go down or to the right along the lines shown, how many different paths can he take from B to H?

(A) 7   (B) 3   (C) 16
(D) 24   (E) 10

12. If $pq = -2$ and $(p + q)^2 = 9$, then $p^2 + q^2 =$

(A) 7   (B) 11   (C) 13
(D) -7 (E) 5

Parallel Lines and Planes

Rows of corn form parallel lines. Describe other real-world examples of parallel lines.

PARALLELISM IN LINES AND PLANES

OBJECTIVE: *Identify parallel planes, parallel lines, and skew lines. Name angle pairs formed when a transversal intersects two lines.*

3-1 Parallel Planes, Lines, and Transversals

In Chapter 1 you learned that two figures that intersect have a set of points in common. Figures that do not intersect have no points in common.

DEFINITION

Parallel planes are planes that do not intersect.

DEFINITION

Parallel lines are coplanar and do not intersect.

Lines that are not coplanar and do not intersect are called **skew lines.**

Planes *M* and *N* are parallel. (*M* ∥ *N*)
Lines *p* and *q* are parallel. (*p* ∥ *q*)

Lines *r* and *s* are skew.

Segments and rays are parallel if they are contained in parallel lines. Two parallel lines determine a unique plane and two intersecting lines determine a unique plane.

Example 1

Refer to the box on the right.
a. Name a pair of parallel planes.
b. Name a pair of parallel lines.

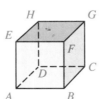

   Solution
   a. plane *ADHE* ∥ *BCGF*   **b.** $\overline{AB} \parallel \overline{HG}$

Try This

Name a pair of skew lines.

◆ THEOREM 3.1

If two parallel planes are cut by a third plane, the lines of intersection are parallel.

Given: Plane *M* is parallel to plane *N*; plane *S* intersects plane *M* in $\overline{AB}$; plane *S* intersects plane *N* in $\overline{CD}$.

Prove: $\overline{AB} \parallel \overline{CD}$

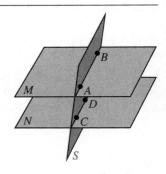

Proof

Statements	Reasons
1. $M \parallel N$; *S* and *M* intersects in $\overline{AB}$; *S* and *N* intersect in $\overline{CD}$.	1. Given
2. $\overline{AB}$ and $\overline{CD}$ do not intersect.	2. Def. of $\parallel$ planes
3. $\overline{AB}$ and $\overline{CD}$ are coplanar.	3. Both lines are in plane *S*.
4. $\overline{AB} \parallel \overline{CD}$	4. Def. of $\parallel$ lines

A line that intersects two coplanar lines in two different points is called a **transversal**. A transversal that intersects two coplanar lines forms eight angles. In the figure to the right, transversal *t* intersects lines *m* and *n*.

Angles 3, 4, 5, and 6 are interior angles.
Angles 1, 2, 7, and 8 are exterior angles.

The pairs of angles have special names.

Alternate interior angles are two nonadjacent interior angles on opposite sides of the transversal. There are two pairs of alternate interior angles: $\angle 3$ and $\angle 6$, $\angle 4$ and $\angle 5$.

Alternate exterior angles are two nonadjacent exterior angles on opposite sides of the transversal. There are two pairs of alternate exterior angles: $\angle 1$ and $\angle 8$, $\angle 2$ and $\angle 7$.

Same-side interior angles are two interior angles on the same side of the transversal. There are two pairs of same-side interior angles: $\angle 3$ and $\angle 5$, $\angle 4$ and $\angle 6$.

Corresponding angles are two nonadjacent angles on the same side of the transversal such that one is an exterior angle and the other is an interior angle. There are four pairs of corresponding angles: $\angle 1$ and $\angle 5$, $\angle 3$ and $\angle 7$, $\angle 2$ and $\angle 6$, $\angle 4$ and $\angle 8$.

Example 2

a. Name two lines in the figure that appear to be parallel.
b. Name two pairs of alternate interior angles for lines *AB* and *CD*.

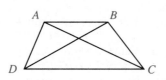

Solution

a. $\overline{AB}, \overline{CD}$
b. $\angle BAC$ and $\angle ACD$, $\angle ABD$ and $\angle BDC$

Try This

Name two pairs of alternate interior angles for lines *AD* and *BC*.

Class Exercises

Short Answer

1. Name three pairs of parallel planes.
2. Name all the lines that are parallel to $\overline{EF}$.
3. How many lines are parallel to each line in the figure?
4. Name all the lines that are skew to $\overline{HE}$.
5. How many lines are skew to each line in the figure?

6. Name two pairs of streets that appear to be parallel.
7. Which streets are transversals for streets a and b?
8. Which streets are transversals for streets d and e?
9. Name the only street that is a transversal for streets a and d.

Sample Exercises

Identify each angle pair as alternate interior, alternate exterior, same-side interior, corresponding, or none of these.

10. $\angle 13$ and $\angle 5$
11. $\angle 1$ and $\angle 3$
12. $\angle 7$ and $\angle 12$
13. $\angle 3$ and $\angle 16$
14. $\angle 7$ and $\angle 10$
15. $\angle 13$ and $\angle 4$

Discussion

16. Draw a diagram to illustrate the statement:
    If plane M is parallel to plane N, not every line in M is parallel to a given line AB in plane N.
17. Draw and label a pair of lines and a transversal. Label the figure so that $\angle 7$ and $\angle 8$ are corresponding angles. Must their supplements be corresponding angles? Give a convincing argument for your answer.

Exercises

A

Refer to the figure to name the plane that is parallel to the given plane.

1. plane $ABHG$
2. plane $CDJI$
3. plane $BCIH$

4. Is plane $ABHG$ parallel to plane $FEKL$? Explain.
5. Name four pairs of parallel planes.
6. Name three lines parallel to $\overline{CD}$.
7. Which lines in plane $AGLF$ are skew to $\overline{CD}$?
8. Name four lines that are skew to both $\overline{EK}$ and $\overline{BH}$.
9. Name two lines that are parallel to $\overline{AB}$ and skew to $\overline{BC}$.
10. Are any lines both parallel and skew to $\overline{FE}$?

Name the indicated angles determined by intersecting lines *q* and *r* cut by transversal *p*.

11. two pairs of alternate interior angles
12. two pairs of alternate exterior angles
13. two pairs of same-side interior angles
14. four pairs of corresponding angles
15. a pair of corresponding angles that includes ∠6
16. a pair of alternate interior angles that includes ∠6

Identify each pair of angles as alternate interior, alternate exterior, same-side interior, corresponding, or none of these.

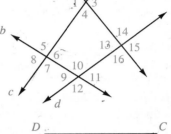

17. ∠1 and ∠13   18. ∠6 and ∠10
19. ∠12 and ∠14   20. ∠4 and ∠10
21. ∠11 and ∠13   22. ∠8 and ∠15
23. ∠1 and ∠15   24. ∠5 and ∠2

25. Name two pairs of alternate interior angles for lines *a* and *b* cut by transversal *c*.
26. Name two pairs of corresponding angles for lines *c* and *d* cut by transversal *a*.

27. For $\overline{AB}$ and $\overline{DC}$ cut by transversal $\overline{AC}$, name the angle that is the alternate interior angle to ∠*BAC*.
28. For $\overline{BC}$ and $\overline{AD}$ cut by transversal $\overline{AC}$, name the angle that is the alternate interior angle to ∠*BCA*.

B

Determine whether each statement is always, sometimes, or never true.

29. If two lines in space are parallel to the same line, then they are parallel to each other.
30. If a plane intersects one of two parallel planes, then it intersects the other parallel plane.
31. If two planes are parallel to the same line, then they are parallel to each other.
32. If a plane is parallel to one of two skew lines, then it intersects the other skew line.
33. If two lines do not intersect, then they are parallel.
34. If a line and a plane do not intersect, then they are parallel.
35. If ∠1 and ∠2 are alternate interior angles, then the vertical angles relative to them are alternate exterior angles.
36. If ∠3 and ∠4 are same-side interior angles, then their supplements are also same-side interior angles.
37. If ∠7 and ∠8 are corresponding angles, then the vertical angles relative to them are alternate interior angles.

38. In the box to the right, opposite sides are parallel. Suppose a plane cuts the box at *A*, *F*, *N*, and *M*. Explain why $\overline{MN} \| \overline{AF}$.

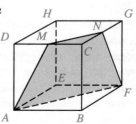

Indicate which of the following are examples of intersecting, parallel, or skew lines.

39. railroad tracks
40. picture frames
41. bowling alleys
42. airplane flight paths
43. rows of corn
44. a picket fence
45. lines on a football field
46. a TV antenna

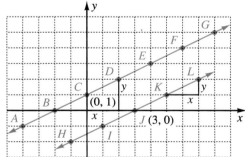

Name each of the following, if it exists, in the crystal.

47. one line that appears to be parallel to $\overline{BE}$
48. the line that appears to be parallel to $\overline{BC}$
49. a plane parallel to *ABCD*
50. a plane parallel to *ABE*
51. one line that appears to be skew to $\overline{AD}$

52. How many edges are skew to $\overline{AD}$?
53. How many segments are shown in the figure?
54. How many pairs of parallel segments do there appear to be?

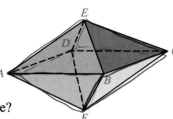

ABCD is a square.

55. A carpenter builds a stairway by cutting triangles like $\triangle ABC$ and $\triangle CDE$ from a piece of lumber. $\angle DCE$ and $\angle FEG$ are corresponding angles relative to what pair of parallel lines and what transversal?

56. In a periscope a pair of mirrors are mounted parallel to each other, as shown. The path of light becomes a transversal. Name a pair of alternate interior angles.

c

In the coordinate graph shown, $\overline{AG}$ and $\overline{HL}$ are parallel.

57. Find the coordinates of each labeled point on $\overline{AG}$ and on $\overline{HL}$.

58. For each pair of points on $\overline{HL}$ construct a triangle like the one shown and calculate the ratio $\frac{y}{x}$ where x and y are the lengths of the sides of the triangle. Do the same for $\overline{AG}$.

59. Write a generalization that is based on your results in Exercise 58

60. Just as any point in an x-y coordinate plane can be named by a pair of coordinates, any point in an x-y-z coordinate space can be named by a triple of coordinates. In the box shown, the x-y-z coordinates of three of the points have been given. Find the coordinates for each of the remaining corners of the box.

61. How many pairs of parallel segments exist in the box to the right?

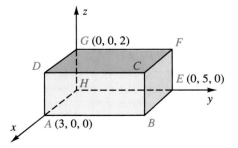

Draw each figure if possible.

62. Line $l \parallel m$, lines l and n are skew, lines m and n are skew.

63. Line $s \parallel t$, line $s \parallel w$, lines t and w are skew.

64. Line $a \perp b$, lines a and c are skew, lines b and c are skew.

65. Line $d \parallel$ plane P, plane $P \parallel$ plane Q, d is $\not\parallel$ to Q.

Critical Thinking

Some statements that are true about lines in a plane are not necessarily true about lines in space. Determine whether each statement is always true about lines in space.

66. Two lines parallel to a third line are parallel to each other

67. If a line is perpendicular to one of two parallel lines, then it is perpendicular to the other parallel line.

68. The number of points that are formed by intersections of a given number of lines depends upon their positions relative to one another. Three lines form 0, 1, 2, or 3 points of intersection. Investigate the number of points of intersection that are possible for four coplanar lines.

0 points   1 point   2 points   3 points

Mixed Review

1. Name a pair of vertical angles.

2. Name an angle that forms a linear pair with $\angle RUS$.

3. Name a pair of adjacent, complementary angles.

4. Name a pair of complementary angles that are not adjacent.

5. Name an angle that is the supplement of $\angle QUR$.

6. Name an angle that is the supplement of $\angle TUS$.

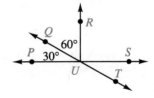

Computer Activity
Parallel Lines and Transversals

Use computer software to draw two parallel lines and a transversal.

1. Measure pairs of corresponding angles in the figure you have drawn. What do you notice? Do you think this is true for any pair of parallel lines and any transversal? State a generalization.

2. Measure other angles and find pairs that are congruent. State an appropriate generalization for each pair.

3. Measure pairs of same-side interior angles. Find the sum of the measures of each pair. What do you notice? State a generalization.

3-2 Properties of Parallel Lines

 EXPLORE Use a ruler to draw two parallel lines, one on each side of the ruler. Draw a transversal and number the angles as shown. Use tracing paper or a protractor to find pairs of congruent angles.

In the last lesson, special pairs of angles formed by two lines and a transversal were defined. You may have discovered while completing the Explore in this lesson, that when the two lines cut by a transversal are parallel, certain pairs of angles are congruent. This observation is the basis for the following postulate.

● **POSTULATE 13**

If two parallel lines are cut by a transversal, then corresponding angles are congruent.

Postulate 13 is used to prove the next theorem.

◆ **THEOREM 3.2**

If two parallel lines are cut by a transversal, then alternate interior angles are congruent.

Given: $a \parallel b$
Prove: $\angle 1 \cong \angle 2$

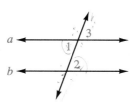

Proof Statements

	Reasons
1. $a \parallel b$	**1.** Given
2. $\angle 2 \cong \angle 3$	**2.** If two parallel lines are cut by a transversal, then corresponding $\angle$s are $\cong$.
3. $\angle 3 \cong \angle 1$	**3.** Vertical $\angle$s are $\cong$.
4. $\angle 1 \cong \angle 2$	**4.** Congruence of $\angle$s is transitive.

Example 1

$p \parallel q$, $m \angle 1 = 100$, $m \angle 2 = 55$ Find $m \angle 3$.

Solution

$m \angle 1 = m \angle ABC$ — *If two parallel lines are cut by a transversal, then alternate interior angles are congruent.*

$m \angle 1 = m \angle 2 + m \angle 3$ — *(Theorem 3.2)*

$100 = 55 + m \angle 3$ — *Substitution*

$45 = m \angle 3$

Try This

$p \parallel q$, $m \angle 1 = 135$, $m \angle 3 = 75$ Find $m \angle 2$.

Two additional relationships you might have discovered in the Explore are stated in Theorems 3.3 and 3.4, which you will be asked to prove in Exercises 30–31.

◆ THEOREM 3.3

If two parallel lines are cut by a transversal, then alternate exterior angles are congruent.

◆ THEOREM 3.4

If two parallel lines are cut by a transversal, then same-side interior angles are supplementary.

Example 2

$\overline{AB} \parallel \overline{CD}$ Find $m \angle B$.

Solution

$m \angle ABC = m \angle DCE$ — *If two parallel lines are cut by a transversal, then corresponding angles are congruent. (Postulate 13)*

$4x - 40 = x + 20$ — *Substitution*

$3x = 60$

$x = 20$ $m \angle B = 40$

Try This

$\overline{AD} \parallel \overline{BC}$, $m \angle D = 3x - 25$, $m \angle DCE = x + 20$ Find $m \angle D$.

Properties of Parallel Lines Cut by a Transversal

1. Corresponding angles are congruent.
2. Alternate interior angles are congruent.
3. Alternate exterior angles are congruent.
4. Same-side interior angles are supplementary.

Class Exercises

Short Answer

$a \parallel b$ State the postulate or theorem that justifies each conclusion.

1. $\angle 1 \cong \angle 8$
2. $\angle 4 \cong \angle 5$
3. $m\angle 4 + m\angle 6 = 180$
4. $\angle 3 \cong \angle 7$
5. $\angle 2 \cong \angle 7$
6. $\angle 6 \cong \angle 3$

Sample Exercises

$a \parallel b$, $m\angle 1 = 65$

7. Find $m\angle 5$.
8. Find $m\angle 8$.
9. Find $m\angle 6$.
10. If $\overline{AB} \parallel \overline{CD}$, name a pair of congruent angles.
11. If $\overline{AD} \parallel \overline{BC}$, name two pairs of supplementary angles.

Discussion

12. If $a \parallel b$, give a convincing argument that $\angle 1$ and $\angle 3$ are supplementary.
13. If $a \parallel b$, give a convincing argument that $\angle 1$ and $\angle 2$ are supplementary.

Exercises

A

$p \parallel q$, $m\angle 3 = 65$

1. Find $m\angle 1$.
2. Find $m\angle 2$.
3. Find $m\angle 4$.
4. Find $m\angle 5$.
5. Find $m\angle 6$.
6. Find $m\angle 7$.

$\overline{AB} \parallel \overline{CD}$, $\overline{AD} \parallel \overline{BC}$, $m\angle ADC = 110$, $m\angle ACD = 28$

7. Find $m\angle 1$.
8. Find $m\angle 2$.
9. Find $m\angle 3$.
10. Find $m\angle 4$.
11. Find $m\angle 5$.
12. Find $m\angle 6$.
13. Find $m\angle 7$.
14. Find $m\angle 8$.
15. Find $m\angle 9$.

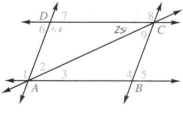

16. Name all the angles congruent to $\angle 1$.
17. Name all the angles congruent to $\angle 3$.
18. Name all the angles supplementary to $\angle 1$.
19. Name all the angles supplementary to $\angle 3$.

$l \parallel m$ Find x.

20. $m\angle 1 = 3x + 7$, $m\angle 5 = 5x - 3$
21. $m\angle 4 = 8x + 12$, $m\angle 6 = 2x + 54$
22. $m\angle 3 = 4x + 7$, $m\angle 6 = 2x + 23$
23. $m\angle 4 = x^2 + 5x$, $m\angle 8 = 9x + 12$
24. $m\angle 2 = x^2 - 6x$, $m\angle 5 = 7x + 220$

Find the values of x and y.

25. $\overline{BE} \parallel \overline{CD}$

26. $\overline{BC}$ bisects $\angle ABD$.
$m\angle ABD = 64$, $\overline{BC} \parallel \overline{DE}$

27. $\overline{AB} \parallel \overline{CD}$, $\overline{AB} \perp \overline{BC}$

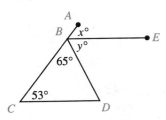

28. $\overline{AB} \parallel \overline{CD}$, $\overline{AB} \perp \overline{AD}$

29. A developer is dividing a plot of land into lots so that the sides of each lot are parallel to the street AC. If $m\angle ACD = 105$, find $m\angle CEF$ and $m\angle CGH$.

30. Complete the proof of Theorem 3.3.

Given: $a \parallel b$

Prove: $\angle 1 \cong \angle 2$

Proof Statements   Reasons

1. $a \parallel b$ 1. ____
2. $\angle 1 \cong \angle 3$ 2. ____
3. $\angle 3 \cong \angle 2$ 3. ____
4. $\angle 1 \cong \angle 2$ 4. ____

31. Write a two-column proof for Theorem 3.4.

Given: $a \parallel b$

Prove: $\angle 1$ and $\angle 2$ are supplementary.

Plan First show that $\angle 2 \cong \angle 3$.
Then use the fact that $\angle 1$
is the supplement of $\angle 3$.

B

$\overline{AB} \parallel \overline{CD}$, $\overline{DG}$ bisects $\angle ADC$.
$\overline{AF}$ bisects $\angle DAB$. $m \angle ADC = 124$

32. Find $m \angle ADG$.
33. Find $m \angle DAF$.
34. Find $m \angle DGB$.

35. $\overline{AB} \parallel \overline{DC}$, $\overline{AD} \parallel \overline{BC}$
    Find $m \angle EAD$.

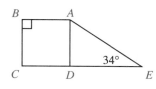

36. **Given:** $m \angle 1 = m \angle 2$, $\overline{DE} \parallel \overline{BC}$
    Prove: $\overline{ED}$ bisects $\angle AEB$.

37. **Given:** $p \parallel q$, $s \parallel t$
    Prove: $\angle 1 \cong \angle 7$
38. **Given:** $p \parallel q$, $s \parallel t$
    Prove: $\angle 2 \cong \angle 9$

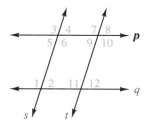

C

39. **Given:** $\overline{CA}$ bisects $\angle DAB$. $\overline{AD} \parallel \overline{BE}$
    $\angle 1$ and $\angle 2$ are complementary.
    Prove: $\overline{BC}$ bisects $\angle ABE$.

40. **Given:** $\overline{BC}$ and $\overline{DE}$ are coplanar.
    plane $M \parallel$ plane N
    Prove: $\angle ABC \cong \angle ADE$, $\angle ACB \cong \angle AED$

41. Draw a diagram and prove the statement: If $\overline{BD}$ bisects $\angle ABC$ and $\overline{AM} \parallel \overline{BD}$ with point M on $\overrightarrow{CB}$, then $m \angle ABD = m \angle AMB$.

Critical Thinking

42. If a theorem is accepted as a postulate, then the statement earlier accepted as a postulate might be proven as a theorem. Suppose Theorem 3.2 is accepted as a postulate. Prove Postulate 13 as a theorem.
43. Assume Theorem 3.4 is a postulate. Prove Postulate 13 as a theorem.

Algebra Review

Solve each system of equations.

1. $x + y = 10$
   $y = x + 8$
2. $y = x - 6$
   $x + y = -2$
3. $x - y = 5$
   $x + 2y = 7$
4. $x + 2y = 10$
   $3x + 4y = 8$

Vectors

Representing quantities that have both direction and magnitude is often done through the use of directed segments called vectors. The vector AB (written $\overrightarrow{AB}$) is a vector whose direction is about 15 degrees above horizontal and whose magnitude, or length, is $\sqrt{53}$.

Vectors can also be represented by an ordered pair of numbers. The vector $\overrightarrow{AB}$ can also be written as (7, 2). The point A is the origin of the vector and the point B is the terminal point of $\overrightarrow{AB}$. The ordered pair notation for a vector results from subtracting the components of the ordered pair representing the origin from the components of the ordered pair representing the terminal point. In the case of $\overrightarrow{AB}$, the origin is $A(1, 1)$ and the terminal point is $B(8, 3)$. Thus, $\overrightarrow{AB} = (8 - 1, 3 - 1)$ or (7, 2).

Two vectors (a, b) and (c, d), or the lines or line segments containing them, are parallel if $\frac{a}{b} = \frac{c}{d}$. Two vectors (a, b) and (c, d), or the lines or line segments containing them, are perpendicular if $\frac{a}{b} \cdot \frac{c}{d} = \frac{ac}{bd} = -1$.

Example

a. Test to see if the vectors (1, 3) and (17, 51) are parallel.

b. Test to see if the vectors (1, 3) and (−12, 4) are perpendicular.

Solution

a. They are parallel since $\frac{1}{3} = \frac{17}{51}$.

b. They are perpendicular since $\frac{1}{3} \cdot \frac{-12}{4} = \frac{-12}{12} = -1$.

Try This

a. Test to see if the vectors (1, 7) and (13, 91) are parallel.

b. Test to see if the vectors (4, 3) and (−6, 8) are perpendicular.

Exercises

Find the ordered pairs representing the following vectors if $A(5, 3)$, $B(4, 0)$, $C(1, 2)$, and $D(2, 5)$.

1. $\overrightarrow{AB}$ 2. $\overrightarrow{AC}$ 3. $\overrightarrow{CD}$ 4. $\overrightarrow{DC}$

5. Is $\overrightarrow{CD}$ the same as $\overrightarrow{DC}$? Explain the relationship between these vectors.
6. Use the distance formula on page 27 to find the magnitude of vectors $\overrightarrow{CD}$ and $\overrightarrow{DC}$.
7. Two vectors having the same ordered pair representation, and therefore the same magnitude, are called equal vectors. What can you say about how equal vectors are related geometrically?
8. What can you say about two vectors that are contained in the same line and are pointed in the same direction?

Indicate which pairs of vectors among the following are parallel and which are perpendicular.

9. (3, 4)   10. (2, −4)   11. (−8, 6)   12. (6, 8)   13. (6, −12)

3-3 Proving Lines Parallel

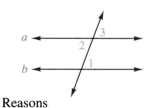

Draw line *m* and point *A* on the line and point *P* above the line. Then draw a transversal through *P* that intersects line *m* at *A*.

Locate and draw the translation image in the direction of vector $\vec{AP}$ of this figure using tracing paper. (Trace the figure and slide the tracing the distance and direction of $\vec{AP}$.) Since translations preserve angle measure $m\angle 1 = m\angle 2$. Do you think line *m* and its translation image are parallel?

In the previous lesson, the hypothesis of each theorem stated that two lines were parallel and the conclusion concerned angle measures. In this lesson, the hypothesis of each theorem is a statement about angle measures and the conclusion states that two lines are parallel.

● **POSTULATE 14**

If two lines are cut by a transversal and a pair of corresponding angles are congruent, then the lines are parallel.

◆ **THEOREM 3.5**

If two lines are cut by a transversal and a pair of alternate interior angles are congruent, then the lines are parallel.

Given: $\angle 1 \cong \angle 2$
Prove: $a \parallel b$

Proof Statements	Reasons
1. $\angle 1 \cong \angle 2$	1. Given
2. $\angle 2 \cong \angle 3$	2. Vertical angles are $\cong$.
3. $\angle 1 \cong \angle 3$	3. Congruence of $\angle$s is transitive.
4. $a \parallel b$	4. If two lines are cut by a transversal and corr. $\angle$s are $\cong$, the lines are $\parallel$.

◆ THEOREM 3.6

If two lines are cut by a transversal and a pair of alternate exterior angles are congruent, then the lines are parallel.

◆ THEOREM 3.7

If two lines are cut by a transversal and a pair of same-side interior angles are supplementary, then the lines are parallel

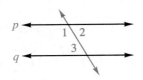

You will be asked to prove Theorems 3.6 and 3.7 in Exercises 20 and 25.

Example 1

Use the given information to determine which lines are parallel. State the theorem or postulate that justifies your answer.

a. $\angle 3 \cong \angle 5$ **b.** $m\angle 1 + m\angle 2 = m\angle 4$

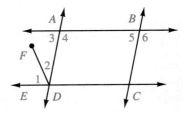

Solution

a. $\overline{AD} \| \overline{BC}$ *If two lines are cut by a transversal and a pair of corr. $\angle$s are $\cong$, then the lines are $\|$.*

b. $\overline{AB} \| \overline{CD}$ *If two lines are cut by a transversal and a pair of alternate interior $\angle$s are $\cong$, then the lines are $\|$.*

Try This

Write a statement about a pair of same-side interior angles that makes $\overline{AD} \| \overline{BC}$.

Example 2

$m\angle 2 = 12x + 7$, $m\angle 3 = 8x - 7$ Find the value of x for which $a \| b$.

Solution

$(12x + 7) + (8x - 7) = 180$ *If same-side interior angles are*
$20x = 180$ *supplementary, then the lines are*
$x = 9$ *parallel.*

Try This

$m\angle 1 = 2x + 6$, $m\angle 3 = 3x - 5$ Find the value of x for which $a \| b$.

◆ THEOREM 3.8

In a plane, two coplanar lines perpendicular to the same line are parallel.

You will be asked to prove Theorems 3.8 and 3.9 in Exercises 30–31.

◆ THEOREM 3.9

Two lines parallel to a third line are parallel to each other.

Ways to Prove Two Lines Parallel Using a Transversal

1. Show that a pair of corresponding angles are congruent.
2. Show that a pair of alternate interior angles are congruent.
3. Show that a pair of alternate exterior angles are congruent.
4. Show that a pair of same-side interior angles are supplementary.
5. Show that two coplanar lines are perpendicular to the same line.

Class Exercises

Short Answer

Congruent angles are marked. State which lines are parallel. Give the theorem or postulate that justifies your answer.

1.   **2.**   **3.**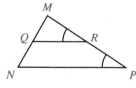

Sample Exercises

Use the given information to state which lines are parallel. Give the theorem or postulate that justifies your answer.

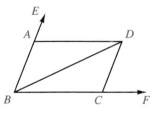

4. $m\angle BAD = 113$, $m\angle ABC = 67$, $m\angle BCD = 103$
5. $m\angle EAD = 57$, $m\angle ABC = 57$, $m\angle DCF = 67$

Find the value of x for which $a \parallel b$.

6. $m\angle 2 = 2x$, $m\angle 3 = 4x$
7. $m\angle 1 = 2x$, $m\angle 6 = 136$
8. $m\angle 1 = 3x$, $m\angle 5 = 60$

Discussion

9. If $\overline{AD} \parallel \overline{BC}$ and $m\angle 1$ is doubled, how must $m\angle 3$ change if $\overline{AD}$ is to remain parallel to $\overline{BC}$?
10. If $\overline{AB} \parallel \overline{DC}$ and $m\angle 1$ is increased by 30 degrees, how must $m\angle 2$ change if $\overline{AB}$ is to remain parallel to $\overline{DC}$?

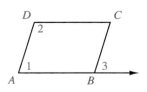

Exercises

A

Use the given information to state which lines are parallel. Give the theorem or postulate that justifies your answer.

1. $\angle 1 \cong \angle 9$ 2. $\angle 3 \cong \angle 6$ 3. $m\angle 8 + m\angle 10 = 180$
4. $\angle 4 \cong \angle 9$ 5. $\angle 8 \cong \angle 12$ 6. $\angle 1 \cong \angle 8$

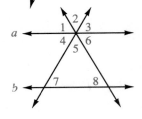

Does the given information allow you to conclude that a is parallel to b? If so, state the theorem or postulate that justifies your answer.

7. $m\angle 4 + m\angle 5 + m\angle 8 = 180$
8. $m\angle 1 + m\angle 2 + m\angle 7 = 180$

9. Name two pairs of corresponding angles that, if congruent, would allow you to conclude that a is parallel b.

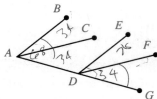

Use the given information to determine if $\overline{AC}$ is parallel to $\overline{DF}$.

10. $m\angle BAD = 42$, $m\angle BAC = 25$, $m\angle FDG = 17$
11. $m\angle BAD = 68$, $m\angle FDG = 34$, $\overline{AC}$ bisects $\angle BAD$.
12. $m\angle EDF = 28$, $m\angle EDA = 100$, $m\angle CAD = 54$
13. $m\angle BAC = 35$, $m\angle BAD = 61$, $m\angle ADE = 119$, $m\angle ADF = 144$

Find the value of x for which p is parallel to q.

14. $m\angle 1 = 3x + 13$, $m\angle 4 = 4x - 6$
15. $m\angle 3 = 4x + 2$, $m\angle 5 = 8x - 2$
16. $m\angle 2 = \frac{2}{3}x - 16$, $m\angle 5 = 24$
17. $m\angle 1 = 2x + 12$, $m\angle 6 = \frac{3}{4}x + 27$
18. $m\angle 2 = x^2 + 7x$, $m\angle 5 = 9x + 3$
19. $m\angle 3 = x^2 + 8x$, $m\angle 5 = 4x + 20$

20. Complete the proof of Theorem 3.6.

    Given: $\angle 1 \cong \angle 2$

    Prove: $a \parallel b$

Proof

Statements	Reasons
1. $\angle 1 \cong \angle 2$	1. ___
2. $\angle 2 \cong \angle 3$	2. ___
3. $\angle 1 \cong \angle 3$	3. ___
4. $a \parallel b$	4. ___

B

Determine the values of x and y for which $m \parallel n$.

21. $m\angle 1 = x + y$, $m\angle 4 = x - y$, $m\angle 8 = 118$
22. $m\angle 3 = 2x - y$, $m\angle 6 = x + 2y$, $m\angle 7 = 75$
23. $m\angle 1 = 6x - 3y$, $m\angle 4 = 2x - 8y$, $m\angle 5 = 126$
24. $m\angle 2 = 63$, $m\angle 3 = x - 3y$, $m\angle 6 = 7x - 2y + 2$

25. Write a two-column proof for Theorem 3.7.

    Given: $\angle 1$ and $\angle 3$ are supplementary.

    Prove: $p \parallel q$

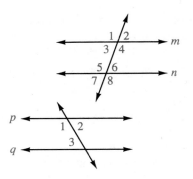

26. In figure $ABCD$, $\overline{AD} \perp \overline{BA}$ and $\overline{CB} \perp \overline{AB}$. Draw the figure and determine which lines, if any, are parallel.

27. In figure $ABCD$, $\overline{CD} \perp \overline{BC}$, $\overline{AB} \perp \overline{BC}$, and $m\angle DAB = 115$. Draw the figure and find the measure of $\angle ADC$.

28. In figure $ABCD$, $m\angle A = 115$, $m\angle ABD = 35$, $m\angle DBC = 30$, and $m\angle BDC = 30$. Draw the figure and determine which lines are parallel.

29. Write a proof for Theorem 3.8.
   Given: $m \perp p$
   $n \perp p$
   Prove: $m \parallel n$

30. Write a proof for Theorem 3.9.
   Given: $a \parallel c$, $b \parallel c$
   Prove: $a \parallel b$

C

31. **Given:** $\angle BCD \cong \angle CDE$, $m\angle B + m\angle D = 180$
   Prove: $\overline{AB} \parallel \overline{DC}$

32. Draw two parallel lines, a and b, and a transversal t. Use a protractor to bisect a pair of alternate exterior angles. Write a statement about these bisectors. Prove the statement.

Critical Thinking

33. Consider the relation "is parallel to." Determine whether the reflexive, symmetric, and transitive properties hold for this relation for **a.** lines in a plane **b.** lines in space.

Mixed Review

Classify each triangle as acute, right, or obtuse.

1.

2.

3.

4.

Quiz

Determine whether each statement is true or false.

1. $\angle 1$ and $\angle 3$ are alternate interior angles.
2. $\angle 3$ and $\angle 2$ are corresponding angles.
3. If $t \parallel v$, then $m\angle 2 + m\angle 5 = 180$.
4. If $\angle 2 \cong \angle 4$, then $t \parallel v$.
5. If $t \parallel v$, $r \parallel s$, and $m\angle 4 = 24$, then $m\angle 3 = 24$.

Use the given information to name the lines, if any, that are parallel.

6. $\angle 3 \cong \angle 7$ 7. $\angle 2 \cong \angle 6$
8. $\angle 2 \cong \angle 3$ 9. $\angle ACE \cong \angle BDC$
10. $m\angle ACD + m\angle BDC = 180$

11. $m\angle 2 = 3x + 10$, $m\angle 5 = x + 28$.
   Find the value of x for which $\overline{AB} \parallel \overline{CD}$.

COMPARING APPROACHES IN GEOMETRY

Synthetic and Transformation Geometry

Theorem 3.5

If two lines are cut by a transversal and a pair of alternate interior angles are congruent, then the lines are parallel.

Theorem 3.5 is proven on page 117 using what is called a synthetic approach, as are all other proofs based on the set of axioms that you are learning.

Transformation proofs are usually based on the properties that are preserved by the transformation being used. For example, on page 31, you learned that translations, reflections, and rotations preserve segment length and angle measure. A property of 180° rotations used below is that a line and its rotation image are parallel.

Compare the synthetic and transformation approaches to a proof of Theorem 3.5.

Synthetic Approach

Transformation Approach

Plan for Proof

It is given that $\angle 1 \cong \angle 2$. By the vertical angles theorem you know that $\angle 2 \cong \angle 3$. Finally use the fact that congruence of angles is transitive to conclude that $\angle 1 \cong \angle 3$. Since corresponding angles are congruent, the lines must be parallel.

Plan for Proof

Consider the 180° rotation with center A—the midpoint of $\overline{BC}$. The rotation image of point B is C and of line r is again line r. Since $\angle 1 \cong \angle 2$, the rotation image of $\angle 1$ must be $\angle 2$. Therefore, the rotation image of p is q. It follows that $p \parallel q$.

Exercises

A is the midpoint of $\overline{BC}$ and the alternate exterior angles $\angle 3$ and $\angle 4$ are congruent. Consider the 180° rotation image centered at A.

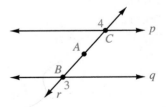

1. Find the rotation image of point B.
2. Find the rotation image of line r.
3. How does the rotation image of $\angle 3$ compare with $\angle 3$ in measure?
4. Find the rotation image of line q.
5. Since the 180° rotation image of line q is parallel to q itself, you can conclude that line p is parallel to __?__ .
6. The statements in Exercises 1–5 outline a transformation proof to what theorem?

ANGLE SUM THEOREMS

OBJECTIVE: *Apply the Angle Sum Theorem for Triangles and related corollaries.*

3-4 Angles of a Triangle

Draw any triangle. Use tracing paper to draw the 180° rotation image of the triangle centered at points A and B—the midpoints of two sides of the triangle. What can you conclude about $m\angle 1 + m\angle 2 + m\angle 3$?

You may have discovered in the Explore that you need the following postulate to prove the theorem.

● POSTULATE 15

Given a line l and a point P not on l, there exists one and only one line through P parallel to l.

A line added to a figure is called an **auxiliary line.** An auxiliary line is added in the proof of the following theorem.

◆ THEOREM 3.10   Angle Sum Theorem for Triangles

The sum of the measures of the angles of a triangle is 180.

Given: $\triangle ABC$

Prove: $m\angle 1 + m\angle 2 + m\angle 3 = 180$

Proof

Statements	Reasons
1. Let l be the only line through A parallel to $\overline{BC}$.	1. Given a line l and a point P not on l, there exists one and only one line through P parallel to l. (Postulate 15)
2. $m\angle 4 = m\angle 2$, $m\angle 1 = m\angle 5$	2. If two ∥ lines are cut by a transversal, then the alternate interior ∠s are ≅.
3. $m\angle 5 + m\angle 4 + m\angle 3 = 180$	3. Linear Pair Postulate
4. $m\angle 1 + m\angle 2 + m\angle 3 = 180$	4. Substitution

Example 1

Find the measure of each angle.
a. $\angle A$ **b.** $\angle B$

Solution

a. $x + 2x + 60 = 180$ *The sum of the measures of*
   $ 3x = 120$ *the angles of a triangle is 180.*
   $ x = 40$
   $m\angle A = 40$

b. $m\angle B = 2x$
   $m\angle B = 2(40)$
   $m\angle B = 80$

Try This

In $\triangle ABC$, $\angle B \cong \angle C$ and $m\angle CAB = 100$.   Find $m\angle B$.

Example 2

The measures of the angles of $\triangle ABC$ are in the ratio $1:2:3$. Classify
the triangle as acute, right, or obtuse.

Solution

 Let $x = m\angle A$
$ 2x = m\angle B$
$ 3x = m\angle C$
$x + 2x + 3x = 180$ *The sum of the measures of the angles*
$ 6x = 180$ *of a triangle is 180.*
$ x = 30$
$m\angle A = 30,\ m\angle B = 60,\ m\angle C = 90$
Therefore $\triangle ABC$ is a right triangle.

Try This

The measures of the angles of $\triangle PQR$ are in the ratio of $2:3:4$. Classify
the triangle as acute, right, or obtuse.

A statement that is a direct consequence of a particular theorem is called a
corollary of the theorem. Below are two corollaries of Theorem 3.10. They
are corollaries because they are easily derived from the Angle Sum Theorem
for Triangles.

▶ **COROLLARY 3.10a**

 The angles of an equiangular triangle each have a measure of 60.

▶ **COROLLARY 3.10b**

 The acute angles of a right triangle are complementary.

You will be asked to prove these corollaries in Exercises 24 and 25.

Class Exercises

Short Answer

Find the value of x.

1.

2.

3.

4. Two angles of a triangle have measures of 50 and 100. Find the measure of the third angle.
5. Two angles of a triangle have measures of 25 and 55. Classify the triangle as acute, right, or obtuse.
6. Two angles of a right triangle are congruent. Find the measures of the angles.

Sample Exercises

Find the value of x. Congruent angles are marked.

7.

8.

9.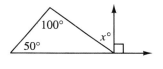

10. $\triangle ABC$ has $\angle B \cong \angle C$. If $m\angle A$ is increased by 20 and $\angle B$ remains congruent to $\angle C$, by how much are $m\angle B$ and $m\angle C$ decreased?
11. $\triangle ABC$ has $\angle B \cong \angle C$. If $m\angle B$ is increased by 15 and $\angle C$ is altered to remain congruent to $\angle B$, what is the effect on $m\angle A$?

Draw the indicated triangle, or write *not possible*.

12. acute equiangular triangle   **13.** obtuse equiangular triangle

Discussion

14. What is the greatest number of right angles a triangle can have?
15. What is the greatest number of acute angles a triangle can have?

Exercises

A

Draw the indicated triangle, or write *not possible*.

1. right triangle with two congruent angles   **2.** right equiangular triangle
3. obtuse right triangle   **4.** acute scalene triangle
5. acute triangle with two congruent angles   **6.** obtuse equiangular triangle
7. right scalene triangle   **8.** scalene isosceles triangle

Find the value of *x*. Congruent angles are marked.

9.

10.

11.

12. 96

13.

14.

15.

$\overline{BC} \parallel \overline{DE}$

16.

$\overleftrightarrow{AD} \parallel \overleftrightarrow{BC}$
(100)

17.

$\overline{AD} \parallel \overline{BC}$

18. The ratio of the measures of the angles of a triangle is $4:5:6$. Find the measures of the angles and classify the triangle as acute, right, or obtuse.

19. The ratio of the measures of the angles of a triangle is $1:3:5$. Find the measures of the angles and classify the triangle as acute, right, or obtuse.

20. The ratio of the measures of the acute angles of a right triangle is $2:3$. Find the measures of the two acute angles.

21. The measure of each of two angles of a triangle is four times that of the third angle. Find the measures of the angles.

22. The rafters of a roof form an angle of 32° at the base. What angle do the rafters form at the ridge?

23. Write a two-column proof for Corollary 3.10a.

    Given: $\triangle ABC$ is equiangular.

    Prove: $m \angle A = m \angle B = m \angle C = 60$

24. Write a two-column proof for Corollary 3.10b.

    Given: $\triangle ABC$, $\angle A$ is a right angle.

    Prove: $\angle B$ and $\angle C$ are complementary.

B

25. The measures of the angles of a triangle are x, x, and $\frac{4}{3}x$. If the largest angle is doubled and the triangle remains isosceles, how would you represent the measures of the angles in the new triangle?

26. The measures of the angles of a triangle are represented by $2x + 15$, $x + 20$, and $3x + 25$. Find the measures of the angles.

27. The measures of the angles of a triangle are x, x, and $3x$. If the measure of the largest angle is increased by ten and the triangle remains isosceles, how would you represent the measures of the angles in the new triangle?

28. In a right triangle, the measure of one acute angle is four times the measure of the other. Find the measures of the angles of $\triangle MNO$.

Find the value of x. Congruent angles are marked.

29.

30.

25
25
25

31.

32.
40°
x°

33. 54°
x°

34.
46°
74°
28°
x° 32°

65
25
80

35. Given: $\overline{AB} \parallel \overline{DE}$
 Prove: $m\angle B + m\angle C + m\angle D = 180$

36. Given: $\overline{DE} \perp \overline{AE}$, $\overline{BD} \perp \overline{AB}$
 Prove: $m\angle CAB = m\angle CDE$

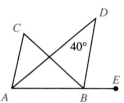

Ex. 35   Ex. 36

37. The pattern of triangles shown, a chain-link fence, illustrates the Angle Sum Theorem for Triangles. Use the figure to demonstrate the Angle Sum Theorem for Triangles.

C

38. Given: $\overline{AD}$ bisects $\angle CAB$.
 $\overline{BD}$ bisects $\angle CBA$.
 $m\angle CAB = m\angle CBA$
 Prove: $\angle ADB \cong \angle CBE$

39. $\overline{AD}$ bisects $\angle CAB$.
 $\overline{BD}$ bisects $\angle EBC$. $m\angle D = 40$
 Find $m\angle C$.

Critical Thinking

40. Accept as a postulate that the acute angles of a right triangle are complementary. Use this to prove that the sum of the measures of the angles of triangles is 180. (HINT: Draw a perpendicular from A to $\overline{BC}$.)

Mixed Review

1. The measure of the supplement of an angle is three times the measure of the angle. Find the measure of the angle and its supplement.
2. The measure of the complement of an angle is five times the measure of the angle. Find the measure of the angle and its complement.

Enrichment

Non-Euclidean Geometry

In this book you are studying Euclidean geometry, in which it is assumed that through a given point P not on a given line l there is exactly one line through P that is parallel to line l. But there are other geometries that differ from Euclidean geometry in their assumptions about the number of lines that contain P and are parallel to line l. Two such assumptions are (1) there are no lines through P parallel to line l, and (2) there are more than one line through P parallel to line l. (See the Historical Note on page 134.)

The "No-Parallel" Geometry

In this geometry, sometimes called "spherical" geometry, points are points on a sphere and lines are "great circles." A great circle on a sphere is a circle whose center is also the center of the sphere. Consider the equator as line l and New York as point P. Are there lines (great circles) through P that do not intersect the equator? Why or why not?

Exercises

Use a string and a globe to answer these questions.

1. Use string to identify three lines (great circles) that intersect to form a spherical triangle ABC. Estimate the measure of each angle of $\triangle ABC$. Does the sum of the measures of $\triangle ABC$ appear to be equal to, less than, or greater than 180?

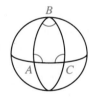

2. Consider the equator as one line and two other lines that pass through the north and south poles to form a triangle. How can BA and BC be placed to maximize the sum of the measures of the angles of $\triangle ABC$?

The "Many-Parallels" Geometry

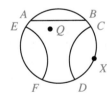

In this geometry, points consist of only those points that are in the interior of a given circle. Lines consist of arcs of circles that form "right angles" with the given circle. Thus CD is a line but AB is not a line, since AB is not the arc of a circle. Line CD is parallel to line EF since they do not intersect. Point Q is a point in this geometry, but point X is not a point, since it is not in the interior of the circle.

Exercises

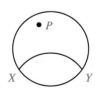

1. How many lines (arcs of circles) can be drawn through P that are parallel to line (arc) XY?

2. Draw a "triangle" consisting of three arcs. Estimate the measure of each of the three angles indicated. Estimate the sum of the measures of the angles of the triangle. Does the sum of the measures appear to be equal to, less than, or greater than 180?

3-5 Theorems Related to the Angle Sum Theorem for Triangles

 EXPLORE Draw triangles with one side extended, as shown. Use a protractor to measure $\angle 1$, $\angle 2$, and $\angle 3$. Compare $m\angle 1$ with $m\angle 2 + m\angle 3$. What do you discover?

If you extend one side of a triangle, an exterior angle is formed. An **exterior angle** of a triangle forms a linear pair with the adjacent interior angle of the triangle. The two angles of the triangle that are not adjacent to the exterior angle are called the **remote interior angles** of that exterior angle.

Every triangle has six exterior angles that form three pairs of vertical angles. Each angle in such a pair of vertical angles has the same remote interior angles. For example, $\angle 3$ and $\angle 4$ have the same remote interior angles.

The following theorem is a consequence of the Angle Sum Theorem for Triangles and states a relationship between an exterior angle of a triangle and its remote interior angles.

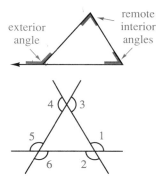

◆ **THEOREM 3.11** The Exterior Angle Theorem

The measure of an exterior angle of a triangle is equal to the sum of the measures of its two remote interior angles.

Given: $\triangle ABC$ with exterior $\angle 1$
Prove: $m\angle 1 = m\angle A + m\angle B$

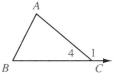

Proof

Statements	Reasons
1. $\triangle ABC$ with exterior $\angle 1$	1. Given
2. $\angle 1$ and $\angle 4$ form a linear pair.	2. Definition of linear pair
3. $m\angle 1 + m\angle 4 = 180$	3. Two angles that form a linear pair are supplementary.
4. $m\angle 1 = 180 - m\angle 4$	4. Addition Property of Equations
5. $m\angle A + m\angle B + m\angle 4 = 180$	5. Angle Sum Theorem for Triangles
6. $m\angle A + m\angle B = 180 - m\angle 4$	6. Addition Property of Equations
7. $m\angle A + m\angle B = m\angle 1$	7. Substitution Property

Example 1

$m \angle 5 = 130$, $m \angle 3 = 38$ Find $m \angle 1$.

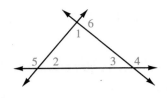

Solution

$m \angle 5 = m \angle 1 + m \angle 3$ *Exterior Angle Theorem*
$130 = m \angle 1 + 38$
$m \angle 1 = 130 - 38$
$m \angle 1 = 92$

Try This

$m \angle 6 = 87$, $m \angle 2 = 42$ Find $m \angle 3$.

Example 2

$m \angle B$ is twice $m \angle A$.   Find $m \angle ABC$.

Solution

$x + 2x = 120$ $m \angle A + m \angle B = m \angle ACD$ by
                            the Exterior Angle Theorem

$3x = 120$
$x = 40$
$2x = 80$ $m \angle ABC = 80$

Try This

$m \angle B$ is five times $m \angle A$.   Find $m \angle B$.

◆ THEOREM 3.12

If two angles of one triangle are congruent to two angles of
another triangle, then the third angles are congruent.

You will be asked to prove this theorem in Exercise 16.

Example 3

Identify which angles of $\triangle ABC$ are congruent to angles of $\triangle CDE$. State
reasons why the angles are congruent.

Solution

$\angle ABC \cong \angle CDE$ *All right angles are congruent.*
$\angle ACB \cong \angle ECD$ *Vertical angles are congruent.*
$\angle BAC \cong \angle CED$ *If two angles of one triangle are congruent to two angles*
                            of another triangle, then the third angles are congruent.

Try This

$\overline{WY}$ bisects $\angle XWZ$. Identify which angles of $\triangle WYX$ are congruent to
angles of $\triangle WYZ$. State reasons why the angles are congruent.

Class Exercises

Short Answer

Name the remote interior angles related to ∠4.

1.

2.

3.

Find the value of x.

4.

5.

6.

Sample Exercises

Find the value of x.

7.

8.

9.

$$\frac{3X = 90 + X}{3} \quad -X$$

$$\frac{2X = 90}{2} \quad \frac{?}{?}$$

$$X = 45$$

10.

11.

12.

13. Complete the proof.

Given: $\overline{AD} \parallel \overline{BC}$, $\overline{AB} \parallel \overline{CD}$

Prove: $\angle B \cong \angle D$

Proof

Statements	Reasons
1. $\overline{AD} \parallel \overline{BC}$	1. Given
2. $\overline{AB} \parallel \overline{CD}$	2. Given
3. $\angle 2 \cong \angle 3$	3. _____
4. $\angle 1 \cong \angle 4$	4. _____
5. $\angle B \cong \angle D$	5. _____

Discussion

14. If two angles of one triangle are congruent to two angles of another triangle, is it possible for the third angles not to be congruent? Give a convincing argument to support your answer.

15. If two sides of one triangle are congruent to two sides of another triangle, is it possible for the third sides not to be congruent? Give a convincing argument to support your answer.

Exercises

A

Find the measure of the indicated angle.

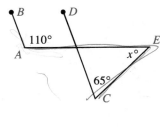

1. If $m\angle 4 = 75$ and $m\angle 2 = 40$, find $m\angle 5$.
2. If $m\angle 1 = 125$ and $m\angle 3 = 90$, find $m\angle 5$.
3. If $m\angle 5 = 40$ and $m\angle 1 = 115$, find $m\angle 4$.
4. If $m\angle 6 = 150$ and $m\angle 2 = m\angle 3$, find $m\angle 2$.
5. If $m\angle 4 = 80$ and $m\angle 2 = m\angle 5$, find $m\angle 2$.
6. If $m\angle 2 = m\angle 5$ and $m\angle 4 = 80$, find $m\angle 6$.
7. If $m\angle 1 = 100$ and $m\angle 4 = 90$, find $m\angle 6$.
8. If $m\angle 4 = 100$ and $m\angle 2$ is three times $m\angle 5$, find $m\angle 2$.
9. If $m\angle 5 = 30$ and $m\angle 4$ is twice $m\angle 2$, find $m\angle 4$.

$\overline{AB} \parallel \overline{CD}$.   **Find $m\angle CEA$.**

10.

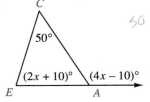

$50 + 2x + 10 = 4x - 10$

11.

12.

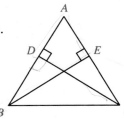

13. **Complete the proof.**

Given: $\angle ADC$ and $\angle AEB$ are right angles.

Prove: $\angle ABE \cong \angle ACD$

Proof Statements	Reasons
1. $\angle ADC$ is a right angle.	1. Given
2. $\angle AEB$ is a right angle.	2. Given
3. $\angle ADC \cong \angle AEB$	3. _____
4. $\angle A \cong \angle A$	4. _____
5. $\angle ABE \cong \angle ACD$	5. _____

14. **Given:** $\angle 1 \cong \angle 2$

  Prove: $\angle 3 \cong \angle 4$

15. **Given:** $\overline{AB} \perp \overline{BD}$, $\overline{CD} \perp \overline{BD}$

  $\angle 1 \cong \angle 2$

  Prove: $\angle A \cong \angle C$

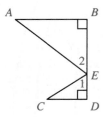

16. Write a two-column proof for Theorem 3.12.

Given: $\angle A \cong \angle D$, $\angle B \cong \angle E$

Prove: $\angle C \cong \angle F$

B

Find the value of x.

17.

18.

19.

20.

21.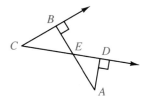

22.

23. If the measures of the exterior angles of the acute angles of a right triangle are $2x + 15$ and $3x + 5$, find the measures of the acute angles.

24. If the ratio of the measures of the angles of a triangle is $1:2:3$, find the ratio of the measures of the exterior angles of the triangle.

25. The design for a drafting table is shown. If the line of the slant of the table top is extended to the floor a $15°$ angle is formed. If $\triangle ABC$ is equiangular, what are the four angles of the table leg $ADEF$?

26. Given: $\overline{AB} \perp \overline{BC}$, $\overline{AD} \perp \overline{CD}$

Prove: $\angle A \cong \angle C$

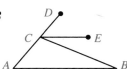

27. Given: $\overline{CE}$ bisects $\angle BCD$. $\angle A \cong \angle B$

Prove: $\overline{CE} \| \overline{AB}$

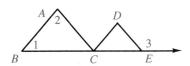

28. Given: $\overline{AC} \| \overline{DE}$

Prove: $m\angle 3 = m\angle 1 + m\angle 2$

C

29. Given: $\overline{AB}$, $\overline{BC}$, $\overline{CD}$, $\overline{AD}$ as shown
Prove: $m\angle 1 + m\angle 2 = m\angle C + m\angle B$

30. Given: $a \parallel b$
Prove: $m\angle 3 = m\angle 1 + m\angle 2$

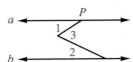

31. Given: figure $ABCD$
Prove: $m\angle 1 = m\angle 2 + m\angle 3 + m\angle 4$

Critical Thinking

32. $\overline{AE} \parallel \overline{BF}$, $\overline{BD}$ and $\overline{BE}$ trisect $\angle ABF$. $\overline{AC}$ and $\overline{AF}$ trisect $\angle BAE$.
Find $m\angle 1$ and $m\angle 2$ if
a. $m\angle ABF = 45$
b. $m\angle ABF = 60$
c. $m\angle ABF = 75$
What seems to be true about $\angle 1$ and $\angle 2$?
Prove your conjecture.

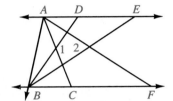

Algebra Review

Translate to a system of equations and solve.

1. Find two integers whose sum is 26 and whose difference is 8.
2. There are 37 students in geometry class. There are 9 more boys than girls. How many girls and boys are in class?

3-6 Angles of a Polygon

Some of the terms you have been using with triangles apply to other polygons as well. A polygon is a union of segments that meet only at endpoints such that

(1) at most two segments meet at one point
(2) each segment meets exactly two other segments.

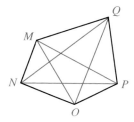

Points M, N, O, P, and Q are vertices of polygon $MNOPQ$.
$\overline{MN}$, $\overline{NO}$, $\overline{OP}$, $\overline{PQ}$, and $\overline{QM}$ are sides of the polygon.
$\overline{MO}$, $\overline{MP}$, $\overline{NP}$, $\overline{NQ}$, and $\overline{OQ}$ are diagonals of polygon $MNOPQ$.

A polygon divides a plane into three parts: the interior of the polygon, the exterior of the polygon, and the polygon itself. A polygon is convex if all the diagonals of the polygon are in the interior of the polygon.

| Convex polygons | | Nonconvex polygons |

A polygon is named by the number of sides it has.

Number of sides	Polygon
4	quadrilateral
5	pentagon
6	hexagon
7	heptagon
8	octagon
9	nonagon
10	decagon
.	.
.	.
.	.
n	n-gon

The sum of the measures of the interior angles of a convex polygon can be determined by drawing diagonals from only one vertex.

Sides	4	5	6	7
Triangles	2	3	4	5
Angle sum	2(180) = 360	3(180) = 540	4(180) = 720	5(180) = 900

Observe that in each case the number of triangles formed is two less than the number of sides. This suggests the following theorem.

◆ **THEOREM 3.13**

The sum of the measures of the angles of a convex polygon of n sides is $(n - 2)\,180$.

Example 1

Find the sum of the measures of the angles of a nonagon.

 Solution

 $(n - 2)\,180$ *Theorem 3.13; a nonagon has nine sides.*
 $(9 - 2)\,180 = 1260$ *n = 9*

Try This

The sum of the measures of the angles of a polygon is 1620. How many sides does the polygon have?

A polygon is *equilateral* if all of its sides are congruent, *equiangular* if all of its angles are congruent. If it is both equilateral and equiangular, it is a *regular polygon*.

Equiangular polygon   Equilateral polygon   Regular polygon

If the sum of the angle measures of a regular polygon is divided by the number of its sides, the resulting quotient is the measure of each angle.

▶ **COROLLARY 3.13a**

The measure of each angle of a regular polygon of n sides is $\dfrac{(n - 2)180}{n}$.

Example 2

Find the measure of each angle of a regular decagon.

Solution

$$m \angle A = \frac{(n-2)180}{n}$$ *Let $m \angle A$ be the measure of one angle of a regular decagon.*

$$m \angle A = \frac{(10-2)180}{10}$$ $n = 10$

$$m \angle A = 144$$

Try This

Each angle of a regular polygon has a measure of 140. How many sides does the polygon have?

A property of the exterior angles of a polygon can be developed by the following method.

At each vertex of pentagon *ABCDE* there is a linear pair of angles.

Use the Linear Pair Postulate.

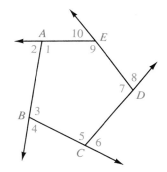

$$m \angle 1 + m \angle 2 = 180$$
$$m \angle 3 + m \angle 4 = 180$$
$$m \angle 5 + m \angle 6 = 180$$
$$m \angle 7 + m \angle 8 = 180$$
$$m \angle 9 + m \angle 10 = 180$$

Add the left members and the right members of the above equations to obtain

$$\text{(exterior sum)} + \text{(interior sum)} = 5(180)$$
$$\text{(exterior } \angle \text{ sum)} + (5-2)180 = 5(180)$$
$$\text{(exterior } \angle \text{ sum)} = 5(180) - 3(180)$$
$$\text{(exterior } \angle \text{ sum)} = 2(180)$$
$$\text{(exterior } \angle \text{ sum)} = 360$$

If five sides is replaced by *n* sides, the sum will still be 360.

◆ THEOREM 3.14

The sum of the measures of the exterior angles of a convex polygon is 360.

Example 3

The measure of an exterior angle of a regular polygon is 24. How many sides does the polygon have?

Solution

$$24x = 360$$ *Let x = the number of sides.*
$$x = 15$$

Try This

The sum of the measures of four exterior angles of a pentagon is 300. What is the measure of the fifth exterior angle?

Class Exercises

Short Answer

Indicate which of the polygons are convex.

1.   2.   3.

Name each polygon and indicate if it is a regular polygon.

4.   5.   6.

Sample Exercises

Complete the table below for regular polygons.

7. Number of sides	6	8	10		20	
8. Measure of each interior ∠				150	162	
9. Measure of each exterior ∠						12

Discussion

10. As the number of sides of a convex polygon increases, what happens to the sum of the measures of its interior angles? What is the greatest possible sum of the measures of the interior angles of a polygon?

11. As the number of sides of a regular polygon increases, what happens to the measure of each exterior angle? What is the least possible measure of an exterior angle of a polygon?

Exercises

A

The number of sides of a convex polygon is given. Find the sum of the measures of the interior angles of each polygon.

1. 8   **2.** 12   **3.** 14   **4.** 16   **5.** p

The sum of the measures of the interior angles of a convex polygon is given. Find the number of sides of each polygon.

6. 7020   **7.** 1980   **8.** 6120   **9.** 1800   **10.** 3420

The number of sides of a regular polygon is given. Find the measure of each interior angle of each polygon.

11. 7   **12.** 9   **13.** 11   **14.** 15   **15.** 17

Find the measure of each exterior angle of the regular polygon.

16. pentagon **17.** heptagon **18.** decagon **19.** 18-gon **20.** 20-gon

21. Home plate on a baseball field has three right angles and two congruent angles shown as $\angle 1$ and $\angle 2$ in the figure. Find $m\angle 1$ and $m\angle 2$.

22. The sum of the measures of seven angles of an octagon is 1000. Find the measure of the eighth angle.

23. How many sides does a regular polygon have if each exterior angle has a measure of 15?

24. How many sides does a regular polygon have if each interior angle has a measure of 108?

B

25. Draw a diagram to show that a floor can be tiled with equilateral triangles. Give a convincing argument that the sum of the measures of the angles sharing a common vertex is 360.

26. The tiling pattern to the right consists of regular hexagons. Find $m\angle 1$, $m\angle 2$, and $m\angle 3$ and verify that their sum is 360.

$$(6-2)180 = \frac{720}{6} = 120 \qquad \frac{120 \times 3}{= 360}$$

27. The tiling pattern to the right consists of regular octagons and a square. Find $m\angle 1$, $m\angle 2$, and $m\angle 3$ and verify that their sum is 360.

28. Explain why three regular pentagons cannot form a tiling pattern.

29. Explain why two regular pentagons and a regular 10-gon will fit around a point.

30. Explain why an equiangular triangle, a regular 7-gon, and a regular 42-gon will fit around a point.

31. Find the number of sides of a polygon if the sum of the measures of its interior angles is twice the sum of the measures of its exterior angles.

32. Find the number of sides of a polygon if the sum of the measures of its interior angles is four times the sum of the measures of its exterior angles.

33. The measure of each interior angle of a regular polygon is eight times that of an exterior angle. How many sides does the polygon have?

34. In quadrilateral $ABCD$ the measures of $\angle A$, $\angle B$, $\angle C$, and $\angle D$ are in the ratio of $1 : 2 : 3 : 4$, respectively. Find the measures of the four angles and determine which segments are parallel.

35. $ABCDEFGH$ is a regular octagon. If sides $\overline{AB}$ and $\overline{GH}$ are extended to meet at X, find $m\angle BXG$.

$(n\ 180)$

$(n-2)180$

c

The numbered angles in each figure are congruent. Find the sum of the numbered angles.

36. **37.** **38.**

39. Write a generalization about the sums you found in Exercises 36–38.

Critical Thinking

40. Complete the table below by drawing each polygon and its diagonals.

Number of sides	3	4	5	6	7	8	9
Number of diagonals	0	2	5				

41. Predict how many diagonals a decagon has.
Write a formula expressing the relationship between the number of sides (*n*) and the number of diagonals (*d*). Use it to check Exercise 40.

Mixed Review

1. The midpoint of $\overline{SV}$ is *T*. Name the congruent segments formed.
2. Line *l* bisects $\overline{MN}$ at *P*. Name the congruent segments formed.
3. $\overrightarrow{BC}$ is the bisector of $\angle ABD$. Name the congruent angles formed.

Quiz

Determine whether each statement is true or false.

1. An obtuse triangle may have a right angle.
2. The acute angles of a right triangle are complementary.
3. A triangle may have an obtuse exterior angle.
4. In any triangle, the remote interior angles are acute.
5. If two angles of one triangle are congruent to two angles of another triangle, then the third pair of angles are congruent.
6. The sum of the measures of the angles of a nonagon is 1440.

$a \parallel b$ **Find the measure of each angle.**

7. $m \angle QRS$ 8. $m \angle PQT$ 9. $m \angle PQR$

10. In an octagon, the sum of the measures of the interior angles is __?__ and the sum of the measures of the exterior angles is __?__ .

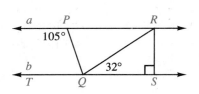

CRITICAL THINKING

Introducing the Process

Critical Thinking has been described as a thinking process used to decide what to believe or do. Consider the following situation.

Inspector Glueso arrived at the scene of a murder at Motley Motel early in the morning. The first thing he found was a broken pocket watch clutched in the victim's hand. Other evidence led Glueso to determine that the murder was committed at the time shown on the watch and that the murderer was one of three people at the motel: Mae East, Mr. Clean, or Joe Monitor. The hotel operator verified that Mae East, an actress, had been talking on the telephone from 12:32 AM to 12:47 AM. Joe Monitor, the motel manager, had been seen using his computer from about 12:20 AM until he shut it off sometime after 12:30 AM. The computer log showed that it was shut off at 12:34 AM. Mr. Clean, the night custodian, had punched out at 12:31 AM and had left promptly. The only fact that Glueso could remember about the watch was that the hour and minute hands were in a straight line when he picked it up. Who should Glueso arrest as the prime suspect?

The major points below outline the steps in Critical Thinking. Answer each question as you work, with Glueso, to solve his problem.

1. **Understand the Situation**
   a. What is the situation about?
   b. What conclusion, decision, or solution is required?
   c. Are there any questions you could ask to clarify the situation?

2. **Deal with the Data/Evidence/Assumptions**
   a. Make a list of the most important data/evidence. Is more needed?
   b. Which evidence is opinion, not fact? Which is not relevant?
   c. What assumptions are made? Can other assumptions be made?

3. **Go Beyond the Data/Evidence/Assumptions**—Read the notes Glueso made in his notebook to the right. How could you use this and the evidence to solve the mystery?
   (HINT: Since the hour hand travels through 5-minute spaces while the minute hand travels through 60-minute spaces, the distance the hour hand had traveled was equal to $\frac{1}{12}$ the distance the minute hand had traveled.)

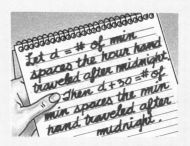

4. **State and Support Your Conclusion**—State your solution to the mystery in writing. Write a paragraph supporting your conclusion.

5. **Apply the Conclusion/Decision/Solution**—The solution of a similar mystery depended upon the fact that a crime occurred the first time after midnight that the hands of a clock were both at the same place. At what time (to the nearest second) did this crime take place?

CHAPTER SUMMARY

Vocabulary

alternate interior angles (3-1)
alternate exterior angles (3-1)
auxiliary line (3-4)
convex polygon (3-6)
corresponding angles (3-1)

diagonal of a polygon (3-6)
exterior angle of a triangle (3-5)
parallel lines (3-1)
parallel planes (3-1)
regular polygon (3-6)

remote interior angles (3-5)
same-side interior angles (3-1)
skew lines (3-1)
transversal (3-1)

Key Ideas

1. Two coplanar lines that do not intersect are called parallel lines.
2. When two parallel lines are cut by a transversal,
   a. corresponding angles are congruent.
   b. alternate interior angles are congruent.
   c. alternate exterior angles are congruent.
   d. same-side interior angles are supplementary.
3. The following are ways to prove two lines parallel.
   a. Show that corresponding angles are congruent.
   b. Show that alternate interior angles are congruent.
   c. Show that alternate exterior angles are congruent.
   d. Show that same-side interior angles are supplementary.
4. The sum of the measures of the angles of a triangle is 180. The measure of an exterior angle of a triangle is equal to the sum of the measures of its remote interior angles.
5. The sum of the measure of the angles of a convex polygon with n sides is $(n - 2)\,180$. The sum of the exterior angles is 360.

CHAPTER REVIEW

3-1

1. Name two pairs of alternate interior angles.
2. Name two pairs of same-side interior angles.
3. Name two pairs of alternate exterior angles.
4. Name four pairs of corresponding angles.

3-2

$\overleftrightarrow{DE} \parallel \overleftrightarrow{FG}$ **State the postulate or theorem that justifies each conclusion.**

5. $\angle EAC \cong \angle ACB$ 6. $m\angle EAC + m\angle ACG = 180$
7. $\angle DAH \cong \angle FBH$ 8. $\angle HAE \cong \angle JBF$
9. $\overleftrightarrow{DE} \parallel \overleftrightarrow{FG}$, $m\angle DAB = 5x - 22$, $m\angle ABC = 2x + 5$.
   Find $m\angle DAH$.

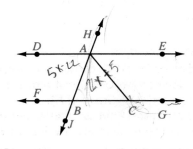

3-3

Use the given information to state which segments are parallel. Identify the postulate or theorem that justifies your answer.

10. $\angle 1 \cong \angle 2$ **11.** $m \angle SRU + m \angle RUT = 180$

12. $\angle SRU \cong \angle TUV$ **13.** $\overline{ST} \perp \overline{TU}, \overline{RU} \perp \overline{TU}$

Find the value of x for which $a \parallel b$.

14. $m \angle 2 = 5x + 12, \ m \angle 4 = 2x + 18$

15. $m \angle 2 = 4x + 6, \ m \angle 5 = 14$

16. $m \angle 1 = \frac{3}{4}x + 42, \ m \angle 6 = x + 2$

17. Given: $\overline{AB} \parallel \overline{CD}, \ \angle 1 \cong \angle 2$

    Prove: $\overline{AD} \parallel \overline{BC}$

3-4

Find the measure of $\angle B$.

18.

136°

19.

$(3x + 30)°$

$6x°$

20. $\overline{BD}$ bisects $\angle ADC$.

    $\angle A \cong \angle DBA$

    $\overline{BC} \perp \overline{BD}, \ m \angle A = 50$

    Find $m \angle C$.

50°

3-5

21. Name an exterior angle of $\triangle RUS$.

22. If $m \angle R = 35$ and $m \angle 1 = 20$, find $m \angle 4$.

23. If $m \angle 3 = 5x + 10, \ m \angle 2 = 50$, and $m \angle T = 3x + 10$, find $m \angle T$.

24. $\angle 3$ is an exterior angle for $\triangle \underline{\ ?\ }$ and its remote interior angles are $\angle \underline{\ ?\ }$ and $\angle \underline{\ ?\ }$.

3-6

25. Find the sum of the measures of the angles of a decagon.

26. Find the number of sides of a convex polygon if the sum of the measures of its interior angles is 4140.

27. Find the measure of an interior angle of a regular hexagon.

28. Find the measure of an exterior angle of a regular octagon.

CHAPTER TEST

Determine whether each statement is true or false.

1. $\overline{AB}$ and $\overline{HG}$ are parallel.
2. $\overline{AB}$ and $\overline{CD}$ are skew.
3. Plane *ABEF* and plane *BCFG* are parallel.
4. If two parallel lines are cut by a transversal, then corresponding angles are congruent.
5. If two parallel lines are cut by a transversal, then same-side interior angles are congruent.
6. If two coplanar lines are perpendicular to the same line, then they are perpendicular to each other.
7. In a triangle, the measure of an exterior angle is equal to the sum of the measures of its remote interior angles.
8. The sum of the angles of a heptagon is 900°.

Identify each pair of angles as alternate interior, alternate exterior, same-side interior, corresponding, or none of these.

9. ∠4 and ∠8
10. ∠3 and ∠6
11. ∠1 and ∠7

Use the given information to determine which segments are parallel.

12. ∠*D* ≅ ∠*BEF*
13. *m*∠*ABE* + *m*∠*BAD* = 180

Find the value of *x*. Congruent angles are marked.

14.

26°   *x*°   70°

15.
x°   135°

16.
95°   *x*°   123°

17. If *m*∠4 = 85 and *m*∠2 = 38, find *m*∠5.
18. If *m*∠1 = 118 and *m*∠3 = 95, find *m*∠5.
19. Find the measure of each interior angle of an 18-sided regular polygon.
20. Find the number of sides of a convex polygon if the measures of its interior angles have a sum of 5940.

21. **Given:** $\overline{AB} \parallel \overline{CE}$, ∠2 ≅ ∠3
    Prove: ∠1 ≅ ∠3

PROBLEM SOLVING

Make a Table, Look for a Pattern

Two strategies useful in solving problems involving numerical relationships are Make a Table and Look for a Pattern. By organizing data in a table you will often be able to recognize patterns more easily.

Example

How many squares are on an 8×8 checkerboard?

Solution

Size of Square	Number of squares
1×1	64
2×2	49
3×3	36
4×4	25
5×5	?
6×6	?
7×7	?
8×8	?

Make a table and record the number of 1×1, 2×2, 3×3, and 4×4 squares. Look for a pattern. The number of 1×1 squares is 8^2 squares. The number of 2×2 squares is 7^2. Note that the pattern appears to be decreasing perfect squares. Complete the table by filling in 16, 9, 4, and 1.

$64 + 49 + 36 + 25 + 16 + 9 + 4 + 1 = 204$

There are 204 squares

Add the numbers in the completed right-hand column.

Problem-Solving Strategies
Draw a Diagram
Make a Table
Look for a Pattern

The problem-solving strategies that have been introduced up to this point in the book are presented in the chart.

Problems

1. How many cubes are in an $8 \times 8 \times 8$ cube? (HINT: Make a table similar to the one above. In one column list the cube sizes—$1 \times 1 \times 1$, $2 \times 2 \times 2$, $3 \times 3 \times 3$, etc. In the second column give the number of cubes for each size.)

2. A yo-yo on a 36-in. string is thrown so that the string is fully extended. On each jerk it comes up 12 in. then falls back 7 in. How many jerks of the string are made by the time the yo-yo returns to the thrower's hand?

3. A triangular number (T) is one that can be represented geometrically. T_1, T_2, T_3, and T_4.

Find T_5 and T_6. Predict what the tenth triangular number (T_{10}) is.

4. A pentagonal number (P) is another number that can be represented geometrically.

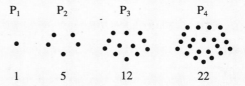

Find P_5 and P_6. Predict what the tenth pentagonal number (P_{10}) will be.

Chapters 1–3

1. Name two pairs of intersecting lines in the figure below. $j \parallel k$

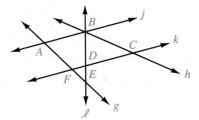

   a. j and k, l, and g
   b. l and g, l and k
   c. $\overline{AF}$ and $\overline{BC}$, $\overline{AB}$ and $\overline{FC}$
   d. h and k, j and k

2. Which of these sets of points is collinear?

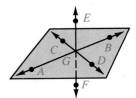

   a. C, G, B b. E, G, D
   c. A, G, B d. C, G, F

3. Which type of statement is accepted as true without proof?
   a. theorem   b. postulate
   c. definition   d. corollary

4. X is between W and Y. If $WY = 12$ and $WX = 5$, find XY.
   a. 7   b. −7   c. 17   d. none of these

5. Which of the following is not another name for $\angle RST$?

   a. $\angle 1$ b. $\angle TSR$ c. $\angle S$ d. $\angle SRT$

6. M is the midpoint of $\overline{AB}$ and $\overline{CD}$. Which conclusion is correct?
   a. $CM = MD$ b. $AM = CM$
   c. $CM = CD$ d. $BM = MD$

7. If $\overline{CS}$ bisects $\angle GCM$, which angles must be congruent?

   a. $\angle 1$ and $\angle 2$ b. $\angle 5$ and $\angle 6$
   c. $\angle 2$ and $\angle 3$ d. $\angle 2, \angle 3,$ and $\angle 4$

8. A triangle with three congruent sides is
   a. isosceles   b. equilateral
   c. scalene   d. obtuse

9. It is not possible for a triangle to be isosceles and also
   a. right   b. obtuse   c. scalene   d. acute

10. What is the hypothesis of the statement "all right angles are congruent"?
    a. two angles are right angles
    b. two angles are congruent
    c. two right angles are congruent
    d. congruent angles are right angles

11. To show that a generalization is false, you can give a(n)
    a. inverse   b. counterexample
    c. hypothesis   d. reason

12. If $\angle 1$ and $\angle 2$ are complementary, then
    a. $\angle 1 \cong \angle 2$ b. $m\angle 1 + m\angle 2 = 180$
    c. $\angle 1$ and $\angle 2$ are adjacent
    d. $m\angle 1 + m\angle 2 = 90$

13. $\angle AOC$ and $\angle COB$ are

    a. complementary   b. vertical angles
    c. a linear pair   d. congruent

14. The measure of an angle is 50 less than its supplement. Find the measure of the smaller angle.

   a. 50   **b.** 65   **c.** 20   **d.** 115

15. If r and t are coplanar, $r \perp t$, and $s \perp t$, then which of the following is true?

   a. $r \parallel s$ **b.** $t \parallel s$
   c. $r \perp s$ **d.** none of these

16. $\overline{AB}$ is the perpendicular bisector of $\overline{CD}$ at point E. Which one of these is not true?

   a. $\overline{AE} \cong \overline{EB}$
   b. $\overline{AB} \perp \overline{CD}$
   c. $\overline{CE} \cong \overline{ED}$
   d. A, E, and B are collinear

17. In RST, $RX = XT$. Which of the following is not correct?

   a. R, X, and T are collinear.
   b. X is the midpoint of $\overline{RT}$.
   c. $RX = \frac{1}{2} RT$
   d. $m\angle RSX = m\angle TSX$

18. If $\angle MON \cong NOR$, $m\angle MON = 15$, and $m\angle NOS = 35$, then $m\angle ROS =$ _____ .

   a. 45   **b.** 20   **c.** 15   **d.** 30

19. $\overline{LM}$ and $\overline{NO}$ intersect at T.
   $m\angle LTN = 3x + 10$
   $m\angle OTM = 5x - 60$
   Find $m\angle LTO$.

   a. 65   **b.** 35   **c.** 70   **d.** 115

20. $\overrightarrow{ST}$ bisects $\angle RSU$. $m\angle RST = 34$ Find $m\angle RSU$.

   a. 34   **b.** 56   **c.** 146   **d.** 68

21. Which one of the statements is false?

   a. If two angles are vertical, then they are congruent.
   b. If two angles are supplements of congruent angles, then they are supplementary.
   c. If two angles are complements of the same angle, then they are congruent.
   d. If two angles are supplements of the same angle, then they are congruent.

22. Which line is skew with $\overleftrightarrow{BC}$?

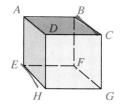

   a. $\overleftrightarrow{AD}$ **b.** $\overleftrightarrow{EF}$ **c.** $\overleftrightarrow{FG}$ **d.** $\overleftrightarrow{AB}$

23. Which of the following would prove $r \parallel s$?

   a. $\angle 2 \cong \angle 8$
   b. $\angle 3 \cong \angle 5$
   c. $m\angle 4 + m\angle 6 = 180$
   d. $\angle 1 \cong \angle 4$

24. In Exercise 23, $r \parallel s$, $m\angle 3 = 5x + 32$, and $m\angle 5 = 4x + 40$. Find $m\angle 5$.

   a. 12   **b.** 92   **c.** 72   **d.** 88

25. Find the sum of the interior angles of a polygon with 12 sides.

   a. 1440   **b.** 1980   **c.** 1800   **d.** 3420

26. If the sum of the measures of four exterior angles of a pentagon is 270, what is the measure of the fifth exterior angle?

   a. 70   **b.** 90   **c.** 45   **d.** 30

Congruent Triangles

Give a convincing argument that the equilateral triangles of this structure are congruent.

TRIANGLES AND CONGRUENCE

OBJECTIVE: *Given two congruent triangles, identify congruent parts.*

4-1 Congruent Triangles

You learned in Chapter 1 that congruent segments have the same length and that congruent angles have the same measure. Use these ideas to define congruent triangles. Two figures are called congruent if they have the same size and shape.

If you were to trace triangle *ABC* shown below and position the tracing over triangle *DEF*, you would see that triangles *ABC* and *DEF* are identical in size and shape.

Individual parts must be made identical in size and shape so that they fit any one of the items on the assembly line.

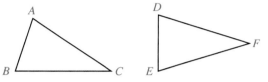

When the tracing of triangle *ABC* matches up with triangle *DEF*, the vertices of the two triangles match up as follows:

$$A \leftrightarrow D \qquad B \leftrightarrow E \qquad C \leftrightarrow F$$

You can also see a **correspondence** between the angles and the sides of the two triangles.

Corresponding angles: $\angle A \leftrightarrow \angle D$, $\angle B \leftrightarrow \angle E$, $\angle C \leftrightarrow \angle F$
Corresponding sides: $\overline{AB} \leftrightarrow \overline{DE}$, $\overline{BC} \leftrightarrow \overline{EF}$, $\overline{AC} \leftrightarrow \overline{DF}$

■ DEFINITION

Two triangles are congruent if and only if there is a correspondence between the vertices such that each pair of corresponding sides and each pair of corresponding angles are congruent.

You write $\triangle ABC \cong \triangle DEF$.

In a diagram congruent sides can be indicated with "hatch" marks and congruent angles by "arc" marks as shown in this figure. When using the notation $\triangle ABC \cong \triangle DEF$, list corresponding vertices in the same order. In this pair of congruent triangles, the corresponding vertices are *A* and *D*, *B* and *E*, and *C* and *F*. These six statements are correct as written.

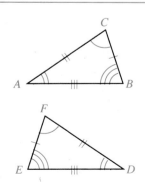

$\triangle ABC \cong \triangle DEF \qquad \triangle ACB \cong \triangle DFE \qquad \triangle BCA \cong \triangle EFD$
$\triangle BAC \cong \triangle EDF \qquad \triangle CAB \cong \triangle FDE \qquad \triangle CBA \cong \triangle FED$

However, it would not be correct to write $\triangle ABC \cong \triangle EDF$ since vertices *A* and *E*, and *B* and *D* are not corresponding vertices.

Example 1

$\triangle UVW \cong \triangle XYZ$ **Complete each statement.**

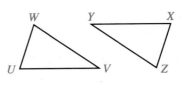

a. $\overline{VW} \cong$ ___ **b.** $\angle V \cong$ ___

Solution

    a. $\overline{VW} \cong \overline{YZ}$ **b.** $\angle V \cong \angle Y$

Try This

Complete each statement.

a. $\overline{YX} \cong$ ___ **b.** $\angle Z \cong$ ___

Example 2

$\triangle ABC \cong \triangle DEC$ **Complete each statement.**

a. $m \angle D =$ ___ **b.** $CD =$ ___

Solution

    a. $m \angle D = 68$ **b.** $CD = 16$

Try This

a. $m \angle E =$ ___ **b.** $BC =$ ___

Class Exercises

Short Answer

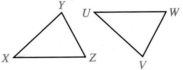

$\triangle XYZ \cong \triangle UVW$

1. Name the three pairs of corresponding angles.
2. Name the three pairs of corresponding sides.

Determine whether each statement is true or false for the above figure.

3. $\triangle YZX \cong \triangle VWU$ 4. $\triangle XZY \cong \triangle UVW$ 5. $\overline{XY} \cong \overline{VY}$ 6. $\angle Y \cong \angle V$

7. Which statement is correct?
    $\triangle YZX \cong \triangle UVW$, $\triangle YZX \cong \triangle VWU$, $\triangle ZXY \cong \triangle WVU$
8. Which statement is not correct? $\overline{XZ} \cong \overline{UW}$, $\angle Y \cong \angle V$, $\overline{XZ} \cong \overline{UV}$

Sample Exercises

$\triangle ABD \cong \triangle CBE$ **Complete each statement.**

9. $\overline{AD} \cong$ ___ 10. $\overline{BE} \cong$ ___ 11. $\angle ABD \cong$ ___
12. $\overline{BC} \cong$ ___ 13. $\triangle BDA \cong$ ___ 14. $\triangle CEB \cong$ ___

$\triangle MOP \cong \triangle HAT$ **Complete each statement.**

15. $\angle M \cong$ ___ 16. $\overline{OP} \cong$ ___ 17. $m \angle P =$ ___
18. $\overline{MP} \cong$ ___ 19. $\angle A \cong$ ___ 20. $\overline{HA} \cong$ ___

Discussion

21. Given that the two triangles to the right are congruent, explain how the figure could be labeled and what notation should be used to show that these triangles are congruent.

Exercises

A

△ABC ≅ △DEF   **Complete each statement.**

1. $\overline{AB}$ ≅ ___   2. $\overline{EF}$ ≅ ___
3. ∠B ≅ ___   4. ∠D ≅ ___
5. ∠F ≅ ___   6. $\overline{AC}$ ≅ ___
7. △FED ≅ ___   8. △BCA ≅ ___

△ABC ≅ △XYZ   **Complete each statement.**

9. AB = ___   10. m∠A = ___
11. m∠C = ___   12. YZ = ___

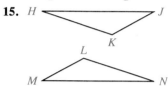

The two triangles shown are congruent. Name three pairs of angles and three pairs of sides that appear to be congruent for each pair of triangles.

13.   14.   15.

△ABF ≅ △CDE, EF = 11, FC = 6   **Complete each statement.**

16. AB = _10_   17. AF = ___
18. m∠AFB = ___   19. m∠CDE = ___
20. m∠CFB = ___   21. m∠FAB = ___

△JIP ≅ △MAT   **Complete each statement.**

22. ∠J ≅ ___   23. ∠P ≅ ___   24. ∠I ≅ ___
25. $\overline{IP}$ ≅ ___   26. $\overline{JP}$ ≅ ___   27. $\overline{JI}$ ≅ ___

28. Draw △ABC. Use a compass and a straightedge to construct a △XYZ, such that △XYZ ≅ △ABC. Use hatch marks and arc marks to label all congruent parts of these figures.

B

△ABC ≅ △CED   **Complete each statement.**

29. m∠ABC = ___   30. m∠ECD = ___
31. m∠ABD = ___   32. m∠ACE = ___

△FKH ≅ △FKG   **Complete each statement.**

33. m∠KFL = ___   34. m∠FKH = ___   35. m∠HKJ = ___
36. m∠FHK = ___   37. m∠FLK = ___   38. m∠FJK = ___

Ex. 29–32

Ex. 33–38

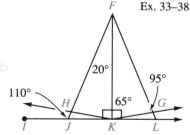

39. This quilt pattern is made by sewing together triangular shapes. How many different (non-congruent) shapes are used? (Consider the shapes of the pieces only, not the fabric design in the shapes.)

40. Explain why these two triangles , though congruent, must be treated as different if you are cutting out the pieces for this quilt.

Plot each point on a rectangular coordinate system. Choose the unit of length large enough that the resulting triangles are easy to measure. Measure the lengths and angles of these triangles. Is △ABC congruent to △DEF?

41. $A(-4, 1)$, $B(-4, 3)$, $C(-1, 3)$, $D(1, 1)$, $E(1, 3)$, $F(4, 3)$
42. $A(-1, -2)$, $B(-3, 1)$, $C(-2, 5)$, $D(1, -2)$, $E(3, 1)$, $F(2, 5)$
43. $A(-3, 1)$, $B(-1, -1)$, $C(-4, 4)$, $D(1, 2)$, $E(1, 4)$, $F(3, 3)$

C

44. Explain why, if one of two congruent triangles is isosceles, then the other triangle is also isosceles.

The three shaded triangles are congruent.

45. List a collection of three sides that are congruent to one another.
46. List a collection of three angles that are congruent to one another.

These figures are congruent, and the congruence symbol in the statement ABCDEF ≅ JKLMNO is interpreted just as it is for triangles. Complete each statement.

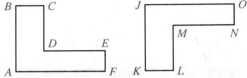

47. $\angle C \cong$ ___   48. $\angle M \cong$ ___
49. $\overline{AB} \cong$ ___   50. $\overline{ON} \cong$ ___

Critical Thinking

51. In the figure at the right, $XY = AB$. For how many different points Z is it true that

   a. triangles ABC and XYZ are congruent?
   b. $\triangle ABC \cong \triangle XYZ$?

   Explain why the answers to these two questions are different.

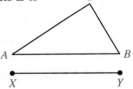

Mixed Review

$\overrightarrow{EB}$ **bisects** $\angle AEC$.   **Complete each statement.**

1. $m\angle AEB =$ ___   2. $m\angle BED =$ ___
3. $m\angle AED =$ ___

4. Name six triangles.
5. What type of triangle is $\triangle AED$?

Study Skills

1. Find a word in this lesson that means "same size and shape."
2. Suppose $\triangle ABC \cong \triangle DEF$. Explain why it is wrong to write $\triangle ABC \cong \triangle FED$.
3. Suppose triangle ABC is congruent to triangle DEF with angles A and F congruent, angles B and D congruent, and angles C and E congruent. Describe the congruence between these triangles using the appropriate symbols.

4-2 Congruence Postulates

EXPLORE

Cut a 4-in., a 5-in., and a 6-in. strip of paper and arrange them to form a triangle. Repeat this experiment. How do the two triangles compare in size and shape? State any generalizations that you discover.

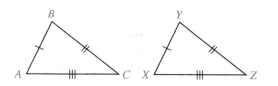

4 in.
5 in.
6 in.

You learned in the last section that when two triangles are congruent, there are three pairs of congruent sides and three pairs of congruent angles. In the Explore above, you may have discovered that you do not need to show all six of these congruence relationships true to conclude that two triangles are congruent as state in the following postulate.

● **POSTULATE 16** SSS Postulate

If each of the three sides of one triangle are congruent respectively to corresponding sides of another triangle, then the two triangles are congruent.

In △ABC, ∠B is *opposite* $\overline{AC}$ and $\overline{AB}$ is *opposite* ∠C. ∠C is *included* between $\overline{AC}$ and $\overline{BC}$, and $\overline{BC}$ is *included* between ∠C and ∠B.

Suppose that a segment and two angles are given as shown here.

If an angle congruent to angle 1 is constructed at point A and an angle congruent to angle 2 is constructed at point B, then the sides of these angles can be extended to intersect at a point C, forming one and only one triangle.

This reasoning can be used as a convincing argument to describe how you might reach the conclusion given in Postulate 17.

● POSTULATE 17 ASA Postulate

If two angles and the included side of one triangle are congruent
to two angles and the included side of another triangle, then the
two triangles are congruent.

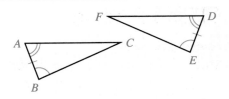

Example 1

Write a congruence between these triangles and state the
postulate by which the triangles are congruent.

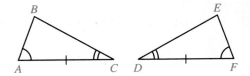

Solution

△ABC ≅ △FED   ASA Postulate

Try This

∠V ≅ ∠Y, ∠W ≅ ∠Z, $\overline{VW}$ ≅ $\overline{YZ}$
Which postulate would you use to show that △UVW ≅ △XYZ?

● POSTULATE 18 SAS Postulate

If two sides and the included angle of one triangle are congruent
to two sides and the included angle of another triangle, then the
two triangles are congruent.

Example 2

Apply the SAS Postulate to show that a pair of triangles are congruent.

Solution

△BAE ≅ △DCB   SAS Postulate

Try This

∠V ≅ ∠Y, $\overline{UV}$ ≅ $\overline{XY}$, $\overline{VW}$ ≅ $\overline{YZ}$
Which postulate would you use to show that △UVW ≅ △XYZ?

Example 3

Name the additional congruent sides or angles needed to show these
triangles are congruent by the given postulate.

a. SAS   **b.** ASA

Solution

   a. $\overline{AB}$ ≅ $\overline{CD}$ **b.** ∠ADB ≅ ∠CBD

Try This

$\overline{UV}$ ≅ $\overline{XY}$, $\overline{VW}$ ≅ $\overline{YZ}$, $\overline{UW}$ ≅ $\overline{XZ}$
Which postulate would you use to show △UVW ≅ △XYZ?

Class Exercises

Short Answer

State the angle or side opposite the given side or angle.

1. $\overline{AD}$ **2.** $\angle A$ **3.** $\overline{AC}$ **4.** $\angle BDC$

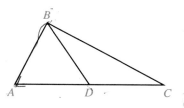

For each pair of sides or angles state the included angle or side.

5. $\overline{AB}, \overline{AD}$ **6.** $\angle A, \angle C$ **7.** $\angle ABD, \angle ADB$ **8.** $\overline{AD}, \overline{BD}$

Sample Exercises

Write a congruence between each pair of triangles and state the postulate applied.

9.   **10.**   **11.**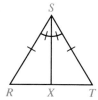

Discussion

12. Give a convincing argument to describe how you might reach the conclusion in Postulate 17.

13. Give a convincing argument to describe how you might reach the conclusion in Postulate 18.

14. Give a convincing argument in favor of or against an AAA method of proving two triangles congruent: If three angles of one triangle are congruent to three angles of another triangle, the triangles are congruent.

Exercises

A

Write a congruence between each pair of triangles and state the postulate applied. If you cannot apply a postulate, write *no conclusion can be made*.

1.   **2.**   **3.**

4.   **5.**   **6.**

Name the additional congruent sides or angles needed to show that the pair of triangles are congruent by the given postulate.

7.
SSS

8.
SAS

9.
SAS

Complete each statement. Give the angle or side that allows you to show that each triangle is congruent to another triangle by the given postulate.

10. SAS for $\triangle ABC$: $\overline{AC}$, ___ , $\overline{BC}$
11. ASA for $\triangle BCE$: $\angle 1$, $\overline{BC}$, ___
12. SSS for $\triangle CDE$: ___ , $\overline{EC}$, $\overline{CD}$
13. SAS for $\triangle BCD$: $\overline{BC}$, ___ , ___

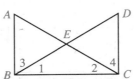

B

Tent pole $\overline{ZX}$ is placed perpendicular to the ground in such a way that X is the midpoint of the opening $\overline{WY}$ at the front of the tent.

14. Name a pair of congruent triangles.
15. What congruence postulate justifies your choice in Exercise 14?
16. Explain why $\triangle WYZ$ is an isosceles triangle.

17. Name a triangle that is congruent to $\triangle ABE$.
18. Name a congruence postulate that can be used to show that the triangles in Exercise 17 are congruent.
19. Explain how you can conclude $\triangle BCE$ is an isosceles triangle.

$\overline{AB} \cong \overline{CD}$

20. Name three triangles that are congruent to $\triangle ABD$.

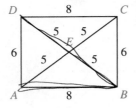

21. The legs of a table are hinged at points A and B. A bolt is placed at F in one of several predrilled holes. The height of the table is determined by the placement of the bolt F. Where should the bolt F be placed if the base CD is equal in length to the top AB? Explain your answer.

$AB \parallel CD$

22. $\angle A \cong \angle D$, $m\angle A = 3x + 15$, $m\angle D = x + 75$
    $AB = 2x + 15$, $DE = 3x - 15$, $AC = x + 4$, $DF = 2x - 26$
    Prove that $\triangle ABC$ and $\triangle DEF$ are congruent.

23. $\angle A \cong \angle D$, $m\angle A = 9x - 48$, $m\angle D = 6x - 15$
    $AB = x + 5$, $DE = 2x - 6$, $AC = x - 1$, $DF = 3x - 23$
    Prove that $\triangle ABC$ and $\triangle DEF$ are congruent.

24. In $\triangle RST$ and $\triangle XYZ$, $\angle R \cong \angle X$, $RS = XY$
    $m\angle R = 11x - 1$, $m\angle X = 9x + 5$, and $RT = 7x + 5$
    Find XZ if $\triangle RST \cong \triangle XYZ$.

25. $\triangle KLM \cong \triangle NOP$, $m\angle K = 3x + 7$, $m\angle N = 2x + 24$, $m\angle L = 5x - 42$,
    $m\angle O = 4x - 25$ Find the measure of $\angle P$.

26. $\triangle CDE \cong \triangle FGH$, $m\angle D = x^2 - 39$, $m\angle G = x + 17$, $m\angle E = 19 - x$,
    $m\angle H = 27 - 2x$, $GH = 39 - 3x$ Find DE.

27. Name the coordinates of point F so that $\triangle ABC \cong \triangle DEF$.
28. Calculate the lengths of the sides and use the SSS Congruence Postulate to verify the congruence stated in Exercise 27.

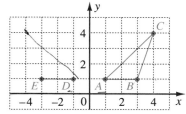

29. Name the coordinates of point R so that $\triangle MNO \cong \triangle PQR$.
30. Calculate the lengths of the sides and use the SSS Congruence Postulate to verify the congruence stated in Exercise 29.

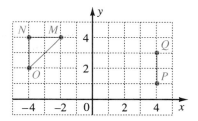

C

31. $\overline{AB} \cong \overline{BC} \cong \overline{CD} \cong \overline{DE}$, $\overline{AF} \cong \overline{EF}$, $\angle A \cong \angle E$
    List all the pairs of triangles that you think could be shown to be congruent in the figure to the right.
32. For each pair of triangles listed in Exercise 31 explain why you think your choice is correct.
33. Which postulate can be used to show that $\triangle ACE \cong \triangle DBF$? Explain your reasoning.
34. Given that $\overline{AE}$ bisects $\angle BAD$, $AD = AB = 21$, find x. Explain how you found the answer.

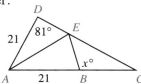

Critical Thinking

35. $ADBEHCFG$ is a cube. Write a paragraph that would convince someone that $\triangle ADC$, $\triangle BDC$, and $\triangle ADB$ are all congruent to one another.

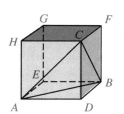

36. The figure to the right shows a square divided into four congruent eight-sided polygons. Draw a second way of doing this.

37. Draw a third way of dividing a square into four congruent eight-sided polygons.

38. Draw a triangle. Label it *RST*. Using a compass and straightedge, construct $\overline{XY} \cong \overline{RS}$, $\angle X \cong \angle R$, and $\angle Y \cong \angle S$. Extend the exterior sides of angles *X* and *Y* so that they meet in a point *Z*. State a congruence between the triangles. What postulate supports your statement?

Mixed Review

$\triangle ACE$ is equilateral. $\angle ACB$ is a right angle. $\angle 1 \cong \angle 3$
Complete each statement.

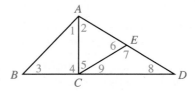

1. $m \angle 1 =$ _____   **2.** $m \angle 2 =$ _____   **3.** $m \angle 3 =$ _____
4. $m \angle 4 =$ _____   **5.** $m \angle 5 =$ _____   **6.** $m \angle 6 =$ _____

Write a congruence between each pair of triangles and state the postulate applied.

7.   **8.**   **9.**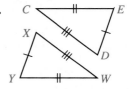

10. $\triangle ABC \cong \triangle LMN$, $m \angle B = x^2$, $m \angle L = 9x$, $BC = x - 2$,
$MN = 16 - x$, $AB = 2x - 14$ How long is $\overline{LM}$?

Quiz

$\triangle DEF \cong \triangle IHF$ **Complete each statement.**

1. $\overline{EF} \cong$ _____   **2.** $m \angle E =$ _____   **3.** $IH =$ _____
4. $\angle I \cong$ _____   **5.** $DF =$ _____   **6.** $\triangle FDE \cong$ _____

Write a congruence between each pair of triangles and state the postulate applied.

7.   **8.**   **9.**

State the additional sides or angles that are needed to prove
$\triangle ABC \cong \triangle YXZ$ **by the indicated postulate.**

10. SAS: $\overline{AB} \cong \overline{YX}$, $\overline{AC} \cong \overline{YZ}$
11. ASA: $\angle C \cong \angle Z$, $\overline{BC} \cong \overline{XZ}$
12. SSS: $\overline{AB} \cong \overline{YX}$, $\overline{BC} \cong \overline{XZ}$

PROVING TRIANGLES CONGRUENT

OBJECTIVE: *Use definitions and the SSS, SAS, and ASA congruence postulates to prove triangles congruent.*

4-3 Proofs: Using Congruence Postulates

In this lesson you will use the SSS, SAS, and ASA congruence postulates to write proofs in the two-column format you learned to use in Chapter 2. The hypothesis and the conclusion of the SAS Postulate are highlighted.

Many professionals must reason carefully and logically. Geometry proofs provide practice in logical thinking.

If | two sides and the included angle of one triangle are congruent to two sides and the included angle of another triangle, | then | the two triangles are congruent.

hypothesis   *conclusion*

When you use a congruence postulate in a two-column proof, you must include statements to show that the hypothesis is true. The final statement is the conclusion.

Example 1

Given: $\overline{AB} \cong \overline{AC}$
$\angle 1 \cong \angle 2$

Prove: $\triangle ABD \cong \triangle ACD$

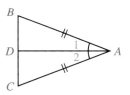

Proof

Statements	Reasons
1. $\overline{AB} \cong \overline{AC}$	1. Given
2. $\angle 1 \cong \angle 2$	2. Given
3. $\overline{AD} \cong \overline{AD}$	3. Reflexive Property
4. $\triangle ABD \cong \triangle ACD$	4. SAS Postulate

In the above proof statements 1, 2, and 3 show that the hypothesis of the SAS Postulate is satisfied. Statement 4 is drawn from the conclusion of the SAS Postulate. Other congruence postulates are used similarly in proofs.

A statement and its reasons often refer to a previously learned definition. Use the sentences listed below as reasons in your proof when you are using the definitions listed. Note the third reason in Example 2.

An angle *bisector* forms two congruent angles.
A segment *bisector* forms two congruent segments.
A segment *midpoint* forms two congruent segments.
Perpendicular segments form right angles.

Example 2

Given: $\overline{AD}$ bisects $\angle BAC$.
$\qquad \overline{AB} \cong \overline{AC}$

Prove: $\triangle ABD \cong \triangle ACD$

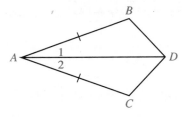

Proof

Statements	Reasons
1. $\overline{AB} \cong \overline{AC}$	1. Given
2. $\overline{AD}$ bisects $\angle BAC$.	2. Given
3. $\angle 1 \cong \angle 2$	3. An angle bisector forms two congruent angles.
4. $\overline{AD} \cong \overline{AD}$	4. Reflexive Property
5. $\triangle ABD \cong \triangle ACD$	5. SAS Postulate

The proof in Example 3 uses the definition of a line perpendicular to a plane introduced in Chapter 1.

Example 3

Given: $\overline{AB} \perp N$
$\qquad B$ in plane N
$\qquad \overline{AB} \cong \overline{CB}$

Prove: $\triangle ABD \cong \triangle CBD$

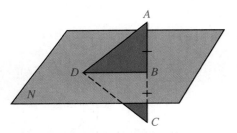

Proof

Statements	Reasons
1. $\overline{AB} \perp N$, B in N	1. Given
2. $\overline{AB} \cong \overline{CB}$	2. Given
3. $\overline{AB} \perp \overline{BD}$	3. If a line is $\perp$ to plane N at B then it is $\perp$ to each line in N through B.
4. $\angle ABD$ and $\angle CBD$ are rt. $\angle$s.	4. $\perp$ lines form rt. $\angle$s.
5. $\angle ABD \cong \angle CBD$	5. All rt. $\angle$s are $\cong$.
6. $\overline{BD} \cong \overline{BD}$	6. Reflexive Property
7. $\triangle ABD \cong \triangle CBD$	7. SAS Postulate

Class Exercises

Short Answer

State the hypothesis and conclusion of each postulate.

1. SSS Congruence Postulate   2. SAS Congruence Postulate   3. ASA Congruence Postulate

4. State the hypothesis and conclusion of this statement.
   Two triangles are congruent if corresponding pairs of angles and sides are congruent.

A conclusion can be drawn from the information given in each of Exercises 5–9. State your conclusion and the postulate or definition on which it is based.

5. $\overline{DF} \cong \overline{AC}$, $\overline{DE} \cong \overline{AB}$, $\angle D \cong \angle A$
6. $\overline{EF} \cong \overline{BC}$, $\angle F \cong \angle C$, $\angle B \cong \angle E$

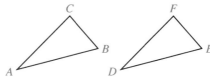

7. $\overline{MN}$ bisects $\angle KML$ and $\angle KNM \cong \angle MNL$.
8. N is the midpoint of $\overline{KL}$. $\overline{KM} \cong \overline{LM}$
9. $\overline{MN}$ bisects $\angle KML$. $\overline{KM} \cong \overline{LM}$

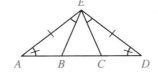

Sample Exercises

Complete each proof.

10. **Given:** $\overline{AE} \cong \overline{DE}$, $\angle A \cong \angle D$
$\angle AEB \cong \angle DEC$

   Prove: $\triangle AEB \cong \triangle DEC$

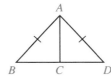

Statements	Reasons
1. $\angle AEB \cong \angle DEC$	1. ___
2. $\overline{AE} \cong \overline{DE}$	2. ___
3. $\angle A \cong \angle D$	3. ___
4. $\triangle AEB \cong \triangle DEC$	4. ___

11. **Given:** $\overline{AB} \cong \overline{AD}$
C is the midpoint of $\overline{BD}$.

   Prove: $\triangle ABC \cong \triangle ADC$

Statements	Reasons
1. $\overline{AB} \cong \overline{AD}$	1. ___
2. C is the midpoint of $\overline{BD}$.	2. ___
3. $\overline{BC} \cong \overline{DC}$	3. ___
4. ___	4. Reflexive Property
5. $\triangle ABC \cong \triangle ADC$	5. ___

12. **Given:** $\overline{RT} \cong \overline{VT}$, $\overline{ST} \cong \overline{UT}$

   Prove: $\triangle RST \cong \triangle VUT$

Statements	Reasons
1. $\overline{RT} \cong \overline{VT}$	1. ___
2. $\angle RTS \cong \angle VTU$	2. ___
3. $\overline{ST} \cong \overline{UT}$	3. ___
4. ___	4. ___

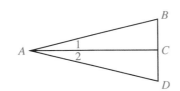

Discussion

13. Suppose that $\overline{AC}$ is the perpendicular bisector of $\overline{BD}$. Give a convincing argument that $\triangle ABC \cong \triangle ADC$.

Exercises

A

Complete each proof.

1. Given: $\angle D \cong \angle X$, $\angle F \cong \angle Z$, $\overline{DF} \cong \overline{XZ}$

Prove: $\triangle DEF \cong \triangle XYZ$

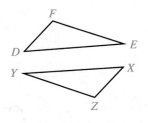

Statements	Reasons
1. $\angle D \cong \angle X$	1. ___
2. $\overline{DF} \cong \overline{XZ}$	2. ___
3. $\angle F \cong \angle Z$	3. ___
4. $\triangle DEF \cong \triangle XYZ$	4. ___

2. Given: $\overline{AC} \cong \overline{AD}$, $\overline{BC} \cong \overline{DE}$, $\overline{AB} \cong \overline{AE}$

Prove: $\triangle ABC \cong \triangle AED$

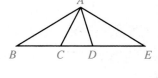

Statements	Reasons
1. $\overline{AC} \cong \overline{AD}$	1. ___
2. $\overline{BC} \cong \overline{DE}$	2. ___
3. ___	3. Given
4. $\triangle ABC \cong \triangle AED$	4. ___

3. Given: $\overline{RT}$ bisects $\angle QRS$. $\angle 1 \cong \angle 2$

Prove: $\triangle RTQ \cong \triangle RTS$

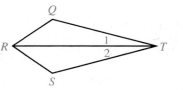

Statements	Reasons
1. $\overline{RT}$ bisects $\angle QRS$.	1. ___
2. $\angle QRT \cong \angle SRT$	2. ___
3. $\overline{RT} \cong \overline{RT}$	3. ___
4. $\angle 1 \cong \angle 2$	4. ___
5. ___	5. ASA

4. Given: $\overline{AE}$ bisects $\overline{BD}$. $\overline{AC} \cong \overline{EC}$

Prove: $\triangle ABC \cong \triangle EDC$

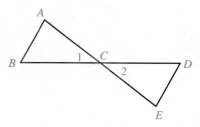

Statements	Reasons
1. $\overline{AE}$ bisects $\overline{BD}$.	1. ___
2. $\overline{BC} \cong \overline{DC}$	2. ___
3. $\angle 1 \cong \angle 2$	3. ___
4. ___	4. ___
5. $\triangle ABC \cong \triangle EDC$	5. ___

Write a two-column proof for each exercise.

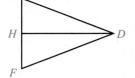

5. Given: $\overline{DE} \cong \overline{DF}$, $\overline{DH}$ bisects $\overline{EF}$.

Prove: $\triangle DHE \cong \triangle DHF$

6. Given: $\overline{DE} \cong \overline{DF}$, $\overline{DH}$ bisects $\angle EDF$.

Prove: $\triangle DHE \cong \triangle DHF$

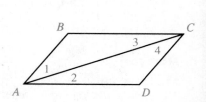

7. Given: $\overline{AB} \cong \overline{CD}$, $\angle 1 \cong \angle 4$

Prove: $\triangle ABC \cong \triangle CDA$

8. Given: $\angle 2 \cong \angle 3$, $\angle 1 \cong \angle 4$

Prove: $\triangle ABC \cong \triangle CDA$

9. Given: $\overline{HI} \cong \overline{KI}$, $\angle 1 \cong \angle 2$
$\overline{JI} \cong \overline{IL}$

Prove: $\triangle HIJ \cong \triangle KIL$

10. Given: $\overline{AB} \cong \overline{CD}$, $\angle 1 \cong \angle 2$
$\overline{AC}$ bisects $\overline{BD}$.

Prove: $\triangle ABE \cong \triangle CDE$

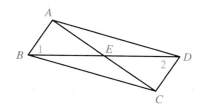

Write a conclusion that follows from the given information. State the congruence postulate and/or definition on which your conclusion is based.

11. $\overline{AB} \cong \overline{AD}$, $\overline{BC} \cong \overline{DC}$
12. $\overline{AB} \cong \overline{AD}$, $\angle 1 \cong \angle 2$
13. $\overline{AC}$ is perpendicular to $\overline{BD}$. $\overline{BC} \cong \overline{DC}$
14. $\overline{AC}$ is perpendicular to $\overline{BD}$. $\angle 1 \cong \angle 2$
15. F is the midpoint of $\overline{EG}$ and $\overline{HI}$.
16. $\overline{EG}$ and $\overline{HI}$ bisect each other.

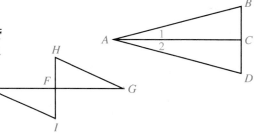

Write a two-column proof for each exercise.

17. Given: $\overline{BD} \perp$ to plane M
$\overline{AB} \cong \overline{BC}$

Prove: $\triangle ABD \cong \triangle CBD$

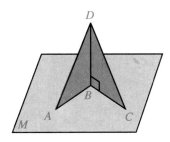

18. Given: $\overline{AB} \perp$ plane M, $\overline{DE} \perp$ plane M
C bisects $\overline{BD}$.

Prove: $\triangle ACB \cong \triangle ECD$

B

Write a two-column proof for each exercise.

19. Given: $\overline{AI}$ bisects $\angle BAC$.
$\overline{AB} \cong \overline{AC}$

Prove: $\triangle ABI \cong \triangle ACI$

20. Given: $\angle 1 \cong \angle 2$, $\angle A \cong \angle E$
N is the midpoint of $\overline{AE}$.

Prove: $\triangle ABN \cong \triangle EDN$

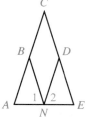

21. Supporting struts are often added to a structure to form triangles so that the structure will become rigid. Explain how the congruence postulates relate to the fact that triangles form rigid figures.

A nonrigid figure collapses.   Triangles form rigid figures.

22. Give a convincing argument that quadrilaterals do not satisfy an SSSS congruence postulate.

23. D is the midpoint of $\overline{BC}$. $AB = 9x + 3$, $BD = 9x - 2$, $AC = 15x - 3$, $CD = 4x + 3$ Show that $\triangle ABD \cong \triangle ACD$.

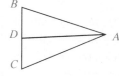

24. $\overline{AD}$ bisects $\angle BAC$. $m\angle BAD = 31 - x$, $m\angle CAD = 15 + 3x$, $AB = 3x + 4$, $AC = 7x - 12$ Show that $\triangle BDA \cong \triangle CDA$.

25. $m\angle AOD = 2x + 9$, $m\angle BOC = 3x + 5$, $AO = x^2 - 2$, $OB = 3x + 2$, $OC = 2x^2 - 17$, $DO = 5x - 5$ Show that $\overline{AB}$ and $\overline{CD}$ bisect each other.

C

26. Given: In figure $ABCD$, O bisects $\overline{AC}$ and $\overline{BD}$.
Prove: $\overline{AB} \parallel \overline{CD}$, $\overline{BC} \parallel \overline{AD}$

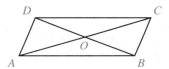

Critical Thinking

Decide whether each statement is always, sometimes, or never true. Draw a figure to explain your answer. Give a convincing argument when the statement is always true.

27. A ray that bisects one angle of a triangle divides the triangle into two congruent triangles.

28. The segment from a vertex of a triangle to the midpoint of the opposite side divides the triangle into a pair of congruent triangles.

29. If two sides of a triangle are congruent, the segment from the common vertex to the midpoint of the third side bisects the angle of the vertex.

Mixed Review

Complete each statement.

1. Two lines in different planes that do not intersect are ___ .

2. Four lines intersect in, at most, ___ points.

3. Adjacent angles have no ___ points in common.

4. Two lines that form congruent adjacent angles are ___ .

5. If two sides of a triangle lie in a plane, the third side ___ .

6. A triangle divides a plane into three sets of points, those on the exterior, those on the interior, and ___ .

Computer Activity

Suppose you have two boxes and each box contains eight dowel rods with lengths 8 cm, 9 cm, 10 cm, 11 cm, 12 cm, 13 cm, 14 cm, and 15 cm. Suppose you reach into one box with your right hand and select three rods at random, and then you reach into the other box with your left hand and select three rods at random.

What are the chances that the triangle made with the right-hand rods will be congruent to the triangle made with the left-hand rods? Are your chances very good?

The program provided here simulates this experiment. When you run the program, it asks how many times you want to simulate the experiment. Then it records the number of times the two randomly selected triangles are congruent. It also records the experimental probability of selecting a pair of congruent triangles.

```
10 INPUT "HOW MANY EXPERIMENTS DO YOU WANT TO RUN ";N
15 FOR COUNT = 1 TO N
20 INDEX = 0
25 FOR TRIANGLE 1 TO 2
30 GOSUB 1000
35 A(INDEX + 1) = NUMBER
40 GOSUB 1000
45 A(INDEX + 2) = NUMBER
50 IF A(INDEX + 1) = A(INDEX + 2) THEN GOTO 40
55 IF A(INDEX + 1) > A(INDEX + 2), THEN SWITCH = A(INDEX + 1):
   A(INDEX + 1) = A(INDEX + 2): A(INDEX + 2) = SWITCH
60 GOSUB 1000
65 A(INDEX + 3) = NUMBER
70 IF A(INDEX + 3) = A(INDEX + 2) OR A(INDEX + 3) = A(INDEX + 1)
   THEN GOTO 60
75 IF A(INDEX + 1) > A(INDEX + 3), THEN SWITCH = A(INDEX + 1):
   A(INDEX + 1) = A(INDEX + 3): A(INDEX + 3) = SWITCH
80 IF A(INDEX + 2) > A(INDEX + 3), THEN SWITCH = A(INDEX + 2);
   A(INDEX + 2) = A(INDEX + 3): A(INDEX + 3) = SWITCH
85 INDEX = 3
90 NEXT TRIANGLE
95 IF A(1) = A(4) AND A(2) = A(5) AND A(3) = A(6) THEN PAIRS = PAIRS + 1
100 NEXT COUNT
110 PRINT "THE NUMBER OF CONGRUENT PAIRS IS "; PAIRS
115 PRINT "THE EXPERIMENTAL PROBABILITY IS "; PAIRS/N
120 END
1000 NUMBER = INT(8*RND(1)) + 8: RETURN
```

Exercises

1. Run the program to simulate the experiment 100 times.
2. Run the program to simulate the experiment 500 times.
3. Which result do you think is closer to the actual probability? Why?

4-4 Proving Segments and Angles Congruent

In this lesson you will prove two triangles are congruent in order to conclude that a pair of angles or sides are congruent. In this first example you will learn how a surveyor can use congruent triangles to find a distance that he or she is unable to measure directly.

Example 1

Application A surveyor is unable to measure the distances from docks A and B to point P on an island. Explain how to find distances AP and BP.

Solution
1. Measure $\angle BAP$ and $\angle ABP$.
2. Locate point C so that $m\angle BAP = m\angle BAC$ and $m\angle ABP = m\angle ABC$.
3. Use the ASA postulate to conclude that $\triangle ABP \cong \triangle ABC$.
4. Since corresponding sides of congruent triangles are the same length, we can conclude that $AP = AC$ and $BP = BC$. Measure $\overline{AC}$ and $\overline{BC}$.

Step 4 in Example 1 uses the fact that corresponding sides of congruent triangles are congruent. It is also true that corresponding angles of congruent triangles are congruent.

> Corresponding parts of congruent triangles are congruent.
> Abbreviation: Corr. parts of $\cong \triangle$s are $\cong$.

Example 2

Complete the proof.

Given: $\overline{AB} \cong \overline{AD}$, $\angle 1 \cong \angle 2$

Prove: $\overline{BE} \cong \overline{DE}$

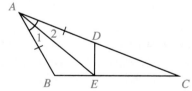

Plan To prove that $\overline{BE} \cong \overline{DE}$, find a pair of congruent triangles that contain these segments. $\triangle ABE$ and $\triangle ADE$ include $\overline{BE}$ and $\overline{DE}$. Angles 1 and 2 are included angles that lead to the use of the SAS postulate.

Proof

Statements	Reasons
1. $\overline{AB} \cong \overline{AD}$	1. Given
2. $\angle 1 \cong \angle 2$	2. Given
3. $\overline{AE} \cong \overline{AE}$	3. Reflexive Property
4. $\triangle ABE \cong \triangle ADE$	4. SAS Postulates
5. $\overline{AB} \cong \overline{CD}$	5. ___

Solution
Corr. parts of $\cong \triangle$s are $\cong$.

A summary of the general procedure that can be used to prove two segments or two angles congruent by using congruent triangles is described as follows.

Proving Two Segments or Two Angles Congruent

1. Identify two triangles that contain the two segments or two angles as corresponding parts.
2. Prove that the two triangles are congruent.
3. State that the two segments or angles are congruent by using "Corr. parts of ≅ △s are ≅."

Example 3

Write a plan for proof and a two-column proof.

Given: $\overline{AC}$ and $\overline{BD}$ bisect each other.

Prove: ∠3 ≅ ∠4

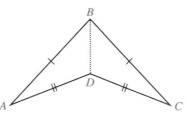

Solution

Plan To prove that ∠3 ≅ ∠4, first prove that △ADC ≅ △CBA or that △AOD ≅ △COB. Since ∠1 and ∠2 are vertical angles, they are congruent. I can use this fact together with the given information to prove △AOD ≅ △COB by SAS.

Proof

Statements	Reasons
1. $\overline{AC}$ and $\overline{BD}$ bisect each other.	1. Given
2. $\overline{AO} \cong \overline{CO}$, $\overline{BO} \cong \overline{DO}$	2. A segment bisector forms two ≅ segments.
3. ∠1 ≅ ∠2	3. Vertical angles are ≅.
4. △AOD ≅ △COB	4. SAS Postulates
5. ∠3 ≅ ∠4	5. Corr. parts of ≅ △s are ≅.

Example 4

Write a plan for proof and a two-column proof. Use an auxiliary line.

Given: $\overline{AB} \cong \overline{CB}$, and $\overline{AD} \cong \overline{CD}$

Proof: ∠A ≅ ∠C

Solution

Plan I can prove ∠A ≅ ∠C if these two angles are corresponding parts of a pair of congruent triangles. If I draw the auxiliary segment $\overline{BD}$, I can use the SSS congruence postulate to prove that △ABD ≅ △CBD.

Proof

Statements	Reasons
1. Draw $\overline{BD}$.	1. For any two points, there is exactly one line containing them.
2. $\overline{BD} \cong \overline{BD}$	2. Reflexive Property
3. $\overline{AB} \cong \overline{CB}$	3. Given
4. $\overline{AD} \cong \overline{CD}$	4. Given
5. △ABD ≅ △CBD	5. SSS Postulate
6. ∠A ≅ ∠C	6. Corr. parts of ≅ △s are ≅.

Class Exercises

Short Answer

Select a pair of triangles that you might try to prove congruent if you wanted to conclude each of the following.

1. $\overline{AD} \cong \overline{CB}$ 2. $\angle 1 \cong \angle 2$

3. Select a second pair of triangles that you could use for Exercise 1.
4. Select a second pair of triangles that you could use for Exercise 2.

Sample Exercises

Give a plan for each proof.

5. **Given:** $\overline{AB} \cong \overline{CD}$, $\angle 1 \cong \angle 2$, $\angle 3 \cong \angle 4$
   Prove: $\overline{BF} \cong \overline{DE}$

6. **Given:** $\angle 5 \cong \angle 6$, $\overline{BC} \cong \overline{DA}$, $\overline{CF} \cong \overline{AE}$
   Prove: $\angle DEA \cong \angle BFC$

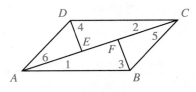

Complete each proof.

7. **Given:** $\angle 1 \cong \angle 2$, $\angle 3 \cong \angle 4$
   Prove: $\angle A \cong \angle C$

Statements	Reasons
1. $\angle 1 \cong \angle 2$	1. ___
2. $\overline{DB} \cong \overline{DB}$	2. ___
3. ___	3. ___
4. $\triangle ADB \cong \triangle CBD$	4. ___
5. $\angle A \cong \angle C$	5. ___

8. **Given:** $\overline{MN} \cong \overline{MP}$, $\overline{NO} \cong \overline{PO}$
   Prove: $\overline{MO}$ bisects $\angle PMN$.

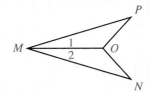

Statements	Reasons
1. $\overline{MN} \cong \overline{MP}$	1. ___
2. ___	2. Given
3. $\overline{MO} \cong \overline{MO}$	3. ___
4. $\triangle PMO \cong \triangle NMO$	4. ___
5. $\angle 1 \cong \angle 2$	5. ___
6. $\overline{MO}$ bisects $\angle PMN$.	6. ___

Write a two-column proof for each exercise.

9. **Given:** $\overline{AB} \cong \overline{CD}$, $\angle 1 \cong \angle 2$
   Prove: $\angle 5 \cong \angle 6$

10. **Given:** $\angle 1 \cong \angle 2$, $\angle 5 \cong \angle 6$
    Prove: $\angle B \cong \angle D$

Discussion

11. Suppose that $\overline{AB} \cong \overline{CD}$ and $\overline{BC} \cong \overline{DA}$. Explain how you would use an auxiliary line to prove that $\angle A \cong \angle C$. How many ways can this be done?

Exercises

A

Suppose that $\triangle ABC \cong \triangle XYZ$. Complete each statement.

1. $XY = 14$ cm, ___ $= 14$ cm
2. $m\angle B = 63$, then ___ $= 63$
3. $m\angle Z = 131$, ___ $= 131$
4. $AC = 21$ cm, ___ $= 21$ cm

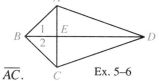

Ex. 5–6

5. **Given:** $\overline{BD}$ bisects $\angle ABC$.
   $\overline{AB} \cong \overline{CB}$

   Prove: $\overline{AD} \cong \overline{CD}$

Statements	Reasons
1. $\overline{AB} \cong \overline{CB}$	1. ___
2. $\overline{BD}$ bisects $\angle ABC$.	2. ___
3. $\angle 1 \cong \angle 2$	3. ___
4. ___	4. Reflexive Property
5. $\triangle ABD \cong \triangle CBD$	5. ___
6. $\overline{AD} \cong \overline{CD}$	6. ___

6. **Given:** $\overline{AC} \perp \overline{BD}$
   $\overline{BD}$ bisects $\overline{AC}$.

   Prove: $\angle ABD \cong \angle CBD$

Statements	Reasons
1. $\overline{AC} \perp \overline{BD}$	1. ___
2. ___	2. $\perp$ lines form $\cong$ adjacent angles.
3. $\overline{BD}$ bisects $\overline{AC}$.	3. ___
4. $\overline{AE} \cong \overline{CE}$	4. ___
5. ___	5. Reflexive Property
6. $\triangle ABE \cong \triangle CBE$	6. ___
7. $\angle ABD \cong \angle CBD$	7. ___

Write a two-column proof for each exercise.

7. **Given:** $\overline{AC}$ and $\overline{BD}$ bisect each other.
   Prove: $\overline{AD} \cong \overline{CB}$

8. **Given:** O bisects $\overline{AC}$. $\angle 3 \cong \angle 4$
   Prove: $\overline{AC}$ and $\overline{BD}$ bisect each other.

9. **Given:** D bisects $\overline{CE}$. $\angle 1 \cong \angle 2$, $\angle C \cong \angle E$
   Prove: $\overline{BD} \cong \overline{FD}$

10. **Given:** N is the midpoint of $\overline{AB}$. $\overline{AD} \cong \overline{BC}$, $\angle 1 \cong \angle 2$
    Prove: $\overline{CN} \cong \overline{DN}$

11. **Given:** O is the midpoint of $\overline{AB}$ and $\overline{CD}$.
    Prove: $\overline{AD} \| \overline{BC}$

12. **Given:** $\overline{AD} \| \overline{BC}$, $\overline{AD} \cong \overline{BC}$
    Prove: O is the midpoint of $\overline{AB}$ and $\overline{CD}$.

13. To find the distance AB across this lake, a surveyor located points C and D with A, P, and D collinear and B, P, and C collinear. $AP = DP$ and $BP = CP$. Explain why distance CD is equal to distance AB.

14. An engineer designing a bridge to be built across a deep canyon needs to find the distance AB across the canyon. He locates points P and C so that $AP = CP$. Next he uses a transit to measure $\angle PAB$. He then locates point D so that $m\angle PAB = m\angle PCD$. How can the engineer find the distance AB?

15. Write a two-column proof.
Add auxiliary lines as needed.
Given: $\overline{AB} \cong \overline{DC}$, $\angle A \cong \angle D$
Prove: $\angle B \cong \angle C$

B

16. $\angle ADE \cong \angle ACB$, $m\angle ACB = 3x + 15$,
$m\angle ADC = 2x + 35$
Find $m\angle ADC$.

17. $\angle XWZ \cong \angle WXZ$, $m\angle XWZ = 3x + 40$,
$m\angle ZXY = 2x + 10$
Find $m\angle ZXY$.

Ex. 16

Ex. 17

List sufficient given information (taken from each figure) and then write a two-column proof.

18. Prove that C is the midpoint of $\overline{BD}$.
19. Prove that $\overline{BF} \cong \overline{DF}$.
20. Prove that $\overline{AB} \cong \overline{AE}$. **21.** Prove that $\angle D \cong \angle C$.

Ex. 18–19

Use the distance formula to calculate each length.

22. AB, DE
23. AC, DF
24. BC, EF

25. Use Exercises 22–24 to show that $\angle A \cong \angle D$.

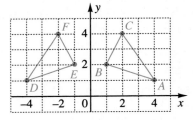

C

26. Given: $\overline{AC} \parallel \overline{DF}$, $\overline{AB} \parallel \overline{DE}$, $\overline{AC} \cong \overline{DF}$, $\overline{AB} \cong \overline{DE}$
Prove: $\angle B \cong \angle E$
(HINT: Draw auxiliary lines.)

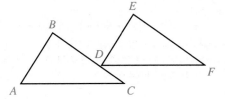

In Exercises 27–30 you may need to prove one pair of triangles congruent in order to gain information needed to show a second pair of triangles congruent. Write a two-column proof for each exercise.

27. Given: In figure $ABCDEFGH$, all sides are congruent to each other.
$\overline{AF} \perp \overline{AB}$, $\overline{BG} \perp \overline{GF}$, $\angle 1 \cong \angle 2$
Prove: $\triangle AHI \cong \triangle GHI$

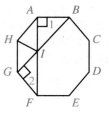

28. Given: $\angle 1 \cong \angle 2$, $\angle 3 \cong \angle 4$,
$\angle 5 \cong \angle 6$, $\angle 7 \cong \angle 8$

Prove: $\angle A \cong \angle C$

29. Prove that if $\overline{AD} \cong \overline{AB}$ and
$\overline{CD} \cong \overline{CB}$, then $\angle D \cong \angle B$.

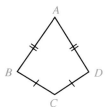

30. Prove that if $\overline{AB} \cong \overline{DE}$, $\overline{AF} \cong \overline{CD}$,
$\overline{EF} \cong \overline{BC}$, and $\angle F \cong \angle C$, then $\overline{AB} \parallel \overline{ED}$.

Critical Thinking

31. In the cube, all faces are squares and all edges are equal in length. Suppose that points B, C, and E are midpoints of edges. Write a convincing argument that $\triangle ABC$ is congruent to $\triangle DCE$.

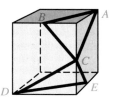

Algebra Review

1. In $\triangle DEF$, $m\angle E$ is six more than $m\angle D$. The measure of $\angle F$ is ten less than twice $m\angle D$. Find the measure of each angle.
2. isosceles $\triangle LOR$ with vertex L, $LO = x^2 + 5$, $LR = 4x + 2$ Find LO and LR.
3. $\triangle CAW$ has $m\angle C = x^2 + 10x + 2$, $m\angle A = x^2 - 9$, and $m\angle W = 8x + 7$. Find the measure of each angle.

Enrichment

Factorials

If three dowel rods are selected from a box of eight rods of different lengths, how many different ways can this selection be completed? (See the Computer Activity on page 165.) If n is a positive whole number, n factorial ($n!$) is defined as $n! = n(n - 1)(n - 2) \ldots 3 \cdot 2 \cdot 1$.

Example

How many ways are there to select
a. three things from nine different things?
b. r things from n different things, where $r < n$?

Solution

a. $\frac{9!}{3!6!} = 84$ **b.** $\frac{n!}{r!(n - r)!}$

Part b of this example gives a general formula to count the number of ways to select r things from n different things.

Select seven points on a circle and use the general formula.

1. How many different segments can be drawn between pairs of these points?
2. How many different triangles can be drawn with vertices selected among these points?
3. How many different segments and triangles can be drawn with vertices selected from among nine points distributed around a circle?

4-5 Proofs: Overlapping Triangles

In the last lesson, you learned that to prove two segments or two angles congruent, it is often necessary to first prove that a pair of triangles are congruent. Sometimes it is difficult to visualize the triangles that you should prove congruent because they overlap.

So it is helpful to separate the triangles mentally, or to redraw the two triangles and then separate them—to help analyze the proof. The first example focuses on formulating a plan for a proof involving overlapping triangles.

Example 1

Write a plan for the proof.

Given: $\angle 1 \cong \angle 6$, $\angle 3 \cong \angle 4$
$\overline{AE} \cong \overline{CD}$

Prove: $\angle ABE \cong \angle CBD$

Solution

Plan I can prove that the overlapping angles $\angle ABE$ and $\angle CBD$ are congruent if I can show that they are corresponding angles in a pair of congruent triangles. Since the angles are overlapping, I can use the ASA Postulate to prove that the overlapping triangles $\triangle ABE$ and $\triangle CBD$ are congruent.

Sometimes the angles or segments that you want to prove congruent are not overlapping so there is no clue that you should be looking for overlapping triangles.

Try This

Write a plan for the proof.

Given: $\angle 1 \cong \angle 6$, $\overline{AE} \cong \overline{CD}$, $\overline{AB} \cong \overline{CB}$

Prove: $\angle 3 \cong \angle 4$

Example 2

Complete the proof.

Given: $\angle 1 \cong \angle 2$, $\overline{AC} \cong \overline{DF}$
$\angle 3 \cong \angle 4$

Prove: $\overline{EF} \cong \overline{BC}$

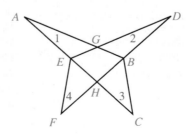

Plan To prove that $\overline{EF} \cong \overline{BC}$, I need to choose a pair of triangles that contain $\overline{EF}$ and $\overline{BC}$ as corresponding sides. I cannot prove $\triangle EFH \cong \triangle BCH$. I can prove overlapping triangles $\triangle EFD \cong \triangle BCA$ by using the ASA postulate.

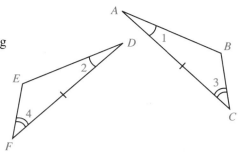

Solution

Proof

Statements	Reasons
1. $\angle 1 \cong \angle 2$	1. Given
2. $\overline{AC} \cong \overline{DF}$	2. Given
3. $\angle 3 \cong \angle 4$	3. Given
4. $\triangle ABC \cong \triangle DEF$	4. ASA Postulate
5. $\overline{EF} \cong \overline{BC}$	5. Corr. parts of $\cong \triangle$s are $\cong$.

Example 3

Complete the proof.

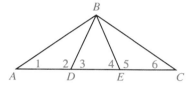

Given: $\angle 1 \cong \angle 6$, $\angle 3 \cong \angle 4$, $\overline{AD} \cong \overline{CE}$

Prove: $\angle ABE \cong \angle CBD$

Plan To prove that $\angle ABE \cong \angle CBD$, I need to prove that a pair of congruent triangles contain these corresponding angles. I can prove (overlapping triangles) $\triangle AEB \cong \triangle CDB$ by ASA if I can show that $\overline{AE} \cong \overline{CD}$. I can do that by using the Common Segment Theorem and the fact that $\overline{AD} \cong \overline{DF}$.

Solution

Proof

Statements	Reasons
1. $\angle 1 \cong \angle 6$	1. Given
2. $\overline{AD} \cong \overline{CE}$	2. Given
3. $\overline{AE} \cong \overline{CD}$	3. Common Segment Theorem
4. $\angle 4 \cong \angle 3$	4. Given
5. $\triangle AEB \cong \triangle CDB$	5. ASA Postulate
6. $\angle ABE \cong \angle CBD$	6. Corr. parts. of $\cong \triangle$s are $\cong$.

Try This

Complete the proof.

Given: $\overline{AB} \cong \overline{CB}$, $\angle 1 \cong \angle 6$, $\overline{AE} \cong \overline{CD}$

Prove: $\angle 2 \cong \angle 5$

Plan First show that $\triangle AEB \cong \triangle CDB$ by SAS. Then $\angle 3 \cong \angle 4$ by corresponding parts of congruent triangles and $\angle 2 \cong \angle 5$ by the Congruent Supplements Theorem.

Proof

Statements	Reasons
1. $\overline{AB} \cong \overline{CB}$, $\angle 1 \cong \angle 6$, $\overline{AE} \cong \overline{CD}$	1. ___
2. ___	2. ___
3. $\angle 3 \cong \angle 4$	3. ___
4. ___	4. ___

Class Exercises

Short Answer

1. Name two different triangles that overlap △AOC.
2. Name two different triangles that overlap △BOD.
3. Name two different triangles that overlap △BOE.
4. Name two different triangles that overlap △AOD.

Sample Exercises

Use the Common Segment Theorem or the Common Angle Theorem to complete each statement.

5. If $\overline{AB} \cong \overline{DE}$, then $\overline{AD} \cong$ ___ .
6. If $\overline{AB} \cong \overline{CD}$, then $\overline{AC} \cong$ ___ .
7. If $\angle 1 \cong \angle 3$, then $\angle AOC \cong$ ___ .
8. If $\angle 2 \cong \angle 4$, then $\angle EOC \cong$ ___ .
9. If $\overline{AC} \cong \overline{BD}$, then $\overline{AB} \cong$ ___ .
10. If $\overline{AD} \cong \overline{BE}$, then $\overline{AB} \cong$ ___ .

11. Write a two-column proof for Example 1 on page 172.

Discussion

12. Suppose that in the above figure $\overline{AO} \cong \overline{EO}$, $\angle 1 \cong \angle 4$, and $\overline{OB} \cong \overline{OD}$.
    Use this information to give a convincing argument that a pair of nonoverlapping triangles are congruent and a pair of overlapping triangles are congruent.

Exercises

A

Name a pair of overlapping triangles that appear to be congruent.

1.   2.   3.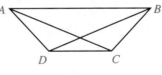

4. Name a second pair of overlapping triangles in Exercise 2.
5. Name a second pair of overlapping triangles in Exercise 3.

Use the Common Segment Theorem and the Common Angle Theorem to complete each statement.

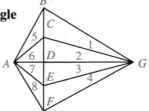

6. If $\angle 1 \cong \angle 4$, then $\angle BGE \cong$ ___ .
7. If $\overline{BE} \cong \overline{FC}$, then $\overline{FE} \cong$ ___ .
8. If $\angle BAE \cong \angle FAC$, then $\angle FAE \cong$ ___ .
9. If $\angle 5 \cong \angle 8$, then $\angle BAE \cong$ ___ .

Redraw each figure, separating the overlapping triangles that you plan to use in the proof. Write a two-column proof.

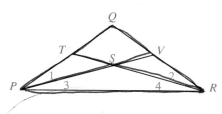

10. Given: $\overline{BC} \cong \overline{ED}$, $\angle ADC \cong \angle ACD$
   Prove: $\overline{BD} \cong \overline{CE}$

11. Given: $\angle ADC \cong \angle ACD$, $\angle 1 \cong \angle 2$
   Prove: $\overline{BC} \cong \overline{ED}$

12. Given: $\overline{BC} \cong \overline{ED}$, $\overline{BD} \cong \overline{EC}$
   Prove: $\angle 3 \cong \angle 4$

13. Given: $\angle 1 \cong \angle 2$, $\overline{PQ} \cong \overline{RQ}$
   Prove: $\overline{QT} \cong \overline{QV}$

14. Given: $\overline{PT} \cong \overline{RV}$, $\overline{TR} \cong \overline{VP}$
   Prove: $\angle 3 \cong \angle 4$

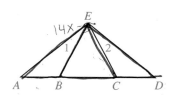

B

15. $AB = CD$, $AC = 3x + 5$, $BD = 4x - 3$, $BC = x + 2$
   Find AB and CD.

16. $\angle 1 \cong \angle 2$, $m\angle AEC = 14x - 3$, $m\angle DEB = 17x - 15$,
   $AE = 4x + 7$, $DE = 3x + 11$, $BE = 3x + 7$, $CE = 5x - 1$
   Show that $\triangle AEC \cong \triangle DEB$.

17. $\angle AEC \cong \angle DEB$, $\triangle AEB \cong \triangle DEC$, $m\angle 1 = 5x - 3$,
   $m\angle 2 = 3x + 5$, $AC = 3x - 1$
   Find DB.

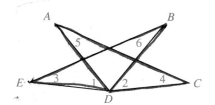

Write a two-column proof for each exercise.

18. Given: $\overline{RS} \cong \overline{UV}$
   $\overline{ST} \cong \overline{VW}$
   $\angle S \cong \angle V$
   Prove: $\overline{RW} \cong \overline{UT}$

19. Given: $\overline{ST} \cong \overline{VW}$
   $\angle S \cong \angle V$
   $\angle STR \cong \angle VWU$
   Prove: $\overline{RS} \parallel \overline{UV}$

20. Given: $\angle 1 \cong \angle 2$
   $\angle 3 \cong \angle 4$
   $\overline{ED} \cong \overline{CD}$
   Prove: $\overline{EB} \cong \overline{CA}$

21. Given: $\angle 1 \cong \angle 2$
   $\overline{AD} \cong \overline{BD}$
   $\overline{ED} \cong \overline{CD}$
   Prove: $\angle 5 \cong \angle 6$

22. Given: $\overline{AB} \cong \overline{DC}$
   $\angle A \cong \angle D$
   $\overline{AE} \cong \overline{DF}$
   Prove: $\overline{EC} \cong \overline{FB}$

23. Given: $\overline{AE} \cong \overline{DF}$
   $\angle E \cong \angle F$
   $\overline{EC} \cong \overline{FB}$
   Prove: $\overline{AB} \cong \overline{CD}$

24. Show that $\angle F \cong \angle G$.

C

Write a two-column proof for each exercise.

25. Given: $\overline{BC} \cong \overline{ED}$
$\angle ADC \cong \angle ACD$
Prove: $\overline{AB} \cong \overline{AE}$

26. Given: $\overline{RS} \cong \overline{RU}$, $\angle 1 \cong \angle 2$
Prove: $\angle 3 \cong \angle 4$

Critical Thinking

27. How many triangles in the figure to the right are congruent to triangle A? triangle B? triangle C?

A   B   C

Algebra Review

1. $\triangle KAW$ is equiangular. $m \angle K = x^2 + 10x + 4$, $m \angle A = x^2 - x + 48$
$m \angle W = 2x^2 + 5x + 8$ Find x.

2. $\triangle JOR$, $\overline{JO} \cong \overline{JR}$, $JO = 2x + 1$, $JR = 4x - 15$, $OR = 3x - 4$
Find OR.

3. $\triangle PSN$, $m \angle P = 3x^2 - 4x - 11$, $m \angle S = x^2 - 2x + 1$
$m \angle N = 2x^2 - 6x - 20$ Find $m \angle P$.

Quiz

Write a two-column proof for each exercise.

1. **Given:** $\overline{JC}$ bisects $\angle EJA$.
$\overline{JE} \cong \overline{JI}$, $\angle E \cong \angle JIA$
Prove: $\overline{EC} \cong \overline{IA}$

2. **Given:** $\overline{JE} \cong \overline{JI}$, $\overline{JC} \cong \overline{JA}$
$\overline{EC} \cong \overline{IA}$
Prove: $\overline{JC}$ bisects $\angle EJA$.

3. **Given:** $\overline{BH} \cong \overline{BE}$, $\overline{BK} \cong \overline{BD}$
Prove: $\angle BDH \cong \angle BKE$

4. **Given:** $\overline{BK} \cong \overline{KE} \cong \overline{BD} \cong \overline{DH}$
$\angle BDH \cong \angle BKE$
Prove: $\angle E \cong \angle H$

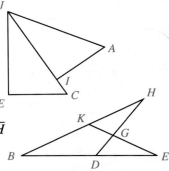

THEOREMS ABOUT TRIANGLES

OBJECTIVE: *Prove and apply the theorems about isosceles triangles.*

4-6 Isosceles Triangles

EXPLORE Use square dot paper or graph paper to draw a large triangle with two sides equal in length. Fold the dot paper with the fold line through the vertex *A* and perpendicular to the side opposite *A*. (This fold line is the reflection line for a reflection transformation.) What do you discover about the angles of this triangle? Repeat for a variety of triangle shapes and state any generalizations that you discover.

You have learned that an isosceles triangle has a pair of congruent sides. The congruent sides are called **legs** and the third side is called the **base.** The angles opposite the legs are called **base angles** and the third angle is called the **vertex angle.**

The following theorem describes a relationship between the legs and the base angles of an isosceles triangle. Note the use of the five steps in proving a theorem as discussed in Chapter 2.

◆ **THEOREM 4.1   Isosceles Triangle Theorem**

If two sides of a triangle are congruent then the angles opposite those sides are congruent.

Given: $\overline{AB} \cong \overline{AC}$

Prove: $\angle 1 \cong \angle 2$

Plan   Let *D* be the midpoint of $\overline{BC}$ and draw the auxiliary line $\overline{AD}$. Then prove that $\triangle ABD \cong \triangle ACD$ using the SSS Postulate and conclude that $\angle 1 \cong \angle 2$.

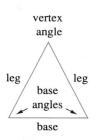

Proof

Statements	Reasons
1. $\overline{AB} \cong \overline{AC}$	1. Given
2. D is the midpoint of $\overline{BC}$.	2. A segment has exactly one midpoint.
3. $\overline{BD} \cong \overline{CD}$	3. A midpoint forms two $\cong$ segments.
4. $\overline{AD} \cong \overline{AD}$	4. Reflexive Property
5. $\triangle ABD \cong \triangle ACD$	5. SSS Postulate
6. $\angle 1 \cong \angle 2$	6. Corr. parts of $\cong \triangle$s are $\cong$.

Sometimes a theorem can be stated concisely in a form that is not if-then form. Theorem 4.1 could have been stated as follows.
The base angles of an isosceles triangle are congruent.

Remember that a theorem that follows directly from another theorem is called a corollary. Below are several corollaries of Theorem 3.1. You will be asked to prove these corollaries in Exercises 30–31.

▶ **COROLLARY 4.1a**

If a triangle is equilateral then it is equiangular.

▶ **COROLLARY 4.1b**

The segment from the vertex of an isosceles triangle to the midpoint of the base bisects the vertex angle.

Recall that the converse of a conditional statement "if *p*, then *q*" is the statement "if *q*, then *p*." The next theorem is the converse of Theorem 4.1.

◆ **THEOREM 4.2**

If two angles of a triangle are congruent, then the sides opposite them are congruent.

You will be asked to prove Theorem 4.2 in Exercise 37.

▶ **COROLLARY 4.2a**

If a triangle is equiangular, then the triangle is equilateral.

Example

Find *BD* and $m \angle ABC$.

Solution

$BD = 14$ *Since* $\angle BAD \cong \angle BDA$, *then*
               $AB = BD$ *by Theorem 4.2.*

$m \angle ABC = x$ *Since* $AC = 8 + 14 = 22$ *and*
               $BC = 22$, *then* $\angle A \cong \angle ABC$
               by Theorem 4.1.

Try This

Explain why $\angle DBC \cong \angle DCB$.

Class Exercises

Short Answer

1. Name the legs of $\triangle ABD$.
2. Name the base angles of $\triangle ABC$.
3. Name the base angles of $\triangle ABD$.
4. Name the legs of $\triangle ABC$.
5. Name the vertex angle of $\triangle ABC$.
6. Name the vertex angle of $\triangle ABD$.

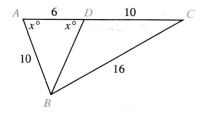

Sample Exercises

Complete each statement based on the theorems in this lesson.

7. The base angles of an isosceles triangle are ___ .
8. If two angles of a triangle are congruent, then ___ .
9. If all three sides of a triangle are congruent then ___ .
10. If all three angles of a triangle are congruent then ___ .
11. The legs of an isosceles triangle are ___ .

12. If $\overline{AE} \cong \overline{DE}$, then ___ $\cong$ ___ .
13. If $\angle 2 \cong \angle 3$, then ___ $\cong$ ___ .
14. If $\overline{BE} \cong \overline{CE}$, then ___ $\cong$ ___ .
15. If $\angle 1 \cong \angle 4$, then ___ $\cong$ ___ .

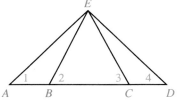

Discussion

16. In the figure to the right $\angle 1 \cong \angle 2$ and $\angle 3 \cong \angle 4$. Give a convincing argument that $AB = CD$.

Exercises

A

Complete each of the following statements. State the theorem that you used.

1. If $\angle 1 \cong \angle 2$, then ___ $\cong$ ___ .
2. If $\angle ABC \cong \angle ACB$, then ___ $\cong$ ___ .
3. If $\overline{DB} \cong \overline{DC}$, then ___ $\cong$ ___ .
4. If $m\angle 1 + m\angle 3 = m\angle 2 + m\angle 4$, then ___ $\cong$ ___ .
5. If $\overline{AB} \cong \overline{AC}$, then ___ $\cong$ ___ .

Use the theorems in this lesson to complete each statement.

6. $m\angle ABC =$ ___
7. $CE =$ ___

Use the theorems in this lesson to complete each statement.

8. $BC =$ ___
9. $AB =$ ___
10. $m\angle ACD =$ ___
11. $m\angle ADB =$ ___
12. $m\angle ABC =$ ___

Use $\triangle ABF$ and $\triangle CED$ in the figure.

13. $CF =$ ___
14. $FE =$ ___

N is the midpoint of $\overline{LO}$ in the figure.

15. Find MN.
16. Find PN.
17. Find PO.

Complete each proof.

18. **Given:** $\overline{AC} \cong \overline{AD}$, $\angle 1 \cong \angle 2$

   Prove: $\triangle ADB \cong \triangle ACE$

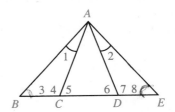

Statements	Reasons
1. $\overline{AC} \cong \overline{AD}$	1. ___
2. $\angle 5 \cong \angle 6$	2. ___
3. $\angle 1 \cong \angle 2$	3. ___
4. $\angle BAD \cong \angle EAC$	4. Common Angle Theorem
5. $\triangle ADB \cong \triangle ACE$	5. ___

19. Use the figure in Exercise 18.

   Given: $\overline{AB} \cong \overline{AE}$, $\angle 1 \cong \angle 2$

   Prove: $\triangle ACD$ is isosceles.

Statements	Reasons
1. $\overline{AB} \cong \overline{AE}$	1. ___
2. $\angle 3 \cong \angle 8$	2. ___
3. $\angle 1 \cong \angle 2$	3. ___
4. $\triangle ABC \cong \triangle AED$	4. ___
5. $\angle 4 \cong \angle 7$	5. ___
6. $\angle 5 \cong \angle 6$	6. Supplements of $\cong \angle$s are $\cong$.
7. $\overline{AD} \cong \overline{AC}$	7. ___
8. $\triangle ACD$ is isosceles.	8. ___

20. The device to the right can be used to determine one half of any angle. Point E is allowed to move along the slot so that $AD = DE$. Explain why the measure of $\angle EAD$ is always one half the measure of $\angle BDE$.

B

21. $\triangle ABC$ is isosceles with $AB = BC$. If $AB = 4x$ and $BC = 6x - 15$, find AB and BC.
22. $\triangle DEF$ is isosceles with base $\overline{DF}$. If $DE = 4x + 15$, $EF = 2x + 45$, and $DF = 3x + 15$, find the lengths of the sides of the triangle.
23. In $\triangle XYZ$, $XY = YZ$. If $m\angle X = 4x + 60$, $m\angle Y = 2x + 30$, and $m\angle Z = 14x + 30$, find $m\angle X$, $m\angle Y$, and $m\angle Z$.
24. In $\triangle ABC$, $\angle A \cong \angle C$. If $AB = 4x + 25$, $BC = 2x + 45$, and $AC = 3x - 15$, find the lengths of the three sides.

Write a two-column proof for each exercise.

25. **Given:** $\triangle ADC$ is isosceles with vertex A.
    $\overline{BC} \cong \overline{ED}$

    Prove: $\triangle ABE$ is isosceles.

26. **Given:** $\triangle ABC$ is isosceles with vertex angle A.
    $\angle 1 \cong \angle 2$

    Prove: $\triangle BCD$ is isosceles.

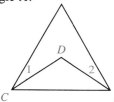

27. **Given:** $\overline{AB} \cong \overline{AC}$
    $\overline{BE}$ bisects $\angle ABC$.
    $\overline{CD}$ bisects $\angle ACB$.

    Prove: $\overline{AD} \cong \overline{AE}$

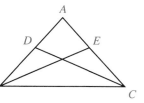

28. **Given:** $\angle ABC \cong \angle ADC$, $\angle 1 \cong \angle 2$
    Prove: $\overline{AB} \cong \overline{AD}$ and $\overline{BC} \cong \overline{DC}$

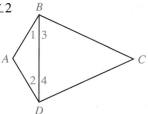

29. If a ship is moving in the direction $\overrightarrow{AD}$, its distance from a point on shore can be determined in the following way. At point A, $m\angle DAC$ can be determined. At some point B along $\overrightarrow{AD}$, $m\angle DBC$ is twice $m\angle DAC$. The distance AB, which can be determined by the ship's log, is the same as the distance BC. Explain why $m\angle DBC = 2m\angle DAC$ means that $AB = BC$.

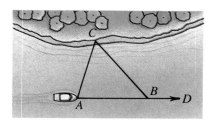

30. Prove Corollary 4.1a.

31. Prove Corollary 4.1b.

32. Use the distance formula and conclude that $m\angle ABC = m\angle ACB$.

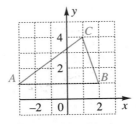

33. Two converging timbers are to be cut along a line as shown so that $m\angle CDB = m\angle ABD$. Two carpenter's squares are positioned so that $BE = DE$. (A carpenter's square has a right-angle corner.)

Prove that $\angle CDB \cong \angle ABD$.

C

34. Suppose that $\triangle ABC$ is an isosceles triangle with vertex angle A and that D is a point on side $\overline{BC}$. Prove that $\overline{AD}$ bisects $\angle A$ if D is the midpoint of $\overline{BC}$.

35. Given: $\overline{AD} \cong \overline{FC}, \overline{AB} \cong \overline{FE}$
$\angle A \cong \angle F$

Prove: $\triangle CDG$ is isosceles.

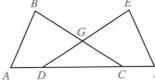

36. $\angle ABD \cong \angle ADB$, $\overline{BF}$ and $\overline{DE}$ bisect $\angle ABD$ and $\angle ADB$ respectively. Prove that $\angle 1 \cong \angle 8$.

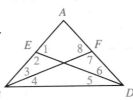

37. Given that, in $\triangle ABC$, $\angle B \cong \angle C$. Prove that $\triangle ABC \cong \triangle ACB$. Explain why you have just proven Theorem 4.2.

38. Given: $M \parallel N$, $\overline{BC}$ in plane M, $\overline{DE}$ in plane N
$m\angle ABC = m\angle ACB$

Prove: $\triangle ADE$ is isosceles.

Critical Thinking

39. Suppose that $\overline{EB} \cong \overline{EC}$ and $\angle 1 \cong \angle 2$. Consider the following argument. Since $\overline{EB} \cong \overline{EC}$, $\triangle EBC$ is an isosceles triangle with the base angles at B and C congruent. This means that $\angle 3 \cong \angle 4$ since they are supplements of congruent angles and $\triangle ABE \cong \triangle DCE$. Therefore, $\overline{AE} \cong \overline{DE}$ since they are corresponding segments in congruent triangles. Consequently $\triangle AED$ is an isosceles triangle. Is this a convincing argument? Why or why not?

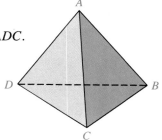

40. For pyramid $ABCD$, $m \angle ABC \cong \angle ACB \cong \angle ACD \cong \angle ADC$. What can you deduce about $\triangle ABD$?

41. Under what conditions is $\triangle ABD$ an equilateral triangle?

Mixed Review

1. The ratio of the measures of the angles of a triangle is $13 : 15 : 17$. Find the measures of the angles and classify the triangle as acute, right, or obtuse.

2. The ratio of the measures of the acute angles of a right triangle is $7 : 8$. Find the measures of the two acute angles.

3. $BC = CD$, $BD = AB - 1$, $AD = 9$ Find AB.

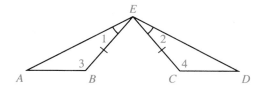

4-7 AAS Congruence and Right Triangle Congruence

EXPLORE

Given angles A and B and a segment with length b. Use a protractor and ruler to draw a triangle DEF with $\angle D$ congruent to the given $\angle A$, $\angle E$ congruent to the given $\angle B$, and whose side opposite $\angle E$ has length b.

You have studied the SSS, SAS, and ASA methods of proving triangles congruent. The above Explore suggests the AAS method.

◆ **THEOREM 4.3**   AAS Congruence

If two angles and a side opposite one of them in one triangle are congruent to the corresponding parts of another triangle, then the two triangles are congruent.

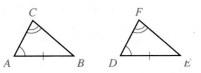

You will be asked to prove the AAS Theorem in Exercise 27. It is used to complete the proof of this example.

Example 1

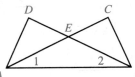

Given: $\angle 1 \cong \angle 2$, $\angle C \cong \angle D$

Prove: $\overline{AD} \cong \overline{BC}$

Solution

Statements	Reasons
1. $\angle 1 \cong \angle 2$, $\angle C \cong \angle D$	1. Given
2. $\overline{AB} \cong \overline{AB}$	2. Reflexive
3. $\triangle ABC \cong \triangle BAD$	3. AAS Congruence Theorem
4. $\overline{AD} \cong \overline{BC}$	4. Corr. parts of $\cong$ $\triangle$s are $\cong$.

In addition to the SSS, SAS, ASA, and AAS methods for proving triangles congruent, there are two methods that apply to right triangles only. The HA Congruence Theorem is a consequence of the AAS Congruence Theorem and will be proven in Exercise 28.

Recall that in a right triangle, the side opposite the right angle is called the *hypotenuse* and the other two sides are called *legs*.

◆ THEOREM 4.4 HA Congruence

If the hypotenuse and one acute angle of a right triangle are congruent to the hypotenuse and one acute angle of another right triangle, then the triangles are congruent.

◆ THEOREM 4.5 HL Congruence

If the hypotenuse and a leg of one right triangle are congruent to the corresponding parts of a second right triangle, then the triangles are congruent.

Given: $\angle Y$ and $\angle RST$ are right $\angle$s in $\triangle XYZ$ and $\triangle RST$.
$\overline{XZ} \cong \overline{RT}$, $\overline{XY} \cong \overline{RS}$

Prove: $\triangle XYZ \cong \triangle RST$

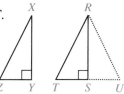

Plan   I will construct $\triangle RUS$, with U selected on $\overline{TS}$ so that $\overline{SU} \cong \overline{YZ}$. If I can show $\triangle XYZ \cong \triangle RSU$, then I can conclude that $\overline{ZX} \cong \overline{UR}$ and that $\triangle TRU$ is isosceles. Consequently $\angle T \cong \angle U$ by Theorem 4.1 and $\angle U \cong \angle Z$ by corr. parts of $\cong \triangle$s are $\cong$. Therefore $\angle T \cong \angle Z$ and I can conclude that $\triangle XYZ \cong \triangle RST$ by HA Congruence.

Example 2

Complete the proof.

Given: $\angle C$ and $\angle F$ are right angles in $\triangle ACB$ and $\triangle DFE$.
$\overline{AE} \cong \overline{DB}$, $\overline{AC} \cong \overline{DF}$

Prove: $\overline{EF} \cong \overline{BC}$

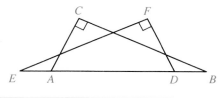

Proof

Statements	Reasons
1. $\angle C$ and $\angle F$ are rt. $\angle$s.	1. Given
2. $\triangle DEF$ and $\triangle ABC$ are rt. $\triangle$s.	2. ____
3. $\overline{AE} \cong \overline{DB}$, $\overline{AC} \cong \overline{DF}$	3. ____
4. $\overline{ED} \cong \overline{BA}$	4. ____
5. $\triangle DEF \cong \triangle ABC$	5. ____
6. $\overline{EF} \cong \overline{BC}$	6. Corr. parts of $\cong \triangle$s are $\cong$.

Solution

2. Definition of a right triangle
3. Given
4. Common Segment Theorem
5. HL Theorem

Six ways to prove triangles congruent have been presented in this chapter. Four ways apply to all triangles and two ways apply to right triangles only.

Summary of Ways To Prove Triangles Congruent

All triangles	SSS	SAS	ASA	AAS
Right triangles	HL	HA		

Class Exercises

Short Answer

Indicate whether the given pair of triangles is congruent by SSS, SAS, ASA, AAS, HA, HL, or none of these.

1.   2.   3.

4.   5.   6.

Sample Exercises

$\overline{CD} \cong \overline{CE}$ State the additional information you need to prove $\triangle ACD \cong \triangle BEC$ by the given method.

7. HA   8. HL   9. SSS
10. AAS   11. ASA   12. SAS

Discussion

13. Formulate a theorem that you would call the LL Congruence Theorem for right triangles. Do you think it is true? Why?
14. Formulate a theorem that you would call the LA Congruence Theorem for right triangles. Do you think it is true? Why?

Exercises

A

State the additional information you need to prove $\triangle ABC \cong \triangle ABD$ by the given method.

1. HA   2. HL   3. AAS
4. SAS   5. ASA   6. SSS

State the additional information you need for the given method to prove that $\triangle ABC \cong \triangle FED$ if $\overline{AD} \cong \overline{CF}$.

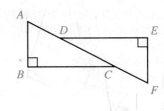

7. HA   8. ASA   9. HL

10. Complete the proof.

Given: B is the midpoint of $\overline{AC}$.
$\angle E$ and $\angle D$ are right $\angle$s. $\overline{EB} \cong \overline{DB}$

Prove: $\angle A \cong \angle C$

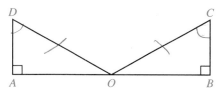

Statements	Reasons
1. $\angle E$, $\angle D$ are rt. $\angle$s.	1. ___
2. $\triangle ABE$ and $\triangle CBD$ are rt. $\triangle$s.	2. ___
3. B is the midpoint of $\overline{AC}$.	3. ___
4. $\overline{AB} \cong \overline{CB}$	4. ___
5. $\overline{EB} \cong \overline{DB}$	5. ___
6. $\triangle ABE \cong \triangle CBD$	6. ___
7. $\angle A \cong \angle C$	7. ___

Write a two-column proof for each exercise.

11. Given: $\angle B$ and $\angle D$ are rt. $\angle$s.
$\overline{AB} \cong \overline{CD}$

Prove: $\triangle ABC \cong \triangle CDA$

12. Given: $\angle B$ and $\angle D$ are rt. $\angle$s.
$\angle 1 \cong \angle 2$

Prove: $\triangle ABC \cong \triangle CDA$

Use each given to prove the right triangles $\triangle AOD$ and $\triangle BOC$ congruent.

13. O is the midpoint of $\overline{AB}$.
$\angle A$ and $\angle B$ are rt. $\angle$s. $\overline{OD} \cong \overline{OC}$
14. $\angle A$ and $\angle B$ are rt. $\angle$s. $\overline{OC} \cong \overline{OD}$, $\angle D \cong \angle C$
15. O is the midpoint of $\overline{AB}$.
$\angle A$ and $\angle B$ are rt. $\angle$s. $\angle AOD \cong \angle BOC$

B

16. A basketball backboard is mounted on a wall with a metal bracket $ABCD$ so that $\angle B$ and $\angle D$ are right angles and $AB = CD$. Show that the two corners A and B of the backboard are equidistant from the wall.

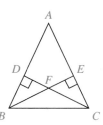

$\overline{DE} \perp \overline{AC}$, $\overline{BF} \perp \overline{AC}$, $\overline{AB} \cong \overline{CD}$, $\overline{DE} \cong \overline{BF}$

17. Prove that $\angle 1 \cong \angle 2$.
18. Prove that $\overline{AD} \cong \overline{CB}$.
19. Prove that $\overline{AE} \cong \overline{CF}$.

20. Given: $\overline{CD} \perp \overline{AB}$, $\overline{BE} \perp \overline{AC}$, $\triangle ABC$ is isosceles.

Prove: $\triangle BFC$ is isosceles.

21. Given: $\overline{CD} \perp \overline{AB}$, $\overline{BE} \perp \overline{AC}$, $\overline{BE} \cong \overline{CD}$

Prove: $\triangle ABC$ is isosceles.

22. $\overline{CD} \perp \overline{AB}$, $\overline{BE} \perp \overline{AC}$, $\overline{CD} \cong \overline{BE}$, $BD = 5x - 7$, $CE = 2x + 14$, $DF = 2x + 5$, $EF = 3x - 2$ Prove that $AEFD$ has two pairs of congruent sides.

23. $\overline{CD} \perp \overline{AB}$, $\overline{BE} \perp \overline{AC}$, $\overline{AC} \cong \overline{AB}$, $AD = 4x - 5$, $AE = 2x + 7$ $m\angle A = 3x + 8$ Find $m\angle A$.

24. A milling cutter with seven teeth is made by cutting seven right triangles out of a seven-sided regular polygon. If $\overline{AB}$ is cut the same length for each tooth, why are the sharp points of the cutter all the same size angle?

25. An antenna tower is perpendicular to a flat roof. Three wires are used to steady the tower, all attached to the same point D on the tower. If the three wires are all the same length, prove that their anchors A, B, and C are all the same distance from the base P.

26. Prove Theorem 4.3.

Given: $\angle A \cong \angle D$, $\angle C \cong \angle F$, $\overline{AB} \cong \overline{DE}$

Prove: $\triangle ABC \cong \triangle DEF$

27. Prove Theorem 4.4.

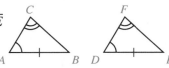

C

28. Prove that segments from the midpoints of the legs of an isosceles triangle perpendicular to the base are congruent.

29. Prove that segments from the midpoint of the base of an isosceles triangle perpendicular to the legs are congruent.

30. Points A, B, and C are in plane M, $\overleftrightarrow{CD} \perp$ plane M, and $\overline{AC} \cong \overline{BC}$. Prove that $\triangle ABD$ is an isosceles triangle.

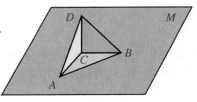

Critical Thinking

31. Write a statement that you would call the SSA Congruence Property. Construct two noncongruent triangles, both named $\triangle ABC$ in which $m\angle A = 45$, $AB = 20$, and $BC = 15$. Do you think that the SSA Property should become a postulate? Why or why not?

Algebra Review

Divide.

1. $(9y^4 - 18y^3 + 27y^2) \div 9y$
2. $(a^2b - a^3b^3 - a^5b^2) \div a^2b$
3. $(y^2 - 25) \div (y + 5)$
4. $(6p^2q^2 - 9p^2q + 12pq^2) \div -3pq$
5. $(y^2 - 8y + 16) \div (y - 4)$
6. $(8x^3 + 27) \div (2x + 3)$

CONNECTIONS ◈

Geometry and Transformations

Congruence as discussed in this chapter is related to concepts studied in algebra. Consider the transformation that associates each point (x, y) in the coordinate plane with the point $(x + 3, y + 2)$. This transformation moves the red triangle to the blue triangle.

1. Calculate the lengths of the sides of the red and blue triangles to show that they are congruent.
2. On graph paper, draw the triangle whose vertices are $(-1, 3)$, $(1, -3)$, and $(2, 1)$. Then draw the position that it moves to after the above transformation is performed.
3. Show that the two triangles in Exercise 2 are congruent.
4. State a generalization about this transformation.

4-8 Medians, Altitudes, and Perpendicular Bisectors

A **median** of a triangle is a segment from a vertex to the midpoint of the opposite side.

  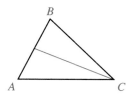

The three medians of △*ABC*

An **altitude** of a triangle is a segment from a vertex perpendicular to the line containing the opposite side.

The three altitudes of △*ABC*

A perpendicular bisector of a side of a triangle is a line through the midpoint and perpendicular to the side.

The three perpendicular bisectors of the sides of △*ABC*

Several theorems relate to perpendicular bisectors.

◆ **THEOREM 4.6**

In an isosceles triangle, the altitude to the base bisects the base and bisects the vertex angle.

Given: An isosceles triangle △*ABC* with legs $\overline{AB}$ and $\overline{AC}$ and $\overline{AD}$ altitude from *A*.

Prove: $\overline{BD} \cong \overline{CD}$, $\angle 1 \cong \angle 2$

Plan Both △*ABD* and △*ACD* are right triangles. Since $\overline{AB} \cong \overline{AC}$ and $\overline{AD}$ is a leg of each, we can use the HL Theorem to conclude that △*ABD* ≅ △*ACD*. Consequently $\overline{BD} \cong \overline{CD}$ and $\angle 1 \cong \angle 2$ by corr. parts of ≅ △s are ≅.

A point *P* is said to be **equidistant** from two points *A* and *B* if *PA* = *PB*. The next two theorems describe the relationship between a point on a perpendicular bisector and a point equidistant from two points.

◆ THEOREM 4.7

If a point is equidistant from the endpoints of a segment, then it is on the perpendicular bisector of the segment.

Given: $\overline{AB}$ and point P with $\overline{PA} \cong \overline{PB}$

Prove: P is on the perpendicular bisector of $\overline{AB}$.

Plan Draw auxiliary lines $\overline{PA}$, $\overline{PB}$, and median $\overline{PC}$ and use the SSS Postulate to prove that $\triangle PAC \cong \triangle PBC$. Then $\angle ACP \cong \angle BCP$ since corr. parts of $\cong \triangle$s are $\cong$. Since these two angles form a linear pair, prove they must both be right angles and $\overline{PC}$ is the perpendicular bisector of $\overline{AB}$.

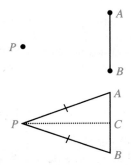

◆ THEOREM 4.8

If a point is on the perpendicular bisector of a segment, then it is equidistant from the endpoints of the segment.

Given: q is the perpendicular bisector of $\overline{AB}$ and P is on q.

Prove: $\overline{PA} \cong \overline{PB}$

Plan Draw $\overline{PA}$ and $\overline{PB}$ and use the SAS Postulate to show that $\triangle PCA \cong \triangle PCB$. Then use the fact that corr. parts of $\cong \triangle$s are $\cong$ to conclude that $\overline{PA} \cong \overline{PB}$.

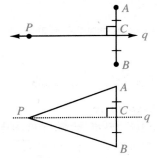

Example 1

Complete the statement in as many ways as possible.
$\overline{EC}$ is ___ in $\triangle AED$.

Solution

1. an altitude
2. a median $\overline{EC}$ *is the altitude to the base of an isosceles triangle. Consequently, it bisects the base by Theorem 4.6 and C is the midpoint of* $\overline{AD}$.
3. a perpendicular bisector

Try This

Complete each statement.

a. $\overline{EB}$ is ___ in $\triangle AEC$.   **b.** $\overline{EC}$ is ___ in $\triangle ABE$.

The distance from a point P to a line r is the distance PQ where Q is the point on r such that $\overline{PQ} \perp r$. For example, the distance from P to line r is d.

◆ THEOREM 4.9

If a point is equidistant from the sides of an angle, then it is on the angle bisector.

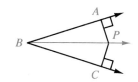

◆ THEOREM 4.10

If a point is on an angle bisector, then it is equidistant from the sides of the angle.

Example 2

What can you deduce from the information given in each part?

a. $AB = AD$ **b.** $\angle ABC$ and $\angle ADC$ are right angles and $BC = DC$.

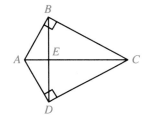

Solution

a. A is on the perpendicular bisector of $\overline{BD}$.
b. C is on the angle bisector of $\angle BAD$.

Try This

What can you deduce if you know that $BE = DE$?

Class Exercises

Short Answer

Determine whether the following statements are true or false.

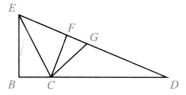

1. If G is the midpoint of $\overline{ED}$, then $\overline{CG}$ is a median of $\triangle EBD$.
2. If $\overline{CF} \perp \overline{ED}$, then $\overline{CF}$ is an altitude of both $\triangle ECD$ and $\triangle ECG$.
3. If $\overline{EB} \perp$ to $\overline{BD}$, then $\overline{EB}$ is an altitude of $\triangle ECD$.
4. If $\overline{CF} \perp$ to $\overline{ED}$, then $\overline{CF}$ is a perpendicular bisector of $\triangle ECD$.
5. If $\overline{CG}$ is a median of $\triangle ECD$, then G is the midpoint of $\overline{ED}$.
6. Each leg of a right triangle is also an altitude of the triangle.

Sample Exercises

Complete each statement in as many ways as possible. Give reasons for your answer.

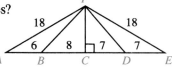

7. $\overline{FD}$ is ___ of $\triangle FCE$.   8. $\overline{FC}$ is ___ of $\triangle AFE$.
9. $\overline{FC}$ is ___ of $\triangle BFE$.   10. $\overline{FC}$ is an altitude of ___ triangles?

11. Trace $\triangle BFE$ and draw all three altitudes of the triangle.
12. Trace $\triangle BFE$ and draw all three medians of the triangle.

Discussion

13. Consider an equilateral triangle. Suppose a segment from a vertex is a median, an altitude, or a perpendicular bisector of the opposite side. Give a convincing argument that the segment is also the other two.

Exercises

A

Complete each statement in as many ways as possible.
Give reasons for your answer.

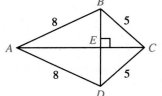

1. $\overline{BE}$ is ___ of $\triangle ABC$.
2. $\overline{AC}$ is ___ of $\overline{BD}$.
3. $\overline{AE}$ is ___ of $\triangle ABD$.
4. $\overline{AC}$ is ___ of $\angle BAD$.

What can you deduce from the information given in each problem?

5. $CD = ED$ 6. $GB = GF$
7. $\angle 1 \cong \angle 2$ 8. $AC = AE$

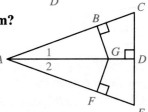

Complete each statement.

9. $\overline{BG}$ is an altitude of $\triangle$ ___ .   10. $\overline{AF}$ is an altitude of $\triangle$ ___ .

Suppose that $\triangle ACE$ is isosceles and segments are perpendicular as shown.

11. Why do you know that $\overline{AD}$ is a median?
12. Why do you know that $BG = GF$?

Lines q and r are perpendicular bisectors of the sides of $\triangle ABC$.

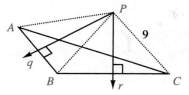

13. If $PC = 9$, then $PB =$ ___ .
14. If $PC = 9$, then $PA =$ ___ .
15. Explain why P is on the perpendicular bisector of $\overline{AC}$.

Complete each statement.

16. $\overline{AP}$ is ___ in $\triangle ABC$.
17. $\overline{CP}$ is ___ in $\triangle ABC$.
18. The distance from P to $\overline{AB}$ is ___ .
19. The distance from P to $\overline{BC}$ is ___ .

20. Give a convincing argument that P is on the angle bisector of $\angle B$.
21. Point P is equidistant from the sides of $\angle ABC$. Explain why
line BP is the angle bisector.

B

22. Suppose that $\overline{BE}$ and $\overline{CD}$ are medians. If $AD = 2x + 3$, $BD = 3x - 2$,
$AE = 4x - 7$, explain why $AB = AC$.
23. Suppose that $\overline{BE}$ is an altitude. If $m\angle AEB = 4x + 10$, $AD = 2x + 5$,
$BD = 3x - 15$, is CD a median?
24. Show that $\overline{AD}$ is a median of $\triangle ABC$.
25. Show that $\overline{AD}$ is an altitude of $\triangle ABC$.
(HINT: Show that $\triangle ABC$ is isosceles.)
26. Show that $\overline{AD}$ is a perpendicular bisector of $\overline{BC}$.
27. Show that the distance from D to $\overline{AB}$ is equal to
the distance from D to $\overline{AC}$.

28. Two electrical power plants are using the same large lake as a cooling tank. Copy the diagram and show the following.
a. Show where, along the lake shoreline, the water intake should be built if they are to be equidistant from both plants.
b. Show where the transformer station should be built if it is to be equidistant from both power plants and the city.

29. Lines p and q represent two major airline routes. A radio transmitter station must be built equidistant from these two routes. The Federal Aviation Administration wants to build it near the city, but a city ordinance does not allow it inside the city limits. Copy the diagram and draw all possible locations for the transmitter station.

C

Write a two-column proof for each exercise. Draw and label a figure as shown in the statement of the theorem.

30. Theorem 4.6   **31.** Theorem 4.8   **32.** Theorem 4.9   **33.** Theorem 4.10

34. Prove that the altitudes from the base angles of an isosceles triangle are congruent.

35. Prove that an altitude to the base of an isosceles triangle is also a median of the triangle and a perpendicular bisector.

Critical Thinking

Inductive reasoning often culminates with a statement, or a conjecture, which the researcher thinks is true. Analyze the following conjectures. If you think they are true, prove them. If not, find a counterexample.

36. Conjecture: If a median of a triangle is also an altitude, then the triangle is isosceles.

37. Conjecture: If an altitude of a triangle bisects the angle it is drawn from, then the triangle is an acute triangle.

38. Conjecture: If two altitudes of an acute triangle are congruent, then the triangle is isosceles.

Algebra Review

Factor.

1. $49y^4 - 81$ **2.** $x^2 - 14x + 49$ **3.** $9y^2 - 64$
4. $a^2b^2 + 7ab + 12$ **5.** $72 - x - x^2$ **6.** $2y^2 - 3y - 2$

Quiz

$\overline{RQ} \cong \overline{RS}, \overline{TQ} \cong \overline{TS}$ Complete each statement.

1. $m\angle RQS = 6x + 10$, $m\angle RSQ = 9x - 17$, $m\angle QRS =$ ___
2. If $QS = RQ$, $m\angle RSQ =$ ___ .
3. If $\angle QVT \cong \angle SVT$, $\triangle QVT \cong \triangle SVT$ by ___ .
4. If $\triangle RVQ$ and $\triangle RVS$ are right triangles, $\triangle RVQ \cong \triangle RVS$ by ___ .
5. If $QV = SV$, $\overline{VT}$ is a(n) ___ or ___ to $\overline{QS}$ and ___ $\angle QTS$.
6. Point W is ___ from $\overline{TQ}$ and $\overline{TS}$.

COMPARING APPROACHES IN GEOMETRY

Introduction to Synthetic and Coordinate Geometry

Theorem 4.8 states that each point on the perpendicular bisector of a segment is equidistant from the two endpoints. The approach taken on page 190 for this theorem is called a **synthetic approach.** A second approach is called a **coordinate approach** since it relies on a coordinate system. Here are the two approaches for a segment $\overline{AB}$ of length 14.

Synthetic Approach

Coordinate Approach

Plan Let C be a point on the $\perp$ bisector of $\overline{AB}$. Then use the SAS Congruence Postulate to prove that $\triangle ACD \cong \triangle BCD$ and conclude that $AC = BC$.

Plan Draw a coordinate system so that the y-axis is the perpendicular bisector of $\overline{AB}$ and point $C(0, b)$ is a general point on this bisector. Use the distance formula to find AC and BC.

In completing the plan for the coordinate proof you obtain the following.

$$AC = \sqrt{(-7 - 0)^2 + (0 - b)^2}$$
$$= \sqrt{49 + b^2}$$
$$BC = \sqrt{(7 - 0)^2 + (0 - b)^2}$$
$$= \sqrt{49 + b^2}$$

Notice that both approaches yield the same result, namely, that $AC = BC$. The exercises below provide more opportunities to use these two approaches.

Exercises

1. Suppose $\overline{AB}$ has length 18. Draw a coordinate system so that $\overline{AB}$ is on the x-axis and the y-axis is the perpendicular bisector of $\overline{AB}$. Find the coordinates of the points A and B.
2. If $C(0, 8)$ is a point on the perpendicular bisector of $\overline{AB}$, use the distance formula to show that $AC = BC$.
3. If C is a general point on the perpendicular bisector of $\overline{AB}$, how can the coordinates of point C be named?
4. If you want to let AB represent a general segment bisected by the y-axis rather than one of length 18, how can the coordinates of point A and B be named?
5. Using the coordinates for A, B, and C from Exercises 3–4, find lengths AC and BC. What theorem does this prove?

CRITICAL THINKING

Deciding on the Truth of a Statement

In the process of dealing with data or evidence in critical thinking, you have to decide if a statement is true. Every statement, no matter how simple or complicated, is either true or false. Statements can be represented by letters of the alphabet.

For example, if statement p "You passed geometry" is true, then the statement $\sim p$ (read "not p") "You did not pass geometry" is false, and vice versa. This is summarized in the truth table to the right.

p	$\sim p$
T	F
F	T

Consider the "p or q" statement below.

p You will pass this geometry course.
q You will be a sophomore again next year.
p or q You will pass this geometry course or you will be a sophomore again next year.

p	q	p or q
T	T	T
T	F	T
F	T	T
F	F	F

The statement is false only when you fail geometry and so you are not a sophomore next year. In the first row p or q is true. You have passed geometry but you could still be a sophomore next year because you failed English!

Check the "p and q" statement below. Do you think the truth table to the right is correct for the "p and q" statement below?

p We will review geometry.
q The geometry test will be easy.
p and q We will review geometry and the geometry test will be easy.

p	q	p and q
T	T	T
T	F	F
F	T	F
F	F	F

Exercises

1. Joe said "It is false that I don't like geometry." Does this mean that Joe doesn't like geometry? Explain. Use symbols to show the statement.
2. Kwan said, "Teenagers like movies or records." If this is true and Kwan likes both movies and records, could Kwan be a teenager? Explain.
3. Bill's mother said, "You can't go out of town and you must be in by 12 o'clock." Bill thought he must not go out of town or he must be in by 12 o'clock. Was he correct? Explain.
4. The salesman said, "You can drive this car home today for nothing down and just $349 a month." Will Corliss be able to drive the car home without having to pay anything on it today?
5. The truth table for "or" statements was defined in a way useful to geometry, but it could be defined in another way. Give a true "or" statement in which both parts cannot be true at the same time.

CHAPTER SUMMARY

Vocabulary

altitude (4-8)	correspondence (4-1)	legs (4-6)
base (4-6)	equidistant (4-8)	median (4-8)
base angles (4-6)	hypotenuse (4-7)	opposite angle (4-2)
corollary (4-6)	included angle (4-2)	vertex angle (4-6)

Key Ideas

1. Prove two triangles congruent using SSS, ASA, SAS, or AAS.
2. Prove two right triangles congruent using HL or HA.
3. Show two angles or two segments congruent by proving that they are corresponding parts of congruent triangles.
4. If two sides of a triangle are congruent, then the *angles* opposite them are congruent.
5. If two angles of a triangle are congruent, then the *sides* opposite them are congruent.
6. Every triangle has three medians, three altitudes, and three perpendicular bisectors.
7. In an isosceles triangle, the altitude to the base bisects the base and bisects the vertex angle.
8. If a point is equidistant from the endpoints of a segment, then it is on the perpendicular bisector of the segment.
9. If a point is equidistant from the sides of an angle, then it is on the angle bisector.

CHAPTER REVIEW

4-1

$\triangle ABC \cong \triangle RST$ **Complete each statement.**

1. $\angle B \cong$ ___
2. $\overline{AB} \cong$ ___
3. $\angle SRT \cong$ ___
4. $TS =$ ___
5. $AC =$ ___
6. $\triangle BCA =$ ___

4-2

Write a congruence between each pair of triangles and state the postulate applied. If you cannot apply a postulate, write *no conclusion can be made.*

7.

8.

9.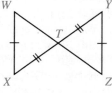

Write a conclusion that follows from the given information. State the congruence postulate or definition on which your conclusion is based.

10. $\overline{AB} \cong \overline{BC}$, $\overline{DA} \cong \overline{DC}$ 11. $\overline{DB}$ bisects $\angle ADC$, $\overline{DA} \cong \overline{DC}$

12. Write a two-column proof.

Given: E is the midpoint of $\overline{DC}$. $\angle 1 \cong \angle 2$

Prove: $\triangle DEB \cong \triangle CEB$

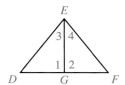

Write a two-column proof.

13. **Given:** G bisects $\overline{DF}$. $\angle 1 \cong \angle 2$

Prove: $\angle 3 \cong \angle 4$

14. **Given:** $\angle 1$ is a right angle. $\angle 3 \cong \angle 4$

Prove: $\overline{DE} \cong \overline{EF}$

Use the Common Segment Theorem and Common Angle Theorem to complete each statement.

15. If $\overline{QW} \cong \overline{ST}$, then $\overline{QS} \cong$ ___ .
16. If $\angle QAS \cong \angle TAW$, then $\angle QAW \cong$ ___ .

17. Write a two-column proof.

Given: $\angle QAS \cong \angle TAW$, $\overline{QA} \cong \overline{TA}$, $\overline{AW} \cong \overline{AS}$

Prove: $\angle 1 \cong \angle 2$

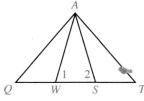

Write a conclusion that follows from the given information. State the theorem on which your conclusion is based.

18. $\angle 4 \cong \angle 7$ 19. $\overline{HJ} \cong \overline{JG}$
20. $\triangle HEG$ is isosceles with vertex H. F is the midpoint of $\overline{EG}$.

State the additional information you need for each method to prove $\triangle AFC \cong \triangle DEB$.

21. HA   22. AAS   23. HL

24. Write a two-column proof.

Given: $\angle 1 \cong \angle 2$, $\overline{AB} \cong \overline{BC}$

Prove: $\triangle AEC \cong \triangle CDA$

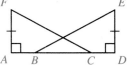

Indicate whether the following statements are true or false.

25. If $\overline{BC} \cong \overline{CD}$ and $\overline{CE} \perp \overline{BD}$, then $\angle 1 \cong \angle 2$.
26. If $\overline{BA} \cong \overline{AD}$, then $\overline{AC}$ is the perpendicular bisector of $\overline{BD}$.
27. If $\overline{AE}$ is an altitude for $\triangle DAB$, then $\overline{BE} \cong \overline{ED}$.
28. In $\triangle ABD$, if $\overline{AB} \cong \overline{AD}$ and $\overline{AE}$ is the median to $\overline{BD}$, then $\angle 3 \cong \angle 4$.

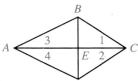

$\triangle ABE \cong \triangle CDF$ **Complete each statement.**

1. $\overline{AB} \cong$ ___   **2.** $\angle BAE$ ___   **3.** ___ $\cong \triangle FDC$

Write a congruence between each triangle and state the postulate applied.

4.   **5.**   **6.**

Write a conclusion that follows from the given information. State the congruence postulate on which your conclusion is based.

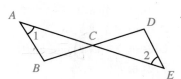

7. $\overline{AC} \cong \overline{CE}$, $\overline{BC} \cong \overline{CD}$

8. $\angle 1 \cong \angle 2$, $\overline{AC} \cong \overline{CE}$

Determine whether each statement is true or false.

9. If $\triangle ABD \cong \triangle CBD$, then $\overline{AD} \cong \overline{CD}$.

10. If $\overline{AB} \cong \overline{BC}$, then $\angle 5 \cong \angle 6$.

11. If $\triangle DEA \cong \triangle DEC$, then $\angle 1 \cong \angle 6$.

12. If $\overline{BD} \perp \overline{AC}$ and $AB = BC$, then $AD = CD$.

13. If $\angle 5 \cong \angle 6$ and $\overline{AB} \cong \overline{BC}$, then $\triangle DAC$ is isosceles.

14. If $\overline{DB}$ bisects $\angle CDA$, then $EA = EC$.

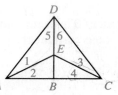

Use the Common Segment Theorem or the Common Angle Theorem to complete each statement.

15. If $\overline{AB} \cong \overline{CD}$, then $AC = $ ___ .

16. If $\angle AEB \cong \angle DEC$, then $\angle AEC \cong$ ___ .

$\overline{AC} \cong \overline{BC}$ **Solve for x.**

17.   **18.**

State the additional information you need to prove $\triangle ABC \cong \triangle DBC$ by the given method.

19. HL   **20.** AAS

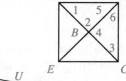

Write a two-column proof.

21. Given: $\overline{AD} \cong \overline{CD}$
         $\angle 5 \cong \angle 6$

   Prove: $\triangle DAB \cong \triangle DCB$

22. Given: B is the midpoint of $\overline{AC}$.
         $\overline{DB} \perp \overline{AC}$

   Prove: $\angle 5 \cong \angle 6$

23. Given: $\angle TUR \cong \angle TSV$
         $\overline{UW} \cong \overline{SW}$

   Prove: $\triangle UVW \cong \triangle SRW$

24. Given: $\triangle UVW \cong \triangle SRW$

   Prove: $\triangle TVS \cong \triangle TRU$

DISCRETE MATH

Graphs

There are several ways of representing data in problems. Mathematicians commonly use *graphs*. A graph is a set of points or *vertices* which are connected by lines or *edges*. In the graph representing airline routes, the vertices C, B, A, D, L represent Chicago, Boston, Atlanta, Dallas, Los Angeles. The edges tell whether the airline has nonstop flights connecting the cities.

Example 1

Is there a route from Boston to Dallas?

Solution

Yes; fly from Boston to Atlanta and then from Atlanta to Dallas.

Due to their sizes and harbor regulations, some ships cannot visit certain cities. Suppose that the Delta can enter the ports of Charleston, Los Angeles, and Miami. The Voyager can enter Los Angeles and Portland. The Tidewater can enter Long Beach and Seattle. The Odyssey can visit Portland and Long Beach. The edges of the graph show which ships can visit which ports.

Example 2

Can cargo be moved by these ships from Charleston to Portland?

Solution

Yes; the cargo can be moved from Charleston to Los Angeles by the Delta and then shipped to Portland by the Voyager.

Exercises

1. Use the airline graph to find all the possible routes from Boston to Dallas which do not visit any city more than once.
2. Use the cargo graph to determine whether cargo can be moved by these ships from Seattle to Miami.

5

Using Congruent Triangles and Parallel Lines

Circuits in a computer chip form a parallelogram. If one angle of the parallelogram is five times as large as another, find the measures of the angles of the parallelogram.

OBJECTIVE: *Apply the definition of a parallelogram and theorems about properties of parallelograms.*

5-1 Properties of Parallelograms

 EXPLORE Use ruled paper and a ruler to draw four different quadrilaterals in which both pairs of opposite sides are parallel. Use a ruler and protractor to measure the sides and angles of each quadrilateral. Make generalizations about properties you find to be true for all four quadrilaterals.

In Chapter 3 you learned that a quadrilateral is a polygon with four sides. In this chapter you will apply theorems you have learned about parallel lines and congruent triangles in your study of special quadrilaterals.

▨ DEFINITION

A **parallelogram** ($\square$) is a quadrilateral with two pairs of parallel sides.

In $\square ABCD$, $\overline{AB}$ and $\overline{CD}$ are opposite sides and so are $\overline{AD}$ and $\overline{BC}$. Sides $\overline{AB}$ and $\overline{BC}$ are adjacent sides. $\angle A$ and $\angle C$ are opposite angles and so are $\angle B$ and $\angle D$. $\angle A$ and $\angle B$ are consecutive angles since they have a common side.

$\overline{AD} \parallel \overline{BC}$
$\overline{AB} \parallel \overline{CD}$

The theorems and corollaries that follow state properties about parallelograms that you may have discovered while completing the Explore.

◆ THEOREM 5.1

Opposite sides of a parallelogram are congruent.

Given: *ABCD* is a parallelogram.
Prove: $\overline{AB} \cong \overline{CD}$, $\overline{AD} \cong \overline{BC}$

Proof Draw $\overline{BD}$. $\angle 1$ and $\angle 2$ are congruent alternate interior angles as are $\angle 3$ and $\angle 4$, since $\overline{AD} \parallel \overline{BC}$ and $\overline{AB} \parallel \overline{CD}$. Since $\overline{BD} \cong \overline{BD}$, $\triangle ABD \cong \triangle CDB$ by the ASA Postulate. So, $\overline{AB} \cong \overline{CD}$ and $\overline{AD} \cong \overline{BC}$ because corresponding parts of congruent triangles are congruent.

▶ COROLLARY 5.1a

Two parallel lines are equidistant at all points.

You will be asked to prove Corollary 5.1a in Exercise 28.

Example 1

Find the lengths of $\overline{AB}$ and $\overline{DC}$ in $\square ABCD$.

Solution

$3x - 10 = 2x + 1$ *Opposite sides of a $\square$ have equal measure.*

$\qquad x = 11$

$2(11) + 1 = 23$ *Replace x with 11 in 2x + 1.*

$AB = DC = 23$

Try This

Find the lengths of $\overline{AD}$ and $\overline{BC}$ if $AD = 2y + 22$ and $BC = 4y - 10$.

◆ THEOREM 5.2

Opposite angles of a parallelogram are congruent.

The following corollary can be proved using Theorem 5.2.

▶ COROLLARY 5.2a

Consecutive angles of a parallelogram are supplementary.

Convincing arguments to support Theorem 5.2 and Corollary 5.2a are asked for in Discussion Exercises 16–17.

Example 2

Find the measures of the four angles of $\square RSTU$ if the measure of $\angle U$ is twice the measure of $\angle R$.

Solution

$x + 2x = 180$ *Consecutive angles of a $\square$ are supplementary.*

$\qquad 3x = 180$

$\qquad x = 60$

$m\angle R = m\angle T = 60 \quad m\angle U = m\angle S = 120$

Try This

Find the measures of the four angles of $\square RSTU$ if the measure of $\angle S$ is ten less than four times the measure of $\angle T$.

◆ **THEOREM 5.3** theorem

The diagonals of a parallelogram bisect each other.

Given: *MNOP* is a parallelogram.
Prove: $\overline{MO}$ and $\overline{PN}$ bisect each other.

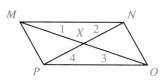

Plan Prove $\angle 1 \cong \angle 3$ and $\angle 2 \cong \angle 4$, since $\overline{MN} \parallel \overline{PO}$. Prove $\triangle MNX \cong \triangle OPX$ by ASA. Then $\overline{MX} \cong \overline{XO}$ and $\overline{NX} \cong \overline{PX}$ by corresponding parts of congruent triangles.

Summary of Properties of Parallelograms

1. Opposite sides are parallel.
2. Opposite sides are congruent.
3. Opposite angles are congruent.
4. Consecutive angles are supplementary.
5. The diagonals bisect each other.

Class Exercises   class excercises

Short Answer

ABCD **is a parallelogram.**

1. Name two pairs of congruent sides.
2. Name two pairs of congruent angles.
3. Name pairs of congruent segments that are not sides.
4. Name two pairs of supplementary angles.
5. If $m\angle CDB = 30$, find $m\angle ABD$.
6. If $m\angle ADC = 100$, find $m\angle ABC$ and $m\angle BAD$.

Sample Exercises

State the definition or theorem that justifies each conclusion.

7. $\overline{AB} \cong \overline{CD}$ 8. $AO = OC$
9. $\overline{AD} \parallel \overline{BC}$ 10. $\angle DAB$ and $\angle ADC$ are supplementary.

ABCD **is a parallelogram. Complete each statement.**

11. If $AB = 3x$, $CD = x + 10$, $AB =$ ___ $AB = CD$
12. If $AD = 3x + 15$, $BC = 21$, $AD =$ ___
13. If $AD = \frac{x}{2}$, $BC = 2x - 12$, $BC =$ ___
14. If $m\angle BAD = 100$, $m\angle DCE =$ ___
15. If $m\angle ADC = 135$, $m\angle ABD = 80$, $m\angle DBC =$ ___

Discussion

16. Explain how Theorem 5.1 can be used to prove Theorem 5.2.
17. Explain how Theorem 5.2 can be used to prove Corollary 5.2a.

Exercises

A

ABCD is a parallelogram. State the theorem that justifies each conclusion.

1. $\angle DAB \cong \angle DCB$ 2. $\overline{BE} \cong \overline{ED}$
3. $\overline{AD} \cong \overline{BC}$ 4. $\overline{DC} \cong \overline{AB}$

Complete each statement.

5. If $AD = 20$, $BC = $ ___ .   6. If $m \angle ADC = 115$, $m \angle ABC$ ___ .
7. If $DB = 22$, $DE = $ ___ .   8. If $AE = 18$, $AC = $ ___ .
9. If $m \angle DAB = 75$, $m \angle ADC = $ ___ .
10. If $m \angle 2 = 30$, $m \angle 3 = $ ___ .
11. If $BD = 10$ and $AE = 8$, $AC = $ ___ .
12. If $m \angle ABC = 2(m \angle BCD)$, $m \angle ADC = $ ___ .
13. If $m \angle ADC = 130$, $m \angle 1 = 35$, $m \angle 2 = $ ___ .

Find the measure of each angle in $\square$ MNST.

14. $m \angle TMN$ 15. $m \angle TSN$
16. $m \angle MSN$ 17. $m \angle SPN$

Complete each statement about $\square$ KLMN.

18. If $KN = 3x - 5$, $LM = x + 9$, $KN = $ ___ .
19. If $KL = \frac{x}{2}$, $MN = 2x - 9$, $KL = $ ___ .
20. If $KL = 8$, $MN = \frac{x^2}{2}$, $x = $ ___ .
21. If $m \angle K = 4x + 11$, $m \angle L = 6x - 1$, $m \angle K = $ ___ .
22. If $m \angle K = 31$, $m \angle M = 2x^2 - 1$, $x = $ ___ .
23. If $m \angle L = x - 40$, $m \angle N = \frac{3x}{4}$, $m \angle L = $ ___ .

B

24. If $\overleftrightarrow{AC} \parallel \overleftrightarrow{XY}$ and the altitude, $\overline{BD}$, of $\triangle BXY$ is 8, what are the lengths of the altitudes of $\triangle AXY$ and $\triangle CXY$ from vertices A and C respectively?

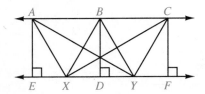

25. Part of the structural support system for a bridge is shown. $\overline{AB} \parallel \overline{CD}$, $\overline{DF} \parallel \overline{CB}$, and $\overline{AD} \parallel \overline{EC}$. Find $m \angle CGF$.

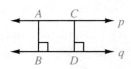

26. Given: $\square ABCD$ with $AB = x + 5$ and $CD = 2x - 7$ Find the length of $\overline{AB}$.

27. Given: $\square ABCD$ with $AB = 2x$, $CD = 3y + 4$, $BC = x + 7$, and $AD = 2y$ Find the lengths of the sides of the parallelogram.

28. Use the figure to the right to prove Corollary 5.1a.
   Given: $p \parallel q$, $\overline{AB} \perp q$, $\overline{CD} \perp q$
   Prove: $\overline{AB} \cong \overline{CD}$

29. Given: $\square ABCD$, $\square AECF$
Prove: $\triangle CDF \cong \triangle ABE$

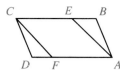

30. Given: $\square ABCD$, $\overline{FG}$ bisects $\overline{DB}$.
Prove: $\overline{DB}$ bisects $\overline{FG}$.

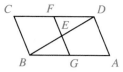

31. Given: $\square ABCD$, A, F, E, and C are collinear. $AF = CE$
Prove: $\overline{DE} \parallel \overline{BF}$

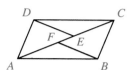

32. Given: $\square ABCD$, $AE = CF$
Prove: $CE = AF$

Assume the figure to the right is a regular 12-gon that has been divided into parallelograms and that $m \angle ALK = 150$. Use the definition of a regular polygon and the theorems from this section for each exercise.

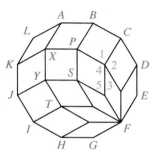

33. Find $m \angle BPX$.   **34.** Find $m \angle 1$.
35. Find $m \angle 2$.   **36.** Find $m \angle 3$.
37. Find $m \angle 4$.   **38.** Find $m \angle 5$.

C

39. Given: $\square ABCD$, $\overline{DE} \cong \overline{FB}$
Prove: X bisects $\overline{EF}$.

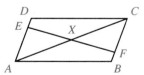

40. Given: $EFGD$ is a $\square$. $\overline{ED} \perp \overline{BE}$, $\overline{BF} \cong \overline{CD}$
Prove: $\triangle ABC$ is isosceles.

41. Prove: If from any point on the base of an isosceles triangle lines are drawn parallel to the congruent sides of the triangle, a parallelogram is formed whose perimeter is equal to the sum of the lengths of the congruent sides.

Critical Thinking

42. Use a ruler to draw several parallelograms. Use a protractor to bisect a pair of consecutive angles in each parallelogram. What generalization can you make about the angle bisectors? Write a paragraph proof to justify your generalization.

43. Write a statement similar to Corollary 5.1a but involving three dimensions. Give a convincing argument that your statement is true.

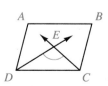

Mixed Review

Use the given information to state which triangles are congruent. Give the postulate or theorem that justifies your answer.

1. $\overline{BD} \perp \overline{AC}$, $\overline{AD} \cong \overline{DC}$
2. $\overline{AB} \cong \overline{BC}$, $\overline{BD}$ bisects $\overline{AC}$.
3. $\overline{AB} \cong \overline{BC}$, $\overline{BD} \perp \overline{AC}$
4. $\angle A \cong \angle C$, $\angle ABD \cong \angle CBD$

Use the given information to state which lines are parallel. Give the postulate or theorem that justifies your answer.

5. $\angle 4 \cong \angle 5$
6. $\angle 3 \cong \angle 10$
7. $\angle 2 \cong \angle 6$
8. $\angle 7 \cong \angle 15$
9. $\angle 1 \cong \angle 8$
10. $\angle 10 \cong \angle 14$
11. $m\angle 4 + m\angle 6 = 180$
12. $m\angle 8 + m\angle 15 = 180$

Study Skills

Working Backward to Check a Proof

While checking a proof you have just completed, it is helpful to start at the conclusion and work backward, as demonstrated with Questions 1–4 with the proof below.

Given: $\angle 1 \cong \angle 2$
Prove: $a \parallel b$

Proof	Statements	Reasons
Question 4	1. $\angle 1 \cong \angle 2$	1. Given
Question 3	2. $\angle 2 \cong \angle 3$	2. Vertical $\angle$s are $\cong$.
Question 2	3. $\angle 1 \cong \angle 3$	3. Congruence of $\angle$s is transitive.
Question 1	4. $a \parallel b$	4. If two lines are cut by a transversal and corr. $\angle$s are $\cong$, the lines are $\parallel$.

Question 1: How can I prove the lines parallel? (Postulate 14, Theorem 3.5, Theorem 3.6, or Theorem 3.7)

Question 2: Which method did I use? (Postulate 14)

Question 3: How do I know that $\angle 1 \cong \angle 3$? (Statements 1–2 and Theorem 1.1)

Question 4: Why is each of those statements true? (Statement 1 is given; statement 2 is justified by the Vertical Angle Theorem.)

In addition to being a good method for checking a proof, working backward is also a helpful problem-solving strategy if you are having difficulty completing a proof.

5-2 Proving Quadrilaterals Are Parallelograms

The theorems in the last section can be given in conditional form as in the following general statement.

If ABCD is a parallelogram, then ABCD has . . . (a given property).

This lesson deals with the converses of those theorems, stating ways of proving that some quadrilaterals are parallelograms, as in the following conditional form.

If . . . (a given property) is true, *then ABCD is a parallelogram.*

One way to prove that a quadrilateral is a parallelogram is to show that both pairs of opposite sides are parallel and then use the definition of a parallelogram. The following theorems state other ways.

Why will the car of this amusement park ride always be parallel to the top frame?

◆ **THEOREM 5.4**

If both pairs of opposite sides of a quadrilateral are congruent, then the quadrilateral is a parallelogram.

Given: $\overline{AB} \cong \overline{CD}$, $\overline{AD} \cong \overline{BC}$
Prove: *ABCD* is a parallelogram.

Proof Draw $\overline{BD}$ so $\triangle ABD \cong \triangle CDB$ by the SSS Postulate. $\angle 1 \cong \angle 2$ and $\angle 3 \cong \angle 4$ by corresponding parts of congruent triangles are congruent. Then $\overline{AB} \parallel \overline{CD}$ and $\overline{AD} \parallel \overline{BC}$ since the alternate interior angles are congruent. Hence, *ABCD* is a parallelogram by definition.

◆ **THEOREM 5.5**

If one pair of opposite sides of a quadrilateral are both parallel and congruent, then it is a parallelogram.

Given: $EF = GH$, $\overline{EF} \parallel \overline{GH}$
Prove: *EFGH* is a parallelogram.

Proof Draw $\overline{HF}$. Since $\overline{EF} \parallel \overline{GH}$, $\angle 1 \cong \angle 2$. Since $\overline{HF} \cong \overline{HF}$, $\triangle HGF \cong \triangle FEH$ by the SAS Postulate. $\overline{HE} \cong \overline{FG}$ by corresponding parts of congruent triangles are congruent. Therefore, *EFGH* is a parallelogram since both pairs of opposite sides are congruent.

The following two theorems give methods of proving that a quadrilateral is a parallelogram by using the angles of the quadrilateral.

◆ THEOREM 5.6

If both pairs of opposite angles of a quadrilateral are congruent, then the quadrilateral is a parallelogram.

◆ THEOREM 5.7

If the consecutive angles of a quadrilateral are supplementary, then the quadrilateral is a parallelogram.

You will be asked to prove Theorems 5.6 and 5.7 in Exercises 33–34.

Example

For what values of x and y will $ABCD$ be a parallelogram?

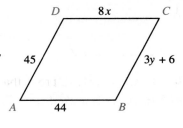

Solution

$8x = 44$ — *If opposite sides of a quadrilateral are congruent,*
$x = 5\frac{1}{2}$ — *then the quadrilateral is a parallelogram.*
$3y + 6 = 45$
$3y = 39$
$y = 13$

Try This

If $m\angle A = 80$, $m\angle B = 6y + 4$, $m\angle C = 5x$, and $m\angle D = 100$, for what values of x and y will $ABCD$ be a parallelogram?

The following method of proving that a quadrilateral is a parallelogram involves the diagonals of a quadrilateral.

◆ THEOREM 5.8

If the diagonals of a quadrilateral bisect each other, then the quadrilateral is a parallelogram.

Given: $\overline{VS}$ and $\overline{RT}$ bisect each other.
Prove: $RSTV$ is a parallelogram.

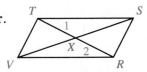

Plan   Prove $\triangle TXS = \triangle RXV$ by the SAS postulate. Conclude $\overline{TS} \cong \overline{RV}$ and $\angle 1 \cong \angle 2$ since they are corresponding parts of congruent triangles. Since $\angle 1 \cong \angle 2$, prove $\overline{TS} \parallel \overline{VR}$. Use Theorem 5.5 to conclude $TSRV$ is a parallelogram.

The methods of proving that a quadrilateral is a parallelogram are summarized below.

Methods of Proving a Quadrilateral a Parallelogram
1. Prove that both pairs of opposite sides are parallel.
2. Prove that both pairs of opposite sides are congruent.
3. Prove that one pair of opposite sides is both congruent and parallel.
4. Prove that both pairs of opposite angles are congruent.
5. Prove that the consecutive angles are supplementary.
6. Prove that the diagonals bisect each other.

Class Exercises

Short Answer

State whether or not the figure is a parallelogram. If it is, state a theorem or definition that justifies your conclusion.

1.

2.

3.

4. Of the six ways to prove that a quadrilateral is a parallelogram summarized in the lesson, which one is not a theorem? What is it?

Sample Exercises

Find the value of x for which each quadrilateral is a parallelogram.

5.

6.

7.

Draw a rectangular coordinate system, plot each point, and find the lengths of AB, BC, CD, and AD. Use Theorem 5.4 to decide whether $ABCD$ is a parallelogram.

8. $A(0, 0)$, $B(0, 3)$, $C(5, 3)$, $D(5, 0)$ 　　**9.** $A(0, 0)$, $B(3, 4)$, $C(9, 4)$, $D(6, 0)$
10. $A(0, 0)$, $B(-4, 0)$, $C(-7, 4)$, $D(-3, 4)$ 　　**11.** $A(3, -2)$, $B(8, -2)$, $C(8, -4)$, $D(3, -4)$

Discussion

Draw a figure, if needed, to support your argument.

12. Is it possible for a quadrilateral to have two congruent opposite sides and two parallel sides but not be a parallelogram? Explain.
13. Is it possible for a polygon to have two sides that are both congruent and parallel but not be a parallelogram? Explain.

Exercises

A

State whether or not you can conclude that the figure is a parallelogram, based on the given information. If it is, state the theorem or definition that justifies your conclusion.

1. $RU = ST, RS = TU$
2. $\overline{RS} \parallel \overline{TU}, \overline{RU} \parallel \overline{ST}$
3. $\overline{RU} \parallel \overline{ST}, \overline{RS} \cong \overline{TU}$
4. $\overline{RS} \parallel \overline{TU}, \overline{RS} \cong \overline{TU}$
5. $RX = \frac{1}{2}RT, XU = \frac{1}{2}SU$
6. $RX = XU, SX = XT$
7. $RU = UT = TS = SR$
8. $m\angle SRU = m\angle UTS, m\angle RST = m\angle RUT$

Determine the values of x and y so that the figure is a parallelogram.

9.

10.

11.

12.

13.

14.

Draw a rectangular coordinate system, plot each point, and find the lengths of $\overline{AB}$, $\overline{BC}$, $\overline{CD}$, and $\overline{DA}$. Use Theorem 5.4 to decide whether $ABCD$ is a parallelogram.

15. $A(0, 0), B(5, 0), C(5, 4), D(0, 4)$
16. $A(0, 0), B(5, 0), C(7, 2), D(2, -2)$
17. $A(0, 0), B(-4, 0), C(-6, 3), D(-1, 3)$
18. $A(0, 7), B(3, 7), C(5, 1), D(2, 1)$
19. $A(1, 0), B(0, 1), C(-2, 0), D(0, 2)$
20. $A(0, 1), B(1, 0), C(4, 3), D(3, 4)$

21. **Given:** $\triangle ABC \cong \triangle CDA$
    Prove: $ABCD$ is a $\square$.

B

22. The ironing board shown on the right is supported by legs that are equal in length. The legs also bisect each other at the point where they cross. Explain why the ironing board will always be parallel to the floor, regardless of the height to which it happens to be adjusted.

23. Consider the children's swing set shown to to right. The hangers $\overline{AD}$ and $\overline{BC}$ are the same length and the distances between the hangers, $\overline{AB}$ and $\overline{DC}$, are equal. Explain why the seat $\overline{DC}$ will always be parallel to the bar $\overline{AB}$ at the top of the swing.

24. A carpenter wants to construct parallel lines on a board. This can be done by using a carpenter square twice. Each time the tool is placed at the same angles with the board and equal units are marked off. Explain why this method assures that $\overline{AB}$ will be parallel to $\overline{CD}$.

25. A parking lot is to be marked for slant parking. A string is stretched from A to B with marks made every 9 ft at $X_1, X_2, \ldots, X_6$. A second string is stretched parallel to $\overline{AB}$ from C to D, with marks located every 9 ft at $Y_1, Y_2, \ldots, Y_6$. Explain why all the painted lines will be parallel.

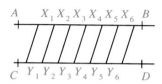

Draw a quadrilateral $ABCD$ and determine the values of x and y for which $ABCD$ is a parallelogram.

26. $AB = 2x + 4$, $CD = 4x - 20$, $AD = 2y$, $BC = y + 5$

27. $m\angle A = 2x - 60$, $m\angle D = x - 5$, $AB = 4y + 6$, $CD = 6y - 10$

28. $AB = 6x + 30$, $BC = 2x - 5$, $CD = 2y - 10$, $AD = y - 35$

Determine the coordinates of D for which $ABCD$ is a parallelogram.

29. $A(0, 0)$, $B(1, 4)$, $C(6, 5)$, $D(x, y)$

30. $A(0, 2)$, $B(2, 0)$, $C(-2, -4)$, $D(x, y)$

31. Given: $ABCD$ is a $\square$.
　　　　$BCEF$ is a $\square$.

Prove: $ADEF$ is a $\square$.

32. Given: $ABCD$ is a $\square$.
　　　　E is the midpoint of $\overline{AD}$.
　　　　F is the midpoint of $\overline{BC}$.

Prove: AFCE is a $\square$.

33. Prove Theorem 5.6.

Given: $\angle A \cong \angle C$
　　　　$\angle B \cong \angle D$

Prove: $ABCD$ is a $\square$.

34. Prove Theorem 5.7.

Given: $\angle 1$ and $\angle 2$ are supplementary.
　　　　$\angle 2$ and $\angle 3$ are supplementary.

Prove: $ABCD$ is a $\square$.

35. Given: $ABCD$ is a $\square$.
　　　　$AE = CF$

Prove: $BFDE$ is a $\square$.

36. Polygon *ABCDE* shown to the right is an equilateral pentagon. The perimeter of *ABCDE* is 20. If $\overline{BD} \parallel \overline{AE}$ and $\overline{CE} \parallel \overline{BA}$, find the perimeter of *ABFE*.

37. If *ABCDEF* is a regular hexagon, prove that *BCEF* is parallelogram.
38. Draw $\triangle ABC$ with median $\overline{AM}$. Extend $\overline{AM}$ so that $\overline{AM} \cong \overline{MD}$. Prove that *ABDC* is a parallelogram.

Critical Thinking

39. Suppose a parallelogram is defined in the following way:
A parallelogram is a quadrilateral with opposite sides congruent.
Use this definition to prove the following statement:
If a quadrilateral has both pairs of opposite sides parallel, then it is a parallelogram.
40. If the definition of a parallelogram that is given in Exercise 39 is accepted, would the statement you proved using that definition in the same exercise be classified as a definition, postulate, or theorem?

Algebra Review

Factor.

1. $x^2 - 4x - 45$ 2. $y^2 + y - 42$ 3. $a^2 + 2a - 15$
4. $a^2 - 7ab + 10b^2$ 5. $x^2 + 5xy - 24y^2$ 6. $b^2 + 9b - 90$

Simplify.

7. $\sqrt{x^2}$ 8. $\sqrt{4y^2}$ 9. $\sqrt{(-5)^2}$ 10. $\sqrt{(-3a)^2}$

Computer Activity

Properties of Special Parallelograms

Use computer software to construct special parallelograms like the ones shown below.

a.   **b.**   **c.**

All right angles   All sides congruent   All right angles
All sides congruent

1. Measure the diagonals in each figure. What do you notice? State a generalization about your observation in each figure.
2. Measure the angles formed by the diagonals in each figure. What do you notice? State a generalization about your observation in each figure.
3. Measure the four segments formed by the diagonals in each figure. What do you notice? State a generalization about your observations.

OBJECTIVE: *Apply definitions and theorems about rectangles, rhombuses, and squares.*

5-3 Rectangles, Rhombuses, and Squares

EXPLORE

Take the linkage that forms a parallelogram (Position 1) and place it in the position of a rectangle (Position 2). What additional properties seem to be true about the rectangle?

Position 1   Position 2

In the last two lessons, you learned about the quadrilateral called a parallelogram. Three special parallelograms, *rectangles*, *rhombuses*, and *squares*, are defined below. They are classified by the special relationships of their angles and sides.

DEFINITION

A **rectangle** is a quadrilateral with four right angles.

DEFINITION

A **rhombus** is a quadrilateral with four congruent sides.

DEFINITION

A **square** is a quadrilateral with four right angles and four congruent sides.

Based on the definitions of rectangle, rhombus, and square, the following statements are true.

Every rectangle is a parallelogram.
Every rhombus is a parallelogram.
Every square is a parallelogram, a rectangle, and a rhombus.

This means that all of the properties of parallelograms—such as opposite sides that are congruent, opposite angles that are congruent, consecutive angles that are supplementary, and diagonals that bisect each other—are also properties of rectangles, rhombuses, and squares.

5-3 Rectangles, Rhombuses, and Squares   **213**

◆ **THEOREM 5.9**

The diagonals of a rectangle are congruent.

Given: $ABCD$ is a rectangle.
Prove: $\overline{AC} \cong \overline{BD}$

Proof Statements

1. $ABCD$ is a rectangle.
2. $\overline{AD} \cong \overline{BC}$
3. $\overline{AB} \cong \overline{AB}$
4. $\angle DAB$ and $\angle CBA$ are rt. $\angle$s.
5. $\angle DAB \cong \angle CBA$
6. $\triangle DAB \cong \triangle CBA$
7. $\overline{AC} \cong \overline{BD}$

Reasons

1. Given
2. Opposite sides of a $\square$ are $\cong$.
3. Congruence of segments is reflexive.
4. Definition of a rectangle
5. All right angles are congruent.
6. SAS Congruence Postulate
7. Corres. parts of $\cong$ $\triangle$s are $\cong$.

◆ **THEOREM 5.10**

The diagonals of a rhombus are perpendicular.

Given: $ABCD$ is a rhombus.
Prove: $\overline{AC} \perp \overline{BD}$

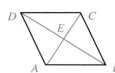

Plan Use the definition of a rhombus and the fact that the diagonals of a parallelogram bisect each other to show that $\triangle AED \cong \triangle CED$. Conclude that $\overline{AC} \perp \overline{BD}$ since $\angle AED$ and $\angle CED$ are supplementary and congruent.

◆ **THEOREM 5.11**

Each diagonal of a rhombus bisects a pair of opposite angles.

You will be asked to prove Theorem 5.11 in Exercise 43.

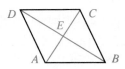

Example 1

If $ABCD$ is a rhombus and $m\angle BDC = 35$, find $m\angle ACD$.

   Solution

   $m\angle ACD = 90 - 35 = 55$ *The acute angles of a right triangle are complementary.*

Try This

If $ABCD$ is a rhombus and $m\angle CAD = 68$, find $m\angle CBD$.

A summary of the properties of rectangles, rhombuses, and squares is given below.

Properties of Rectangles

A rectangle has all properties of a parallelogram as well as having
all angles, right angles and
congruent diagonals.

Properties of Rhombuses

A rhombus has all properties of a parallelogram as well as having
all sides congruent,
perpendicular diagonals, and
diagonals that bisect opposite angles.

Properties of Squares

A square has all properties of a parallelogram, a rectangle, and a rhombus.

While it is the case that every rectangle, rhombus, and square is a
parallelogram, it is not the case that every parallelogram is a rectangle,
rhombus, or square. The following two theorems state conditions for which
a parallelogram is either a rectangle or a rhombus.

 THEOREM 5.12

If a parallelogram has a right angle, then it is a rectangle.

 THEOREM 5.13

If a parallelogram has two adjacent sides congruent, then it is a rhombus.

You will be asked to prove Theorems 5.12 and 5.13 in Exercises 44–45.
From Theorems 5.12 and 5.13, it follows that a parallelogram with a right
angle and two adjacent sides congruent is a square.

Example 2

$ABCD$ is a parallelogram. If $AD = 2x + 10$ and $CD = 4x - 20$, for what
value of x will $ABCD$ be a rhombus?

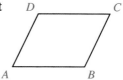

Solution

$$4x - 20 = 2x + 10 \quad \textit{If a parallelogram has two adjacent sides}$$
$$2x = 30 \quad \textit{congruent, then it is a rhombus.}$$
$$x = 15$$

Try This

If $AB = 5 - 2x$ and $BC = 3x + 80$, for what value of x will $ABCD$ be a rhombus?

Class Exercises

Short Answer

Determine whether each statement is true or false.

1. The diagonals of a rectangle are perpendicular.
2. The diagonals of a rectangle bisect the opposite angles.
3. If *ABCD* is a square, then *ABCD* is a rhombus.
4. If *ABCD* is a parallelogram, then *ABCD* is a rhombus.
5. If *ABCD* is a rectangle, then *ABCD* is a rhombus.

Sample Exercises

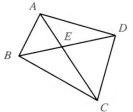

6. If *ABCD* is a rectangle, name all pairs of congruent segments.
7. If *ABCD* is a rhombus, name all pairs of congruent segments.
8. If *ABCD* is a rhombus, name all the angles that are right angles.
9. If *ABCD* is a square, name all the angles that are congruent to $\angle CAB$.
10. If *ABCD* is a square, what is $m\angle AED$?
11. If *ABCD* is a rectangle and $BE = 6$, what is length AC?
12. If *ABCD* is a rhombus and $m\angle BAC = 35$, what is $m\angle BCD$?

Discussion

Name two properties that are true for each of the following.

13. all squares but not all rectangles
14. all rhombuses but not all parallelograms
15. all rectangles but not all parallelograms

Exercises

A

1. State three properties that are true about the diagonals of a square.
2. *ABCD* is a parallelogram. If $m\angle A = 90$, must *ABCD* be a rectangle, a rhombus, or a square?
3. *ABCD* is a parallelogram. If $\overline{AB} \cong \overline{BC}$, must *ABCD* be a rectangle, a rhombus, or a square?
4. *ABCD* is a parallelogram. If $m\angle A = 90$ and $\overline{AB} \cong \overline{BC}$, must *ABCD* be a rectangle, a rhombus, or a square?

Assume that *GWAD* is a rectangle. Find the indicated measure.

5. $GX = 6$ Find *XW*.
6. $XA = 9$ Find *DW*.
7. $m\angle GXD = 40$ Find $m\angle GDX$.
8. $m\angle WAG = 65$ Find $m\angle GXW$.

Assume that *GWAD* is a rhombus. Find the indicated measure.

9. $m\angle GDX = 47$ Find $m\angle XGD$.
10. $m\angle GWA = 86$ Find $m\angle GWD$.

Assume that *GWAD* is a square. Find the indicated measure.

11. Find $m\angle XDA$.
12. $GX = 3x + 6$, $XW = 4x - 10$ Find *GA*.

216   *Chapter 5   Using Congruent Triangles and Parallel Lines*

Determine whether each statement is true or false.

13. Every rectangle is a parallelogram.
14. Every rhombus is a rectangle.
15. Every parallelogram is a rectangle.
16. Every property of a parallelogram is also a property of a square.
17. Every property of a square is also a property of a rectangle.
18. The diagonals of a square bisect each other.

19. A picture frame is constructed of four pieces of wood that are glued together so that $AB = BC = CD = DA$. The ends of each piece of wood are cut at a 45° angle. Explain why the completed frame will form a square.

20. **Given:** $ABCD$ is a ▱. $m\angle 3 = m\angle 4$
    Prove: $ABCD$ is a rhombus.
21. **Given:** $ABCD$ is a ▱. $m\angle 3 + m\angle 4 = 90$
    Prove: $ABCD$ is a rectangle.

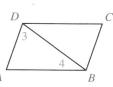

B

Draw a parallelogram for the given conditions or write *not possible*.

22. all angles congruent
23. diagonals that bisect each other
24. no right angles, diagonals congruent
25. congruent and perpendicular diagonals
26. all sides congruent with diagonals that are not perpendicular

27. $ABCD$ is a parallelogram. $AB = 2x + 4$, $DC = 3x - 11$, $AD = x + 19$ Show that $ABCD$ is a rhombus.
28. $ABCD$ is a rhombus. $m\angle DEC = 4x + 10$, $m\angle DAB = 3x + 4$ Find $m\angle ABC$.

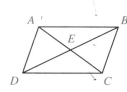

$ABCD$ is a rectangle with the given coordinates. Find the lengths of the diagonals and verify that they are congruent.

29. $A(2, 5)$, $B(2, 1)$, $C(7, 1)$, $D(7, 5)$ 30. $A(-2, 3)$, $B(-4, 3)$, $C(-4, -2)$, $D(-2, -2)$

Determine the coordinates of D for which $ABCD$ is a rectangle.

31. $A(-2, 5)$, $B(1, 5)$, $C(1, -2)$, $D(x, y)$ 32. $A(-3, -2)$, $B(4, -2)$, $C(4, -3)$, $D(x, y)$

Determine the coordinates of D for which $ABCD$ is a square.

33. $A(3, -1)$, $B(-1, 3)$, $C(-5, -1)$, $D(x, y)$ 34. $A(3, 0)$, $B(1, 2)$, $C(3, 4)$, $D(x, y)$

35. A contractor is measuring for the foundation of a building that is to be 85 ft by 40 ft. Stakes and string are placed as shown. The outside corners of the building will be at the points where the strings cross. To make sure that $WXYZ$ is a rectangle, the contractor constructs $WX = ZY$ and $WZ = XY$. Prove that if $WY = ZX$, $WXYZ$ will be a rectangle.

36. If $WY = 93$ ft and $XZ = 94$ ft, is $WXYZ$ a rectangle? If not, which way should stakes E and F be moved to make $WXYZ$ a rectangle?

37. Given: *WXYZ* is a rhombus.
  R is the midpoint of $\overline{WV}$.
  T is the midpoint of $\overline{VY}$.
  S is any point on $\overline{ZV}$.
Prove: $\triangle SRT$ is isosceles.

38. Given: *ABCD* is a rectangle.
  ACBE is a parallelogram.
Prove: $\triangle DBE$ is isosceles.

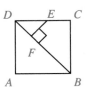

C

39. Given: *ABCD* is a square.
  $FB = CB$
  $\overline{EF} \perp \overline{BD}$
Prove: $DF = FE = EC$

What quadrilateral is determined by a cross section of the cube containing the given vertices? Write a paragraph proof to justify your choice.

40. vertices *A*, *B*, *G*, and *H*   **41.** vertices *A*, *C*, *G*, and *E*

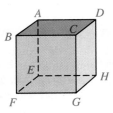

42. Draw and label a rectangle *ABCD* and equilateral triangles *ABX* and *BCY* entirely outside the rectangle. Prove that $\triangle XDY$ is isosceles.

43. Prove Theorem 5.11   **44.** Prove Theorem 5.12   **45.** Prove Theorem 5.13

Critical Thinking

Answer the questions in Exercises 46–50 for each figure (a–f).

46. Must the figure be a quadrilateral?
47. Must the figure be a parallelogram?
48. Must the figure be a rectangle?
49. Must the figure be a rhombus?
50. Must the figure be a square?

Algebra Review

Solve.

  1. $x^2 - 9 = 6$ **2.** $25a^2 = 16$ **3.** $y^2 = \frac{4}{9}$

Math Contest Problem

The figure shown is a cube. $\overline{BC}$ and $\overline{BH}$ are diagonals of faces of the cube. Find the measure of $\angle CBH$.

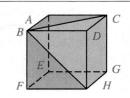

COMPARING APPROACHES IN GEOMETRY

Synthetic and Coordinate Geometry

In the last lesson, we proved that the diagonals of a rectangle are congruent. The approach that was used, a synthetic approach, does not rely on algebra. Recall from its introduction on page 194 that a coordinate approach relies on a coordinate system. Compare the two approaches for a 5 by 7 rectangle.

Synthetic Approach

Coordinate Approach

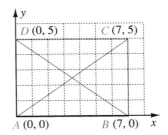

Plan Prove $\triangle ABC \cong \triangle DCB$ and use corresponding parts of congruent triangles are congruent to conclude that $AC = BD$.

Plan Name the coordinates of the vertices and use the distance formula to conclude that $AC = BD$.

In the coordinate approach use the distance formula to find AC and BD. Observe that these lengths are equal.

$$AC = \sqrt{(7-0)^2 + (5-0)^2} = \sqrt{49 + 25}$$
$$BD = \sqrt{(0-7)^2 + (5-0)^2} = \sqrt{49 + 25}$$

Exercises

When using a coordinate proof it is important to name the figure correctly after it has been positioned on a coordinate system.

1. Suppose that a coordinate system is selected as shown for a 4 by 9 rectangle. What are the x and y coordinates of vertex C?

2. Suppose that a coordinate system is placed on an 8 by 11 rectangle in the same manner as is shown for the 4 by 9 rectangle in the figure to the right. What are the coordinates of all four vertices A, B, C, and D?

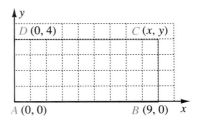

3. A general rectangle is represented by using variable coordinates rather than numerical coordinates. For example, suppose that a coordinate system is placed on a rectangle that is a units long and b units wide as is shown in the figure. What are the coordinates of all four vertices A, B, C, and D in terms of a and b?

4. Use the distance formula to find the distances AC and BD in the figure for Exercise 3. What theorem does your work prove?

5-4 Trapezoids

Take several styrofoam cubes and cut three cross sections.

a. a cross section containing vertices *A*, *B*, *C*, and *D*
b. a cross section containing vertices *A* and *B* and
    midpoints *F* and *G*
c. a cross section containing vertices *A*, *B*, and *E*

Sketch the figure formed by each of the three cross sections.

Another classification of quadrilateral is the trapezoid.

▪ DEFINITION

A **trapezoid** is a quadrilateral with exactly one pair of parallel sides.

The parallel sides of a trapezoid are called **bases.** The nonparallel sides are
called **legs.** The pairs of angles formed by a base and the legs are called
base angles. In trapezoid *ABCD*, ∠*ADC* and ∠*BCD* are base angles and
∠*DAB* and ∠*CBA* are base angles. An **isosceles trapezoid** is a trapezoid
with congruent nonparallel sides.

◆ THEOREM 5.14

Each pair of base angles of an isosceles trapezoid are congruent.

Given: Isosceles trapezoid *ABCD*, $\overline{AB} \cong \overline{DC}$
Prove: ∠*B* ≅ ∠*C*, ∠*BAD* ≅ ∠*CDA*

Plan Draw $\overline{AE}$ and $\overline{DF}$ perpendicular to $\overline{BC}$. Prove △*ABE* ≅ △*DCF* by the
Hypotenuse-Leg Theorem. It follows that ∠*B* ≅ ∠*C*. Prove that
∠*BAD* ≅ ∠*CDA* since supplements of congruent angles are congruent.

Example 1

Given isosceles trapezoid *EFGH* with *m*∠*EFG* = 55, find *m*∠*FGH*.

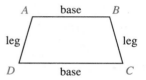

Solution

m∠*FGH* = 55   *Base angles of an isosceles trapezoid have the same measure.*

Try This

If *m*∠*E* is twice *m*∠*F*, find the measures of the four angles of trapezoid *EFGH*.

◆ THEOREM 5.15

The diagonals of an isosceles trapezoid are congruent.

The **median of a trapezoid** is the segment joining the midpoints of the legs. $\overline{PQ}$ is the median of trapezoid $WXYZ$. The median and the bases of a trapezoid are related in a special way.

◆ THEOREM 5.16

The median of a trapezoid is parallel to the bases and has a length equal to half the sum of the lengths of the bases. That is, $PQ = \frac{1}{2}(XY + WZ)$.

You will be asked to prove Theorems 5.15 and 5.16 in Exercises 20 and 23.

Example 2

$ABCD$ is a trapezoid. $AB = 13$, $CD = 20$
Find the length EF of the median.

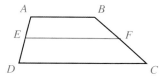

Solution

$EF = \frac{1}{2}(AB + CD)$ *Theorem 5.17*
$EF = \frac{1}{2}(13 + 20)$
$EF = 16.5$

Try This

Find the length of $\overline{CD}$ if $AB = 15$ and $EF = 21$.

Class Exercises

Short Answer

$ABCD$ is an isosceles trapezoid with median $\overline{XY}$.

1. Name the bases of trapezoid $ABCD$.   **2.** Name the legs of trapezoid $ABCD$.
3. Name two pairs of congruent angles.   **4.** Name two pairs of congruent segments.

Sample Exercises

Use isosceles trapezoid $ABCD$ with median $\overline{XY}$ to complete each statement.

5. $AX = 4$, $CD = $ ___   **6.** $m\angle ABC = 110$, $m\angle BAD = $ ___
7. $m\angle BAD = 65$, $m\angle CDA = $ ___   **8.** $AD = 22$, $BC = 10$, $XY = $ ___
9. $BC = 20$, $XY = 32$, $AD = $ ___   **10.** $m\angle DCB = 105$, $m\angle DAB = $ ___

Discussion

Draw a trapezoid satisfying the following conditions. If not possible, explain.

11. two right angles   **12.** three right angles   **13.** three congruent sides
14. four congruent sides   **15.** congruent legs   **16.** congruent bases

Exercises

A

ABCD is a trapezoid with median $\overline{EF}$.

1. $AB = 24$, $CD = 43$ Find EF.
2. $AB = 2\frac{1}{2}$, $CD = 4\frac{1}{2}$ Find EF.
3. $AB = 9.7$, $CD = 24.6$ Find EF.
4. $CD = 32$, $EF = 23$ Find AB.
5. $AB = x + 1$, $EF = 5x$, $CD = 35$ Find AB.
6. $AB = x + 11$, $EF = x - 20$, $CD = 9$ Find EF.

Indicate whether each statement is always, sometimes, or never true.

7. If the diagonals of a trapezoid are congruent, then the trapezoid is isosceles.
8. If a quadrilateral has more than two right angles, then it is not a trapezoid.
9. The opposite angles of an isosceles trapezoid are supplementary.
10. The diagonals of an isosceles trapezoid bisect each other.
11. If the consecutive angles of a quadrilateral are supplementary, it is a trapezoid.
12. A dam is constructed with a trapezoidal cross section that measures 38 ft across the top and 10 ft across the base. What is the average width of the dam?

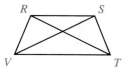

B

13. The length of one base of a trapezoid is four times the length of the other base. If the length of the median is 40, find the length of each base.
14. If the length of the shorter base of a trapezoid is doubled but the length of the median is not changed, how does the length of the longer base change?
15. If one base of a trapezoid is increased 12 cm and the other base remains the same length, by how much is the length of the median increased?
16. Suppose the lengths of the bases of a trapezoid are represented by x and y. If the length of the median is doubled, write an expression that represents the length of the median of the larger trapezoid.

17. **Given:** $ABCD$ is a trapezoid.
    $\overline{AB} \| \overline{CD}$
    $\overline{AP}$ bisects $\angle A$.

    Prove: $\triangle APD$ is isosceles.

18. **Given:** $ABCD$ is a trapezoid.
    $\overline{AB} \| \overline{CD}$, $\overline{AD} \cong \overline{BC}$
    $\overline{AC}$ and $\overline{BD}$ intersect at E.

    Prove: $\triangle CDE$ is isosceles.

19. **Given:** $\triangle ABC$ is isosceles with base $\overline{BC}$.
    $\angle AED \cong \angle B$

    Prove: $BEDC$ is an isosceles trapezoid.

20. Prove Theorem 5.15
    Given: $RSTV$ is a trapezoid with $\overline{RV} \cong \overline{ST}$.
    Prove: $\overline{RT} \cong \overline{VS}$

Graph the given coordinates and determine if *ABCD* is an isosceles trapezoid.

21. $A(3, 3)$, $B(5, 3)$, $C(8, 1)$, $D(1, 1)$ **22.** $A(-4, 1)$, $B(-4, 6)$, $C(2, 4)$, $D(2, 3)$

C

23. Prove Theorem 5.16.

Given: In trapezoid *ABCD*, *M* is a midpoint of leg $\overline{AB}$.
   N is a midpoint of leg $\overline{DC}$.

Prove: a. $\overline{MN} \| \overline{AD}$, $\overline{MN} \| \overline{BC}$ **b.** $MN = \frac{1}{2}(AD + BC)$
(HINT: Draw a line through *N* parallel to $\overline{AB}$.
Prove that *AMNF* is a parallelogram.)

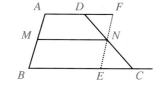

24. Prove Theorem 5.14 by constructing a line through *D* parallel to $\overline{AB}$.
(NOTE: This is an alternate method of proving Theorem 5.15.)

Given: *ABCD* is an isosceles trapezoid with $\overline{AB} \cong \overline{CD}$.

Prove: $\angle B \cong \angle C$

25. Prove that if the base angles of a trapezoid are congruent, then the trapezoid is isosceles.

26. Prove that if *ABCDEF* is a regular hexagon, then *ABEF* is an isosceles trapezoid.

Critical Thinking

27. *P* is a point above the plane *M* determined by the equilateral triangle *ABC*. If a plane parallel to *M* cuts the segments $\overline{PA}$, $\overline{PB}$, and $\overline{PC}$, how many trapezoids are formed? Where must *P* be located in order for the trapezoids to be isosceles?

Mixed Review

1. Find the sum of the measures of the angles of a regular hexagon.
2. Find the measure of each angle of a regular hexagon.
3. Find the measure of an exterior angle of a regular hexagon.

Quiz

ABCD **is a parallelogram.**

1. If $AD = 6$, find BC.   2. If $m\angle 1 = 32$, find $m\angle 2$.
3. If $m\angle ABC = 4x - 6$ and $m\angle BCD = 2x + 54$, find $m\angle CDA$.

Determine whether each statement is true or false.

4. If $\overline{AB} \| \overline{CD}$ and $\overline{AD} \cong \overline{BC}$, then *ABCD* is a parallelogram.
5. If *ABCD* is a square, then $\overline{AC} \cong \overline{BD}$.
6. If *ABCD* is a rhombus and $m\angle ABC = 90$, then *ABCD* is also a square.

ABCD **is an isosceles trapezoid with median** $\overline{EF}$.

7. If $AB = 6$ and $DC = 18$, find EF.
8. If $AB = 2x$, $EF = 3x + 2$, and $DC = 24$, find EF.

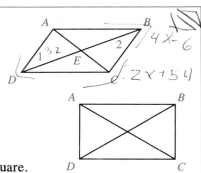

TRIANGLES AND INEQUALITIES

OBJECTIVE: *Apply theorems about segments that join midpoints of sides of triangles and quadrilaterals.*

5-5 The Midsegment Theorem

Draw right triangles ABC_1, ABC_2, ABC_3 with $BC_1 = 1$ in., $BC_2 = 2$ in., and $BC_3 = 3$ in. Let D, E_1, E_2, and E_3 be the midpoints of their respective segments. Compare the lengths of $\overline{DE_1}$, $\overline{DE_2}$, and $\overline{DE_3}$ with the lengths of $\overline{BC_1}$, $\overline{BC_2}$, and BC_3. State a conclusion about your findings.

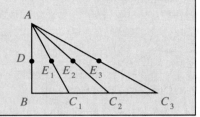

Consider the trapezoids $NEAT$ and medians $\overline{XY}$ below. Note that in each figure the base $\overline{NT}$ gets smaller until finally the base is the point N (or T).

By Theorem 5.16, $\overline{XY} \parallel \overline{EA}$ and $XY = \frac{1}{2}(EA + NT)$. However, in the last case $\overline{NT}$ has length zero so $XY = \frac{1}{2}EA$. This suggests the next theorem. You will be asked to prove Theorem 5.17 in Exercise 31.

◆ **THEOREM 5.17**   Midsegment Theorem

The segment that joins the midpoints of two sides of a triangle is parallel to the third side and has a length equal to half the length of the third side.

Example 1

D and E are midpoints of the sides of $\triangle ABC$. If $DE = x + 5$ and $AB = 4x - 16$, find the length of $\overline{AB}$.

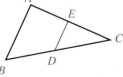

Solution

$$\frac{1}{2}(AB) = DE \qquad \textit{Midsegment Theorem}$$
$$\frac{1}{2}(4x - 16) = x + 5$$
$$2x - 8 = x + 5$$
$$x = 13$$
$$AB = 4(13) - 16 = 36$$

Try This

If D and E are midpoints and $AB + DE = 36$, find the lengths of $\overline{AB}$ and $\overline{DE}$.

Example 2

P, Q, and R are midpoints of the sides of $\triangle MNO$. Find the perimeter of $\triangle PQR$ if $MN = 12$, $NO = 16$, and $OM = 14$.

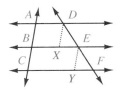

Solution

$PQ = \frac{1}{2}(ON) = \frac{1}{2}(16) = 8$ *Midsegment Theorem*

$QR = \frac{1}{2}(OM) = \frac{1}{2}(14) = 7$

$RP = \frac{1}{2}(MN) = \frac{1}{2}(12) = 6$

Perimeter $\triangle PQR = PQ + QR + RP$
$$= 8 + 7 + 6$$
$$= 21 \quad \text{The perimeter of } \triangle PQR \text{ is } 21.$$

Try This

P, Q, and R are midpoints of the sides of $\triangle MNO$. If $MP = 3$, $QN = 5$ and $NR = 7$, find the perimeter of $\triangle PQR$.

The following theorem can be proved by using the Midsegment Theorem.

◆ THEOREM 5.18

The quadrilateral formed by joining the midpoints of the consecutive sides of another quadrilateral is a parallelogram.

Given: M, N, P, and Q are midpoints of the sides of quadrilateral $ABCD$.
Prove: $MNPQ$ is a parallelogram.

Plan   Draw $\overline{BD}$, forming triangles ABD and CBD. Prove that $MN = \frac{1}{2}BD$ and $\overline{MN} \parallel \overline{BD}$ by the Midsegment Theorem. Prove that $QP = \frac{1}{2}BD$ and $\overline{QP} \parallel \overline{BD}$ by the Midsegment Theorem. Conclude that $MN = QP$ and $\overline{MN} \parallel \overline{QP}$, and hence $MNPQ$ is a parallelogram.

◆ THEOREM 5.19

If three or more parallel lines cut off congruent segments on one transversal, then they will cut off congruent segments on every transversal.

You will be asked to prove Theorem 5.19 in Exercise 35.

▶ COROLLARY 5.19a

A line that contains the midpoint of one side of a triangle and is parallel to another side bisects the third side.

Class Exercises

Short Answer

D and *E* are midpoints of the sides of △*ABC*. Complete each statement.

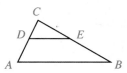

1. If $AB = 8$, then $DE = $ ___ . 2. If $AC = 9$, then $AD = $ ___ .
3. If $BE = 5$, then $BC = $ ___ . 4. If $AB = 15$, then $DE = $ ___ .

Sample Exercises

Find the value of *x* or state *cannot determine*.

5.

6.

7.
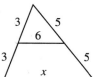

Determine whether Theorem 5.18 allows you to conclude that ABCD is a ▱.

8.

9.

Discussion

10. Determine values for *x* and *y* so that only one of the segments *a*, *b*, and *c* can be determined. Explain your choices.

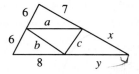

Exercises

A

D and *E* are midpoints of the sides of △*ABC*. Complete each statement.

1. $DE = 10$, $BC = $ ___ 2. $BC = 12$, $DE = $ ___ 3. $DE = 8$, $BC = $ ___
4. $DE = 2x$, $BC = x + 10$, $DE = $ ___
5. $DE = x - 4$, $BC = x + 12$, $BC = $ ___
6. $DE = x + 2$, $BC = \frac{1}{2}x + 19$, $DE = $ ___

Find the value of *x*.

7.

8.

9.

Determine whether Theorem 5.18 allows you to conclude that ABCD is a parallelogram.

10.

11.

12.

D, E, and F are midpoints of the sides of △ABC. Find the perimeter of △DEF.

13. $AB = 20$, $BC = 36$, $AC = 24$
14. $AB = 15$, $BC = 25$, $AC = 17$
15. $AD = 3$, $BF = 6$, $EC = 4$

Exactly one of the values a, b, or c can be determined. Find it.

16.

17.

18.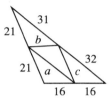

19. If the dowel is cut where the diagram indicates, will it be divided into five equal lengths? Why or why not?

B

Determine the coordinates of the midpoint X of side $\overline{AB}$ and the midpoint Y of side $\overline{AC}$ of △ABC. Find XY and BC and verify that $XY = \frac{1}{2}BC$.

20. $A(0, 0)$, $B(8, 0)$, $C(0, 4)$ **21.** $A(0, 5)$, $B(0, 1)$, $C(-8, 5)$
22. $A(-2, -1)$, $B(2, -1)$, $C(-2, -7)$

23. Explain how the distance across the pond (XY) can be found by using △ZXY where Z is any point other than X or Y.
(HINT: Consider the midpoints of $\overline{XZ}$ and $\overline{ZY}$.)

M and N are midpoints of sides $\overline{AC}$ and $\overline{BC}$.

24. If $MN = x^2 + x - 8$ and $AB = x^2 + x + 14$, find MN and AB.
25. If $AM = x + 5$, $MC = 2y + 6$, $MN = 2x - 5$, and $AB = y + 8$, find MN and AB.

D is the midpoint of $\overline{AB}$ and $\overline{DE} \parallel \overline{BC}$.

26. Find AC if $AE = 2x^2 - 4x$ and $EC = 2x + 20$.
27. Find EC if $AE = 3x + 4$ and $AC = x + 20$.

28. Given: F is the midpoint of $\overline{AC}$.
  D is the midpoint of $\overline{BC}$.
  E is the midpoint of $\overline{AB}$.
  Prove: $AEDF$ is a parallelogram.

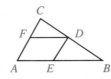

29. Given: $\overline{AB} \cong \overline{AC}$
  E is the midpoint of $\overline{AB}$.
  D is the midpoint of $\overline{CB}$.
  Prove: $\triangle BDE$ is isosceles.

30. Given: $ABCDEF$ is a hexagon.
  $\overline{AB} \| \overline{DE}, \ \overline{AB} \cong \overline{DE}$
  $W, X, Y,$ and Z are midpoints.
  Prove: $WXYZ$ is a parallelogram.
  (HINT: Draw $\overline{AE}$ and $\overline{BD}$.)

31. Prove Theorem 5.17.
  Given: D and E are midpoints.
  Prove: a. $\overline{DE} \| \overline{BC}$ **b.** $DE = \frac{1}{2}BC$
  (HINT: Extend $\overline{DE}$ until $\overline{DE} \cong \overline{EF}$ as shown in the figure to the right.
  Prove $ADCF$ is a parallelogram. Then prove $DBCF$ is a parallelogram.)

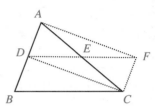

c

32. If the length of each diagonal of a given rectangle is ten, find the perimeter of the quadrilateral formed by joining the midpoints of the sides of the rectangle.

33. $ABCD$ is a trapezoid with diagonals $\overline{AC}$ and $\overline{BD}$ and median $\overline{MN}$. Find FG if $MN = 27$, $AB = 7x$ and $CD = 4x^2 - x$.

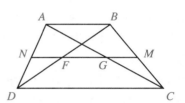

34. Given a regular pentagon $ABCDE$ in which M is the midpoint of side $\overline{AB}$ and N is the midpoint of side $\overline{BC}$, prove $\overline{MN} \| \overline{ED}$.

35. Prove Theorem 5.19.
  Given: $\overleftrightarrow{AD} \| \overleftrightarrow{BE} \| \overleftrightarrow{CF}, \overline{AB} \cong \overline{BC}$
  Prove: $\overline{DE} \cong \overline{EF}$
  (HINT: Draw $\overline{DX}$ and $\overline{EY}$ parallel to $\overline{AC}$.)

Critical Thinking

36. Draw several isosceles trapezoids and connect the midpoints of the sides. In each case, what kind of quadrilateral is formed? Write a theorem that describes your discovery. Then write a paragraph proof.

37. A student studied the figure to the right and concluded that $ABCD$ is not a parallelogram, giving Theorem 5.19 as the reason for this conclusion. Do you agree? Why or why not?

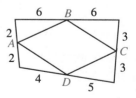

Algebra Review

Solve.

1. $x + 7 > 9$ **2.** $y + 12 < 6$ **3.** $2a + 3 - a > 5$
4. $b - 10 > -16$ **5.** $6x > 72$ **6.** $9a < 81$

Enrichment
Tessellations

Regular hexagon

M. C. Escher, a Dutch graphic artist, created more than 150 drawings using tessellations. A **tessellation** is an arrangement of polygonal shapes that cover a plane such that no polygons overlap and there are no gaps. A question of interest to mathematicians is, "Which shapes or combinations of shapes tessellate the plane?" It is easy to show that a square tessellates the plane by using tracing paper to repeatedly trace the square until the entire sheet of paper is covered. As shown to the right, a plane can also be tessellated by a regular hexagon.

Exercises

Determine which of the polygons shown tessellate the plane.

1.
   Parallelogram

2.
   Trapezoid

3.
   Kite

4.
   Any quadrilateral

5.
   Equilateral triangle

6.
   Nonconvex quadrilateral

7.
   Regular pentagon

8.
   Regular octagon

9. Cut out several copies each of an equilateral triangle, a square, a regular hexagon, and a regular octagon so that each side of each polygon has the same length. Find several combinations of two or more of these polygons that will tessellate the plane.

5-6 Indirect Proof

In some cases it is easier to use indirect reasoning rather than to use direct reasoning as you have been doing in the proofs you have written so far. Indirect reasoning involves assuming the opposite of what you want to conclude. You then reason logically until you reach a **contradiction** involving two conflicting statements.

Indirect reasoning is illustrated by what might happen in this cartoon—if B.C. cooperates! Suppose B.C. eats the berry but does not die. The following illustrates the use of indirect reasoning to conclude that the berry is not poison.

B.C. by permission of Johnny Hart and Field Enterprises, Inc.

> Suppose the berry is poison.
> If B.C. eats it, he will die.
> B.C. ate it but didn't die.
> Therefore, the berry is not poison!

In an **indirect proof** you use indirect reasoning to establish a statement or theorem. An important part of an indirect proof is assuming the negation of a statement. The **negation** of a statement is the opposite of the original statement. In·an indirect proof you first assume the negation of what you want to prove. Then you reason logically until you have shown that the assumption leads to a contradiction involving two conflicting statements.

Example 1

State the negation of each statement.

a. $m\angle 1 = m\angle 2$

b. $\overline{AB} \not\perp \overline{CD}$ (NOTE: $\not\perp$ means "is not perpendicular to.")

> **Solution**
> **a.** $m\angle 1 \neq m\angle 2$ **b.** $\overline{AB} \perp \overline{CD}$

Try This

State the negation of "$\overline{AB}$ intersects $\overline{CD}$."

Another part of an indirect proof is reaching a contradiction. The following pairs of statements each form a contradiction since they cannot both be true.

$\overline{XY}$ is longer than $\overline{MN}$. $\overline{MN}$ is longer than $\overline{XY}$.

$\angle A$ and $\angle B$ are right angles. $\angle A$ and $\angle B$ are not congruent angles.

Example 2

Determine which pairs of statements form a contradiction.

a. $\overline{AB} \parallel \overline{CD}$
$\overline{AB}$ and $\overline{CD}$ are perpendicular.

b. In $\triangle ABC$, $m\angle A = m\angle B$.
$\triangle ABC$ is scalene.

c. $ABCD$ is a rhombus.
$ABCD$ is a square.

Solution

Statements in **a** and **b** form a contradiction.

Try This

Which two of the following three statements form a contradiction?

a. $\triangle ABC$ is isosceles.   **b.** $\triangle ABC$ is equilateral.   **c.** ABC is a right triangle.

The steps for indirect proof are summarized below.

Steps for Using Indirect Proof

Step 1 Assume the negation of the *Prove* statement.

Step 2 Reason logically to show that the assumption leads to the contradiction of a known fact (theorem, definition, postulate, given information, etc.).

Step 3 Conclude that the assumption is false and that the *Prove* statement is true.

An indirect proof can be written in paragraph form, as in Examples 3 and 4.

Example 3

Given: $\angle 1$ and $\angle 2$ are not congruent.

Prove: $\angle 1$ and $\angle 2$ are not vertical angles.

Proof Assume that $\angle 1$ and $\angle 2$ are vertical angles. Then $\angle 1 \cong \angle 2$ by the Vertical Angle Theorem. This statement contradicts the given information which says that $\angle 1 \not\cong \angle 2$. Therefore, this assumption must be false. It follows that $\angle 1$ and $\angle 2$ are not vertical angles.

Example 4 presents an indirect proof for the statement: The base angles of an isosceles triangle must be acute.

Example 4

Given: $AB = AC$

Prove: $m\angle B < 90$

Proof Assume $m\angle B \geq 90$. Since $AB = AC$ then $m\angle B = m\angle C$ by the Isosceles Triangle Theorem. Therefore, $m\angle C \geq 90$. By addition, $m\angle B + m\angle C \geq 180$. This contradicts the fact that the sum of the measures of the angles of a triangle is 180. The assumption that $m\angle B = 90$ must be false. Therefore, $m\angle B < 90$.

Class Exercises

Short Answer

State the negation of each statement.

1. The sun is shining.
2. It will not rain.
3. $m \perp n$
4. The adjacent sides are not parallel.
5. $\overline{AB} \cong \overline{CD}$
6. $\angle A$ is not acute.
7. $\triangle ABC$ is an isosceles triangle.
8. $\triangle ABC$ is congruent to $\triangle DEF$.

Sample Exercises

Identify which two of the three statements, a, b, and c, form a contradiction.

9. **a.** $\triangle ABC$ is equilateral.
   b. $\triangle ABC$ is acute.
   c. $\triangle ABC$ is scalene.
10. **a.** $\angle A \cong \angle B$
    b. $\angle A$ and $\angle B$ are supplementary.
    c. $\angle A$ and $\angle B$ are complementary.
11. **a.** $\angle A$ and $\angle B$ are adjacent angles.
    b. $\angle A$ and $\angle B$ form a linear pair of angles.
    c. $\angle A$ and $\angle B$ are acute angles.
12. **a.** $\angle A$ and $\angle B$ are supplementary.
    b. $\angle A$ and $\angle B$ are both acute angles.
    c. $\angle A$ and $\angle B$ are vertical angles.
13. **a.** Lines p and q are not parallel.
    b. Lines p and q have no points in common.
    c. Lines p and q lie in the same plane and have no points in common.
14. **a.** $\angle A$ and $\angle B$ are not right angles.
    b. $\angle A$ and $\angle B$ are congruent angles.
    c. $m\angle A \neq m\angle B$

Discussion

Discuss how an indirect proof could be used to prove the following.

15. **Given:** $m\angle B \neq m\angle C$
    Prove: $AB \neq AC$
    (HINT: Begin by assuming the negation $AB = AC$.)
16. **Given:** $AB > AC$
    Prove: $\triangle ABC$ is not equiangular.

Exercises

A

Write the negation you would use to begin an indirect proof.

1. Prove: $\angle A$ is supplementary to $\angle B$.
2. Prove: $\angle A$ is not a right angle.
3. Prove: $\angle A$ and $\angle B$ are not vertical angles.
4. Prove: There is at most one line through P that is parallel to m.
5. Prove: ABC is not an equilateral triangle.

Indicate whether each pair of statements would enable you to arrive at a contradiction in an indirect proof.

6. Lines p and q are parallel.
   Lines p and q do not intersect.

7. $\angle A \cong \angle B$
   $m\angle A > m\angle B$

8. $m \perp n$
   $m \not\perp n$

9. $\angle A$ and $\angle B$ form a linear pair.
   $m\angle A < 90$, $m\angle B < 90$

10. $\angle A$ and $\angle B$ are congruent.
    $\angle A$ and $\angle B$ are supplementary.

11. $\angle A$ and $\angle B$ are obtuse angles.
    $\angle A$ and $\angle B$ are supplementary.

12. Arrange statements **a–f** in the correct order to write the indirect proof in paragraph form.

    Given: $\overline{AB} \perp \ell$

    Prove: Any other line $\overline{AC}$ is not perpendicular to ℓ.

    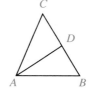

    a. $m\angle ABC = 90$
    b. Contradiction of Angle Sum Theorem for Triangles; therefore, $\overline{AC} \not\perp \ell$.
    c. $\overline{AB} \perp \ell$ **d.** $m\angle ABC + m\angle ACB = 180$
    e. Assume $\overline{AC} \perp \ell$.   **f.** $m\angle ACB = 90$

13. Complete the following indirect proof.

    Given: In $\triangle ABC$, $AC \neq AB$, D is the midpoint of $\overline{BC}$.

    Prove: $\overline{AD} \not\perp \overline{BC}$

    Proof Assume $\overline{AD} \perp \overline{BC}$. Then $\angle ADC \cong \angle ADB$. Since D is the midpoint of $\overline{BC}$, then $\overline{CD} \cong \overline{BD}$. By the Reflexive Property, $\overline{AD} \cong \overline{AD}$. Therefore, $\triangle ADC \cong \triangle ADB$.

    (HINT: Obtain a statement that contradicts a statement in the given information.)

Write an indirect proof in paragraph form.

14. **Given:** $\angle 4 \not\cong \angle 6$
    Prove: $a \not\parallel b$

15. **Given:** $a \not\parallel b$
    Prove: $\angle 3 \not\cong \angle 5$

16. **Given:** $\angle 1 \not\cong \angle 8$
    Prove: $\angle 4 \not\cong \angle 5$

17. **Given:** $\overline{AB} \cong \overline{AD}$, $\angle 1 \not\cong \angle 2$
    Prove: $\overline{BC} \not\cong \overline{CD}$

B

18. **Given:** $\overline{AB} \cong \overline{AD}$, $\overline{BC} \not\cong \overline{CD}$
    Prove: $\angle 1 \not\cong \angle 2$

19. **Given:** $\triangle ABD$ is scalene. $\overline{AC}$ is a median.
    Prove: $\overline{AC} \not\perp \overline{BD}$

20. **Given:** $\overline{AC}$ bisects $\angle BAD$. $\overline{AC} \not\perp \overline{BD}$
    Prove: $AB \neq AD$

21. Given: $\overline{MN} \perp \overline{NP}$
$\qquad \overline{QP} \perp \overline{NP}$
$\qquad \angle M \not\cong \angle Q$
Prove: $\overline{MN} \not\cong \overline{QP}$

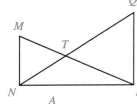

22. Given: $AB = AE$
$\qquad AC \neq AD$
Prove: $BC \neq DE$

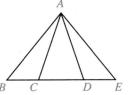

23. Given: $\overline{AC} \perp M$
$\qquad \angle B \not\cong \angle D$
Prove: $\angle BAC \not\cong \angle DAC$

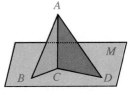

24. Given: $\triangle ABC$ is equilateral.
$\qquad \triangle DAC$ is equilateral.
$\qquad \triangle ABD$ is not equilateral.
Prove: $\triangle BCD$ is not equilateral.

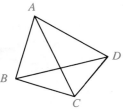

C

25. Write an indirect proof in paragraph form to prove the following statement. If a line is perpendicular to one side of an angle, it is not perpendicular to the other side of the angle.

26. Write an indirect proof in paragraph form to prove the following statement. Two lines perpendicular to the same plane do not intersect.

27. Write an indirect proof in paragraph form to prove the following statement. If point D is not in the same plane as $\triangle ABC$, then $\overline{BD}$ and $\overline{AC}$ are skew lines.

Critical Thinking

28. A store owner claimed that an expensive radio had been stolen from her store. She was convinced that either Anna, Brenda, Carlos, or Dee had stolen the radio. Each person made a statement but only one of the four statements was true.
Anna said, "I didn't take it."
Brenda said, "Anna is lying."
Carlos said, "Brenda is lying."
Dee said, "Brenda took it."
Who told the truth? Who took the radio? Use indirect reasoning and write a paragraph proof to justify your choice.

Mixed Review

Find the measure of the indicated angle.

1. If $m\angle 4 = 50$ and $m\angle 5 = 75$, find $m\angle 1$.
2. If $m\angle 6 = 135$ and $m\angle 2 = m\angle 5$, find $m\angle 2$.
3. If $m\angle 3 = 120$ and $m\angle 4$ is twice $m\angle 5$, find $m\angle 4$.
4. If $m\angle 1$ is 160 and $m\angle 5$ is three times $m\angle 4$, find $m\angle 5$.

Determine whether each statement is always, sometimes, or never true. Draw a figure to illustrate your answer.

5. Two adjacent angles form a linear pair.
6. Adjacent angles are congruent.
7. Vertical angles are complementary.
8. An angle and its complement are congruent.
9. Vertical angles are congruent.
10. Two acute angles are supplementary.

Career

Technical Illustrator

The professional artist who prepares drawings that show how machines, tools, and equipment operate is a technical illustrator. Working from blueprints, designs, mockups, and photoprints, he or she may draw an object from different points of view to show its function, its relationship to other equipment, or the assembly sequence of its parts.

One skill technical illustrators develop is drawing in perspective. Using congruent triangles, the artist produces a two-dimensional representation in which parallel lines appear to converge at some distant point. He or she may also draw from schematic, orthographic, or oblique-angle views. Color or shading with ink, crayon, airbrush, or overlays helps emphasize details or eliminate unwanted backgrounds.

The artist may include instructions, comments, or cartoons to help describe how the object works. A technical illustrator uses drafting or optical equipment, photo-offset techniques, and projections transparencies. His or her work appears in reference or technical manuals, brochures, and safety manuals and on posters. Related professions include engineering and production illustration.

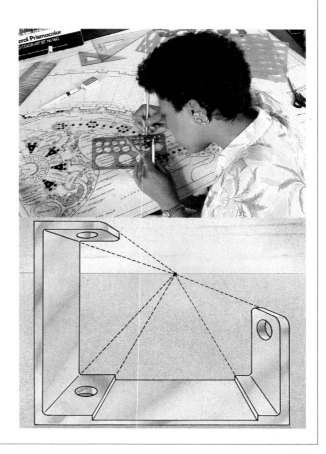

5-7 Inequalities in One Triangle

Many theorems concern equality of measures. This lesson deals with inequalities. The first theorem is related to the Exterior Angle Theorem.

◆ **THEOREM 5.20** Exterior Angle Inequality Theorem

The measure of an exterior angle of a triangle is greater than the measure of either remote interior angle.

Given: $\angle 1$ is an exterior angle of $\triangle ABC$.
Prove: $m\angle 1 > m\angle 2$, $m\angle 1 > m\angle 3$

Plan By the Exterior Angle Theorem for Triangles, $m\angle 1 = m\angle 2 + m\angle 3$. It follows that $m\angle 1 > m\angle 2$ and $m\angle 1 > m\angle 3$.

◆ **THEOREM 5.21**

If one side of a triangle is longer than a second side, then the measure of the angle opposite the longer side is greater than the measure of the angle opposite the shorter side.

Given: $BC > AB$
Prove: $m\angle A > m\angle C$

Proof Use the Ruler Postulate to select D on $\overline{AC}$ so $AB = BD$. Then $m\angle A = m\angle BDA$, since if two sides of a triangle are congruent, the angles opposite them are congruent. Therefore $m\angle ADB > m\angle C$ by the Exterior Angle Inequality Theorem. It follows that $m\angle A > m\angle C$ by substitution.

Example 1

Name the largest angle of $\triangle ABC$.

Solution

$\angle B$ Theorem 5.21

Try This

Name the smallest angle of $\triangle ABC$.

◆ THEOREM 5.22

If one angle of a triangle is larger than another angle, then the side opposite the larger angle is longer than the side opposite the smaller angle.

Given: $m \angle A > m \angle C$
Prove: $BC > AB$

Proof Assume $BC = AB$. It follows that $m \angle A = m \angle C$. This contradicts the given information. Assume $AB > BC$. By Theorem 5.22, $m \angle C > m \angle A$. This contradicts the given information. Therefore, $BC > AB$.

▶ COROLLARY 5.22a

The perpendicular segment from a point to a line is the shortest segment from the point to the line.

You will be asked to prove Corollary 5.22a in Exercise 33.

Example 2

Name the longest side of quadrilateral ABCD.

Solution

$\overline{AB}$ (or $\overline{AD}$)   *Theorem 5.22*

Try This

Name the shortest side of quadrilateral *ABCD*.

You will be asked to prove Theorem 5.23 in Exercise 41.

◆ THEOREM 5.23 Triangle Inequality Theorem

The sum of the lengths of any two sides of a triangle is greater than the length of the third side.

Example 3

Which numbers could represent the lengths of the sides of a triangle?

a. 3, 4, 6   **b.** 10, 11, 21   **c.** 2, 6, 9   **d.** 34, 35, 36

Solution

a and **d**   *Triangle Inequality Theorem*

Try This

Two sides of a triangle measure 5 and 13. Which could be the measure of the third side?

a. 16   **b.** 8   **c.** 9   **d.** 19

Class Exercises

Short Answer

Name the largest angle and the smallest angle for each figure.

1.

2.

3.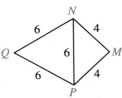

Name the longest side and the shortest side for each figure.

4.

5.

6.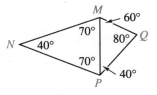

Sample Exercises

Decide which angle is the larger based on the Exterior Angle Inequality Theorem or state that it is not possible to determine which angle is larger.

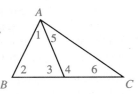

7. ∠3 and ∠6   8. ∠4 and ∠1   9. ∠3 and ∠1   10. ∠2 and ∠4

11. If the lengths of two sides of a triangle are 6 and 12, what are the possible whole numbers for the length of the third side?
12. If two sides of a parallelogram have lengths 7 and 11, then the lengths of the diagonals must be greater than __?__ and less than __?__.
13. In △ABC, m∠A = 30, m∠B = 50, and m∠C = 100. List the sides of the triangle from the shortest to the longest.
14. In △DEF, DE = 5, EF = 6, and DF = 8. List the angles of the triangle from the largest to the smallest.

Discussion

15. Which side of a right triangle must be the longest side? Explain.
16. Is the base of an isosceles triangle always the shortest side? Explain.

Exercises

A

List the sides of each figure from the shortest to the longest.

1.

2.

3.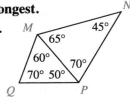

List the sides of △ABC from the shortest to the longest.

4. $m\angle A = 46$, $m\angle B = 30$ **5.** $m\angle C = 101$, $m\angle B = 70$

6. $m\angle A = 59$, $m\angle C = 61$ **7.** $m\angle B = 48$, $m\angle A = 47$

4.) $\overline{AC}, \overline{BC}, \overline{AB}$

List the angles of △ABC from the smallest to the largest.

8. $AB = 17$, $BC = 21$, $AC = 18$ **9.** $AB = 15$, $AC = 16$, $BC = 17$

10. List the sides of quadrilateral $ABCD$ from the shortest to the longest.

11. List all the segments in the figure from the shortest to the longest.

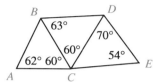

Which numbers could represent the lengths of the sides of a triangle?

12. 10, 20, 30 **13.** 10, 8, 6 **14.** 5, 14, 7

15. 4, 9, 15 **16.** 6, 6, 11 **17.** 1, 3, 5

18. If the sum of the lengths of two sides of a triangle is 15, what is the largest possible integral value for the third side?

19. If the base of an isosceles triangle is 10, what is the shortest possible integral value for each of the equal sides?

20. If the perimeter of a triangle is 8 and the lengths of the sides are integers, what is the length of the shortest side?

Use the Exterior Angle Inequality Theorem to determine which angle is larger or state *not possible*.

21. ∠1 and ∠6 **22.** ∠1 and ∠2

23. ∠2 and ∠4 **24.** ∠5 and ∠2

25. The three main work centers in the kitchen are the refrigerator, the sink, and the stove. You could picture them as the points of a triangle. It is recommended that the three sides of the kitchen triangle add up to more than 12 ft and less than 22 ft, with the shortest side of the triangle between the sink and the stove. Decide whether each kitchen triangle in the chart below is possible. Then state whether it follows the recommendation.

	a	b	c	d	e
stove/sink	5 ft	10 ft	6 ft	3 ft	3 ft
stove/refrigerator	4 ft	11 ft	8 ft	7 ft	8 ft
refrigerator/sink	8 ft	8 ft	7 ft	4 ft	4 ft

B

26. If the lengths of two sides of a triangle are 6 and p, where p is a whole number, give the possible whole numbers for the length of the third side.

27. If the longer side of a parallelogram has a length x, where x is a whole number, and the longer diagonal has a length of 10, give the possible whole numbers for the length of the shorter side of the parallelogram.

28. Given: $AB = BC$
Prove: $m \angle 1 > m \angle C$

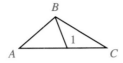

29. Given: E is in the interior of $\angle BAC$:
Prove: $m \angle 1 > m \angle 2$
(HINT: Compare $m \angle 1$ and $m \angle 2$ with $m \angle EDC$.)

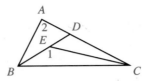

30. Given: quadrilateral $ABCD$
Prove: $AB + BC + CD + DA > 2(AC)$

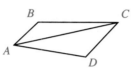

31. Given: quadrilateral $ABCD$
Prove: $AB + BC + CD > AD$

32. A railroad company is to build an engine house to service four cities located at the vertices $ABCD$ of a quadrilateral as shown here. Where should the engine house H be located so that the length, and hence the construction costs, of the roadbed $AH + BH + CH + DH$ is as small as possible?

33. Use the figure to the right to prove Corollary 5.22a.
Given: Line ℓ with P not on ℓ, $\overline{PQ} \perp \ell$
Prove: $\overline{PQ}$ is the shortest segment from P to ℓ.

34. Use the figure to the right to prove Theorem 2.9.
Only one perpendicular can be drawn from a point not on a line to a line.
Given: Line ℓ and point P not on ℓ
Prove: a. There is one line through P perpendicular to ℓ.
b. There is only one line through P perpendicular to ℓ.

35. Cities are located at A, B, C, and D as shown in the figure to the right. Railroad tracks are to be laid from H to each of the cities. What is the total length of track needed?
(HINT: The length of an altitude of an equilateral triangle is $\frac{\sqrt{3}}{2}$ times the length of a side.) Where should H be located so that the total length of the tracks is the least possible?

36. Suppose cities are located at points A, B, C, and D as shown on the coordinate grid. Where is a point H located if $AH + BH + CH + DH$ is a minimum? What is the value of this minimum? (Use the distance formula and a calculator.)

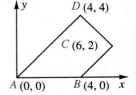

Determine the largest angle of $\triangle ABC$ for the given coordinates of A, B, and C.

37. $A(0, 0)$, $B(5, 0)$, $C(1, 5)$
38. $A(-1, 2)$, $B(-2, -1)$, $C(2, 0)$
39. $A(2, -5)$, $B(4, -1)$, $C(7, -4)$

40. Use the figure to the right to prove the statement.
The median $\overline{YM}$ from vertex Y of scalene $\triangle XYZ$ is longer
than the altitude $\overline{YN}$ from vertex Y.

Given: $\triangle XYZ$ is scalene. $\overline{YN}$ is an altitude. $\overline{YM}$ is a median.

Prove: $YM > YN$

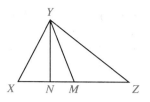

c

41. Use the figure to the right to prove Theorem 5.23.

Given: $\triangle ABC$

Prove: a. $AB + BC > AC$
      b. $BC + AC > AB$
      c. $AB + AC > BC$

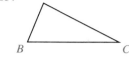

(HINT: Assume one of the sides is the longest. Two of the statements
are then easily established. To prove the third statement, drop a
perpendicular from the appropriate vertex to the opposite side.)

42. Given: P is in the interior of $\triangle ABC$.

Prove: $PB + PC < AB + AC$

43. Prove that the sum of the lengths of the three altitudes of $\triangle ABC$ is less
than the sum of the lengths of the sides of the triangle.

44. Prove that the sum of the lengths of the medians of $\triangle ABC$ is greater
than half the perimeter.

Critical Thinking

45. Suppose a triangle is made of 12 chain linkages. List the lengths of the
sides of possible triangles. Assume each link is one unit.

Algebra Review

Find all values of x.

1. $|x| = 7$ **2.** $|-x| = -7$ **3.** $|-x| = 7$
4. $x = |7|$ **5.** $2|x| = 7$ **6.** $x = |-7|$
7. $|x| + 1 = 7$ **8.** $|x| + |-1| = 7$ **9.** $x - |-1| = 7$
10. $-2|x| = -14$ **11.** $|2x + 1| = 14$ **12.** $|x - 1| - 1 = 7$

Translate to an equation and solve.

13. The product of two consecutive integers is
132. Find the integers

14. The product of two consecutive even integers
is 168. Find the integers.

15. The square of a number is six more than the
number. Find the number.

16. Twice the square of a number is 10 more
than the number. Find the number.

17. Twice the square of a number plus one is 73.
Find the number.

18. The square of a number minus twice the
number is 48. Find the number.

Geometric and Algebraic Inequalities

The Triangle Inequality Theorem, one of the most famous in geometry, has an important counterpart with the same name in algebra. There the theorem states that for any two real numbers a and b, $|a| + |b| > |a + b|$. The triangle inequality takes many other forms. With vectors, which were introduced in the Connections on page 116, the vector sum of two vectors (a, b) and (c, d) can be defined as the vector $(a + c, b + d)$. Then, as shown by the graph of these three vectors, we can see that the triangle inequality could be written as

$$\sqrt{a^2 + b^2} + \sqrt{c^2 + d^2} > \sqrt{(a + c)^2 + (b + d)^2}$$

Many other famous inequalities that occur in geometry have algebraic counterparts. Two of the most famous are the arithmetic mean and the geometric mean of numbers. Two numbers a and b have an arithmetic mean $\frac{(a + b)}{2}$ and a geometric mean $\sqrt{ab}$. A famous result provides an inequality relating these two means.

$$\frac{(a + b)}{2} > \sqrt{ab} \text{ for all nonnegative real numbers } a \text{ and } b$$

The arithmetic mean of two numbers is simply their common average. The geometric mean of two nonnegative real numbers a and b can be illustrated by the following process. Find a segment having lengths a and b. Put these segments end to end and draw a semicircle having the two segments as diameter. Construct a segment perpendicular to the two segments at their common endpoint and extend it until it intersects the circle. The length of this segment is the geometric mean of a and b, which is $\sqrt{ab}$.

You will study more about the geometric mean in Chapter 7.

Exercises

1. For what real numbers a and b is it the case that $|a| + |b| = |a + b|$?

2. Use the fact that the length of the vector (x, y) is $\sqrt{x^2 + y^2}$ and the geometric Triangle Inequality Theorem presented in this section to argue that $\sqrt{a^2 + b^2} + \sqrt{c^2 + d^2} > \sqrt{(a + c)^2 + (b + d)^2}$ for the vectors (a, b), (c, d), and their sum, $(a + c, b + d)$.

3. Under what conditions will the arithmetic mean, $\frac{(a + b)}{2}$, of two numbers a and b be equal to the numbers themselves?

4. Under what conditions will the inequality involving the arithmetic mean and geometric mean of two numbers a and b assume the equality $\frac{(a + b)}{2} = \sqrt{ab}$?

5. Give a convincing argument that, for all nonnegative values of a and b, other than those cited in the answer to Exercise 4, $\frac{(a + b)}{2} > \sqrt{ab}$.

5-8 Inequalities in Two Triangles

EXPLORE Use straws or other suitable objects to make three triangles with the following lengths (in inches): **a.** 3, 4, 2 **b.** 3, 4, 5 **c.** 3, 4, 6. In which triangle is the angle included between the sides of length 3 and 4 the smallest? the largest?

Write a generalization about your findings.

The theorems in this lesson involve two triangles in which two sides of one triangle are congruent to two sides of another triangle.

◆ **THEOREM 5.24** SAS Inequality Theorem

If two sides of one triangle are congruent to two sides of a second triangle and the included angle of the first triangle is larger than the included angle of the second triangle, then the third side of the first triangle is longer than the third side of the second triangle.

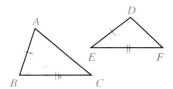

The above theorem says that if $AB = DE$ and $BC = EF$, then the relationship between the lengths of $\overline{AC}$ and $\overline{DF}$ depends on the measures of $\angle B$ and $\angle E$.

You will be asked to prove Theorem 5.24 in Exercise 28.

◆ **THEOREM 5.25** SSS Inequality Theorem

If two sides of one triangle are congruent to two sides of a second triangle, and the third side of the first triangle is longer than the third side of the second triangle, then the angle opposite the third side of the first triangle is larger than the angle opposite the third side of the second triangle.

Given: $AB = DE$, $BC = EF$, $AC > DF$
Prove: $m \angle B > m \angle E$

Plan Use an indirect proof. Assume $m \angle B \not> m \angle E$.
Case 1: Let $m \angle B = m \angle E$. Show $\triangle ABC \cong \triangle DEF$ by SAS and obtain the contradiction that $AC = DF$.
Case 2: Let $m \angle B < m \angle E$. Obtain the contradiction that $AC < DF$ by the SAS Triangle Inequality Theorem. Conclude that $m \angle B > m \angle E$.

Example 1

What conclusions can be drawn from the given information?

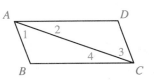

a. $AB = CD$, $m\angle 1 > m\angle 3$
b. $AB = CD$, $m\angle 1 = m\angle 3$
c. $AD = BC$, $AB > CD$

Solution

a. $BC > AD$ **b.** $\triangle ABC \cong \triangle CDA$ **c.** $m\angle 4 > m\angle 2$

Try This

What conclusions can be drawn if $AB = CD$ and $BC > AD$?

Class Exercises

Short Answer

Given $\triangle ABC$ and $\triangle DEF$, $AB = DE$ and $BC = EF$, complete each statement by using $>$, $<$, or $=$.

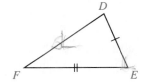

1. If $m\angle B > m\angle E$, then AC ___ DF.
2. If $DF < AC$, then $m\angle B$ ___ $m\angle E$.
3. If $AC = DF$, then $m\angle E$ ___ $m\angle B$.
4. If $m\angle E > m\angle B$, then DF ___ AC.
5. If $AC < DF$, then $m\angle E$ ___ $m\angle B$.

Sample Exercises

Complete each statement by using $>$, $<$, or $=$.

6.
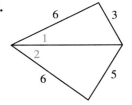

$m\angle 1$ ___ $m\angle 2$

7.

CD ___ BD

8.
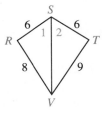

$m\angle 1$ ___ $m\angle 2$

Determine whether the statement is always, sometimes, or never true.

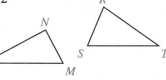

9. If $PN = RT$, $MN = RS$, and $m\angle N < m\angle R$, then $PM > ST$.
10. If $PM = ST$, $MN = RS$ and $PN > RT$, then $m\angle M > m\angle S$.

Discussion

11. Consider the cube to the right. Each edge of the cube has a length of one unit. Consider $\triangle EGC$ and $\triangle EGF$ and use the SAS Inequality Theorem to explain why $EC > FE$.

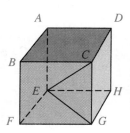

Exercises

A

What conclusion can be drawn from the given information?

1. $BD = DC$, $m\angle 1 > m\angle 2$
2. $AB = AC$, $m\angle 3 > m\angle 4$
3. $\overline{AD}$ is a median. $AB > AC$
4. $\triangle ABC$ is isosceles with base $\overline{BC}$. $CD > BD$

Determine whether each statement is always, sometimes, or never true.

5. If $AB = DE$, $BC = FD$, and $m\angle B > m\angle D$, then $FE > AC$.
6. If $AB = DE$, $AC = FE$ and $BC < FD$, then $m\angle A < m\angle E$. always
7. If $m\angle B < m\angle D$, $m\angle C < m\angle F$, then $m\angle A > m\angle E$.
8. If $BC = FD$, $m\angle C > m\angle F$ then $m\angle A > m\angle E$. sometimes
9. If $AB = DE$, $BC = FD$, $AC > FE$, then $m\angle D > m\angle B$.
10. If $BC = FD$, $AC = FE$, and $m\angle C < m\angle F$, then $DE > AB$. always

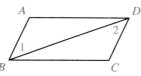

11. **Given:** $AB = CD$, $m\angle ABC > m\angle BCD$
    Prove: $AC > BD$

12. **Given:** $AB = CD$, $m\angle 1 > m\angle 2$
    Prove: $ABCD$ is not a $\square$.
    (HINT: Use an indirect proof.)

13. **Given:** $\overline{AC}$ is a median. $m\angle 1 > m\angle 2$
    Prove: $AB > AD$

B

14. In $\triangle MNP$, $\overline{MX}$ is a median, $m\angle MXN = 4x + 6$ and $m\angle MXP = 7x - 2$.
    Which side is longer, $\overline{MN}$ or $\overline{MP}$? Which angle is larger, $\angle N$ or $\angle P$?

N > P

15. Quadrilateral $ABCD$ has $AB = AC = AD$, $m\angle DCA = 50$, and $m\angle ACB = 55$.
    Which side is longer, $\overline{CD}$ or $\overline{BC}$? Which angle is larger, $\angle B$ or $\angle D$?
16. P is a point above the plane determined by equilateral $\triangle ABC$. If $PC > PB$, which
    angle is larger, $\angle PAC$ or $\angle PAB$?

A > D

Determine whether $m\angle A < m\angle D$, $m\angle A = m\angle D$, or $m\angle A > m\angle D$, given the following coordinates for triangles ABC and DEF.

17. $A(1, 1)$, $B(2, 3)$, $C(4, 0)$,
    $D(1, -2)$, $E(2, 0)$, $F(-2, -3)$
18. $A(-2, 3)$, $B(-3, 0)$, $C(1, 2)$,
    $D(3, 0)$, $E(2, 3)$, $F(0, 1)$

19. Given: D is the midpoint of $\overline{AB}$.
$\quad\quad\quad AE = BF$
$\quad\quad\quad AC < BC$
Prove: $DF < DE$

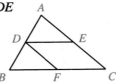

20. Given: $AB = AD$
$\quad\quad\quad BC > DC$
Prove: $m\angle 2 > m\angle 1$

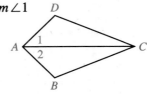

21. Given: $RU > RT$
$\quad\quad\quad VU = ST$
Prove: $SU > TV$

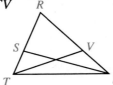

22. Given: $\overline{CD} \perp$ bisector of $\overline{AB}$
$\quad\quad\quad E$ is on $\overleftrightarrow{AC}$.
Prove: $AE > BE$

23. Given: N, P, Q are in plane T.
$\quad\quad\quad m\angle MNQ > m\angle MNP$
$\quad\quad\quad NP = NQ$
Prove: $m\angle MPQ > m\angle MQP$

C

24. Given: $AC > AB$
$\quad\quad\quad \overline{DC}$ and $\overline{EC}$ trisect $\angle ACB$.
$\quad\quad\quad \overline{DB}$ and $\overline{EB}$ trisect $\angle ABC$.
Prove: $EC > BE$

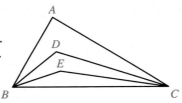

25. Given: $m\angle 1 = m\angle 2$
$\quad\quad\quad m\angle 3 > m\angle 4$
Prove: $AC > AB$

26. Given: $m\angle 1 = m\angle 2$
$\quad\quad\quad AB > AC$
Prove: $m\angle 3 < m\angle 4$

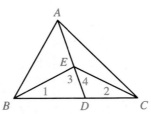

27. Given: $\overline{AC} \perp$ plane N
$\quad\quad\quad AD > AB$
Prove: $CD > BC$
(HINT: Select point E on $\overleftrightarrow{CD}$ so that $BC = CE$.)

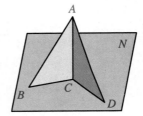

28. Complete the following proof for Theorem 5.24. Draw $\overline{BP}$ so that $\angle PBC \cong \angle E$. Select M so that $BM = DE$. There are two possibilities. Either M is on $\overline{AC}$ or M is not on $\overline{AC}$. Regardless, $\triangle BMC \cong \triangle EDF$ and $MC = DF$.
Case 1: M is on $\overline{AC}$. Explain why $AC > DF$.
Case 2: M is not on $\overline{AC}$. Let $\overline{BN}$ bisect $\angle ABM$. Draw $\overline{NM}$ and $\overline{MC}$. $AB = BM = DE$. Use the fact that $\triangle ABN \cong \triangle MBN$ and that $AN = NM$ to explain why $AC > DF$.

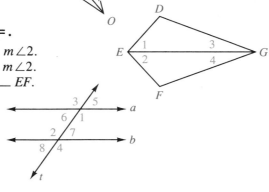

Critical Thinking

29. $\overline{PA}$ is perpendicular to the plane determined by the equilateral triangle ABC. Which segment is the longest: $\overline{AB}$, $\overline{BC}$, $\overline{CA}$, $\overline{PA}$, $\overline{PB}$, or $\overline{PC}$? Write a paragraph proof to justify your choice.

Algebra Review

Solve for x.

1. $\frac{x}{3} = \frac{4}{2}$ **2.** $\frac{12}{16} = \frac{6}{x}$ **3.** $\frac{16}{x} = \frac{x}{4}$

Quiz

E, F, and G are the midpoints of sides $\overline{AC}$, $\overline{AB}$, and $\overline{CB}$ respectively.

1. If $AC = 24$, find FG.
2. If $EG = 2x + 12$ and $AF = 16$, find EG.
3. If $EG = 7$, $FG = 8$, and $CB = 12$, find the perimeter of $\triangle ABC$.

Refer to the figure to the right.

4. In $\triangle LMO$, name the smallest angle.
5. In $\triangle MNO$, name the shortest side.
6. Which is shorter, $\overline{LO}$ or $\overline{MN}$?
7. Using the Triangle Inequality Theorem, $m \angle NMO > m\underline{\ ?\ }$ and $m\underline{\ ?\ }$.

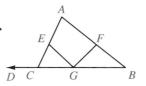

Complete each statement by using $>$, $<$, or $=$.

8. If $DE = EF$ and $DG < FG$, then $m \angle 1 \underline{\ \ } m \angle 2$.
9. If $DG = GF$ and $EF = DE$, then $m \angle 1 \underline{\ \ } m \angle 2$.
10. If $m \angle 3 > m \angle 4$ and $DG = FG$, then $DE \underline{\ \ } EF$.

11. Write an indirect proof for the following.

Given: $\angle 1 \not\cong \angle 2$
Prove: $\angle 3 \not\cong \angle 4$

Finding Shortest Connections

Mathematics is used in planning telephone or other services to find the optimal way of hooking towns, offices, etc. together using the minimal amount of cable or wire. Consider the map for several towns to be served by a cable television network. The problem is to find the minimum amount of cable to connect all of the towns.

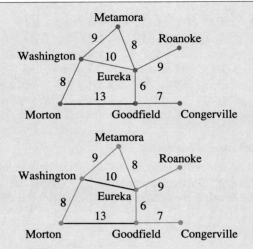

The path shown in red illustrates one method of connecting the towns but it uses more than the minimum; as it connects Washington into the network of towns twice, once through Eureka and once through Metamora. Since the link through Eureka is not needed to connect any other town, it can be deleted. This reduces the amount of cable required by 10 mi.

To find the minimum amount for a task such as shown to the right, you start by identifying one of the towns as the beginning point. This choice has no bearing on the minimal amount, as each town must eventually be connected into the network. Start at this town, say Eureka, and look for the closest town. This is Goodfield, so you would connect the two with a cable. Now look for the next closest town to either town connected and add it to the network, in this case, Congerville. Next look for the town not yet connected that is closest to Eureka, Goodfield, or Congerville. This is Metamora. Include it and then continue asking for the next closest town. In this example, you can see that there is a tie between Washington and Roanoke, so either can be chosen at this point. Suppose you choose Washington. You would next add Morton and then Roanoke. What would have happened if you had chosen Roanoke instead of Washington? All of the towns are now connected and the amount of cable needed to complete the cable network is the sum of the lengths shown in blue, 6 + 7 + 8 + 9 + 8 + 9, or 47 mi of cable.

A collection of edges that touch all of the points in a graph, but which allow only one way of traveling from point to point without repeating other points is called a tree. The process of finding this shortest connecting set of links is known as finding a minimal spanning tree. Sometimes more than one minimal spanning tree exists, but the minimal distances for each tree will be the same.

Exercises

Find the minimal spanning tree and the total length for each of the following.

1.

2.

3.

CRITICAL THINKING

Analyzing and Evaluating Evidence

Sometimes it is possible to jump to a conclusion on the basis of evidence that is unreliable or incomplete. Some evidence is **possibly true,** other evidence is **probably true,** and still other evidence is **accepted as true.** Consider the following examples.

Example 1

a. By observation only, decide if line k, when extended, will meet point A, B, C, or none of these points.

b. Read the following silently and then aloud.

> A BIRD IN THE
> THE HAND IS WORTH
> TWO IN THE BUSH

What do you notice? What kind of evidence are you using in these examples?

Solution

a. point A

b. The word *the* is repeated.

In both cases, observational evidence was used. These examples show that we do not always see what we think we see. Observational evidence should be treated with caution and classified as possibly or probably true.

Example 2

As Jerry came around a corner, he saw his steady girlfriend Rhonda walking into a theater with another boy. Jerry concluded that Rhonda was dating someone else and was very angry. What kind of evidence was Jerry using in his decision?

Solution

Jerry based his conclusion on circumstantial evidence. The truth was that Rhonda was meeting her aunt at the theater and was only walking through the door next to a boy from school. Circumstantial evidence should be considered as possibly true.

Example 3

Mr. Higami was clocked traveling 48 mph in a 35 mph zone by a policeman's radar gun. Two reputable witnesses, who had checked the radar gun before and after Mr. Higami's ticket was issued, testified that the gun was working properly. Another policeman who was riding in the car with the officer verified the officer's story. What kind of evidence do you have in this case?

Solution

The evidence here is of the type that is accepted to be true. In a case such as this, many different facts corroborate the fact in contention. Even in such cases where the evidence is considered true beyond any reasonable doubt, there is always a small possibility that it could be false.

Exercises

1. After Karen began dating Javier, her report card showed she was getting a lower grade in each of her classes. Her mother checked Karen's study time and found that she spent an average of only four hours a week on homework. Karen seemed to be trying to get better grades and did not want to talk about her lower grades. Decide if each of the following statements of evidence is possibly true, probably true, or accepted as true.
   a. Karen was getting better grades before she started dating Javier.
   b. Karen is spending less time on homework since she started dating Javier.
   c. Karen feels guilty or embarrassed about her lower grades.

2. Plan and rehearse a brief incident that a group of three or four students could act out in class. After a group presents an incident, write a careful "eyewitness report" of exactly what happened. How does your report compare to that of a classmate?

3. Describe a situation in which you drew an incorrect conclusion based on circumstantial evidence.

CHAPTER SUMMARY

Vocabulary

bases of a trapezoid (5-4) median of a trapezoid (5-4) rhombus (5-3)
contradiction (5-6) midsegment of a triangle (5-5) rectangle (5-3)
indirect proof (5-6) negation (5-6) square (5-3)
isosceles trapezoid (5-4) parallelogram (5-1) trapezoid (5-4)

Key Ideas

1. A parallelogram has the following properties.
   a. Opposite sides are parallel.　　**b.** Opposite sides are congruent.
   c. Opposite angles are congruent.　**d.** Consecutive angles are supplementary.
   e. Diagonals bisect each other.
2. Rectangles, rhombuses, and squares are special types of parallelograms.
3. A quadrilateral is a parallelogram if any one of the following is true.
   a. Both pairs of opposite sides are parallel.
   b. Both pairs of opposite sides are congruent.
   c. One pair of sides are parallel and congruent.
   d. Both pairs of opposite angles are congruent.
   e. Consecutive angles are supplementary.
   f. Diagonals bisect each other.
4. The median of a trapezoid is parallel to the bases and its length is half the sum of the lengths of the bases.
5. A segment that joins the midpoints of two sides of a triangle is parallel to the third side and its length is half the length of the third side.
6. In an indirect proof, you assume the negation of the *prove* statement and reason logically to reach a contradiction. Then conclude that the assumption is false and the *prove* statement is true.
7. In a triangle, the measure of an exterior angle is greater than the measure of either of the remote interior angles.
8. In a triangle, the longer side is opposite the largest angle. The converse is also true.
9. The sum of any two sides of a triangle is greater than the third side.
10. The SAS and SSS Inequality Theorems are two methods for comparing angles and sides of two triangles.

CHAPTER REVIEW

5-1

Use parallelogram *STAR* to complete each statement.

1. If $m\angle 1 = 32$, then $m\angle 2 =$ ___ .
2. If $m\angle TSR = 125$, then $m\angle SRA =$ ___ and $m\angle TAR =$ ___ .
3. If $ST = 8$, then ___ $= 8$.
4. If $RT = 16$, then $XT =$ ___ .
5. If $SR = 5x + 10$ and $TA = 2x + 43$, then $TA =$ ___ .

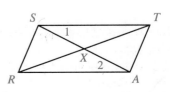

5-2

Determine if the quadrilateral is a parallelogram. If so, state the theorem or definition that justifies the conclusion. If not, write *no conclusion*.

6. **7.** **8.** **9.**

5-3

Classify each statement as always, sometimes, or never true.

10. Opposite sides of a rhombus are parallel.

11. All angles of a rhombus are right angles.

12. Diagonals of a square bisect the opposite angles.

13. All sides of a parallelogram are congruent.

5-4

MATH is a trapezoid and $\overline{XY}$ is a median. Complete each statement.

14. $\overline{MA}$ and $\overline{HT}$ are called the ___ of the trapezoid.

15. If $m\angle H = 35$, then $m\angle MXY = $ ___ .

16. If $AY = 5$, then $AT = $ ___ .

17. If $MA = 10$ and $HT = 24$, then $XY = $ ___ .

5-5

Indicate whether each statement is true or false.

18. If $\overline{SV} \parallel \overline{TU}$, then $SV = \frac{1}{2}TU$.

19. If $\overline{RW} \parallel \overline{SX} \parallel \overline{TU}$ and $RS = ST$, then $WX = XU$.

20. A parallelogram results if the midpoints of the consecutive sides of quadrilateral $RWUT$ are joined.

21. If S is the midpoint of $\overline{RT}$, then $\overline{SV}$ bisects $\overline{RU}$.

5-6

22. Write the negation of the following statement. $\angle ABC$ is an obtuse angle.

23. The statement "$\angle A \cong \angle B$ and $\angle A \not\equiv \angle B$" is called a __?__ .

5-7

24. In $\triangle RST$, $m\angle R = 35$ and $m\angle S = 40$. List the sides of the triangle from shortest to longest.

25. In $\triangle WXY$, if $WX > WY > XY$, name the largest angle in the triangle.

26. A triangle has two sides of lengths 3 and 7. The length of the third side must be greater than __?__ and less than __?__ .

5-8

Complete each statement and state the theorem that supports your conclusion.

27. If $ED = DG$ and $m\angle 1 = m\angle 2$, then ___ = ___ .

28. If $EF = FG$ and ___ < ___ , then $m\angle 3 < m\angle 4$.

29. If $EF = GD$ and $m\angle 3 > m\angle 2$, then ___ > ___ .

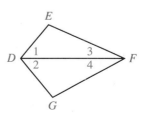

List the letters of all the figures that have each of the following properties.

1. Diagonals are congruent.
2. Both pairs of opposite sides are congruent.
3. Diagonals are perpendicular.
4. Exactly one pair of opposite sides are parallel.
5. Diagonals bisect each other.
6. Opposite sides are parallel.

a. quadrilateral
b. trapezoid
c. parallelogram
d. rectangle
e. rhombus
f. square

Use the given information to write the theorem or definition that supports the conclusion that *RSTU* is a parallelogram.

7. $RS = UT$ and $RU = ST$
8. $\overline{RU} \parallel \overline{ST}$ and $RU = ST$
9. $RV = VT$ and $UV = VS$
10. $\overline{RS} \parallel \overline{UT}$ and $\overline{RU} \parallel \overline{ST}$

Refer to trapezoid *LMNO* and median $\overline{PQ}$.

11. If $LM = 7$ and $ON = 13$, find PQ.
12. If $PQ = 2x - 6$, $LM = 5x - 25$, and $ON = 7$, find LM.
13. If $\overline{LM} \parallel \overline{PQ}$ and $LP = PO$, then MQ __?__ QN.

14. Find the perimeter of the triangle that is formed by joining the midpoints of the sides of a triangle with sides of lengths 8 cm, 12 cm, and 14 cm.

Classify each statement as true or false.

15. A triangle can have sides of lengths 7 in., 13 in., and 15 in.
16. In $\triangle ABC$, if $AB > AC$, then $m\angle B > m\angle C$.
17. In $\triangle RST$, if $m\angle R < m\angle S$, then $ST < RT$.
18. If a line is parallel to one side of a triangle, then it contains the midpoints of the other two sides.
19. If $RQ = TS$ and $m\angle 1 > m\angle 4$, then $QT > RS$.
20. If $RQ = TS$ and $QT > RS$, then $m\angle 1 < m\angle 4$.
21. The negation of $QR = RT$ is $\overline{QR} \parallel \overline{RT}$.

22. Write the negation you would use to begin an indirect proof.
    Prove: $\triangle ABC$ is not an isosceles triangle.

23. Write a two-column proof.
    Given: $\square ABCD$
    $m\angle 1 > m\angle B$
    Prove: $BC > AE$

24. Write an indirect proof.
    Given: trapezoid $RSTU$
    $\overline{RT} \not\equiv \overline{US}$
    Prove: $RSTU$ is not isosceles.

PROBLEM SOLVING

Work Backward

The strategy Work Backward is sometimes helpful in solving problems. Ask yourself, "What information do I need in order to reach the conclusion I want?" Consider statements **a–f** in the following example.

Example

Suppose you have one pail that holds 4 L of water and another that holds 9 L. There are no markings on either pail to indicate how many liters it contains. How can you measure out exactly 6 L of water using these two pails?

Solution

a. I want to end with 6 L. I can do this if I can pour 3 L from the 9 L pail.
b. I can pour 3 L from the 9 L pail if there is space for only 3 L in the 4 L pail.
c. There would be space for only 3 L in the 4 L pail if I could first put 1 L in it.
d. I can put 1 L in the 4 L pail if I can use the 9 L to measure 1 L.
e. I can measure 1 L in the 9 L pail if I can pour out 8 L.
f. I can pour 8 L from the 9 L pail by filling the 4 L pail twice.

Now work backward and use statements **a–f** to write a solution to the problem.

Problem-Solving Strategies	
Draw a Diagram	Find a Pattern
Make a Table	Work Backward

The problem-solving strategies that have been introduced up to this point in the book are presented in the chart.

Problems

Solve each problem by using one of the strategies presented so far.

1. How can you measure out exactly 4 L if you have only an unmarked 5 L pail and an unmarked 7 L pail?

2. A goat owner wanted to make a rectangular pen with as much grazing area as possible. He had only 72 m of fence and wanted the length and width of his pen to be whole numbers. What should the dimensions of his pen be?

3. Suppose there are eight balls that look alike. All are the same weight except one, which is heavier than all the rest. How could you use a balance scale only twice to find the heavier ball? (HINT: Start with the second use of the balance scale. Figure out how you could decide which of two (or three) balls is heavier in only one balancing and work backward.)

4. What is the minimum number of pieces of pizza than can be obtained if a circular pizza is cut eight times with straight cuts.

5. A rhombus-shaped flower bed is to be built in the center of a circular patio. The plans show the rhombus inside a dotted rectangle. $EF = 4$ m and $FG = 6$ m. The builder thinks it will be difficult to calculate the length of the side of the flower bed. Her assistant thinks it will be very easy to find the length with almost no calculation at all. What do you think? Find the length.

6

Similarity

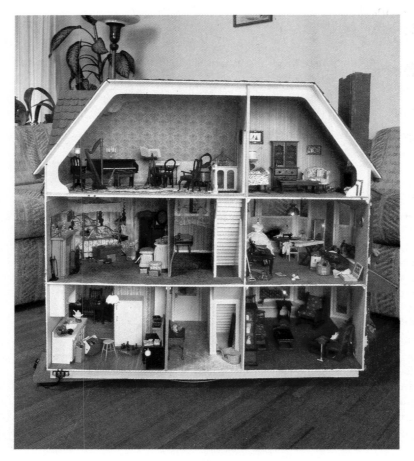

A dollhouse is built using a scale factor of $\frac{1}{24}$. Find the dimensions of the dollhouse kitchen if the actual kitchen measures 8 ft by 10 ft.

RATIO, PROPORTION, AND SIMILARITY

OBJECTIVE: *Express a ratio in simplest form. Write a proportion and solve for an unknown part.*

6-1 Ratio and Proportion

For any two numbers, x and y, the **ratio** of x to y is the quotient obtained by dividing x by y. For example, the ratio of the length to the width of the poster on the left is 42 to 24. The ratio is represented in any of the following ways.

42

24

$42:24$ 42 to 24 $\frac{42}{24}$ $42 \div 24$

Note that the ratio 42 to 24 is not the same as the ratio 24 to 42. A ratio that is expressed in lowest terms is said to be in *simplest* form. For example, the ratio 6 to 8 or $\frac{6}{8}$ in simplest form is 3 to 4 or $\frac{3}{4}$.

18

72

These posters are much alike but differ in their ratio of width to length.

Example 1

Give each ratio in simplest form.

a. AB to BD **b.** $m\angle A$ to $m\angle C$ **c.** BD to CD

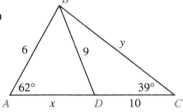

Solution

a. $\frac{AB}{BD} = \frac{6}{9} = \frac{2}{3}$ **b.** $\frac{m\angle A}{m\angle C} = \frac{62}{39}$ **c.** $\frac{BD}{CD} = \frac{9}{10}$

Try This

Give each ratio in simplest form.

a. AB to CD **b.** CD to BD

Example 2

$x = 5, y = 15, z = 12$

Give each ratio in simplest form.

a. $\frac{x}{y}$ **b.** y to z **c.** $x + y : z$

$$\underset{x}{5} \qquad \underset{y}{15} \qquad \underset{z}{12}$$

Solution

a. $\frac{x}{y}$ is $\frac{5}{15}$ or $\frac{1}{3}$.   **b.** y to z is 15 to 12 or 5 to 4.

c. $x + y : z$ is $20 : 12$ or $5 : 3$.

Try This

Give the ratio $\frac{y}{x + z}$ in simplest form.

A **proportion** is an equation stating that two ratios are equal. Two ways of expressing the same proportion are $\frac{3}{4} = \frac{12}{16}$ or $3 : 4 = 12 : 16$.

In the proportions to the right, a is the first term, b is the second term, c is the third term, and d is the fourth term. The blue first and fourth terms are called the **extremes,** and the red second and third terms are called the **means** of the proportion. This proportion is read: a is to b as c is to d. The next theorem describes a relationship between the means and extremes.

$$\frac{a}{b} = \frac{c}{d}$$

$$a : b = c : d$$

THEOREM 6.1 Means—Extremes Products Theorem
In a proportion, the product of the means equals the product of the extremes.

Given: $\frac{a}{b} = \frac{c}{d}$

Prove: $ad = bc$

Proof

Statements	Reasons
1. $\frac{a}{b} = \frac{c}{d}$	1. Given
2. $\frac{a}{b} \cdot bd = \frac{c}{d} \cdot bd$	2. Multiplication Property of Equality
3. $ad = bc$	3. Property of Real Numbers

The converse of Theorem 6.1 is also true.

Example 3
Determine whether each pair of ratios can be written as a proportion.

a. $\frac{6}{15}, \frac{9}{22}$ b. $\frac{6}{8}, \frac{9}{12}$

Solution

a. $\frac{6}{15} \stackrel{?}{=} \frac{9}{22}$

$6 \cdot 22 \stackrel{?}{=} 15 \cdot 9$ *Check the product of the means and the extremes.*

$132 \neq 135$ *Since the product of the means and the extremes are not equal, these ratios do not form a proportion.*

$\frac{6}{15} \neq \frac{9}{22}$ *Note how the contrapositive of Theorem 6.1 is used.*

b. $\frac{6}{8} \stackrel{?}{=} \frac{9}{12}$

$6 \cdot 12 \stackrel{?}{=} 8 \cdot 9$

$72 = 72$ *Since the product of the means and the extremes are equal, these ratios form a proportion.*

$\frac{6}{8} = \frac{9}{12}$

Try This
Determine whether each pair of ratios form a proportion.

a. $\frac{3}{5}, \frac{27}{45}$ b. $\frac{4}{7}, \frac{9}{17}$ c. $\frac{3x}{2y}, \frac{6x}{4y}$

Example 4
Find x in the proportion $6 : x = 5 : 15$.

Solution

$\frac{6}{x} = \frac{5}{15}$

$5x = 6 \cdot 15$ *The product of the means equals the product of the extremes.*

$(\frac{1}{5})5x = (\frac{1}{5}) \cdot 6 \cdot 15$

$x = 18$

Try This
Find x in each proportion.

a. $4 : 20 = x : 25$ b. $x : 9 = 6 : 18$

Class Exercises

Short Answer

Give each ratio in simplest form.

1. $\frac{4}{20}$ 2. $2x$ to $3x$ 3. $35x : 7x^2$ 4. $\frac{3xy}{6y}$

State the means and the extremes in each proportion.

5. $5:8 = 10:16$ 6. $\frac{7}{12} = \frac{35}{60}$ 7. $8:2 = 100:x$ 8. $\frac{17}{48} = \frac{96}{x}$

Determine whether each pair of ratios form a proportion.

9. $\frac{2}{5}, \frac{4}{10}$ 10. $\frac{3}{9}, \frac{4}{12}$ 11. $\frac{2}{7}, \frac{3}{14}$ 12. $\frac{1}{2}, \frac{3}{8}$

Sample Exercises

Find the value of x in each proportion.

13. $1:2 = x:4$ 14. $3:5 = 6:x$ 15. $x:3 = 3:9$ 16. $3:4 = 6:x$

Discussion

17. $ad = bc$ How many different proportions can you obtain using a, b, c, and d?

2

Exercises

A

Give each ratio in simplest form.

1. $\frac{UT}{TW}$ 2. $\frac{VW}{TW}$ 3. $\frac{m\angle UTV}{m\angle VTW}$ 4. $\frac{m\angle VTW}{m\angle W}$

5. TV to TW 6. UT to VW $\frac{5}{3}$

$x = 6, \; y = 10, \; z = 15$ Give each ratio in simplest terms.

7. $\frac{x}{y}$ 8. $(x + y):z$ 9. $(z - y):x$ 10. $(y - x):z - x$

Determine whether each pair of ratios form a proportion.

11. $\frac{5}{8}, \frac{15}{24}$ 12. $\frac{4}{9}, \frac{12}{27}$ yes   13. $\frac{3x}{5}, \frac{6x}{10}$ 14. $\frac{xy}{3}, \frac{14}{6xy}$

Find the value of x in each proportion.

15. $x:15 = 20:25$ 12   16. $\frac{x}{7} = \frac{12}{25}$ 17. $5:x = 8:15$ 18. $\frac{3}{7} = \frac{5}{x}$ $\frac{35}{3}$ 11.6

B

Write two proportions for each equation.

21.) $\frac{3}{4} = \frac{9}{12}$ $\frac{9}{3} = \frac{12}{4}$

19. $3 \cdot 4 = 6 \cdot 2$ 20. $6 \cdot 4 = 8 \cdot 3$ 21. $3 \cdot 12 = 9 \cdot 4$

22. $9 \cdot x = 15 \cdot 8$ 23. If $2y = 3z$, find the ratio z to y.

24. If $x + 3 = 2y$, find the ratio $x + 3 : y$.

$x + 3 = 2y$ $x + 3 : y$

$\frac{2y}{y}$ $2 : 1$

Give the measure of each angle.

25. Two supplementary angles are in a ratio of 2 to 1.

26. The acute angles of a right triangle are in a ratio of 5 to 4.

27. Two numbers are in a ratio of $2:3$. What is the ratio of their squares? $\frac{4}{9}$ $\frac{2}{3}$ $\frac{4}{9}$

28. A 56-cm segment is divided in a ratio of 3 to 5. What is the length of each segment?

The gear ratio of a bicycle can be defined in two ways.

$$\text{gear ratio} = \frac{\text{number of pedal gear teeth}}{\text{number of sprocket gear teeth}} = \frac{\text{number of sprocket revolutions}}{\text{number of pedal revolutions}}$$

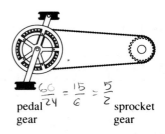

29. If a bicycle has 60 teeth on the pedal gear and 24 teeth on the sprocket gear, find its gear ratio in simplest form?

30. If the pedal on the bicycle in Exercise 29 makes two revolutions, how many revolutions does the sprocket gear make? 5

$$\frac{60}{24} = \frac{15}{6} = \frac{5}{2}$$

pedal gear   sprocket gear

31. Calculate the lengths of the segments to verify that $\frac{AD}{DB} = \frac{AE}{EC}$ is a proportion.

32. Calculate the lengths of the segments to verify that $\frac{AC}{AE} = \frac{AB}{AD}$ is a proportion.

33. Write and verify two other proportions from this figure.

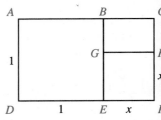

C

In rectangle *ACFH*, *ABED* is a square and *EFHG* is a square. Suppose that $DF:AD = AD:FH$.

34. Show that $\frac{1+x}{1} = \frac{1}{x}$.   **35.** Show that $\frac{DF}{AD} = \frac{FH}{HC}$.

36. Show that $x = \frac{-1 + \sqrt{5}}{2}$.

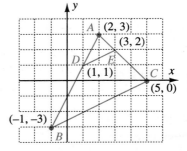

Critical Thinking

37. Suppose a polygon has n sides. Give a convincing argument that the number of diagonals from one vertex is $n - 3$. Give a convincing argument that the ratio $n - 3$ to 360 can never be 2 to 7.

38. Suppose a polygon has n sides. Give a convincing argument that the total number of diagonals is $\frac{n(n-3)}{2}$. Give a convincing argument that the ratio of the number of diagonals from one vertex to the total number of diagonals can never be 3 to 5.

Mixed Review

$\overline{AB} \parallel \overline{CE}$, $BC = BD$, $\overline{AC} \parallel \overline{BD}$ **Find the measure of each angle.**

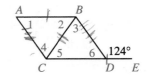

1. $m\angle 1 =$ ___   **2.** $m\angle 2 =$ ___   **3.** $m\angle 3 =$ ___

4. $m\angle 4 =$ ___   **5.** $m\angle 5 =$ ___   **6.** $m\angle 6 =$ ___

Calculator Investigation

1. Use a calculator to calculate the ratio $\frac{DF}{AD}$ in Exercises 34–36 and verify that it is 1.618.

2. Calculate the ratio $\frac{DF}{FH}$ and verify that it is 2.618.

3. Show that DF is a solution of the equation $x^2 = x + 1$.

4. The sequence 1, 1, 2, 3, 5, 8, 13, 21, 34, 55, 89 is called the Fibonacci sequence. Discover the pattern and write the next three terms of the sequence.

5. Calculate the sequence of ratios of successive terms $\frac{2}{1}, \frac{3}{2}, \frac{5}{3}, \frac{8}{5}, \ldots$ of the Fibonacci sequence. How does this sequence relate to the ratio $\frac{DF}{AD}$ in Exercises 34–36?

6-2 Properties of Proportions

 EXPLORE Form a proportion by substituting the numbers 4, 6, 10, and 15 in these boxes.

$$\Box : \Box = \Box : \Box$$

Find other proportions by rearranging these numbers. State any generalizations you discover.

In geometry, proportions are used to compare lengths of segments. Often an unknown length can be found by solving a proportion. Solving proportions sometimes requires you to first rewrite a proportion into an equivalent form.

To obtain equivalent forms of a proportion you can use the properties summarized in the following theorem. You will be asked to prove this theorem in Exercises 43–47.

◆ **THEOREM 6.2** Properties of Proportions

If $\frac{a}{b} = \frac{c}{d}$, and a, b, c, and $d \neq 0$, then each of the following is true.

    a. $\frac{a}{c} = \frac{b}{d}$

    b. $\frac{d}{b} = \frac{c}{a}$

    c. $\frac{b}{a} = \frac{d}{c}$

    d. $\frac{a + b}{b} = \frac{c + d}{d}$

    e. $\frac{a - b}{b} = \frac{c - d}{d}$

Example 1

Complete the statement in three different ways. Justify each answer.

If $\frac{6}{9} = \frac{8}{12}$, then ____ .

    Solution

       $\frac{6}{8} = \frac{9}{12}$ *Switch the means.*

      $\frac{12}{9} = \frac{8}{6}$ *Switch the extremes.*

       $\frac{9}{6} = \frac{12}{8}$ *Invert the proportion.*

Try This

Complete the statement in five different ways. Justify each answer.

If $\frac{3}{7} = \frac{18}{42}$, then ____ .

Examples 2 and 3 illustrate the use of the properties of proportions.

Example 2

Use the proportion $\frac{x}{y} = \frac{5}{8}$ to complete each proportion.

a. $\frac{y}{8} = $ ___ **b.** $\frac{5}{x} = $ ___ **c.** $\frac{y}{x} = $ ___ **d.** $\frac{y+x}{x} = $ ___

Solution

a. $\frac{y}{8} = \frac{x}{5}$ **b.** $\frac{5}{x} = \frac{8}{y}$ **c.** $\frac{y}{x} = \frac{8}{5}$ **d.** $\frac{y+x}{x} = \frac{13}{5}$

Try This

Use the proportion $\frac{x}{y} = \frac{5}{8}$ to complete each proportion.

a. $\frac{x+y}{x} = $ ___ **b.** $\frac{x+5}{5} = $ ___

Example 3

Given: $\frac{AD}{DB} = \frac{AE}{EC}$

Prove: $\frac{AB}{DB} = \frac{AC}{EC}$

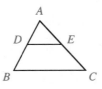

Proof

Statements	Reasons
1. $\frac{AD}{DB} = \frac{AE}{EC}$	1. Given
2. $\frac{AD + DB}{DB} = \frac{AE + EC}{EC}$	2. Property of Proportions. Add the denominator to the numerator.
3. $\frac{AB}{DB} = \frac{AC}{EC}$	3. Segment Addition Postulate

Try This

Given: $\frac{AB}{AD} = \frac{AC}{AE}$

Prove: $\frac{BD}{AD} = \frac{CE}{AE}$

Class Exercises

Short Answer

Complete each statement by switching the means.

1. If $\frac{3}{8} = \frac{6}{16}$, then ___ . **2.** If $\frac{9}{5} = \frac{45}{25}$, then ___ . **3.** If $\frac{18}{12} = \frac{6}{4}$, then ___ .

Complete each statement by switching the extremes.

4. If $\frac{2}{x} = \frac{y}{7}$, then ___ . **5.** If $\frac{x}{y} = \frac{7}{8}$, then ___ . **6.** If $\frac{x}{4} = \frac{y}{4}$, then ___ .

Sample Exercises

Complete each statement in five different ways. Justify your answer.

7. If $\frac{9}{16} = \frac{u}{v}$, then ___ . **8.** If $\frac{y}{8} = \frac{x}{4}$, then ___ . **9.** If $\frac{6}{m} = \frac{n}{8}$, then ___ .

10. If $\frac{y}{x} = \frac{9}{5}$, then ___ . **11.** If $\frac{u}{7} = \frac{3}{v}$, then ___ . **12.** If $\frac{21}{q} = \frac{4}{r}$, then ___ .

Discussion

13. Suppose that $\frac{a}{b} = \frac{c}{d}$. One student concluded that $\frac{a+b}{b} = \frac{c+b}{d}$ by adding b to both sides of the equation. Do you think this reasoning is correct? Explain why or why not.

Exercises

A

Complete each statement in five different ways. Justify your answer.

1. If $\frac{7}{8} = \frac{14}{16}$, then ___.
2. If $\frac{4}{5} = \frac{36}{45}$, then ___.
3. If $\frac{5}{3} = \frac{125}{75}$, then ___.
4. If $\frac{x}{y} = \frac{7}{11}$, then ___.
5. If $\frac{u}{8} = \frac{v}{9}$, then ___.
6. If $\frac{5}{a} = \frac{7}{b}$, then ___.

Use the proportion $\frac{3}{4} = \frac{x}{y}$ to complete each proportion.

7. $\frac{3}{x} = $ ___
8. $\frac{y}{4} = $ ___
9. $\frac{7}{4} = $ ___
10. $\frac{x - y}{y} = $ ___
11. $\frac{y}{x} = $ ___
12. $\frac{y + x}{x} = \frac{4+3}{3}$

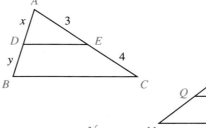

$\frac{LQ}{QM} = \frac{LR}{RN}$ **Prove each of the following.**

13. $\frac{LQ}{LR} = \frac{QM}{RN}$
14. $\frac{LM}{QM} = \frac{LN}{RN}$
15. $\frac{LM}{LQ} = \frac{LN}{LR}$
16. $\frac{LQ + QM}{QM} = \frac{LR + RN}{RN}$
17. $\frac{LQ + QM}{LQ} = \frac{LR + RN}{LR}$

B

given, property of proportion

Use the proportion $\frac{a}{b} = \frac{x}{y}$ to complete each proportion.

18. $\frac{a}{x} = \frac{x}{a}$
19. $\frac{y}{x} = $ ___
20. $\frac{y}{b} = $ ___

Use the proportion $\frac{c + d}{d} = \frac{u + v}{v}$ to complete each proportion.

$2x \times 6 = 36$
$\frac{}{6} \quad \frac{}{6}$
$2x^2 = \frac{30}{2}$

21. $\frac{c}{d} = $ ___
22. $\frac{v}{u} = $ ___
23. $\frac{c + 2d}{d} = $ ___

Find the value of x.

24. $\frac{x + 3}{4} = \frac{9}{2}$ 15
25. $\frac{x - 2}{x} = \frac{3}{5}$
26. $\frac{2x - 3}{3} = \frac{3x - 7}{2}$
27. $\frac{x + 2}{2} = \frac{9}{5}$
28. $\frac{6x - 3}{3} = \frac{12}{2x}$
29. $\frac{x - 3}{5} = \frac{2}{x}$
30. $\frac{x + 2}{3} = \frac{4x}{6}$
31. $\frac{16}{4x} = \frac{4x}{9}$
32. $\frac{x + 2}{6} = \frac{6}{x + 2}$

28.) $12x^2 - 6x = 36$
$12x^2 - 6x - 36 = 0$
$6(2x^2 - x - 6) = 0$
$2x^2 - x - 6 = 0$
$(2x + 3)(x - 2)$
$= 0$
$x = 2, \frac{-3}{2}$

$\frac{TU}{UV} = \frac{TX}{XW}$ **Use the figure to complete the table.**

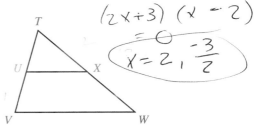

	TU	UV	TV	TX	XW	TW
33.	14	16	—	—	24	—
34.	—	10	18	12	—	—
35.	12	—	26	—	21	—
36.	16	—	—	24	33	—
37.	—	—	21	12	—	28
38.	—	—	16	9	15	—
39.	10	18	—	—	—	42
40.	—	12	—	12	—	30
41.	—	—	26	—	24	39
42.	6	—	—	—	20	28

$\frac{a}{b} = \frac{c}{d}$ **Prove that each proportion is correct.**

43. $\frac{a}{c} = \frac{b}{d}$
44. $\frac{d}{b} = \frac{c}{a}$
45. $\frac{b}{a} = \frac{d}{c}$
46. $\frac{a + b}{b} = \frac{c + d}{d}$
47. $\frac{a - b}{b} = \frac{c - d}{d}$

48. A photographer enlarged a 6 in. × 10 in. photograph by multiplying each dimension by a factor of $\frac{3}{2}$. Use proportions to find the width x and length y of the enlarged photograph.

49. Repeat Exercise 48 using a factor of $\frac{5}{4}$.

10 original
6

y

enlargement
x

The $\frac{1}{4}$-in. line on the blueprint shown represents 12 ft.

50. If the distance measured from A to B is $2\frac{1}{2}$ in., what is the actual distance from A to B?

51. If the distance measured from C to D is $1\frac{5}{8}$ in., what is the actual distance from C to D?

52. If it costs $45 per foot to build a wall from A to B in this blueprint, what is the total cost of building the wall?

C

Given: $\triangle ABC$, $\frac{CD}{AD} = \frac{CE}{BE}$ **Complete each statement.**

53. If $CD = x$, $AD = x + 3$, $CE = x + 1$, and $BE = x + 5$; then $CD =$ ___, $AD =$ ___, $CE =$ ___, and $BE =$ ___.

54. If $CD = 2x$, $AD = x + 3$, $CE = x + 5$, and $BE = x - 3$; then $CD =$ ___, $AD =$ ___, $CE =$ ___, and $BE =$ ___.

55. If $CD = 3x$, $AD = x + 2$, $CE = x + 2$, and $BE = x - 1$; then $CD =$ ___, $AD =$ ___, $CE =$ ___, and $BE =$ ___.

56. If $\frac{a}{b} = \frac{c}{d} = \frac{e}{f}$, then show that $\frac{a}{b} = \frac{a + c + e}{b + d + f}$.

57. Complete this generalization. If $\frac{a}{b} = \frac{c}{d} = \frac{e}{f} = \frac{g}{h} = \ldots$, then $\frac{a}{b} = \frac{(a + \ldots)}{(b + \ldots)}$.

Critical Thinking

Decide whether each statement is always true, sometimes true, or never true. Explain your answer.

58. When two terms of the proportion $a:b = c:d$ are interchanged, the two ratios that result form a proportion.

59. If one term of the proportion $a:b = c:d$ is added to another term, the two ratios that result form a proportion.

Mixed Review

$\overline{AB} \parallel \overline{DC}$, $AC = BD$, $m\angle BDC = 34$, $m\angle DAC = 84$
Find the measure of each angle.

1. $m\angle ACD$ **2.** $m\angle AEB$ **3.** $m\angle BEC$
4. $m\angle ADE$ **5.** $m\angle ABC$ **6.** $m\angle ABD$

$\triangle PQR$ is isosceles with legs $\overline{PQ}$ and $\overline{PR}$. $\overline{PT}$ is an altitude.
$m\angle PQR = 64°$, $m\angle RST = 44°$ **Find the measure of each angle.**

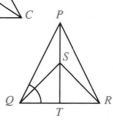

7. $m\angle PRT$ **8.** $m\angle QPR$ **9.** $m\angle SQT$
10. $m\angle PQS$ **11.** $m\angle QPT$ **12.** $m\angle PSQ$

13. Prove that $\triangle PQS \cong \triangle PRS$. **14.** Prove that $\angle SQT \cong \angle SRT$.

Enrichment

The Golden Rectangle

For centuries architects and artists have found the **golden rectangle** an especially pleasing form. You can find it in the front of the Parthenon in Athens and in vases from different periods of history. In nature, the spiral of the chambered nautilus shell fits within a golden rectangle.

The ratio of the length to the width distinguishes a golden rectangle from other rectangles. Imagine a square within the rectangle to the right whose sides are the same length as the width of the rectangle. The new rectangle formed has length and width in proportion to the original rectangle. That is, $\frac{1}{x} = \frac{x}{y}$. Because $y = 1 - x$, you can also express the proportion as follows. $\frac{1}{x} = \frac{x}{1 - x}$.

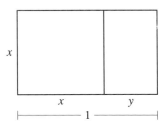

Exercises

1. State the product of the means and extremes for the proportion $\frac{1}{x} = \frac{x}{1 - x}$.
2. Express the solution above as a quadratic equation (that is, in the form $ax^2 + bx + c = 0$).
3. Use the formula $x = \frac{-b \pm \sqrt{b^2 - 4ac}}{2a}$ to solve the quadratic equation.
4. In the photograph of the vase above, measure the lengths and widths of several rectangles to the nearest millimeter. Use your calculator to compute the ratios of each length to width.
5. The ratio of the length to the width, $\frac{l}{w}$ or $\frac{1}{x}$, is the golden ratio. Use your answer to Exercise 3 to express the golden ratio as a decimal. How does your answer compare to the ratios in Exercise 4?

6-3 Similar Polygons

You learned in Chapter 3 that triangles having the same size and shape are called congruent figures. In this lesson you will learn about triangles and other polygons that have the same shape but not necessarily the same size.

Polygon *WXYZ* is the same shape as polygon *ABCD*. Each side of *WXYZ* is double the length of the corresponding side of *ABCD*. That is, the ratio of the length of each side of *WXYZ* to its corresponding side of *ABCD* is 2. A characteristic of figures that have the same shape is that ratios of corresponding sides are equal. Two polygons that have the same shape are called **similar**.

The photograph of bacteria on the left has been enlarged by a factor of 10 to make it easier for scientists to study.

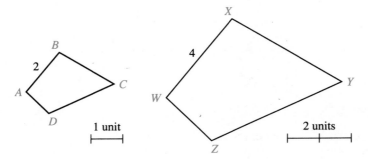

■ DEFINITION

Two polygons are similar (~) if their vertices can be matched so that
a. corresponding angles are congruent, and
b. ratios of lengths of corresponding sides are equal.

To indicate that polygon *ABCD* is similar to polygon *WXYZ*, write *ABCD* ~ *WXYZ*. When using this notation write corresponding vertices in the same order.

If *ABCD* ~ *WXYZ*, you know that
a. $\angle A \cong \angle W$, $\angle B \cong \angle X$, $\angle C \cong \angle Y$, $\angle D \cong \angle Z$, and
b. $\frac{AB}{WX} = \frac{BC}{XY} = \frac{CD}{YZ} = \frac{AD}{WZ}$
Conversely, if you know that all parts of *a* and *b* above are true, you can conclude that *ABCD* ~ *WXYZ*.

The ratio of lengths of corresponding sides of two similar polygons is called the **scale factor** between the similar polygons. Since $\frac{AB}{WX} = \frac{2}{4} = \frac{1}{2}$, the scale factor of *ABCD* to *WXYZ* is $\frac{1}{2}$. Since $\frac{WX}{AB} = \frac{4}{2} = 2$, the scale factor of *WXYZ* to *ABCD* is 2.

Example

$ABCDE \sim JFGHI$ **Complete each statement.**

a. $m\angle J =$ ___   **b.** $m\angle G =$ ___   **c.** $\frac{ED}{IH} =$ ___

d. $x =$ ___   **e.** The scale factor of $JFGHI$ to $ABCDE$ is ___ .

Solution

a. $m\angle J = 90$ **b.** $m\angle G = 120$ *Corresponding angles are congruent.*

c. $\frac{ED}{IH} = \frac{AE}{JI} = \frac{2}{3}$ *Corresponding sides are proportional.*

d. $\frac{AE}{JI} = \frac{BC}{FG}$ *Corresponding sides are proportional.*

$\quad \frac{2}{3} = \frac{4}{x}$ *Substitute segment lengths and solve for x.*

$\quad 2x = 12 \quad$ or $x = 6$

e. The scale factor of $JFGHI$ to $\frac{JI}{AE} = \frac{3}{2}$

$\quad ABCDE$ is $\frac{3}{2}$.

Try This

In polygon $ABCDE$, find y.

Class Exercises

Short Answer

Complete each statement.

1. If two polygons are similar, then corresponding ___ are congruent.
2. If two polygons are similar, then corresponding ___ are proportional.
3. If for two polygons corresponding angles are ___ and corresponding sides are ___ , then the polygons are similar.
4. If the scale factor between two similar triangles is one, then the triangles are ___ .

$\triangle ABC \sim \triangle XYZ$ **Complete each statement.**

5. $\angle A \cong$ ___   6. $\angle C \cong$ ___
7. $\frac{AC}{XZ} =$ ___   8. $\frac{XY}{AB} =$ ___

Sample Exercises

$\triangle RST \sim \triangle VUW$ **Complete each statement.**

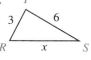

9. $\angle R \cong$ ___   10. $\frac{RT}{VW} =$ ___
11. $x =$ ___   12. $y =$ ___

Discussion

Determine whether each statement is always true, sometimes true, or never true. Explain your answer.

13. If two triangles are congruent, then they are similar.
14. If two triangles are similar, then they are congruent.
15. Squares $ABCD$ and $EFGH$ are similar.
16. Isosceles triangles ABC and DEF are similar.
17. If corresponding sides of two rectangles are proportional, then the rectangles are similar.

Exercises

A

RSTU ~ EFGH   **Complete each statement.**

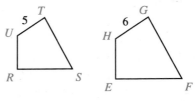

1. ∠R ≅ ___
2. ∠S ≅ ___
3. ∠H ≅ ___
4. ∠G ≅ ___
5. $\frac{HG}{UT}$ = ___
6. $\frac{RU}{EH}$ = ___
7. $\frac{ST}{FG}$ = ___
8. $\frac{RS}{EF}$ = ___

ABCDE ~ RSTUV   **Complete each statement.**

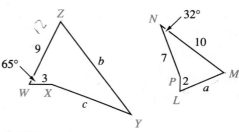

9. $m\angle E$ = ___
10. $m\angle A$ = ___
11. ∠T ≅ ___
12. $m\angle B$ = ___
13. x = ___
14. y = ___
15. UT = ___
16. UV = 20, DE = ___
17. $\frac{RS}{AB}$ = ___
18. $\frac{UV}{DE}$ = ___
19. The scale factor of ABCDE to RSTUV is ___ .

WXYZ ~ LPNM   **Complete each statement.**

20. $m\angle L$ = ___
21. $m\angle Y$ = ___
22. ∠M ≅ ___
23. ∠X ≅ ___
24. a = ___
25. b = ___
26. c = ___
27. If WZ = 12, LM = ___ .
28. The scale factor of WXYZ to LPNM is ___ .

B

Find the coordinates of a point A so that △ABC ~ △DEF.

29.

30.

31. Plot points A(1, 1), B(7, 1), C(6, 3), and D(2, 3) and draw quadrilateral ABCD. Then plot points A'(−3, 4) and B'(−3, 1). Find points C' and D' so that A'B'C'D' is similar to ABCD.

$\triangle ABC \sim \triangle DEF$ The scale factor of $\triangle ABC$ to $\triangle DEF$ is $\frac{3}{7}$.
Complete each statement.

32. If $AB = 15$, then $DE = $ ___ .
33. If $EF = 42$, then $BC = $ ___ .
34. $\frac{AB}{DE} = $ ___
35. If $DF = 56$, then $AC = $ ___ .

36. In order to find the distance AB across a lake, a surveyor constructed $\triangle OCD$ similar to $\triangle OBA$. He measured OB, OC, and CD directly to obtain the lengths shown. Find the length of AB.

$\triangle ABC \sim \triangle ADE$

37. $m\angle A = 87$, $m\angle AED = 41$ Find $m\angle B$.
38. $AD = 8$, $AB = 12$, $AE = 14$ Find AC.
39. $AD = 9$, $AB = 13$, $AE = 14$ Find EC.
40. Prove that $\overline{DE} \parallel \overline{BC}$.

41. **Given:** $\overline{AB} \parallel \overline{DE}$
    Prove: $\triangle ABC \sim \triangle DEC$

42. Keiko uses the sight marks to aim the ball. Suppose she misses the mark by 5 cm in a bowling alley that is 15 m long. If the mark is 2 m from the point A when the ball is released, by how much will she miss the pin?

C

$\triangle ACD$ and $\triangle ABC$ are right triangles and $y = x\sqrt{2}$.
Complete each statement.

43. $CD = $ ___   44. $DB = $ ___
45. $BC = $ ___   46. $\frac{AB}{AC} = $ ___

47. Prove that $\triangle ACD \sim \triangle ABC$.

Determine whether each statement is always true, sometimes true, or never true.

48. An equilateral triangle and an equiangular triangle are similar.
49. If an angle of one rhombus is congruent to an angle of another rhombus, the two rhombi are similar.
50. Two isosceles trapezoids are similar.
51. Two parallelograms that each have a 132° angle are similar.
52. Two rectangles, each with the property that two sides are twice the length of the other two sides, are similar.

Critical Thinking

53. An arithmetic progression is a sequence of the form x, $x + a$, $x + 2a$, $x + 3a$, ... Write the first five terms of each of these arithmetic progressions.

    a. $x = 3$, $a = 2$ **b.** $x = 4$, $a = 3$ **c.** $x = 2$, $a = 5$

54. Suppose the length of the sides of a triangle are the first three terms of an arithmetic progression. Show that the lengths of the sides of any similar triangle also form an arithmetic progression. (HINT: Assume that the lengths of the sides of one triangle are x, $x + a$, and $x + 2a$ and the lengths of the corresponding sides of the second triangle are y, $y + b$, and $y + c$ and show that $c = 2b$.)

Algebra Review

Write an equation and solve each problem.

1. In a triangle the second angle is 12° greater than the first angle. The third angle is 12° greater than the second angle. Find the measures of the three angles.

2. The measures of the angles of a triangle are in the ratio $4:5:6$. Find the measure of each angle.

3. The perimeter of a triangle is 39. If the ratio of the lengths of the sides is $3:4:6$, find the length of each side.

4. The vertex angle of an isosceles triangle has a measure 25 less than three times the measure of a base angle. Find the measures of the three angles.

5. The ratio of the measures of the angles of a quadrilateral is $2:4:7:11$. Find the measure of each angle.

Quiz

Express each ratio in the simplest form.

1. $\dfrac{AB}{CD}$ **2.** $m\angle ACB : m\angle BAC$

3. CD to AD **4.** $BC + CD : AC$

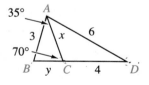

5. The width and length of a rectangle are in the ratio $2:3$. If the perimeter of the rectangle is 20, find the width and length.

Given the proportion $\dfrac{x}{2} = \dfrac{7}{y}$, indicate whether the following proportions are true or false.

6. $\dfrac{2}{x} = \dfrac{y}{7}$ **7.** $\dfrac{y}{2} = \dfrac{x}{7}$ **8.** $7 : x = y : 2$ **9.** $\dfrac{x+2}{2} = \dfrac{y+7}{y}$

quadrilateral $ABCD$ ~ quadrilateral $KLMN$ **Complete each statement.**

10. $\angle C \cong \angle$ _____

11. $AD = 20$, $BC = 32$, $LM = 24$ $KN =$ _____

12. The scale factor of $ABCD$ to $KLMN$ is _____ .

SIMILAR TRIANGLES

OBJECTIVE: *Use the AA Similarity Postulate to draw conclusions about triangles.*

6-4 AA Similarity Postulate

Trace angles *A*, *B*, and *C* in this triangle. Then draw a large triangle *ABC* on dot paper so that the corresponding angles of the two triangles are congruent. Use a protractor if necessary.

Compare the ratios of corresponding sides of the two triangles.

State a generalization.

In order to prove that two triangles are similar using the definition of similarity, you must verify six relationships. You must establish that all three pairs of corresponding angles are congruent and that the three ratios of corresponding sides are equal.

In the Explore you may have discovered that if all three pairs of corresponding angles are congruent, then the two triangles are similar. In fact, knowing that two pairs of angles are congruent is sufficient to conclude similarity. Consider $\triangle ABC$ and $\triangle DEF$ in which two pairs of angles are congruent. You can use the Triangle Angle Sum Theorem to conclude that

$$m\angle C = 180 - (x + y) \text{ and } m\angle F = 180 - (x + y)$$

Consequently, if two pairs of angles are congruent, all three pairs of angles are congruent.

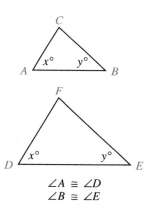

$\angle A \cong \angle D$
$\angle B \cong \angle E$

● **POSTULATE 19**   AA Similarity

If two angles of one triangle are congruent respectively to two angles of another triangle, then the two triangles are similar.

Example 1

$\angle G \cong \angle J, \angle H \cong \angle K$

Find *x* and *y*.

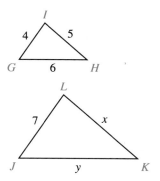

Solution

$\triangle GHI \sim \triangle JKL$ *AA Similarity Postulate*

$\frac{x}{5} = \frac{7}{4}$ or $x = \frac{35}{4}$ *Ratios of corresponding sides are equal.*

$\frac{y}{6} = \frac{7}{4}$ or $y = \frac{21}{2}$

Try This

In the figure to the right, $JL = 12$.   Find *JK* and *KL*.

Example 2

$\angle A \cong \angle F$, $\overline{AB} \parallel \overline{EF}$, $BC = 4$, $AC = 5$, $DF = 8$ Find ED.

Solution

$\frac{BC}{ED} = \frac{AC}{FD}$ $\angle A \cong \angle F$ When parallel lines are cut by a
$\frac{4}{x} = \frac{5}{8}$ transversal, alternate interior angles are
$5x = 32$ congruent so $\angle B \cong \angle E$. Therefore
$x = \frac{32}{5}$ $\triangle ABC \sim \triangle FED$ by the AA Postulate.

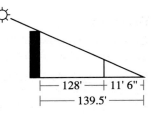

Try This

If $EF = 15$, find AB.

THEOREM 6.3   Right Triangle Similarity

If an acute angle of one right triangle is congruent to an acute angle of
another right triangle, then the triangles are similar.

Example 3

Application   A man 6 ft tall casts a shadow that is 11 ft 6 in. long. The
end of his shadow coincides with the end of the shadow cast
by a building 128 ft from the man. Find the height of the building.

Solution

Let x = height of the building.
$\frac{6}{11.5} = \frac{x}{139.5}$
$x = \frac{139.5(6)}{11.5}$
$x \approx 72.78$ ft   The building is about 73 ft high.

Try This

How tall would the building be if the man's shadow were 10 ft long?

Example 4

Given: $\triangle ABC$ is isosceles with base $\overline{BC}$. $\overline{DE} \perp \overline{BC}$, $\overline{FG} \perp \overline{BC}$

Prove: $\frac{DE}{FG} = \frac{BE}{CG}$

Proof

Statements	Reasons
1. $\triangle ABC$ is isosceles.	1. Given
2. $\angle B \cong \angle C$	2. Base $\angle$s of an isos. $\triangle$ are $\cong$.
3. $\overline{DE} \perp \overline{BC}$, $\overline{FG} \perp \overline{BC}$	3. Given
4. $\angle BED$ and $\angle CGF$ are rt. $\angle$s.	4. __?__
5. $\triangle BED$ and $\triangle CGF$ are rt. $\triangle$s.	5. Definition of rt. $\triangle$
6. $\triangle DEB \sim \triangle FGC$	6. Rt. $\triangle$ Similarity Theorem
7. $\frac{DE}{FG} = \frac{BE}{CG}$	7. Ratios of corr. sides of $\sim\triangle$s are $=$.

Solution

4. Definition of $\perp$ line segments

Class Exercises

Short Answer

Which of these statements about △DEF and △GHI are true?

1. If $m\angle E = 32$, $m\angle H = 32$, $m\angle D = 68$, and $m\angle G = 68$, then $\triangle DEF \sim \triangle GHI$.
2. If $m\angle F = m\angle I = 90$, $m\angle D = 35$, and $m\angle H = 50$, then $\triangle DEF \sim \triangle GHI$.
3. If $m\angle F = m\angle I = 115$, $m\angle E = 30$, and $m\angle H = 40$, then $\triangle DEF \sim \triangle GHI$.

State the measure of $\angle A$ that would make the given triangles similar.

4.

5.

6.

Sample Exercises

$\overline{BE} \parallel \overline{DF}$, $\overline{BC} \perp \overline{AC}$, $\overline{DE} \perp \overline{AE}$ **Complete each statement.**

7. $\triangle ABC \sim$ ___   8. $\triangle ADF \sim$ ___   9. $\frac{AE}{AC} =$ ___

10. Write a proportion that can be used to find x.
11. Find x.

Discussion

Determine whether each statement is always true, sometimes true, or never true. Draw pictures as needed and explain your answer.

12. Two right triangles are similar.   13. Two obtuse triangles are similar.
14. Two isosceles triangles with congruent vertex angles are similar.
15. Two isosceles right triangles are similar.

Exercises

A

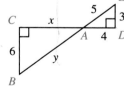

Complete each statement.

1. $\triangle ABC \sim$ ___   2. The proportion ___ can be used to find x.
3. $x =$ ___   4. The proportion ___ can be used to find y.
5. $y =$ ___

$\overline{BC} \parallel \overline{DE}$ **Find x and y.**

6.

7.

8.

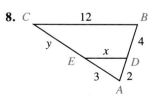

Identify a pair of similar triangles and find x and y.

9.

10.

11.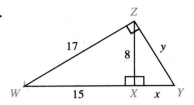

Prove that each pair of triangles is similar.

12. $\triangle ABC \sim \triangle DEC$ **13.** $\triangle ABC \sim \triangle BDC$ **14.** $\triangle BED \sim \triangle ADB$ **15.** $\triangle ADB \sim \triangle DEC$

16. Prove Theorem 6.3.

    Given: right triangles ABC and XYZ with
           $\angle A$ and $\angle X$ right angles, $\angle B \cong \angle Y$
    Prove: $\triangle ABC \sim \triangle XYZ$

17. A person 5 ft 6 in. tall casts a shadow that is 14 ft long, the end of which lies at the end of the shadow cast by a building that is 328 ft away from the person. How tall is the building?

18. When a mirror is placed on the ground so that the top of a building can be seen beside a person standing by the mirror, $m\angle BMA = m\angle DMC$. A person 150 cm tall who is 6 m from the mirror observes the top of the tower when the mirror is 120 m from the tower. Find the height of the building.

19. To find the distance x across a river, a surveyor located points A, B, C, and D through direct measurement. Find the distance x.

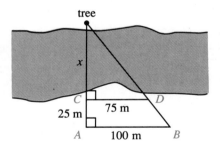

20. Given: $\angle 3 \cong \angle 4$
    Prove: $\triangle ABC \sim \triangle EDC$

21. Given: $\overline{AB} \parallel \overline{ED}$
    Prove: $\dfrac{AB}{ED} = \dfrac{BC}{DC}$

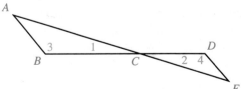

B

$ABCD$ is a trapezoid with bases $\overline{AD}$ and $\overline{BC}$. Identify a pair of similar triangles and find x and y.

22.

23.

24.

25. Rectangle *LMNO* coincides with rectangle *STUO* in such a way that $\overline{OL}$ lies on $\overline{OS}$ and $\overline{ON}$ lies on $\overline{OU}$. Show that when the diagonal from point *O* to point *T* passes through point *M*, the rectangles are similar.

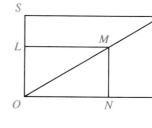

Use a straightedge and the diagonal test to determine whether the rectangles are similar.

26.   **27.**   **28.**

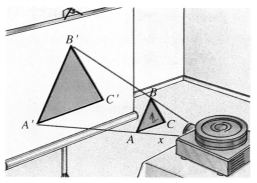

29. When a photograph is taken, the image formed on the film is similar to the object being photographed. Similar triangles help to explain this. If $\overline{AB}$ and $\overline{A'B'}$ are parallel, prove $\triangle LAB$ and $\triangle LB'A'$ are similar.

Suppose a slide projector and screen are set up as shown with the screen 20 ft from the projector. Assume *ABC* is similar to *A′B′C′* and these planes are parallel.

30. If the triangular cutout *ABC* is placed 2 ft in front of the projector, find the length of *A′B′* in terms of *AB*.

31. If the triangular cutout *ABC* is placed *x* ft in front of the projector, calculate the length *A′B′* in terms of the length *AB* and the distance *x*.

32. If *x* is halved, what happens to *A′B′*?

33. If *x* is doubled, what happens to *A′B′*?

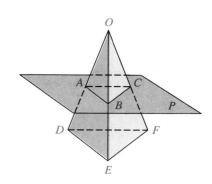

34. Given: $\overline{BE}$ and $\overline{AD}$ are altitudes.
    Prove: $\dfrac{AD}{AC} = \dfrac{BE}{BC}$

35. Given: $\triangle AEB$ is isosceles.
    Prove: $AD \cdot AF = CF \cdot BD$

     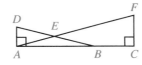

36. Given: *ABCD* is a parallelogram.
    $\overline{AE} \perp \overline{CD}$, $\overline{AF} \perp \overline{BC}$
    Prove: $AE \cdot CD = AF \cdot BC$

37. Given: $\overline{AB} \cong \overline{AC}$,
    $\angle A \cong \angle CBD$
    Prove: $\dfrac{AB}{BD} = \dfrac{BC}{CD}$

     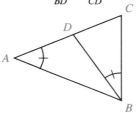

C

38. Given: Plane *P* is parallel to $\triangle DEF$.
    Prove: $\dfrac{AB}{DE} = \dfrac{BC}{EF} = \dfrac{AC}{DF}$.

39. *ABCD* is a parallelogram. Find *x*.
(HINT: Set up two proportions by using △*AED* and △*AEB* and triangles similar to them.)

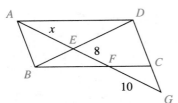

40. Given: $\overline{AD}$, $\overline{BE}$, and $\overline{CF}$ are altitudes.
Prove: $\dfrac{AF}{BF} \cdot \dfrac{BD}{CD} \cdot \dfrac{CE}{AE} = 1$
(HINT: Begin by writing three proportions using three pairs of similar right triangles.)

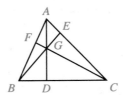

Critical Thinking

41. Trace pentagon *ABCDE* and all its diagonals as shown in the figure to the right. Assume that all sides of *ABCDE* are equal in length and all vertex angles are equal in measure. Label the angle measures of as many angles in your tracing as possible.

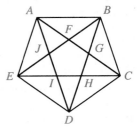

42. Show that △*JAE* ~ △*ABE* and conclude that $\dfrac{EJ}{AE} = \dfrac{AE}{EB}$. Show that *AE* = *EF* and write a proportion using *EJ*, *EF*, and *EB*.

43. Suppose that *AE* = *EF* = 1. Let *x* = *EJ*. Use the proportion from Exercise 42 to show that $\dfrac{x}{1} = \dfrac{1}{1+x}$. Show that $x = \dfrac{-1 + \sqrt{5}}{2}$.

Mixed Review

Any two equilateral triangles are similar.

1. Write the statement as a conditional.
2. Write the inverse of the statement.
3. Write the contrapositive of the statement

If two triangles are congruent, then they are similar.

4. Write the converse of the statement.
5. Show that the converse is false.
6. If the inverse is false, give a counterexample.

CONNECTIONS ◇◇

Transformations

Similarity as discussed in this lesson is related to concepts studied in algebra. Consider the transformation that associates each point (*x*, *y*) in the coordinate plane with the point (2*x* + 2, 2*y* + 3)—the red triangle with the blue triangle.

1. Calculate the lengths of the sides of each triangle to show that the three ratios of corresponding sides are proportional.
2. Draw on graph paper the triangle whose vertices are (−2, −1), (4, −1), and (2, 3). Then draw the triangle associated with it by the transformation above.
3. Show that the ratios of corresponding sides are proportional.

$(x, y) \rightarrow (2x + 2, 2y + 3)$

6-5 SAS and SSS Similarity Theorems

The AA Similarity Postulate provides what is probably the most often used method of showing that two triangles are similar, since it requires proving only two pairs of angles congruent.

However, there are other methods for proving triangles similar. The SAS Theorem below describes a comparison between two pairs of sides and one pair of included angles.

A mechanical linkage, called a pantograph, is used by draftsmen to enlarge or reduce drawings.

◆ **THEOREM 6.4**   SAS Similarity Theorem

If an angle of one triangle is congruent to an angle of another triangle and if the lengths of the sides including these angles are proportional, then the triangles are similar.

Given: $\angle C \cong \angle F, \frac{AC}{DF} = \frac{BC}{EF}$

Prove: $\triangle ABC \sim \triangle DEF$

Plan   Suppose that $CA < FD$. Choose point U on $\overline{FD}$ so that $UF = AC$ and point V on $\overline{FE}$ so that $\angle 1 \cong \angle FDE$. Then $\triangle UVF \sim \triangle DEF$ by AA Similarity. Use this similarity to conclude that $\frac{UF}{DF} = \frac{VF}{EF}$. It is given that $\frac{AC}{DF} = \frac{BC}{EF}$ from which it can be concluded that $VF = BC$ (recall, $AC = UF$). Conclude that $\triangle UFV \cong \triangle ACB$ by SAS and that $\triangle ACB \sim \triangle UFV \sim \triangle DEF$.

Example 1

Find the value of x for which $\triangle ABC \sim \triangle DEF$. State the theorem that justifies your answer.

Solution

$\frac{5}{7} = \frac{8}{x}$

$5x = 56$

$x = \frac{56}{5}$

The triangles are similar by the SAS Similarity Theorem.

Try This

Given: $\triangle ABC$ and $\triangle XYZ$ If $\angle A \cong \angle X$, state the proportion that must be true to conclude that $\triangle ABC \sim \triangle XYZ$ by SAS Similarity.

Example 2

Application: In the pantograph, P, D, and E are collinear, $AD = BC$, $AB = CD$, and $\frac{AB}{AP} = \frac{CE}{BC}$. How does PD compare to DE?

Solution

$ABCD$ is a parallelogram.	*By construction opposite sides of ABCD are congruent.*
$\angle PAD \cong \angle B \cong \angle DCE$	*If parallel lines are cut by a transversal, corresponding angles are congruent.*
$\frac{x}{u} = \frac{v}{y}$	*This is true by the pantograph construction.*
$\triangle APD \sim \triangle CDE$	*SAS Similarity Theorem*
$\frac{PD}{DE} = \frac{u}{x}$	*Corresponding sides of similar triangles are proportional.*
or $PD = \frac{u}{x} \cdot DE$	

Try This

In the pantograph shown, if $PA = 5$ cm and $AB = 10$ cm, find $\frac{DE}{PD}$.

The next theorem describes a situation where three pairs of sides of two triangles allow you to conclude that the triangles are similar.

◆ **THEOREM 6.5** SSS Similarity Theorem

If corresponding sides of two triangles are proportional, then the two triangles are similar.

Given: $\frac{AC}{DF} = \frac{AB}{DE} = \frac{AB}{DE}$

Prove: $\triangle ABC \sim \triangle DEF$

Plan Suppose that $AB < DE$. Choose point X on $\overline{DE}$ so that $DX = AB$ and choose point Y on $\overline{DF}$ so that $\overline{XY}$ is parallel to $\overline{EF}$. It follows that $\angle 1 \cong \angle 2$ and $\triangle DXY \sim \triangle DEF$ by AA Similarity. Consequently, $\frac{DY}{DF} = \frac{XY}{EF}$. Use this proportion together with the given proportion to conclude that $AC = DY$, $AB = DX$, and $XY = BC$. It follows that $\triangle ABC \cong \triangle DXY$. Therefore, $\triangle ABC \sim \triangle DXY \sim \triangle DEF$.

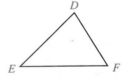

Example 3

Find the value of x for which $\triangle ABC \sim \triangle EDA$.

Solution

$\frac{6}{4} = \frac{9}{6} = \frac{x+4}{x}$ $\quad$ If $\frac{AB}{ED} = \frac{BC}{DA} = \frac{AC}{EA}$,

$\frac{3}{2} = \frac{x+4}{x}$ $\qquad$ *then the triangles are similar.*

$3x = 2x + 8$

$x = 8$

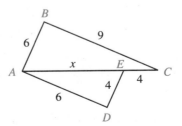

Try This

If $EC = 3$ and the triangles are similar, show that the two triangles are isosceles.

Class Exercises

Short Answer

Determine whether the two triangles shown are similar. If so, state the postulate or theorem that justifies your answer.

(handwritten) similat

(handwritten top right) 1.5 × 2 / 3.0

(handwritten) $\frac{3}{5}$ $\frac{5}{9}$ = $\frac{25}{27}$

1.

2.   *(handwritten)* SAS

3.   *(handwritten)* NO

4.

5.

6.

7.

8.

9. *(see figure)*

3.

6. *(figure for 6 under id 10)*

Sample Exercises

State whether you can conclude that $\triangle ABC \sim \triangle DEF$ from the given information.

10. $\angle A \cong \angle D$, $\frac{AC}{DF} = \frac{AB}{DE}$

11. $\frac{DF}{AC} = \frac{DE}{AB} = \frac{EF}{BC}$

12. $\angle B \cong \angle E$, $\frac{EF}{BC} = \frac{AC}{FD}$

13. $\angle C \cong \angle F$, $\frac{AC}{BC} = \frac{DF}{EF}$

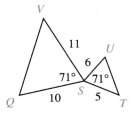

14. Given: $\triangle ABC$ and $\triangle DEF$, $\angle B \cong \angle E$, $AB = 6$, $DE = 2$, $BC = 4$
Find the length of $\overline{EF}$ for which $\triangle ABC \sim \triangle DEF$.

15. Given: $\triangle RST$ and $\triangle UVW$, $RS = 6$, $UV = 8$, $ST = 9$, $RT = 12$
Find lengths of $\overline{VW}$ and $\overline{UW}$ for which $\triangle RST \sim \triangle UVW$.

16. Given: $\triangle ABC$ and $\triangle DEF$, $DE = 6$, $EF = 3$, $DF = 9$, $AB = 4$, $BC = 2$
Find the length of $\overline{AC}$ for which $\triangle ABC \sim \triangle DEF$.

Discussion

17. Given: quadrilaterals $ABCD$ and $WXYZ$, $\frac{AB}{WX} = \frac{BC}{XY} = \frac{CD}{YZ} = \frac{AD}{WZ}$
Are the quadrilaterals similar? If so, give a convincing argument to support your answer. If not, give a counterexample.

Exercises

A

Find a value of x for which the triangles are similar. State the theorem that justifies your answer.

1.

2.

3.

4.

5.

6.

7.

8.

9.

Draw and label figures for each exercise.

10. Given: $\triangle ABC$ and $\triangle DEF$ If $\angle B \cong \angle E$, state the proportion that must be true if $\triangle ABC \sim \triangle DEF$ by SAS Similarity.

11. Given: $\triangle UAZ$ and $\triangle RBN$ If $\angle U \cong \angle R$, state the proportion that must be true if $\triangle UAZ \sim \triangle RBN$ by SAS Similarity.

12. Given: $\triangle GHI$ and $\triangle KLM$ If $\angle I \cong \angle M$, state the proportion that must be true if $\triangle GHI \sim \triangle KLM$ by SAS Similarity.

13. Given: $\triangle XYZ$ and $\triangle UVW$ State the proportions that must be true if $\triangle XYZ \sim \triangle UVW$ by SSS Similarity.

14. $\triangle ADE \sim \triangle ABC$ Find AD and BD.

15. $y = 7$ Is $\triangle ADE \sim \triangle ABC$?

16. Find the value of y that makes $\overline{DE} \parallel \overline{BC}$.

17. **Given:** $\frac{AO}{CO} = \frac{BO}{DO}$

   Prove: $\angle B \cong \angle D$

Ex. 17

18. **Given:** $\frac{AB}{CD} = \frac{AO}{OC} = \frac{BO}{OD}$

   Prove: $\angle 1 \cong \angle 2$

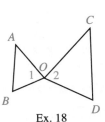

Ex. 18

19. In the pantograph in Example 2, the ratio $\frac{PE}{PD}$ is called the magnification factor. If $PA = 5$ in. and $AB = 7$ in., what is the magnification factor of the pantograph?

The figure describes a camera with film width *XY* that is 35 mm and with focal length 50 mm. The scene has width *AB*.

20. What assumptions do you make about this figure that allow the conclusion △*ALB* ~ △*XLY*?

21. What is the width of the scene *AB*?

22. If the lens of the camera has a focal length of 100 mm, what is the width of the scene?

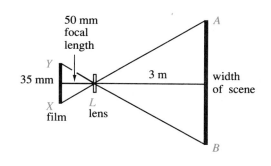

B

Use this figure for Exercises 23–25.

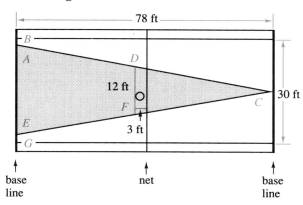

23. Suppose that a tennis player standing 3 ft from the net at the center of the court can return all balls hit within 6 ft on each side of him. Then his opponent standing at the center of the base line would have to hit the ball outside the shaded region in order to hit a "winner." What assumptions do you make in order to ensure that △*ACE* ~ △*DCF*?

24. What is the distance *AB* from the corner of the shaded triangle to the corner of the singles court?

25. If the distance from the player to the net is 6 ft, will the distance *AB* increase or decrease? by how much?

Use the figure and the table to identify which triangles, if any, are similar.

	AB	BC	CD	DE	FE	AF	BF	FD
26.	1	1	1	1	1	1	1	1
27.	3	6	6	3	6	3	3	5.2
28.	1	2	2	4	4	2	2	2
29.	8	16	24	3	20	4	8	18
30.	1	2	2	1	1	2	1.7	1
31.	4	10	10	2	4	8	6.5	4

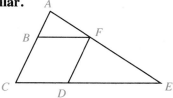

32. Given: △*ABD* ~ △*EFH*

C is the midpoint of $\overline{BD}$.

G is the midpoint of $\overline{FH}$.

Prove: △*ABC* ~ △*EFG*

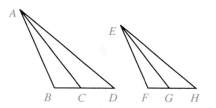

33. Proportional dividers are used to construct segments of proportional length. Two pieces of the same length are connected with a set screw. Suppose the set screw O is set so that $OW = OY = 3OX = 3OZ$. How does the length WY compare to the length XZ? Explain.

34. Find the lengths of the sides of these triangles.

35. Use the SSS Similarity Theorem to show that $\angle DFE \cong \angle CAB$.

36. Name the coordinates of points X, Y, Z so that $\triangle XYZ \sim \triangle ABC$.

37. Given: $\angle A \cong \angle CBD$
  Prove: $AC \cdot DC = BC \cdot BC$

38. Given: $AC \cdot DC = BC \cdot BC$
  Prove: $\angle A \cong \angle CBD$

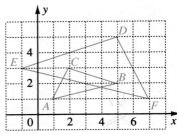

Ex. 34–36

C

39. Give a counterexample to show that this statement is false. If two sides of one triangle are proportional to two sides of another triangle and an angle of the first triangle is congruent to an angle of the second triangle, the triangles are similar.

40. Given: point O on lines $\overline{AA'}$, $\overline{BB'}$, $\overline{CC'}$, $\dfrac{OA'}{OA} = \dfrac{OB'}{OB} = \dfrac{OC'}{OC}$
  Prove: $\overline{AB} \| \overline{A'B'}$, $\overline{BC} \| \overline{B'C'}$, $\overline{AC} \| \overline{A'C'}$

Critical Thinking

41. Suppose that lines p and q intersect at A and points B_1, B_2, B_3, . . . are on p and C_1, C_2, C_3, . . . are on q so that the following pattern of equations is true. State the next two equations in each of these patterns.
  a. $AC_1 \cdot AC_2 = (AB_1)^2$
  $\quad AC_2 \cdot AC_3 = (AB_2)^2$
  b. $AB_1 \cdot AB_2 = (AC_2)^2$
  $\quad AB_2 \cdot AB_3 = (AC_3)^2$

42. Use the equations in Exercise 41 to show that $\triangle AC_1B_1 \sim \triangle AB_1C_2 \sim \triangle AC_2B_2 \sim \triangle AB_2C_3 \sim \triangle AC_3B_3$. (HINT: Rewrite each equation as a proportion.)

Algebra Review

Solve.

1. $n^2 - 9 = 0$ **2.** $n^2 - 6 = 0$ **3.** $n^2 - 4 = 0$ **4.** $n^2 - 25 = 0$
5. $2n^2 - 8 = 0$ **6.** $(3n)^2 = 81$ **7.** $3n^2 + 9 = 2n^2 + 25$ **8.** $n^2 + 6n = 18$

Computer Activity
Computer Construction

Use a computer software program to complete the following constructions. Then measure the ratios of the segment lengths. Suggest theorems that you think could be proven.

a line parallel to
a side of a triangle

three parallel lines cut
by transversals

6-6 Segments Divided Proportionally

EXPLORE

Draw a segment AB and a point X between A and B. Then draw a second segment CD parallel to $\overline{AB}$.

Using a straightedge only, devise a method for constructing a point Y on $\overline{CD}$ so that $\frac{AX}{XB} = \frac{CY}{YD}$.

Segments $\overline{AB}$ and $\overline{CD}$ are **divided proportionally** by points X on $\overline{AB}$ and Y on $\overline{CD}$ if $\frac{AX}{XB} = \frac{CY}{YD}$.

In the Explore you may have discovered a method of constructing a point Y so that $\overline{AB}$ and $\overline{CD}$ are divided proportionally by X and Y.

◆ **THEOREM 6.6**   Triangle Proportional Segment Theorem

If a line parallel to one side of a triangle intersects the other two sides, then it divides the two sides proportionally.

Given: $\triangle ABC$, $\overline{DE} \| \overline{BC}$

Prove: $\frac{AD}{DB} = \frac{AE}{EC}$

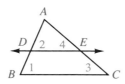

*IF those lines
are parellel
then thesides
are
proportional*

Proof

Statements	Reasons
1. $\overline{DE} \| \overline{BC}$	1. Given
2. $\angle 1 \cong \angle 2$, $\angle 3 \cong \angle 4$	2. If $\|$ lines are cut by a trans., corr. $\angle$s are $\cong$.
3. $\triangle ABC \sim \triangle ADE$	3. AA Similarity Theorem
4. $\frac{AB}{AD} = \frac{AC}{AE}$	4. Corr. sides of similar $\triangle$s are proportional.
5. $\frac{AB - AD}{AD} = \frac{AC - AE}{AE}$	5. Property of Proportions
6. $\frac{DB}{AD} = \frac{EC}{AE}$	6. Segment Addition Property
7. $\frac{AD}{DB} = \frac{AE}{EC}$	7. Property of Proportions

Example 1

Given: $\triangle ABC$ with $\overline{DE} \parallel \overline{AC}$
Find x.

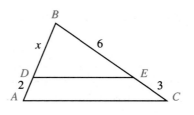

Solution

$\frac{x}{2} = \frac{6}{3}$ *This proportion is true by the Triangle*
$3x = 12$ *Proportional Segment Theorem.*
$x = 4$

Try This

Given: $\triangle ABC$ with $\overline{DE} \parallel \overline{AC}$ If $BE = 5$, find x.

The next theorem is the converse of Theorem 6.6. Its proof will be completed in Exercise 24.

If those sides are proportional then the lines ~~sides~~ are parellel

◆ **THEOREM 6.7**

If a line divides two sides of a triangle proportionally, then the line is parallel to the third side.

◆ **THEOREM 6.8**   Parallels Proportional Segment Theorem

If three parallel lines intersect two transversals, then they divide the transversals proportionally.

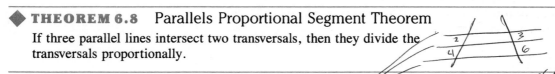

If 3 lines orparellel then the sides are proportional

Given: $\overline{AX} \parallel \overline{BY} \parallel \overline{CZ}$

Prove: $\frac{AB}{BC} = \frac{XY}{YZ}$

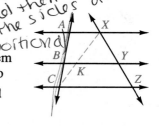

Plan   Draw the auxiliary segment $\overline{CX}$ intersecting $\overline{BY}$ at K. Apply Theorem 6.6 to $\triangle CAX$ to conclude that $\frac{CB}{BA} = \frac{CK}{KX}$. Then apply this theorem to $\triangle XCZ$ to conclude that $\frac{XK}{KC} = \frac{XY}{YZ}$. Use properties of proportions and equality to conclude that $\frac{AB}{BC} = \frac{XY}{YZ}$.

Example 2

$\overline{AD} \parallel \overline{BE} \parallel \overline{CF}$
EF is $\frac{3}{2}$ less than three times the length of DE.
Find DE and EF.

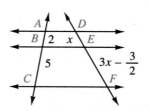

Solution

Let $DE = x$. Then $EF = 3x - \frac{3}{2}$.

$\frac{AB}{BC} = \frac{DE}{EF}$ *Parallels Proportional Segment Theorem*

$\frac{2}{5} = \frac{x}{3x - \frac{3}{2}}$

$6x - 3 = 5x$

$x = 3$

$DE = 3$ $EF = 3(3) - \frac{3}{2} = \frac{15}{2}$

Try This

If $\overline{EF}$ is three more than $\frac{3}{2}$ times as long as $\overline{DE}$, find DE and EF.

The Triangle Proportional Segment Theorem is used to prove the next theorem.

◆ **THEOREM 6.9**   Triangle Angle Bisector Theorem
If a ray bisects an angle of a triangle, then it divides the opposite side into two segments whose lengths are proportional to the lengths of the other two sides.

These are Proportional 2 these

Given: $\angle 1 \cong \angle 2$
Prove: $\frac{AD}{DB} = \frac{AC}{CB}$

Plan   Draw auxiliary segment $\overline{BE}$ parallel to $\overline{CD}$. Extend $\overline{AC}$ to point E. Use properties of parallel lines to conclude that $\angle 1 \cong \angle 4$ and $\angle 2 \cong \angle 3$, and conclude that $CE = CB$. Apply the Triangle Proportional Segment Theorem to show that $\frac{AD}{DB} = \frac{AC}{CE}$. By substitution $\frac{AD}{DB} = \frac{AC}{CB}$.

Example 3   E   Example 3 3
If $\angle 1 \cong \angle 2$, find AD and DB.

   Solution
   $\frac{x}{15-x} = \frac{5}{12}$ *Triangle Angle Bisector Theorem*
   $12x = 75 - 5x$
   $17x = 75$
   $x = \frac{75}{17} = AD$ $BD = 15 - x = 15 - \frac{75}{17} = \frac{180}{17} \approx 10.59$

Try This   Try This   Try this
Use the figure to the right above.
If $AB = 13$, find AD and DB.

Three additional theorems also concern ratios in similar triangles.

◆ **THEOREM 6.10**
The lengths of bisectors of corresponding angles of two similar triangles are in the same ratio as the lengths of corresponding sides.

proportional

◆ **THEOREM 6.11**
The lengths of altitudes from corresponding vertices of similar triangles are in the same ratio as the lengths of corresponding sides.

◆ **THEOREM 6.12**
The lengths of medians from corresponding vertices of similar triangles are in the same ratio as the lengths of corresponding sides.

Class Exercises

Short Answer

Determine whether segments $\overline{AB}$ and $\overline{CD}$ are divided proportionally.

1.
A   5   X   2   B

C   10   Y   4   D

2.
A   8   X   5   B

C   16   Y   10   D

3.
A   7   X   4   B

C   14   Y   10   D

$\overline{BC}\|\overline{DE}$, $\angle 1 \cong \angle 2$ Complete each statement.

4. $\frac{a}{b} = $ _____

5. $\frac{AE}{AD} = $ _____

6. $\frac{AE}{AB} = $ _____

Line p, q, and r are parallel. Complete each statement.

7. $\frac{c}{d} = $ _____

8. $\frac{AB}{BC} = $ _____

Sample Problems

Find x. State the theorem that justifies each answer.

9.

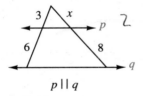

$p\|q$

10. $\angle 1 \cong \angle 2$

11.

$p\|q\|r$

Discussion

12. Suppose that $\overline{DE}$ is parallel to $\overline{AB}$. One student claimed AB could be found by solving the proportion $\frac{3}{2} = \frac{7}{x}$. Discuss this method. Explain why this method does or does not work.

Exercises

A

Find x. State the theorem that justifies each answer.

1.

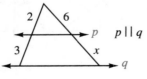

$p\|q$

2. $\angle 1 \cong \angle 2$

3.

$p\|q\|r$

4. $\angle 1 \cong \angle 2$

5.

$p\|q\|r$

6.

$p\|q$

In the figure, $\overline{BE}$ bisects $\angle B$ and $\overline{DE}\,\|\,\overline{BC}$.

7. Use the Triangle Proportional Segment Theorem to complete the proportion $\frac{x}{y} = $ ___ .
8. Use the Triangle Angle Bisector Theorem to complete $\frac{x}{y} = $ ___ .
9. Combine the results of Exercises 7–8 to find z.
10. Find the length of $\overline{DE}$.   11. If $y = 7$, find x.

Given $\triangle ADH$, $\overline{DF}$ bisects $\angle D$ and $p\,\|\,q\,\|\,r$. Find the indicated length and state the theorem applied.

12. If $AB = 2$, $BD = 7$, and $EH = 14$, find AE.
13. If $AD = 12$, $DH = 15$, and $FH = 10$, find AF.
14. If $AC = 8$, $CD = 3$, and $AH = 15$, find AG and GH.
15. If $AF = 6$, $FH = 8$, $AC = 7$, and $DH = 13$, find CD.

 B

16. In a new subdivision three trapezoidal lots are each 125 ft across the front. The lot lines on the side are all perpendicular to the front. What is the length of the property line across the back of each lot?
17. A carpenter wants to cut a $9\frac{1}{4}$ in.-wide board into five pieces equal in width. (NOTE: $9\frac{1}{4} \div 5 = 1\frac{17}{20}$, a unit that does not appear on a carpenter's ruler) Since he cannot divide $9\frac{1}{4}$ by 5 and measure directly, he places a ruler diagonally so that 10 units show across the board. Then he draws a horizontal line every 2 units. Explain why this method works.

$ABCD$ is a trapezoid with bases $\overline{AB}$ and $\overline{CD}$, and $\overline{EF}\,\|\,\overline{AB}$.

18. If $\frac{AE}{ED} = \frac{1}{4}$ and $BC = 30$, find BF and FC.
19. If $\frac{BG}{BD} = \frac{3}{4}$, $AD = 8$, and $BC = 14$, find AE, ED, BF, and FC.
20. If $BG = 3$, $GD = 5$, and $GF = 4$, find CD.
21. If $AE = 2$, $ED = 3$, and $GF = 4$, find CD.

22. Two people walk away from each other at an angle, one moving straight ahead at 6 ft per second, the other moving straight ahead at 4 ft per second. After 5 seconds they are 24 ft apart. If they continue at the same angle and pace, how far apart will they be after 1 minute?
23. Prove that the construction you developed in the Explore is correct.
24. Prove Theorem 6.7.   25. Prove Theorem 6.9   26. Prove Theorem 6.10.
27. Prove Theorem 6.11   28. Prove Theorem 6.12.

C

29. In the pentagon-based pyramid on the left, $\overline{WX}\,\|\,\overline{BC}$, $\overline{XY}\,\|\,\overline{CD}$, $\overline{YZ}\,\|\,\overline{DE}$, $AW = 2$, $WB = 3$, and $AE = 6$. Find AZ and ZE.
30. If $\overline{DE}\,\|\,\overline{BC}$, show algebraically that $\overline{BF}$ cannot be the angle bisector of $\angle B$ in the figure on the right. (HINT: Obtain two equations involving x assuming that $\overline{DF}$ is the angle bisector. Show that the two equations imply different values for x, which is not possible.)

Critical Thinking

31. Given: Planes $P_1 \parallel P_2 \parallel P_3$ and transversals p and q that are skew lines.

    a. Is $\overleftrightarrow{AX}$ always, sometimes, or never parallel to $\overleftrightarrow{CZ}$?

    b. Prove that $\frac{AB}{BC} = \frac{XY}{YZ}$.

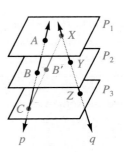

Mixed Review

1. If an airplane climbs 6000 ft while traveling 15 mi during its ascent, how many miles will it take to climb 33,000 ft?

2. At its current rate of ascent how high will the airplane be after 46 mi?

3. How many miles did the plane travel in climbing from 16,000 ft to 20,000 ft?

6000 ft

15 mi

Complete each statement. Use acute, right, obtuse, equilateral, isosceles, or scalene.

4. A right triangle may never have a(n) ____ angle.

5. An isosceles triangle is never ____ .

6. The acute angles of a(n) ____ triangle are complementary.

7. An equilateral triangle is always ____ .

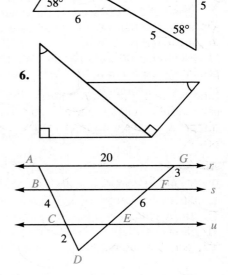

CRITICAL THINKING

Recognizing Quantifier Errors in Reasoning

Many reasoning errors occur in critical thinking because people do not know how to use the **quantifier** words *all*, *no*, and *some*. Consider these examples.

Example 1—All

Nino said, "All my friends dislike me."
"You're wrong," said Tico, "All your friends like you a lot."

Since *all* means *every* member of a certain set, Tico could have negated Nino's statement by giving a counterexample, "You're wrong—I'm your friend and I like you."

Example 2—No

Jenny said, "No student from Lincoln High is friendly."
"I don't agree," said Sara, "All of the ones I've met are really friendly."

Since *no* means *not one, or none* Sara found one example to contradict Jenny's statement and could say, "I disagree. I've met Sandy Sloan and she is very friendly."

Example 3—Some

Tip said, "Some theorems in geometry are easy to prove."
"I disagree," said Bill, "Some theorems in geometry are not easy to prove."

Since *some* means *at least one,* Bill would have to say the following to negate Tip's statement, "I disagree. No theorem in geometry is easy to prove."

All, no, and *some* statements can be written in one of the following four forms.

I. All A are B.
II. No A is B.
III. Some A are B.
IV. Some A are not B.

Exercises

What would you have to do to prove that the statements in Exercises 1–4 are false?

1. Tom said, "All frogs are green."
2. Katy said, "No compact disk costs less than $10."
3. A teacher said, "Some students in our class are absent today."
4. A geometry student said, "Some triangles have two lines of symmetry."

Use statements I–IV above.

5. Give examples to explain why statements I and II are not negations of each other. Do the same for statements III and IV.
6. Which pairs from statements I, II, III, and IV are negations of each other? Give examples to explain why you think so.
7. What if-then statement means the same as statement I? statement II?
8. Which statement means the same as "Anytime an A is found to exist, it is guaranteed to be a B."? as "Anytime an A is found to exist, it is guaranteed not to be a B."?

CHAPTER SUMMARY

Vocabulary

extremes (6-1)	proportion (6-1)	scale factor (6-3)
means (6-1)	ratio (6-1)	similar polygons (6-3)

Key Ideas

1. The properties of proportions are used to change proportions into equivalent forms.
2. In similar polygons, the corresponding angles are congruent and the lengths of the corresponding sides are proportional.
3. Prove two triangles similar by AA, SAS, or SSS.
4. Prove two right triangles similar by showing a pair of acute angles congruent.
5. If a line is parallel to one side of a triangle and intersects the other two sides, then it divides those two sides proportionally.
6. Three parallel lines cut a pair of transversals proportionally.
7. If a ray bisects an angle of a triangle, then it divides the opposite side into segments whose lengths are proportional to the lengths of the other two sides.

CHAPTER REVIEW

6-1

Give each ratio in simplest form.

1. $\frac{3t}{15}$ 2. 33 to 9   3. $16xy : 20x$ 4. $\frac{45x^2y}{18xy^2}$

5. If $3 : 5 = 7 : x$, then $x = \underline{\ ?\ }$.   6. If $2 : 6 = x : 18$, then $x = \underline{\ ?\ }$.
7. The measures of two supplementary angles are in a ratio $3 : 15$. What are the measures of the angles?
8. A 42-cm line segment is divided into two segments whose lengths are in a ratio of 5 to 9. How long is each segment?

6-2

Complete each statement and state which property of proportions you are using.

9. If $\frac{x}{y} = \frac{5}{7}$, then $7x = \underline{\ \ \ }$.   10. If $\frac{8}{t} = \frac{4}{w}$, then $\frac{t}{8} = \underline{\ \ \ }$.

11. If $\frac{3}{4} = \frac{x}{y}$, then $\frac{y}{4} = \underline{\ \ \ }$.   12. If $\frac{x}{3} = \frac{4}{w}$, then $\frac{x-3}{3} = \underline{\ \ \ }$.

Find the value of x.

13. $\frac{5}{4} = \frac{x-7}{8}$ 14. $\frac{x+1}{4} = \frac{7}{2}$ 15. $\frac{2}{5} = \frac{6}{x-4}$

16. $\frac{3x}{8} = \frac{9}{6}$ 17. $\frac{x+2}{2} = \frac{16}{2x+4}$ 18. $\frac{2x}{3} = \frac{4}{x-1}$

19. On a map, $\frac{1}{2}$ in. represents 2 mi. If the distance from a shopping mall to the high school is $\frac{3}{4}$ in. on the map, what is the distance in miles?
20. A 75 yd × 50 yd parking area was decreased in size by multiplying each dimension by a factor of $\frac{4}{5}$. Find the new length and width.

6-3

$\triangle ABC \sim \triangle DEF$
Complete each of the following.

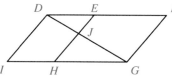

21. $m\angle E =$ ___
22. $m\angle F =$ ___
23. $EF =$ ___
24. $AC =$ ___
25. The scale factor of $\triangle ABC$ to $\triangle DEF$ is ___ .

10 5
5 2

157.
7
180
157
23

6-4

26. If $\angle R \cong \angle SWX$, then $\triangle SRU \sim$ _?_
by the _?_ postulate.
27. **Given:** $\overline{RS} \parallel \overline{UT}$
Prove: $\triangle WXS \sim \triangle VXU$

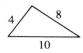

$\overline{RU} \parallel \overline{WV}$

28. A person 5 ft 9 in. tall casts a $3\frac{1}{2}$-ft shadow, the foot of which lies at the end of the shadow cast by a tree 12 ft away. How tall is the tree?
29. If a person 6-ft tall casts a shadow 9 ft long, how long a shadow would a person 4 ft 6 in. tall cast?

6-5

State if the two triangles are similar. If so, state a theorem or postulate that justifies your answer. If not, write *triangles not similar.*

30.

31.

32.
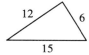

33. Given: $\triangle RST$ and $\triangle GHI$ If $\angle T \cong \angle I$, state the proportion that must be true if $\triangle RST \sim \triangle GHI$ by SAS Similarity.
34. Given: $\triangle WXY$ and $\triangle DEF$ State the proportions that must be true if $\triangle WXY \sim \triangle DEF$ by SSS Similarity.
35. Write a two-column proof.
Given: $\square DFGI$
Prove: $DE \cdot HJ = EJ \cdot GH$

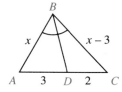

6-6

Find BC.

36.

$\overline{BE} \parallel \overline{CD}$

37.
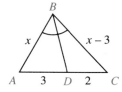

CHAPTER TEST

Give each ratio in simplest form.

1. BD to BC **2.** $CD:CB$ **3.** $\frac{BC}{AB}$

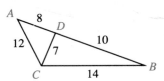

Find x in each proportion.

4. $x:12 = 8:16$ **5.** $6:x = 9:6$ **6.** $2:3 = 12:x$

Complete each statement.

7. If $\frac{3}{y} = \frac{7}{5}$, then $\frac{y}{3} =$ ___ .

8. If $7:4 = x:y$, then $\frac{y}{4} =$ ___ .

9. If $\frac{m}{2} = \frac{5}{3}$, then $\frac{m-2}{2} =$ ___ .

$ABCD \sim KLMN$ **Complete each statement.**

10. $m\angle B =$ ___

11. $\angle D \cong$ ___

12. $x =$ ___

Determine if each pair of triangles are similar. If so, state a theorem or postulate that supports your answer.

13.

14.

15.

16.

17.

18.

$\overleftrightarrow{CQ} \parallel \overleftrightarrow{DR} \parallel \overleftrightarrow{ES}$ **Complete each statement.**

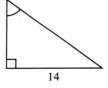

19. $\frac{QR}{RS} =$ ___

20. If $CD = 2$, $DE = 5$, and $RS = 10$, then $QR =$ ___ .

21. If DE is twice CD and $QS = 16$, then $QR =$ ___ .

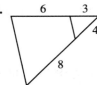

$\angle 1 \cong \angle 2$, $\angle 3 \cong \angle 4$ **Complete each statement.**

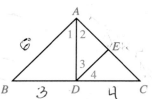

22. $\frac{AE}{EC} =$ ___

23. $\frac{AB}{AC} =$ ___

24. If $BD = 3$, $DC = 4$, and $AB = 6$, then $AC =$ ___ .

PREPARING FOR COLLEGE ENTRANCE EXAMS

1.

The ratio of the surface area of cube 1 to the surface area of cube 2 is

(A) $1:5$ (B) $1:6$ (C) $1:2$
(D) $1:8$ (E) $1:4$

2. What is the next number in the sequence 1, 4, 9, 16, . . . ?

(A) 9   (B) 36   (C) 21
(D) 25   (E) 42

3.

The area of trapezoid $ABCD = 55$. Find w.

(A) 9   (B) 10   (C) 11
(D) 12   (E) $\frac{55}{12}$

4. An item normally costs $10.00, but it has been marked down 10%. How much does it now cost?

(A) $9.00   (B) $7.50   (C) $5.00
(D) $4.00   (E) $1.00

5.

$ABCD$ is a parallelogram. Find x.

(A) 10   (B) 15   (C) 25
(D) 30   (E) 40

6. Solve for x. $x^2 - 36 = 0$

(A) $6, -6$ (B) $5, -5$ (C) $6, 0$
(D) $6, 4$ (E) 36

7. For any integer n, which of the following represents three consecutive odd integers?

(A) $n, n + 1, n + 2$
(B) $n + 1, n + 3, n + 5$
(C) $3n, 5n, 7n$
(D) $2n + 1, 2n + 3, 2n + 5$
(E) $2n, 2n + 2, 2n + 4$

8.

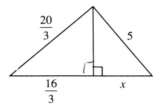

Find x.

(A) $\frac{10}{3}$ (B) $\frac{20}{3}$ (C) 3   (D) 4   (E) 5

9. In one week, sailboat production at four different factories was 8, 10, 5, 5. What was the average production per factory that week?

(A) 5   (B) 6   (C) 7   (D) 14   (E) 28

10.

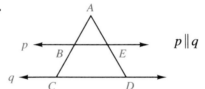

Which of the following is not necessarily true?

(A) $AB:AC = AE:AD$
(B) $\angle ACD \cong \angle ABE$
(C) $AB:BC = AE:ED$
(D) $AB:ED = AE:BC$
(E) $m\angle BED + m\angle CDA = 180$

11. On the moon, objects weigh only $\frac{1}{6}$ their earth weight. If an astronaut weighs 22 lb on the moon, how much does she weigh on earth?

(A) 66 lb   (B) 120 lb   (C) 124 lb
(D) 132 lb   (E) 148 lb

12. Three angles in a quadrilateral are 90, 145, and 80. The measure of the fourth angle is

(A) 25   (B) 45   (C) 115
(D) 205   (E) 225

CUMULATIVE REVIEW

Chapters 1–6

1. Points A, B, and C are collinear. If $AC = 9$, $BC = 10$, and $AB = 19$, which point is between the other two?
   a. A is between B and C.
   b. B is between A and C.
   c. C is between A and B.
   d. none of these

2. $\angle FED$ and $\angle FEG$ form a linear pair. If $m\angle FEG = x$, find $m\angle FED$.
   a. $x + 180$ b. $180 - x$
   c. 180 d. $90 - x$

3. What is the statement formed by negating both the hypothesis and the conclusion of a conditional called?
   a. converse   b. inverse
   c. contrapositive   d. biconditional

4. If $\overline{AB} \perp \overline{XY}$ at E, what conclusion can be drawn?
   a. $m\angle AEX + m\angle AEY = 180$
   b. $XE = EY$
   c. $m\angle AEB = 90$
   d. $AB = XY$

5. If $\overrightarrow{AC}$ is between $\overrightarrow{AB}$ and $\overrightarrow{AD}$, then ___ .
   a. $m\angle BAC = m\angle CAD$
   b. $m\angle CAB + m\angle DAB = m\angle CAD$
   c. $\overline{AB} \perp \overline{AD}$
   d. $m\angle BAC + m\angle CAD = m\angle BAD$

6. $\overline{RS}$ and $\overline{TU}$ intersect at V. If $m\angle RVT = 2x + 2$ and $m\angle RVU = x + 4$, find $m\angle RVT$.
   a. 58   b. 118   c. 62   d. 6

7. Which of the following statements is false?
   a. If one angle of a linear pair is a right angle, then the other angle is a right angle.
   b. If one angle of a linear pair is acute, then the other angle is obtuse.
   c. Perpendicular lines form congruent adjacent angles.
   d. If two angles are complements of congruent angles, then they are complementary.

8. If $l \parallel m$, then ___ .

   a. $\angle 3 \cong \angle 5$.
   b. $\angle 1 \cong \angle 8$.
   c. $m\angle 1 + m\angle 5 = 180$.
   d. $m\angle 4 + m\angle 5 = 180$.

9. Find $m\angle 1$.

   a. 80   b. 150
   c. 100   d. 110

10. How many sides does a polygon have if the sum of the interior angles is 900?
    a. 6 sides   b. 7 sides
    c. 8 sides   d. 9 sides

11. $\triangle ABC \cong \triangle XYZ$. Which pair of angles are congruent?
    a. $\angle C \cong \angle Z$ b. $\angle B \cong \angle X$
    c. $\angle C \cong \angle X$ d. $\angle A \cong \angle Z$

12. $\overline{AE}$ and $\overline{BD}$ bisect each other at C. $\triangle ABC \cong \triangle DEC$ by which postulate?

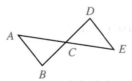

    a. SSS   b. ASA
    c. SAS   d. AAS

13. An equiangular triangle is both equilateral and ___ .
    a. right   b. isosceles
    c. scalene   d. obtuse

14. $\triangle RSU \cong \triangle WVT$
Which of these would not necessarily be true?

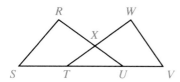

a. $\overline{RU} \cong \overline{WT}$
b. X is the midpoint of $\overline{WT}$.
c. $\overline{ST} \cong \overline{UV}$
d. $\overline{XR} \cong \overline{XW}$

15. $\overline{OM}$ is a median in $\triangle LON$. Which conclusion is correct?

a. $\angle 1 \cong \angle 2$
b. $\overline{OM} \parallel \overline{LN}$
c. $LM = MN$
d. all of the above

16. If $FGHI$ is a parallelogram, which conclusion is *not* correct?

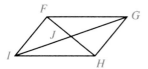

a. $\overline{FG} \cong \overline{IH}$
b. $m\angle FIH + m\angle IHG = 180$
c. $\overline{FH} \cong \overline{GI}$
d. $\overline{IJ} \cong \overline{JG}$

17. The altitude of a right triangle ___.
a. may lie on the exterior of the triangle
b. may be congruent to the hypotenuse
c. may be a leg of the triangle
d. none of the above

18. Which quadrilateral has perpendicular diagonals?
a. rhombus   b. rectangle
c. parallelogram   d. all of the above

19. Find the length of the median of a trapezoid if the lengths of the bases are $2x$ and $3x + 15$, and the median is $2x + 20$.
a. 25   b. 50
c. $23\frac{1}{3}$ d. 70

20. What is the negation of $a \parallel b$?
a. $a \nparallel b$ b. a and b intersect.
c. $a \perp b$ d. a and b are skew.

21. $\triangle ABC \sim \triangle DEF$, $AB = 8$, $AC = 10$, $DE = 12$
Find DF.
a. 30   b. $6\frac{2}{3}$
c. 15   d. 14

22. In $\triangle ABC$, $\angle 1 \cong \angle 2$, $AD = x + 2$, $DC = 3x - 3$, $AB = 8$, and $BC = 6$.
Find x.

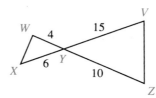

a. 3   b. 2
c. 7   d. 4

23. $\triangle WYX \sim \triangle ZYV$ by which postulate or theorem?

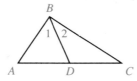

a. SSS   b. SAS
c. AA   d. The triangles are not similar.

24. The diagonals of a parallelogram make ___.
a. 4 pairs of similar triangles
b. 6 pairs of similar triangles
c. 8 pairs of similar triangles
d. 12 pairs of similar triangles

Right Triangles

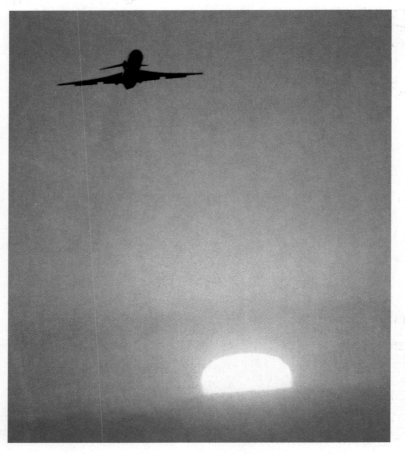

A plane takes off at an angle of 20° and covers a ground distance of 15,000 ft. Find the altitude of the plane.

RIGHT TRIANGLE RELATIONSHIPS

OBJECTIVE: *Identify and apply proportions in right triangles.*

7-1 Right Triangle Proportions

In this section you will analyze the relationships among the triangles and segments formed when an altitude is drawn to the hypotenuse of a right triangle. To do this, the following idea is helpful.

When a, b, and x are positive numbers and $\frac{a}{x} = \frac{x}{b}$, x is called the **geometric mean** between a and b.

In order to prepare for finding the geometric mean between two numbers, you could review the process for writing a radical, such as $\sqrt{32}$, in simplest form. Recall that in such a radical, 32 is called the radicand. For a radical expression to be in simplest form, the following must be true.

- A radicand can have no factor (other than 1) that is a perfect square.
- A radicand cannot be a fraction.
- There can be no radicals in a denominator.

The idea of a geometric mean can be used to describe some relationships in a starfish. AB is the geometric mean between BC and AC.

Example 1
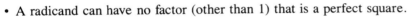
Simplify each radical.   **a.** $\sqrt{32}$ **b.** $\sqrt{(\frac{16}{2})}$

    Solution

    a. $\sqrt{32} = \sqrt{(16 \cdot 2)} = \sqrt{16} \cdot \sqrt{2} = 4\sqrt{2}$

    b. $\sqrt{(\frac{16}{2})} = \frac{\sqrt{16}}{\sqrt{2}} = \frac{4}{\sqrt{2}}$

            $= \frac{4}{\sqrt{2}} \cdot \frac{\sqrt{2}}{\sqrt{2}}$ *Multiply by $\frac{\sqrt{2}}{\sqrt{2}}$ to remove the*

            $= \frac{4\sqrt{2}}{2} = 2\sqrt{2}$ *radical from the denominator.*

Try This
Simplify $\frac{2}{\sqrt{5}}$.

The idea of the geometric mean is illustrated in the example below and used in the theorems that follow.

Example 2
Find the geometric mean between 3 and 6.

    Solution

    $\frac{3}{x} = \frac{x}{6}$ *Use the definition of geometric mean to write a proportion.*

    $x^2 = 18$ *The product of the means equals the product of the extremes.*

    $x = \sqrt{18} = \sqrt{9 \cdot 2} = \sqrt{9} \cdot \sqrt{2} = 3\sqrt{2}$

Try This
Find the geometric mean between 4 and 9.

Theorems 7.1, 7.2, and 7.3 present some right-triangle relationships that will be used later to prove other theorems about right triangles called the "altitude on the hypotenuse" theorems.

◆ THEOREM 7.1

The altitude to the hypotenuse of a right triangle forms two triangles that are similar to each other and to the original triangle.

Given: $\triangle ABC$ is a right triangle.
$\overline{CD}$ is the altitude to the hypotenuse $\overline{AB}$.

Prove: $\triangle ADC \sim \triangle CDB \sim \triangle ACB$

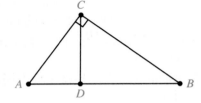

Proof The right angles in $\triangle ADC$, $\triangle CDB$, and $\triangle ACB$ are congruent. Also, since $\angle DCB$ and $\angle A$ are both complementary to $\angle ACD$, it follows that $\angle DCB \cong \angle A$. By the AA Similarity Postulates, $\triangle ADC \sim \triangle CDB$, Also, since $\angle A \cong \angle A$, it follows that $\triangle ADC \sim \triangle ACB$. By the properties of similarity, $\triangle ADC \sim \triangle CDB \sim \triangle ACB$.

◆ THEOREM 7.2

In a right triangle, the length of the altitude to the hypotenuse is the geometric mean between the lengths of the two segments on the hypotenuse.

Given: $\triangle ABC$ is a right triangle.
$\overline{CD}$ is an altitude to the hypotenuse $\overline{AB}$.

Prove: $\frac{x}{h} = \frac{h}{y}$

Proof From Theorem 7.1, we know that $\triangle ADC \sim \triangle CDB$. Since the ratios of corresponding sides of these similar triangles are equal, it follows that $\frac{x}{h} = \frac{h}{y}$.

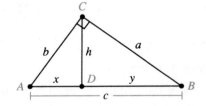

◆ THEOREM 7.3

In a right triangle with an altitude to the hypotenuse, each leg is the geometric mean between the length of the hypotenuse and the length of the segment of the hypotenuse adjacent to that leg.

You will be asked to prove Theorem 7.3 in Exercise 45.

Example 3

Find the length of the altitude $\overline{FH}$ of right $\triangle EFG$.

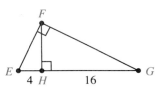

Solution

$\frac{4}{FH} = \frac{FH}{16}$ *Theorem 7.2*

$FH^2 = 64$

$FH = 8$

Try This

Find HG if $EH = 5$ and $FH = 10$.

Example 4

Find the length of leg $\overline{AB}$ of right $\triangle ABC$.

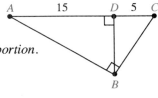

Solution

$\frac{20}{AB} = \frac{AB}{15}$ *Use Theorem 7.3 to set up the proportion.*

$AB^2 = 300$

$AB = \sqrt{300} = 10\sqrt{3}$

Try This

Find the length of leg $\overline{BC}$ of right $\triangle ABC$.

Class Exercises

Short Answer

1. $\overline{EG}$ is the altitude to the hypotenuse in right $\triangle DEF$.
   Name three similar triangles.

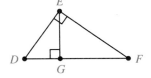

Use Theorems 7.2 and 7.3 to complete these proportions.

2. $\frac{EG}{DG} = \frac{?}{EG}$ 3. $\frac{?}{DF} = \frac{DG}{?}$ 4. $\frac{EF}{GF} = \frac{?}{EF}$

5. Simplify the radical. $\sqrt{27} = \sqrt{9 \cdot 3} = \underline{\ ?\ }$

Sample Exercises

6. Find the geometric mean between 3 and 9.

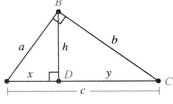

Complete each statement, write a proportion, and state a theorem that supports your answer.

7. h is the geometric mean between ___ and ___ .

8. a is the geometric mean between ___ and ___ .

9. b is the geometric mean between ___ and ___ .

10. If $x = 5$ and $y = 9$, find the lengths of the legs and the altitude of $\triangle ABC$.

Discussion

11. Suppose you wanted to find x, y, and z. Does it make any difference
    which variable you tried to find first? Explain your reasoning and discuss
    how to find the value of each variable.

Exercises

A

Simplify each radical.

1. $\sqrt{8}$ 2. $\sqrt{48}$ 3. $\frac{1}{\sqrt{2}}$ 4. $\sqrt{\frac{3}{5}}$ 5. $\frac{2}{3\sqrt{5}}$

Find the geometric mean between each pair of numbers.

6. 2 and 8   7. 9 and 16   8. 4 and 5   9. $\sqrt{3}$ and $\sqrt{5}$ 10. 5 and 1.25

Use Theorems 7.2 and 7.3 to complete each proportion and find the values of x, y, or z.

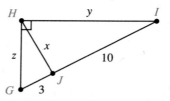

11. $\frac{3}{x} = \frac{x}{?}$ 12. $\frac{3}{?} = \frac{?}{10}$

13. $\frac{13}{z} = \frac{z}{?}$ 14. $\frac{?}{y} = \frac{y}{10}$

15. $\frac{10}{?} = \frac{?}{13}$ 16. $\frac{13}{?} = \frac{?}{3}$

Find the length of the altitude of right $\triangle PQR$.

17.   18.   19.

Find the length of each leg of right $\triangle GHK$.

20.   21.   22.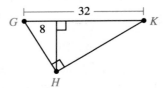

Complete each equation using Theorem 7.2 or 7.3.

23. Theorem 7.2: $h^2 =$ ____
24. Theorem 7.3: $a^2 =$ ____
25. Theorem 7.3: $b^2 =$ ____

Find each of the following.

26. $PQ = 9$, $QN = 4$ Find MQ.
27. $QN = 3$, $MQ = 9$ Find PQ.
28. $PM = 12$, $PQ = 9$ Find PN.
29. $MN = 8$, $QN = 6$ Find PN.
30. $PN = 75$, $PQ = 72$ Find MN.
31. $MQ = 4$, $PQ = 10$ Find QN.
32. $PN = 13$, $PM = 12$ Find PQ.
33. $PN = 16$, $QN = 4$ Find QM.

34. How far is it across the lake?

B

35. If $EO = 4$ and $GH = 10$, find GO.
36. If $GH = 16$ and $EH = 12$, find EO.
37. If $EH = 16$ and $EG = 12$, find OH.
38. If $HO = 6$ and $EG = 4$, find OG.
39. If $EO = 8$ and $\frac{HO}{OG} = \frac{2}{1}$, find HO.
40. If $HO = 10$ and $OG = 8$, find $HE \cdot EG$.

41. How far is it from home, past the gym, to school?

42. The altitude, $\overline{XR}$, to the hypotenuse of right $\triangle WXY$ divides the hypotenuse into segments that are 8 and 10 cm long. Find the length of the altitude.

43. A 12-cm long altitude of a right triangle divides the hypotenuse into two segments, one three times as long as the other. How long is the hypotenuse?

44. Use a ruler and compass to (a) construct a right triangle and (b) construct an altitude to its hypotenuse. Measure all segments to the nearest millimeter and verify that Theorems 7.2 and 7.3 hold for your triangle.

45. Prove Theorem 7.3.

   Given: $\triangle ABC$ is a right triangle.
   $\overline{CD}$ is an altitude to the hypotenuse $\overline{AB}$.

   Prove: $\frac{y}{a} = \frac{a}{c}$ and $\frac{x}{b} = \frac{b}{c}$

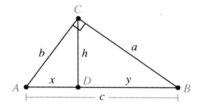

46. Use Theorem 7.3 to prove that if the altitude to the hypotenuse of a right triangle bisects the hypotenuse, then the right triangle is isosceles.

47. Use the information given below the starfish picture on page 295 to show that if $AB = CD$, then AC is the geometric mean between AB and AD. (HINT: Use the properties of proportions.)

C

48. Use Theorem 7.3 to find d.
   (HINT: Let x represent the length of one of the segments of the hypotenuse.)

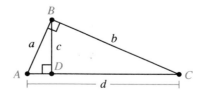

49. Given the information shown in the figure, prove that $cd = ab$. State in words the theorem you have proved.

Critical Thinking

50. Euclid, a Greek mathematician, described a segment divided into two parts so that "the greater part is the geometric mean between the whole and the lesser part."

   a. Draw a diagram and use variables to describe this situation.

   b. Test the triples circled in the Fibonacci sequence below to see if they are close to being possible lengths for Euclid's segment and its parts. Form a conjecture about this situation.

$$1, 1, (2, 3, 5), 8, (13, 21, 34), 55, (89, 144, 233), \ldots$$

Algebra Review

Assume that *a*, *b*, and *c* are positive real numbers. Simplify each expression.

1. $(\sqrt{2})^2$ **2.** $(3\sqrt{5})^2$ **3.** $(2\sqrt{a})^2$

4. $(\sqrt{5b})^2$ **5.** $(\frac{\sqrt{3}}{2})^2$ **6.** $(\frac{5}{\sqrt{2}})^2$

7. $(\sqrt{5a})^2$ **8.** $\sqrt{\frac{b^2}{5}}$ **9.** $\frac{\sqrt{a}}{\sqrt{3}}$

10. $\frac{\sqrt{2b^2}}{\sqrt{2}}$ **11.** $\sqrt{\frac{4c^2}{5}}$ **12.** $\sqrt{\frac{36a^2}{7}}$

Careers

Architect

Architects design most of the structures we work and live in; every school, theater, and hospital was planned by an architect. Since rectangular windows, triangular roofs, and spiral staircases are common features of these structures, mathematics—especially geometry—plays an important role in an architect's training.

A project usually begins with a contract to design a particular type of building. A design is developed by the architect who prepares drawings and models showing how the building will look when it is completed. Thereafter, the architect oversees the construction of the building and works closely with contractors who provide plumbing, landscaping, and other components of the project. Often, the architect gets a percentage of the contruction budget as a fee.

Frank Lloyd Wright, one of the best-known American architects of the twentieth century, designed the Guggenheim Museum in New York pictured to the right.

7-2 The Pythagorean Theorem

EXPLORE How does the sum of the areas of the squares on the legs of this right triangle compare to the area of the square on the hypotenuse? Make a generalization.

Use graph paper to decide if this generalization is true for right triangles with legs $a = 5$, $b = 12$, and $a = 8$, $b = 15$.

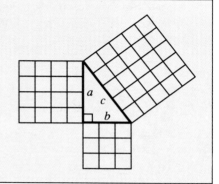

The Pythagorean Theorem is one of the most famous and useful theorems in plane geometry. It can be used to find the length of the third side of a right triangle when the lengths of two of the sides are known. It was named after the Greek mathematician Pythagoras who is thought to have given the first proof of the theorem around 500 BC. In the Explore, you may have "discovered" this famous theorem.

◆ **THEOREM 7.4** Pythagorean Theorem

In a right triangle, the square of the length of the hypotenuse equals the sum of the squares of the lengths of the legs.

Given: $\triangle ABC$ is a right triangle.
$\angle C$ is a right angle.
Prove: $a^2 + b^2 = c^2$

Proof Statements   Reasons

    1. $\triangle ABC$ is a right triangle.   1. Given
       $\angle C$ is a right angle.
    2. Draw a perpendicular from C to $\overline{AB}$.   2. Theorem 2.9
    3. $\frac{c}{a} = \frac{a}{x}, \frac{c}{b} = \frac{b}{y}$ 3. Theorem 7.3
    4. $a^2 = cx, b^2 = cy$ 4. Product of mean equals product of extremes.
    5. $a^2 + b^2 = cx + cy$ 5. Addition Property
    6. $a^2 + b^2 = c(x + y)$ 6. Distributive Property
    7. $a^2 + b^2 = c^2$ 7. Segment Addition Postulate, Substitution

The following example shows how to use the Pythagorean Theorem.

Example

Find the value of *a*.

Solution

$5^2 + a^2 = 13^2$ *Use the Pythagorean Theorem to write this equation.*

$25 + a^2 = 169$

$a^2 = 144$

$a = 12$ *Note that $a = -12$ is another solution to the equation, but the length of a segment must be a positive number.*

Try This

Find the value of *c* in the figure to the right.

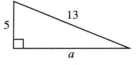

Class Exercises

Short Answer

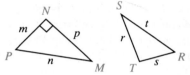

1. State the Pythagorean Theorem in your own words.
2. What equation gives the relationship of the sides in $\triangle MNP$?
3. What information must you know about $\triangle RST$ to conclude that $r^2 + s^2 = t^2$.
4. Give an equation that can be solved to find the length of the hypotenuse of a right triangle with a 10-cm leg and a 24-cm leg.

Sample Exercises

Find the value of *x*.

5.

6.

7.

8. Find the length of a diagonal of a square with side length $2\sqrt{2}$.
9. Find the perimeter of a rhombus with diagonals of 10 and 24 inches.

Discussion

10. If $\triangle ABC$ has sides with lengths 3, 4, and 5, why can you not conclude directly from the Pythagorean Theorem that it is a right triangle?

Determine whether each statement about the Pythagorean Theorem is always, sometimes, or never true.

11. It states a relationship among the sides of an obtuse triangle.
12. It states a relationship among the sides of an isosceles triangle.
13. It states a relationship among the sides of a scalene triangle.
14. It states a relationship among the sides of a right triangle.

Exercises

A

Find the value of x.

1.

2.

3.

4.

5.

6.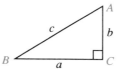

Find each missing length. Express radicals in simplest form.

7. If $a = 6$ and $b = 8$, then $c =$ ___ .
8. If $c = 15$ and $a = 9$, then $b =$ ___ .
9. If $b = 2$ and $a = 2$, then $c =$ ___ .
10. If $c = \sqrt{15}$ and $a = \sqrt{10}$, then $b =$ ___ .
11. If $b = \sqrt{2}$ and $a = \sqrt{3}$, then $c =$ ___ .
12. If $a = 2\sqrt{3}$ and $c = 6$, then $b =$ ___ .

13. If the legs of an isosceles right triangle are 6 units long, find the length of the hypotenuse.
14. The length of a rectangle is 24 cm and the width is 10 cm. How long is the diagonal?
15. A television screen measures approximately 15.5 in. high and 19.5 in. wide. A television is advertised by giving the approximate length of the diagonal of its screen. How should this television be advertised?

Find each missing length x.

16.

17.

18.

The length of the side of a square is given. Find the length of the diagonal of the square. Express radicals in simplest form.

19. $s = 2$ **20.** $s = 3$ **21.** $s = 4$ **22.** $s = 5$

B

23. Look for a pattern in the answers to Exercises 19–22. Predict the formula for finding the diagonal of any square with side length s. Use the Pythagorean Theorem to show that your prediction is correct.

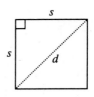

24. Find the length of each leg of an isosceles right triangle with hypotenuse 30 cm long.

Find the value of each variable.

25.

26.

27.

28.

29.

30.

31.

Cube

32.

33.

Rectangular prism

34. The base of an isosceles triangle is $2x$ cm long. The altitude to the base is $3x$ cm long. Find the length of one other side of the triangle.

35. The hypotenuse of a right triangle is three times the length of a leg. The sum of the sides of the triangle is between 6 and 8. How long are the legs and the hypotenuse of the triangle if the length of the hypotenuse is an integer?

36. Find the altitude of an equilateral triangle with side length ten.

37. Find the perimeter of a rectangle that has diagonal length eight and a side of length five.

38. Find the perimeter of an isosceles trapezoid that has a base with length 10, another base with length 18, and height 8.

39. A 6-ft ladder is placed against a wall with its base 2 ft from the wall. How high above the ground is the top of the ladder?

40. A person travels 8 mi due north, 3 mi due west, 7 mi due north, and 11 mi due east. How far is that person from the starting point?

41. A door is 6 ft 6 in. high and 36 in. wide. Can a thin piece of plywood 7 ft wide be carried through the door?

C

42. In $\triangle ABC$, a, b, and c are the lengths of the sides opposite vertices A, B, and C. If $a = 7$, $b = 8$, and $c = 9$, find the length of the altitude of the triangle from vertex C.

43. In isosceles $\triangle DEF$, $DE = EF = 25$ and $DF = 30$. Find the length of the altitude of the triangle from vertex F.

44. Will a fishing rod that collapses to a length of 80 cm fit into a suitcase with the dimensions shown?

45. The faces of this triangular pyramid are equilateral triangles with side length 6. Find the altitude h of the pyramid.
(HINT: Point E is the intersection of the medians of $\triangle ADC$.)

46. $\triangle ABC$ is a right triangle. Show that $AC^2 = AB^2 + BC^2$.

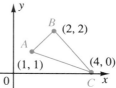

47. Mark and connect the points $(2, 4)$, $(-2, 2)$, $(4, 0)$, and $(-4, 4)$ on a coordinate grid. Find the perimeter of this quadrilateral and express it as simply as possible.

48. Find the length, to the nearest tenth, of the median m of this triangle. (HINT: Draw the altitude of the triangle from B.)

49. Use a straightedge and compass to construct a right triangle with hypotenuse equal to the length of this segment.

50. The 3-mi road from Cisco to Rockton forms a right angle with the 4-mi road from Rockton to Bayville. Emerson is on the straight road from Bayville to Cisco 2 mi from Bayville. Find the distance from Emerson to Rockton.

51. Find the lengths of $\overline{AB}$, $\overline{AC}$, $\overline{AD}$, and $\overline{AE}$. Then, use a compass and straightedge to construct segments with lengths $\sqrt{6}$ and $\sqrt{7}$.

52. A surveyor wants to measure the distance between points A and B on rough land. She wants to find the actual horizontal distance AB. If the land is 0.75 m higher midway between the two stakes, and the measuring tape reads 27.0 m, use a calculator to find the actual distance AB.

Critical Thinking

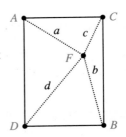

53. Four cities A, B, C, and D are located at the corners of a rectangle. If a factory is built at any point F inside the rectangle, the builders claim that the following relationship between the distances from the factory to the cities holds. $a^2 + b^2 = c^2 + d^2$

Draw two or three accurate rectangles and test this conjecture by measuring to the nearest millimeter. If you think the conjecture is true, give a convincing argument to support your conclusion.

54. A student looked at a right triangle and stated "b^2 can be found by multiplying the sum of the other leg and the hypotenuse by the difference of that leg and the hypotenuse." Test several cases and decide if this generalization is true. If you think it is, give a convincing argument to support your conclusion.

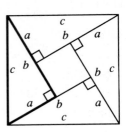

55. Give a general rule for finding the length of the diagonal of a cube when you know the length of one of its sides.

Mixed Review

Complete each statement.

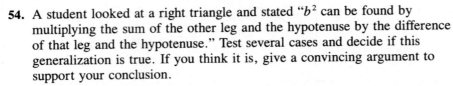

1. $\angle ABE$ and $\angle BEF$ are ___ angles.   **2.** If $\overleftrightarrow{AC} \parallel \overleftrightarrow{DG}$, then $\angle DEB \cong$ ___ .

3. If $\overleftrightarrow{AC} \parallel \overleftrightarrow{DG}$, $m \angle ABE = 60$, and $m \angle EBF = 50$, then $m \angle BFG =$ ___ .

4. If $\angle CBF$ is supplementary to ___ , then $\overleftrightarrow{AC} \parallel \overleftrightarrow{DG}$.

5. $m \angle EBF + m \angle BFE =$ ___

6. Find the sum of the measures of the angles of $RSTUVW$.

7. If $RSTUVW$ is a regular hexagon, find the measure of each of its angles.

8. Find the sum of the measures of the exterior angles of $RSTUVW$.

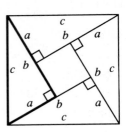

7-3 The Converse of the Pythagorean Theorem

EXPLORE Cut a string or piece of yarn 12 in. long. At what two locations could you tie knots in the string so that it could be used to accurately form a right angle? Why does your method work?

When using the Pythagorean Theorem, you are given a right triangle and conclude a relationship among its side lengths. When using the *converse* of the Pythagorean Theorem, you are given a relationship among the side lengths and conclude that the given triangle is a right triangle. You may have used this idea in the Explore.

◆ **THEOREM 7.5** Converse of the Pythagorean Theorem

If a triangle has side lengths a, b, and c, and $a^2 + b^2 = c^2$, then the triangle is a right triangle with right angle opposite the side of length c.

Given: $\triangle ABC$ with $a^2 + b^2 = c^2$
Prove: $\triangle ABC$ is a right triangle.

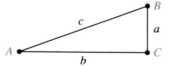

Plan Draw a right triangle $\triangle PQR$ with $\angle Q$ a right angle, legs of lengths a and b, and hypotenuse length x. Use the Pythagorean Theorem to show that $x = c$. Then prove that the two triangles are congruent and use this to show that $\angle C$ is a right angle.

You will be asked to prove this theorem in Exercise 24.

Example 1
Is a triangle with sides 8, 15, and 17 a right triangle?
Solution
$8^2 + 15^2 = 289$, $17^2 = 289$
Since $8^2 + 15^2 = 17^2$, a triangle with sides 8, 15, and 17 is a right triangle.   *Theorem 7.4*

Try This
Is a triangle with sides 5, 6, and 8 a right triangle?

Consider the diagram below showing the result of increasing or decreasing the length c.

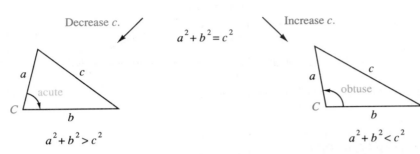

Decrease c. Increase c.

$$a^2 + b^2 = c^2$$

$$a^2 + b^2 > c^2$$ $$a^2 + b^2 < c^2$$

This diagram suggests the following convincing argument that the next theorem is true. If c is decreased, while keeping a and b the same, $a^2 + b^2$ will be greater than c^2 and $\angle C$ will be smaller and acute. If c is increased, while keeping a and b the same, $a^2 + b^2$ will be less than c^2 and $\angle C$ will be larger and obtuse.

These ideas are summarized in Theorem 7.6

◆ **THEOREM 7.6**

If $a < b < c$ are lengths of the sides of a triangle and

a. $a^2 + b^2 < c^2$, then the triangle is an obtuse triangle.
b. $a^2 + b^2 > c^2$, then the triangle is an acute triangle.

Example 2

Is a triangle with sides of lengths 2, 3, and 4 acute, right, or obtuse?

Solution

$2^2 + 3^2 = 4 + 9 = 13$
$4^2 = 16$
$2^2 + 3^2 < 4^2$, so the triangle is obtuse.   *Theorem 7.6*

Try This

Is a triangle with sides $\sqrt{3}$, $\sqrt{4}$, and $\sqrt{5}$ a right triangle? Explain.

A **Pythagorean Triple** is any three whole numbers a, b, and c that satisfy the equation $a^2 + b^2 = c^2$. Theorem 7.5 allows you to conclude that the numbers in a Pythagorean Triple are sides of a right triangle. Some commonly used Pythagorean Triples are (3, 4, 5), (5, 12, 13), (8, 15, 17), and (7, 24, 25). Any multiple of a Pythagorean Triple is also a Pythagorean Triple. For example, (6, 8, 10), (9, 12, 15), and so on, are multiples of (3, 4, 5) and are all Pythagorean Triples.

Class Exercises

Short Answer

1. State the Pythagorean Theorem in your own words.
2. State the converse of the Pythagorean Theorem in your own words.

Complete each statement.

3. If $r^2 + t^2 < s^2$, then $\angle S$ is ___ .
4. If $r^2 + t^2 > s^2$, then $\angle S$ is ___ .
5. If $r^2 + t^2 = s^2$, then $\angle S$ is ___ .
6. The converse of the Pythagorean Theorem helps you tell if a triangle is ___ .
7. If x, y, and z are a Pythagorean Triple, they satisfy the equation ___ .

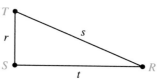

Sample Exercises

Which of these triples are sides of a right triangle?

8. (2, 3, 4) 9. (6, 8, 10) 10. (0.1, 0.4, 0.5)
11. (1, 1, 2) 12. $(\sqrt{2}, \sqrt{3}, \sqrt{5})$ 13. $(\frac{1}{3}, \frac{1}{4}, \frac{1}{5})$

Classify each triangle as acute, right, or obtuse.

14.

15.

16.

17. A rhombus has side length 5 and diagonal length $5\sqrt{2}$. Is the quadrilateral a square? Why or why not?
18. Certain side lengths and pairs of congruent angles are marked in the figure. How do you know that $\angle S$ is a right angle?

Discussion

Determine whether each statement is true or false. Give a convincing argument to support your decision.

19. The numbers $\sqrt{3}$, $\sqrt{4}$, and $\sqrt{7}$ do not form a Pythagorean Triple.
20. The converse of the Pythagorean Theorem allows you to conclude that the sum of the squares of the lengths of the legs of a right triangle is equal to the square of the length of the hypotenuse.
21. The numbers 0.3, 0.4, and 0.5 form a Pythagorean Triple.
22. If the sum of the squares of the lengths of the two shorter sides of a triangle is less than the square of the length of the longer side, the triangle is acute.

23. A student claimed that if each number in a Pythagorean Triple is multiplied by the same number, another Pythagorean Triple results. Use the triple (3, 4, 5) and discuss whether you think this is true. Give another example of a "family of triples."

Exercises

A

36 r 64 = 100

Classify each triangle with the given side lengths as acute, right, or obtuse.

1. 4, 5, 7   **2.** 6, 8, 10   **3.** 0.4, 0.5, 0.6   **4.** 0.9, 4.0, 4.1

5. $\sqrt{3}, \sqrt{2}, \sqrt{5}$ **6.** $\sqrt{2}, \sqrt{3}, \sqrt{4}$ **7.** 9, 10, 12   **8.** $\frac{3}{5}, \frac{4}{5}, 1$

Decide if ∠1 is acute, right or obtuse. Give reasons for your decision.

9.

10.
obtuse
acute
$\overleftrightarrow{AC} \parallel \overleftrightarrow{FG}$

11.
right

12.

13.
obtuse
$\ell \parallel m$

14.
right

15. The sides of a triangle are 9, 40, and 41. Is the triangle a right triangle? Is a triangle with side lengths twice these a right triangle? Why or why not?

B

Classify each triangle with the given side lengths as acute, right or obtuse, or state that no conclusion can be made. Assume that *n* is a nonzero whole number.

16. $3n, 4n, 5n$ **17.** $8n, 15n, 17n+1$ **18.** $11n, 60n-1, 61n$

19. The shortest side of a triangle has length 14. The other sides have lengths $x + 1$ and $x + 3$. Find the value of x that would make the triangle a right triangle and give the length of each side.

20. The shortest side of a triangle has length 4. The other sides have lengths x and $x + 1$. Find the value of x that would make the triangle a right triangle and give the length of each side.

21. A grounds crew was laying out a baseball diamond. They measured the distance from home plate to second base to check that the baseline angle at first base was a right angle. Find distance d.

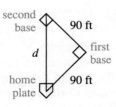
second base   90 ft
d   first base
home plate   90 ft

Decide if △ABC is right, acute, or obtuse. Explain.

22.

23.
$AB = 23, CD = 24, \overline{EC} \cong \overline{AC}$

24. Prove Theorem 7.5.
25. Use Theorem 7.6 to decide if $\triangle ABC$ is an acute, obtuse, or right triangle.

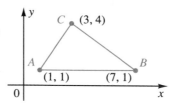

C

26. The sides of a triangle were given as m, $(\frac{m^2}{4} - 1)$, and $(\frac{m^2}{4} + 1)$, where m is an even number not equal to 2. Prove that it is a right triangle.
27. Prove that if n is an integer and $a = 2n + 1$, $b = 2n^2 + 2n$, and $c = 2n^2 + 2n + 1$, then a, b, c is a Pythagorean Triple.
28. Show that the $3-4-5$ right triangle is the only right triangle with sides that are consecutive integers. (HINT: Use x, $x + 1$, and $x + 2$ to represent consecutive integers.)
29. **Given:** Right $\triangle ABC$ with leg lengths a and b, and hypotenuse length c.
   $\triangle A'B'C'$ with side lengths $a + k$, $b + k$, and $c + k$ (where k is a positive integer).
   Prove: $\triangle A'B'C'$ is acute.

Critical Thinking

30. A teacher gave this easy method for finding a missing leg of a right triangle and it works whenever the other leg and the hypotenuse differ by one. "Just add 24 and 25. b is the square root of this sum." Use variables to prove that this method works.

Algebra Review

Find the slope of each line.

1. $y = 3x + 1$	2. $y = -2x + 1$	3. $y = 5x$
4. $x + y = 7$	5. $3y + 6x = 2$	6. $y = -4$
7. $2y - 4x - 9 = 0$	8. $2y + x = 1$	9. $3x - 9y = 1$

Computer Activity

The following BASIC program produces some Pythagorean Triples.

```
10 FOR M = 2 TO 5
20 FOR N = 1 TO M-1
30 LET A = M*M-N*N
40 LET B = 2*M*N
50 LET C = M*M+N*N
60 PRINT A;", ";B;", ";C
70 NEXT N
80 NEXT M
90 END
```

1. What formula is used to produce the Pythagorean Triples? How does M relate to N?
2. Run the program. Change the program so it will produce more triples.
3. If n is a positive integer, then $(2n + 1, 2n^2 + 2n, 2n^2 + 2n + 1)$ is a Pythagorean Triple. Change the program so that it uses this formula to produce triples. Do the two programs produce the same triples? Describe any differences.

7-4 Special Right Triangles

EXPLORE

Construct three squares and three equilateral triangles of different sizes. Label each as shown.

Measure segments to the nearest millimeter. Find the ratios $\frac{c}{a}$ for each square. Find the ratios $\frac{c}{a}$ and $\frac{b}{a}$ for each triangle.

Recall that $\sqrt{2} \approx 1.414$ and $\sqrt{3} \approx 1.732$. What conjectures can you make about the two special triangles shown above in blue?

Certain special right triangles are frequently involved in applications of mathematics. One of these, an isosceles right triangle, has two 45° angles and is called a **45°–45°–90° triangle.** It is often necessary to find the length of the hypotenuse of a 45°–45°–90° triangle when the length of a leg is known. Theorem 7.7, proved using the Pythagorean Theorem, gives an efficient way to do this.

◆ **THEOREM 7.7** 45°–45°–90° Triangle Theorem

The length of the hypotenuse of a 45°–45°–90° triangle is $\sqrt{2}$ times the length of a leg.

Given: $\triangle ABC$ is a 45°–45°–90° triangle.
Prove: $c = a\sqrt{2}$.

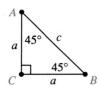

Proof $\triangle ABC$ is a 45°–45°–90° triangle. Using the Pythagorean Theorem, $a^2 + a^2 = c^2$. Simplifying, it follows that $c^2 = 2a^2$, $c = \sqrt{2a^2}$, and $c = a\sqrt{2}$.

Example 1

Find the value of c.

Solution

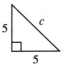

$c = a\sqrt{2}$ *Theorem 7.7*
$c = 5\sqrt{2}$ *Substitute 5 for a.*

Try This

Find the length of the diagonal of a square with side length 12 cm.

A special right triangle with a 30° and a 60° angle is called a **30°–60°–90° triangle.** The hypotenuse and the longer leg in a 30°–60°–90° triangle can be found when the shorter leg is known by using Theorem 7.8 below. Note that the shorter leg is opposite the 30° angle and the longer leg is opposite the 60° angle. The Pythagorean Theorem is used to prove Theorem 7.8.

◆ **THEOREM 7.8**   30°–60°–90° Triangle Theorem

In a 30°–60°–90° triangle, the length of the hypotenuse is 2 times the length of the shorter leg and the length of the longer leg is $\sqrt{3}$ times the length of the shorter leg.

Given: $\triangle ABC$ is a 30°–60°–90° triangle.

Prove: $c = 2a$
$b = a\sqrt{3}$

Plan   Draw $\triangle ADC$ so that $\triangle ABC \cong \triangle ADC$. Show that $\triangle ABD$ is equiangular, and hence, equilateral. It follows that $c = 2a$. Then use the Pythagorean Theorem to show that $a^2 + b^2 = c^2 = 4a^2$. Finally, simplify to show that $b^2 = 3a^2$, or $b = a\sqrt{3}$.

The proof of this theorem will be called for in Exercise 41.

Example 2

Find the length of the hypotenuse and the longer leg.

Solution

Hypotenuse: $x = 2(6) = 12$ *hypotenuse* $= 2 \cdot$ *shorter leg*
Longer leg: $y = 6\sqrt{3}$ *longer leg* $= \sqrt{3} \cdot$ *shorter leg*

Try This

Find the length and diagonal length of the rectangle to the right.

Theorems 7.7 and 7.8 are summarized as follows.

Special Right Triangle Relationships

The ratio of side lengths opposite the 45°–45°–90° angles is $x : x : x\sqrt{2}$.

The ratio of side lengths opposite the 30°–60°–90° angles is $x : x\sqrt{3} : 2x$.

Class Exercises

Short Answer

Complete each statement.

1. To find the length of the hypotenuse of a 45°–45°–90° triangle, multiply the length of one of the legs by ___ .

2. To find the length of the hypotenuse of a 30°–60°–90° triangle, multiply the length of the shorter leg by ___ .

3. To find the length of the longer leg of a 30°–60°–90° triangle, multiply the length of the shorter leg by ___ .

Sample Exercises

Find the value of x.

4.

5.

6.

7.

8.

9.

10.

11.

12.

13. The length of the hypotenuse of a 45°–45°–90° triangle is $5\sqrt{2}$. Find the length of a leg.

14. The length of the hypotenuse of a 30°–60°–90° triangle is 20. What is the length of the shorter leg?

15. The length of the longer leg of a 30°–60°–90° triangle is $4\sqrt{3}$. What is the length of the shorter leg?

16. The length of the hypotenuse of a 30°–60°–90° triangle is 10. Find the length of the two legs.

17. Find the length of the diagonal of a square with sides 8 cm long.

18. Find the length of the altitude of an equilateral triangle if a side is 10 mm long.

19. If the perimeter of a square is 64 cm, how long is its diagonal?

Discussion

20. Draw a 45°–45°–90° triangle and explain how to use variable expressions to give the relative lengths of the sides in terms of x. Do this for a 30°–60°–90° triangle in terms of y.

Discuss how to complete each statement. Explain your decision.

21. The length of a leg of a $45°$–$45°$–$90°$ triangle is ___ times the length of the hypotenuse.
22. The length of the hypotenuse of a $30°$–$60°$–$90°$ triangle is ___ times the length of the longer leg.
23. The length of the shorter leg of a $30°$–$60°$–$90°$ triangle is ___ times the length of the hypotenuse.
24. The length of the shorter leg of a $30°$–$60°$–$90°$ triangle is ___ times the length of the longer leg.

Exercises

A

Find the missing lengths to complete the table.

	a	b	c
1.	6	—	—
2.	—	10	—
3.	2.5	—	—
4.	—	$\sqrt{2}$	—
5.	—	—	$7\sqrt{2}$
6.	—	—	8

	a	b	c
7.	4	$4\sqrt{3}$	8
8.	$\frac{2}{3}$	$\frac{2\sqrt{3}}{3}$	$\frac{4}{\sqrt{3}}$
9.	$\frac{3}{3}$	$3\sqrt{3}$	6
10.	$\frac{3}{8}$	$\frac{3\sqrt{3}}{8}$	$\frac{3}{4}$
11.	5	$5\sqrt{3}$	10
12.	$3\sqrt{3}$	9	$6\sqrt{3}$

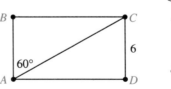

Figure _ABCD_ is a rectangle with the measures shown.

13. Find the length of the diagonal of rectangle _ABCD_.
14. Find the length of $\overline{AD}$.
15. Find the perimeter of rectangle _ABCD_.

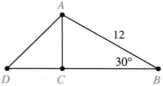

16. Find the length of a diagonal of a square with side length 10 cm.
17. Find the side length of a square with diagonal length 10 cm.
18. Find the length of the altitude of an equilateral triangle with side length 12 cm.

$\overline{AC} \perp \overline{DB}$, $m \angle BAD = 105$ **Complete each statement.**

19. $AC =$ ___
20. $BC =$ ___
21. $CD =$ ___
22. $AD =$ ___
23. $m \angle BAC =$ ___
24. $m \angle CDA =$ ___

Complete each statement.

25. $m \angle RTS = $ ___
26. $m \angle TRS = $ ___
27. $m \angle TQR = $ ___
28. $TR = $ ___
29. $TQ = $ ___
30. $QR = $ ___
31. $TS = $ ___
32. $TP = $ ___
33. $PS = $ ___
34. $PQ = $ ___

35. A ladder leaning against a wall makes a $60°$ angle with the ground. The base of the ladder is 3 m from the building. How high above the ground is the top of the ladder?

B

36. The perimeter of a square is 36. Find the length of the diagonal of the square.
37. Find the perimeter of hexagon $RSTUVW$.

38. Find the length of an altitude of an equilateral triangle with perimeter 24.
39. Find lengths x, y, and z.

40. A right triangle has a $30°$ angle and altitude to the hypotenuse of 5 cm. Find the length of its sides and of the segments on its hypotenuse.
41. Prove the $30°–60°–90°$ Triangle Theorem (Theorem 7.8).
42. The machine nut to the right has a regular hexagonal shape. Find the distances x and y.

2 cm

C

43. The figure is a pyramid with a regular hexagonal base with center C. $DB = 4$, $AB = 17$ Find the height h of the hexagonal pyramid.

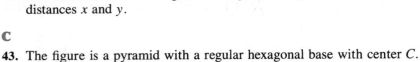

44. An equilateral triangle has side length s. Find the distance to a vertex from the point where its medians intersect.
45. A-$BCDE$ is a pyramid with a square base with center F. $\overline{AF}$ is the altitude of the pyramid and $\overline{AG}$ is a perpendicular bisector of $\overline{ED}$. $m \angle AGF = 60$ If $BD = 8\sqrt{2}$, find AF and AG.

46. An architect is calculating the dimensions for a regular hexagonal window that must fit into an opening with height 120 cm. Find the distance *AB* from one corner of the opening to the opposite corner.

120 cm

47. Show that the altitude to the hypotenuse of a 30°–60°–90° triangle divides the hypotenuse into two segments, one three times as long as the other.

Critical Thinking

48. Devise a formula for finding (a) the length of the altitude of an equilateral triangle with side length *s*, and (b) the area of an equilateral triangle with side length *s*.

Make and test a conjecture about how the area of an equilateral triangle changes as the length of its sides are doubled.

Mixed Review

Use □JKLM to determine whether each statement is always, sometimes, or never true.

1. $\overline{MN} \cong \overline{NK}$ **2.** $\overline{JL} \perp \overline{MK}$
3. $m\angle JKL + m\angle KLM = 90$ **4.** $\angle MJK \cong \angle KLM$
5. If $m\angle J = 90$, then *JKLM* is a rectangle.
6. If $\overline{JK} \cong \overline{KL} \cong \overline{LM} \cong \overline{JM}$, then *JKLM* is a square.
7. *JKLM* is a trapezoid.

Quiz

Complete each statement.

1. $\frac{y}{4} = $ ___   **2.** $\frac{y}{9} = $ ___
3. $\frac{z}{13} = $ ___   **4.** $x = $ ___
5. $y = $ ___   **6.** $z = $ ___

7. Find the geometric mean between 5 and 15.

Find *x* and/or *y*.

8.

9.

10.

11. Is a triangle with sides 7, 9, and 11 an acute, right, or obtuse triangle?
12. Find the perimeter of a rhombus if the diagonals have lengths 16 and 30.

COMPARING APPROACHES IN GEOMETRY

Symmetry and Metric Properties

When a coordinate system is placed on a figure, it is important to name the coordinates of the vertices correctly. Often you will use symmetry properties as well as the relationships from Theorems 7.7 and 7.8. In this figure, review the reflectional symmetry of rectangles, equilateral triangles, and regular hexagons.

Lines of reflectional symmetry

Example

Suppose that an equilateral triangle ten units on a side is placed on coordinate system as shown. If $A(5, 0)$ is one vertex, find the coordinates of B and C.

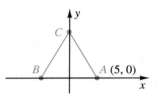

Solution

$B = B(-5, 0)$ *By symmetry, the x-coordinate of B is the opposite of the x-coordinate of A. All points on the x-axis have y-coordinate 0.*

$C = C(0, 5\sqrt{3})$ *All points on the y-axis have x-coordinate 0. The long leg of a 30°–60°–90° triangle is $\sqrt{3}$ times the short leg.*

Exercises

Suppose that a coordinate system is placed on a rectangle 12 units long and 6 units wide so that the *x*- and *y*-axes are both lines of symmetry as shown in this figure.

1. Find the coordinates of A.
2. Find the coordinates of B.
3. Find the coordinates of C.
4. Find the coordinates of D.

Suppose that an equilateral triangle 8 units on a side is placed on a coordinate system as shown.

5. Find the coordinates of C.
6. Use Theorem 7.8 to find the coordinates of B.

Suppose that a regular hexagon is placed on a coordinate system as shown.

7. Find the coordinates of B.
8. Use symmetry to find the coordinates of C, D, E, and F.

TRIGONOMETRIC RATIOS

OBJECTIVE: *Identify and use the tangent ratio.*

7-5 The Tangent Ratio

Trigonometry, which means *triangle measurement* in Greek, is the study of the relationships between the sides and angles of triangles. Trigonometry is a widely used part of mathematics. In sailing, surveying, photography, physics, and other situations, it serves daily as a valuable tool. The idea of similar triangles and the Pythagorean Theorem is used in this lesson to develop the trigonometry of right triangles.

This draftsman uses trigonometry in situations involving right triangles.

A **trigonometric ratio** is a ratio of the lengths of two sides of a right triangle. Consider the following ratio in the similar right triangles below.

$$\frac{\text{length of leg } opposite \text{ the } 60° \text{ angle}}{\text{length of leg } adjacent \text{ to the } 60° \text{ angle}}$$

$$\frac{\text{opposite leg}}{\text{adjacent leg}} = \frac{\sqrt{3}}{1} = \frac{2\sqrt{3}}{2} = \frac{3\sqrt{3}}{3} = \sqrt{3}$$

Note that this ratio is the same in all three of the similar right triangles shown. The ratio of the length of the opposite leg to the length of the adjacent leg of a right triangle is called the **tangent ratio.** You can abbreviate this as tan 60° = $\sqrt{3}$. In general, the tangent of an acute angle of a right triangle is the following ratio.

$$\tan A = \frac{\text{length of opposite leg}}{\text{length of adjacent leg}} = \frac{a}{b}$$

You will study other trigonometric ratios in Lesson 7-6. This example shows how to find the tangent ratio.

Example 1

Use right triangle ABC to find tan A and tan B.

Solution

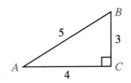

$\tan A = \frac{3}{4} = 0.75$ $\tan A = \frac{opposite\ leg}{adjacent\ leg}$

$\tan B = \frac{4}{3} \approx 1.33$ *Round to the nearest hundredth.*

Try This

Find tan A and tan B if $AB = 13$ and $AC = 12$.

Since ratios of corresponding sides of similar triangles are equal, the tangent ratio of an angle depends only on the size of the angle—not on the size of the triangle. For example, on page 319 you saw that tan $60° = \sqrt{3}$, regardless of the size of the triangle. You can use the table on page 636 or a calculator with trigonometric functions to find decimal approximations of tangent and other trigonometric ratios.

Example 2

Write an equation and solve for x.
Round to the nearest hundredth.

Solution

$\tan 54° = \frac{16}{x}$

$1.3764 \approx \frac{16}{x}$ *Read this value to the right of 54° under "tan" in the table or use a calculator.*

$x(1.3764) \approx 16$

$x \approx \frac{16}{1.3764}$ *Solve for x.*

$x \approx 11.6245 \approx 11.62$ *Use a calculator. Round to the nearest hundredth.*

Try This

What is the value of x if $\angle A$ is not given and $\angle B$ is 27°?

The following example shows how to use the tangent ratio to find the measure of an acute angle when the measures of the legs are given.

Example 3

Find the measure of $\angle R$.

Solution

$\tan R = \frac{25}{14} \approx 1.786$

$m\angle R \approx 61°$ *Use a calculator or look in the "tan" column in the table for the number closest to 1.786. Read the angle that corresponds to this number.*

Try This

Find $m\angle T$ if $TS = 30$ and $RS = 12$.

Class Exercises

Short Answer

Use the right triangles below.

1. Give the length of the leg opposite each of these angles:
   $\angle A$, $\angle B$, $\angle D$, $\angle F$, $\angle G$, $\angle I$
2. Give the length of the leg adjacent to each of these angles:
   $\angle A$, $\angle B$, $\angle D$, $\angle F$, $\angle G$, $\angle I$
3. Use one of the triangles above and describe the tangent ratio in your own words.
4. Express the tangent of each of these angles as a ratio of whole numbers:
   $\angle A$, $\angle B$, $\angle D$, $\angle F$, $\angle G$, $\angle I$
5. Express the tangent of $\angle B$ as a decimal rounded to four places.
6. Use the table on page 636 to find the measure of $\angle B$ to the nearest degree.

Sample Exercises

Use the table on page 636 or a calculator to complete each of the following.

7. $\tan 34° \approx$ ___
8. $\tan 75° \approx$ ___
9. $\tan 5° \approx$ ___
10. $\tan$ ___ ≈ 2.6051
11. $\tan$ ___ ≈ 0.9657
12. $\tan$ ___ ≈ 0.6745

13. Find the width of rectangle $ABDE$.
14. Find the length of the altitude, CF, of $\triangle BCD$.

15. The long leg of a right triangle has length 12. The short leg has length 8. Find the measures of the acute angles of the triangle to the nearest degree.
16. A diagonal of a rectangle forms a 30° angle with the 25-cm base of the rectangle. What is the width of the rectangle?

Discussion

17. Compare the tangents of $\angle A$ and $\angle B$ in a 45°–45°–90° triangle ABC, where $\angle C$ is the right angle.
18. Discuss how the tangent of one acute angle of a right triangle compares to the tangent of the other acute angle of that triangle. Explain using examples.
19. How would you use figures like this to give a convincing argument that tan A decreases as $m \angle A$ decreases?

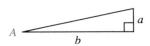

Exercises

A

Express the tangents of ∠A and ∠B as ratios.

1.

2.

3.

4. Express tan B for the triangle in Exercise 1 as a three-place decimal.
5. Express tan A for the triangle in Exercise 2 as a three-place decimal.
6. Express tan B for the triangle in Exercise 3 as a three-place decimal. 1.875
7. Find the measure of ∠B for the triangle in Exercise 3 to the nearest degree.

Use the table on page 636 or a calculator to complete each statement.

8. tan 19° ≈ ___
9. tan 35° ≈ ___
10. tan 62° ≈ ___
11. tan 89° ≈ ___
12. tan ___ ≈ 0.5774
13. tan ___ ≈ 1.1918
14. tan ___ ≈ 0.2493
15. tan ___ ≈ 5.6713
16. tan ___ ≈ 1.0355
17. If tan G = 1, then m∠G = ___ .

Write an equation and solve for s. Round to the nearest hundredth.

18.

$$TAN \, 63 = \frac{S}{15}$$
$$15 \, TAN \, 63 = S$$

29.44

19.

$$TAN \, 27 = \frac{15}{S}$$
$$S = \frac{15}{TAN \, 25}$$

20.

1.9626
15

Find the measure of ∠A. Round to the nearest degree.

21.

22.

23.

24. Find m∠B in Exercise 21.   **25.** Find m∠B in Exercise 22.
26. Find m∠B in Exercise 23.
27. Find the width of rectangle ABCD.

28. Find the length of the altitude of this triangle.

322   *Chapter 7 Right Triangles*

29. Find the height of the building.

50°

⊢ 30 m ⊣

B

30. Write the tangents of the two acute angles of a 30°–60°–90° triangle as ratios in simplest form.

31. Find the altitude h to the base of an isosceles triangle with congruent sides of length 12 cm and base angles of 72°.

32. The length of a rectangle is 16. Its width is 10. Find the measure of each angle formed at the intersection of the diagonals. Round to the nearest degree.

33. Suppose $AB = 3$, $BC = 4$, and $AC = 5$ in $\triangle ABC$. Use a calculator to find $m\angle A$ and $m\angle C$ to the nearest degree.

34. A landscape architect wants to build a bridge across a pond. He lays out $\angle I$ to equal 44° and finds the length of $\overline{IH}$ to be 50 m. How far is it across the pond?

35. An airplane that climbs at a steady rate to reach an altitude of 30,000 ft covers 32 mi of ground distance. Find the measure of $\angle T$, the angle of climb. You may wish to use a calculator.

30,000 ft

T ⎯⎯⎯ 32 mi

36. A person 1000 ft from the base of the Washington Monument finds the angle the ground makes with the line of sight to the top of the monument to be about 29°. About how high is the monument?

37. If $m\angle A$ is 43° and $BC = 20$, find AB.

38. If $BC = 7$ and $AB = 19$, find $m\angle A$.

39. Find the measures of the angles of a right triangle with leg lengths 9 and 40.

C

40. Molten gold is poured into a mold like this to form a brick. The "draft angle" $\angle 1$ is the degree of slant of the walls of the mold. The draft angle is 5° and the depth of the mold BE is 6 cm. How much wider is $\overline{AB}$ than $\overline{CD}$?

41. Suppose you are unable to measure $\overline{AC}$ or $\overline{BC}$ directly, but want to find the height of the tower. Find the height of the tower DC if the known measures are those shown in the diagram.

42. The diagonals of a rhombus are 5 cm and 12 cm long. Find the measures of the angles of the rhombus.

Critical Thinking

43. How would you use figures like those to the right to give a convincing argument that tan A increases as $m\angle A$ increases? Do you think tan A could ever be as large as 100? Explain.

Mixed Review

Determine whether each pair of triangles is congruent by SSS, SAS, ASA, AAS, HA, or HL.

1.   **2.**   **3.**

Calculator Investigation

A calculator with trigonometric functions can be used instead of a table of trigonometric ratios to find the tangent of an angle. Here is a summary of how these calculator functions can be used.

- To use a calculator to find tan 42°

  Enter: 42 [tan]   Display: 0.900404

- To use a calculator to find $m\angle A$, where tan $A \approx 1.4281$

  Enter: 1.4281 [2nd] [tan]   Display: 54.999095

1. Round the numbers on the display to give the tan 42° to the nearest ten-thousandth and $m\angle A$ to the nearest degree.
2. Select a right triangle that has acute angles A and B with whole-number measures. Use a calculator to find tan A, tan B, and tan $A \cdot$ tan B. Do this for several different right triangles. Make a table to show your results. What did you discover? Can you prove that this is true?
3. Use your calculator to find the measures (to the nearest degree) of the acute angles in right triangles that have these Pythagorean Triples as side lengths. **a.** 3, 4, 5   **b.** 5, 12, 13   **c.** 8, 15, 17

7-6 The Sine and Cosine Ratios

You have seen that the tangent ratio is the ratio of two legs of a right triangle. Two other useful trigonometric ratios, involving a leg and the hypotenuse of a right triangle, are the **sine** and **cosine** of an acute angle. These three ratios are given below for $\angle A$. They can also be given for $\angle B$. Note that the sine of $\angle A$ is usually abbreviated sin A and the cosine of $\angle A$ is usually abbreviated cos A.

The sine and cosine ratios are used in navigation to determine distances, establish locations, and chart a course.

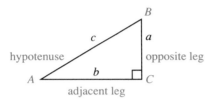

$$\tan A = \frac{\text{length of the opposite leg}}{\text{length of the adjacent leg}} = \frac{a}{b}$$

$$\sin A = \frac{\text{length of the opposite leg}}{\text{length of the hypotenuse}} = \frac{a}{c}$$

$$\cos A = \frac{\text{length of the adjacent leg}}{\text{length of the hypotenuse}} = \frac{b}{c}$$

Example 1

Write an equation and solve it to find an approximate value for x. Round to the nearest hundredth.

Solution

$\sin 56° = \frac{x}{24}$ *The sine is the ratio of the side opposite the angle to the hypotenuse*

$0.829 \approx \frac{x}{24}$ *Use a calculator or a table of trigonometric ratios. sin 56° ≈ 0.829*

$x \approx 0.829 \cdot 24$

$x \approx 19.896$ or 19.90 *Round to the nearest hundredth.*

Try This

Find the approximate value of y in the figure.

In Example 1, you were given the hypotenuse and the angle and used the sine and cosine ratios to find the legs. The next example gives the hypotenuse and a leg and uses the sine and cosine ratios to find the angle.

Example 2

Find the measure of $\angle A$ to the nearest degree.

Solution

$\sin A = \frac{7}{16}$ *The sine is the ratio of opposite to hypotenuse.*

$\sin A = 0.4375$

$m\angle A \approx 26$ *$\sin 25° = 0.4256$ and $\sin 26° = 0.4384$*
                        $26°$ is the closer angle.

Try This

Use trigonometric ratios to find $m\angle B$ to the nearest degree.

In Example 3, an angle and a leg are given and the sine and cosine ratios are used to find the hypotenuse.

Example 3

Find the length of the hypotenuse, to the nearest hundredth.

Solution

$\cos 28° = \frac{12}{h}$

$0.8829 \approx \frac{12}{h}$

$0.8829 \cdot h \approx 12$

$h \approx 12 \div 0.8829 \approx 13.59$

Try This

Find the length of the hypotenuse if $m\angle B = 74$ and $AC = 32$.

Class Exercises

Short Answer

Use these triangles for Exercise 1–5.

1. Name and give the length of the hypotenuse in each right triangle above.
2. Give the length of the leg opposite each of these angles.
   $\angle P, \angle Q, \angle G, \angle I, \angle X, \angle Y$
3. Give the length of the leg adjacent to each of these angles.
   $\angle P, \angle Q, \angle G, \angle I, \angle X, \angle Y$
4. Express the sine of each of these angles as a ratio.
   $\angle P, \angle Q, \angle G, \angle I, \angle X, \angle Y$
5. Express the cosine of each of these angles as a ratio.
   $\angle P, \angle Q, \angle G, \angle I, \angle X, \angle Y$

Sample Exercises

Use the table on page 636 or a calculator to complete each statement.

6. $\sin 13° \approx$ ___   **7.** $\cos 18° \approx$ ___   **8.** $\sin 87° \approx$ ___

9. $\cos 82° \approx$ ___   **10.** $\sin$ ___ ≈ 0.5736 **11.** $\cos$ ___ ≈ 0.7314

12. $\sin$ ___ ≈ 0.9816 **13.** $\cos$ ___ ≈ 0.2588 **14.** $\sin$ ___ ≈ 0.7986

15. $\sin$ ___ ≈ 0.5000 **16.** $\cos$ ___ ≈ 0.7071 **17.** $\cos$ ___ $= 0.5000$

18. Use $\triangle LMN$ to express $\sin L$ and $\cos M$ in decimal notation.

19. Use the table on page 636 or a calculator to find $m \angle L$ to the nearest degree.

20. Find x, y, and $m \angle C$.

21. Find the height of the tree to the nearest foot.

Discussion

22. In $\triangle FGH$, how does $\sin F$ compare to $\cos G$? Is this true for the other triangles above? State a generalization.

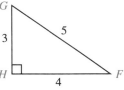

23. A student drew these pictures and asserted, "As the angle gets larger, the sine ratio increases and gets closer and closer to 1." Do you agree with this claim? Why or why not?

$\dfrac{a}{c} \longrightarrow 1$

Use *sine* or *cosine* to complete each statement. Give a convincing argument to support your answer.

24. As the angle gets larger, the ___ gets closer to 1 and the ___ gets closer to 0.

25. As the angle gets smaller, the ___ gets closer to 1 and the ___ gets closer to 0.

26. For what angle, if any, are the sine and cosine ratios equal? Explain your reasoning.

Exercises

A

Express the sine and cosine of $\angle A$ and $\angle B$ as ratios.

1.

2.

3.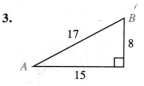

Find these sines and cosines using the table on page 636 or a calculator.

4. $\sin 32° \approx$ ___ **5.** $\cos 49° \approx$ ___ **6.** $\sin 75° \approx$ ___ 0.9695

Find the measure of the angle to the nearest degree. Use the table on page 636 or a calculator.

7. $\sin A \approx 0.6428$ **8.** $\cos B \approx 0.9613$ **9.** $\sin C \approx 0.9962$

Write and solve equations involving the sine ratio to find x and y. Round to the nearest hundredth.

10.

11.

12.

13. Write an equation using the cosine ratio to find each of the lengths in Exercises 10–12.

Find the measure of $\angle A$ and $\angle B$ to the nearest degree.

14.

15.

16.

Find the length of the hypotenuse. Round to the nearest hundredth.

17.

18.

19. B

20. Write two different equations, each of which could be used to find the length r of the slanted part of this roof.
Use one of the equations to find r to the nearest tenth.

B

21. It is often helpful to know the trigonometric ratios for 30°, 45°, and 60° angles without looking at a table. Use the special triangles reviewed here to complete the following. Write as ratios. Copy and complete the table for your reference.

	30°	45°	60°
sin	$\frac{1}{2}$	——	——
cos	——	——	——
tan	——	——	——

22. The diagonal of a rectangle is 10. The length is 2 more than the width and the perimeter is 28. Find the measures of two angles of different sizes formed by a side and a diagonal.

23. The length of the altitude to the base of an isosceles triangle is 12 cm. The angle not congruent to the other two has measure 72°. Find the length of one of the congruent sides.

24. The length of a side of a rhombus is 24 cm. The smaller angle of the rhombus has measure 64°. Find the length of the shorter diagonal of the rhombus.

25. Given that $\angle B$ is an acute angle of a right triangle and $\sin B = \frac{5}{8}$, find $\cos B$ without referring to a table of trigonometric ratios or using a calculator.

Given $\triangle PQR$ with $\angle Q$ a right angle, decide whether each statement is always, sometimes, or never true.

26. Tan P is the reciprocal of tan R.
27. $\sin P = \sin R$
28. $\cos R = \sin P$
29. $\cos R = \tan P$

30. In this rhombus, $IK = 8$ and $m\angle LIJ = 44$. Find LJ and the perimeter of the rhombus.

31. If $d = 4$ and $e = 12$, find a and the measure of $\angle B$.
32. If $m\angle BCD = 38$ and $d = 5$, find a and h.
33. If $b = 10$ and $m\angle A = 26$, find a and c.
34. If $b = 16$ and $e = 8\sqrt{3}$, find a and $m\angle B$.

35. A cable is used to support a 245-m television tower. If the angle the cable makes with the ground is 78°, how long is the cable?

36. When flying, the string of a kite forms a straight line and makes a 36° angle with the ground. If the string is 175 m long, how high is the kite?

37. Find the sine and cosine of the acute angles of this right triangle.

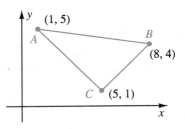

C

38. The area of the square base of an Egyptian Pyramid is 52,900 m². The faces of the pyramid make an angle of about 52° with the base. What is the shortest distance you would have to climb up a face to reach the top?

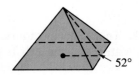

39. A boat at location P is directly east of lighthouse A. The navigator sights a lighthouse B at 53° south of the east-west direction. The boat then travels 60 km in a path 16° east of the north-south direction to point Q. It is then directly east of lighthouse B. How far is the boat from B?

40. Given △XYZ with acute angles X and Y,
Prove that $x \sin Y = y \sin X$.
(HINT: Would it help to draw an altitude?)

Critical Thinking

41. Use a calculator to find the values of w and y.
   a. $(\sin 54°)^2 + (\cos 54°)^2 = w$ **b.** $(\sin 7°)^2 + (\cos 7°)^2 = y$
   c. Make a conjecture about $(\sin x°)^2 + (\cos x°)^2$, where x is the measure of any angle.
   d. Use a calculator to make a conjecture about how $\frac{\sin x°}{\cos x°}$ relates to $\tan x°$, where x is the measure of any angle.
   e. Draw a right triangle, label it using variables, and prove the the two relationships you discovered above are true.

Algebra Review

Solve for x.

1. $|x| = 5$ 2. $|x| = 0$ 3. $|x - 3| = 7$ 4. $|x + 12| = 1$
5. $|5 - x| = 6$ 6. $|7x - 2| = 5$ 7. $|4x + 3| = 67$ 8. $|x^2 - 10| = 6$

Math Contest Problem

In a room 8 ft wide, 8 ft high, and 15 ft long—a bug crawls from the middle of the front wall, 1 ft above the floor, to the middle of the back wall, 1 ft below the ceiling. What is the shortest path? How far is it?

7-7 Angles of Elevation and Depression

Trigonometric ratios are often used to indirectly find lengths or distances that cannot be found by direct measurement. It is important to be able to identify special angles that are often used in these applications. For example, when an observer sights from a boat up to a plane, as shown in this picture, the angle the line of sight makes with the horizontal is called the **angle of elevation.**

Example 1

Application An observer in an airport control tower sights an airplane at an angle of elevation 32°. The pilot reports the plane's altitude as 3.5 km. What is the airplane's horizontal ground distance d from the tower?

Solution

$$\tan 32° = \frac{3.5}{d}$$
$$d \tan 32° = 3.5$$
$$d = \frac{3.5}{\tan 32°} \approx \frac{3.5}{0.6248} \approx 5.6$$

The plane's ground distance from the airport is about 5.6 km.

Try This

Solve the above problem if the angle of elevation is 24°.

When an observer sights downward, as from the plane to the boat in this picture, the angle the line of sight makes with the horizontal is called the **angle of depression.**

Example 2

Application An airplane pilot sights a life raft. The angle of depression is 26° and the plane's altitude is 3 km. What is the plane's distance d from the raft?

Solution

$$\sin 26° = \frac{3}{d}$$
$$d \sin 26° = 3$$
$$d = \frac{3}{\sin 26°} \approx \frac{3}{0.4384} \approx 6.84$$

The plane is about 6.8 km from the raft.

Try This

Solve the above problem if the angle of depression is 35°.

Class Exercises

Short Answer

A person standing on a cliff looks up to see a hot air balloon and then looks down to see a sailboat.

1. Find the angle of elevation.
2. Find the angle of depression.
3. Suppose you knew the height h of the cliff above the water. Which trigonometric function would you use to find the line-of-sight distance to the sailboat?
4. Suppose you knew the distance d to a point directly below the balloon. Which trigonometric function would you use to find the height of the balloon?

$\overleftrightarrow{AE}$ **and** $\overleftrightarrow{FC}$ **are horizontal and** $\overrightarrow{BD}$ **is vertical. Name each angle and tell whether it is an angle of depression or an angle of elevation.**

5. An observer at A sights F.
6. An observer at C sights D.
7. An observer at A sights D.
8. An observer at C sights B.

Sample Exercises

9. The angle of elevation of a helicopter from a ship is $35°$. The altitude of the helicopter is 2800 m. How far is it from a buoy, directly below the helicopter, to the ship?
10. If the angle of depression of the ship from the helicopter is $29°$ and the water-surface distance from the helicopter to the ship is 2640 ft, find the altitude of the helicopter.

Draw a picture and solve each problem.

11. A person 1320 ft from a television tower sights its top. The angle of elevation is $24°$. How tall is the tower?
12. A person in a hot air balloon that is directly over a school building sights her house. The angle of depression is $42°$. The house is 1 mi from the school. Find the altitude of the balloon.

Discussion

Determine whether each statement is true or false. If true, give a convincing argument.

13. As you move farther away from a flagpole, the angle of elevation of its top increases.
14. If you look out the window of a tall building at a car, the angle of depression decreases as the car moves away from you.
15. If you look at a fountain from the windows of a tall building, the angle of depression decreases as you move to higher and higher floors of the building.
16. As an airplane flies toward you, its angle of elevation increases.
17. An object directly overhead has an angle of elevation of $90°$.

Exercises

A

1. A monument casts a shadow 215 ft long when the angle of elevation of the sun is 52°. Find the height of the monument.
2. The angle of depression of a tree from the top of the monument in Exercise 1 is 78°. How far is the tree from the base of the monument?

Draw a picture, then solve.

3. The angle of depression of a car from an air balloon basket is 40°. The balloon is directly over a water tower that is 5 km from the car. Find the altitude of the balloon.
4. A person on a building 180 ft high looked at a bench in a park below. The angle of depression was 24°. How far is the bench from the foot of the building?
5. The length of a guywire supporting a radio tower is 175 ft. The angle of elevation of the top of the radio tower from the foot of the guywire is 65°. How tall is the tower?

B

6. The Chrysler Building in New York is 1046 ft tall. A person stands half a mile away and views the top of the building. Find the angle of elevation of the top.
7. A Mission Control observer, 4.5 km from the launch pad, observes a space shuttle ascending. The angle of elevation of the shuttle is 38°. How far (air distance) is the shuttle from the observer?
8. A television tower 150 ft high casts a shadow 200 ft long. Find the angle of elevation of the sun.

9. How far is the surface of the lake below the level land on the bank?

10. A ramp is 120 ft long and rises vertically 15 ft. Find the angle of elevation of the ramp.

C

11. A person on a bridge sights a boat at an angle of depression of 6°. The bridge is 96 ft above the water. If the boat is traveling 440 ft per minute, about how long will it take the boat to reach the bridge?

12. An observer at the top of a 50 m lighthouse sights two ships approaching, one behind the other. The angles of depression of the ships are 36° and 25°. Find the distance between the ships to the nearest meter.

13. A surveyor could not measure a distance ending directly under the top of a mountain so he marked two locations, A and B, 1000 m apart. He then measured the angle of elevation of the top of the mountain from each of these locations and drew this diagram. Find the height of the mountain. (HINT: Write and solve a pair of equations.)

Critical Thinking

14. When the horizon is sighted from the top of the world's tallest mountain, Mt. Everest, the angle of depression is 3°. The height of Mt. Everest, to the nearest hundredth of a mile is 5.50 miles.

   a. How can you use this information to find the distance R from the center of the earth to the earth's surface (the radius of the earth)?

   b. Investigate how an error in measuring the angle of depression or the height of the mountain would affect the value of R. Explain your findings.

Mixed Review

$\triangle ABC \sim \triangle RST$ **Complete each of the following.**

1. $\angle B \cong$ ____   **2.** $\angle T \cong$ ____

3. $\frac{AB}{RS} = \frac{AC}{?}$ **4.** $\frac{?}{BC} = \frac{RT}{ST}$

5. $x =$ ____   **6.** $y =$ ____

7. The scale factor of $\triangle ABC$ to $\triangle RST$ is ____ .

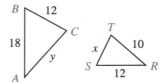

Quiz

Indicate whether each equation is true or false.

1. $\sin A = \frac{12}{13}$ **2.** $\cos B = \frac{5}{13}$

3. $\tan B = \frac{5}{13}$ **4.** $\tan A = \frac{12}{5}$

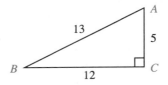

Find the indicated lengths to the nearest hundredth and angles to the nearest degree.

5.   **6.**   **7.**

8. A person in a lighthouse spots a boat. If he is 25 m above sea level and the angle of depression is 15°, find the distance from the boat to the foot of the lighthouse.

CRITICAL THINKING

Common Errors in Drawing a Conclusion

There are several common reasoning errors that are made every day in the critical thinking process. The ones described below often result in "proofs" which do not support the conclusion. Consider the following examples.

Example 1

Mr. Vasquez said, "All politicians are dishonest." Ms. Tsujimura said, "I agree with you. I've known a lot of politicians in my time, and none of them were honest."

This is an instance of *drawing a conclusion in the absence of a counterexample*. You have seen that a counterexample is a single example that shows a general statement to be false. In Example 1, the reasoning error was deciding a general statement to be true (all politicians are dishonest) just because a counterexample had not been found. This is similar to *drawing a conclusion from selected examples*, illustrated by the freshman who says, "The teachers in this school are strict—look at the ones I have this year."

Example 2

Jackie said, "The neighbors drive a big new car so they must be rich."

This is an example of *drawing a conclusion that does not follow from the supporting statements*. An expensive-looking car is, of course, not enough evidence to support the conclusion that those who drive it are rich.

Example 3

Rose decided she needed a job. Her mother asked why. Rose said, "I need to work to pay for a car." Her mother asked, "Why do you need a car?" Rose answered, "I need it to drive to my job."

This illustrates *drawing a conclusion by assuming it is true* (or *circular reasoning*). Notice that Rose used the assumption that she needed a job to convince her mother that she needed a job.

Exercises

Which reasoning error described above occurs in each situation? Explain.

1. Fred said, "My geometry teacher assigns a lot of homework. She must not like our class."
2. Janelle said to Samantha, "You joined our club because you're strange." Samantha asked, "Why do you think I'm strange?" Janelle responded, "You must be, or you wouldn't have joined our club."
3. Maurice said, "All four-sided figures are quadrilaterals." Su Ming agreed, "I've never seen a four-sided figure that wasn't a quadrilateral."
4. Niki said, "I've ordered two items from a bike catalog and they have both been of low quality. That company obviously sells only inferior items."
5. Victoria said, "I'm running for mayor." Marc asked her why. She answered, "I'm quite intelligent." When Marc asked Victoria how she knew she was intelligent, she responded, "I must be, otherwise I wouldn't be running for mayor."
6. Roger drew three right triangles, measured their sides, and found that the Pythagorean Theorem held for all of them. He concluded, "The Pythagorean Theorem must be true because I can't draw a triangle for which it doesn't hold."
7. Consider the advertisement below.

Which reasoning error occurs in the advertisement?

CHAPTER SUMMARY

Vocabulary

angle of depression (7-7)
angle of elevation (7-7)
cosine ratio (7-6)
45°–45°–90° triangle (7-4)

geometric mean (7-1)
Pythagorean Triple (7-3)
sine ratio (7-6)
tangent ratio (7-5)

30°–60°–90° triangle (7-4)
trigonometric ratio (7-5)
trigonometry (7-5)

Key Ideas

1. The altitude to the hypotenuse of a right triangle
   a. forms two triangles that are similar to each other and to the original triangle.
   b. is the geometric mean between the length of the two segments on the hypotenuse.
2. The Pythagorean Theorem states that in a right triangle, the square of the length of the hypotenuse equals the sum of the squares of the lengths of the legs.
3. If a, b, and c are the lengths of the sides of a triangle (c being the longest side) and
   a. $a^2 + b^2 < c^2$, then the triangle is obtuse.
   b. $a^2 + b^2 > c^2$, then the triangle is acute.
   c. $a^2 + b^2 = c^2$, then the triangle is right.
4. In a 45°–45°–90° triangle with legs of length x, the hypotenuse has length $x\sqrt{2}$.
5. In a 30°–60°–90° triangle with shorter leg of length x, the hypotenuse has length $2x$ and the longer leg has length $x\sqrt{3}$.
6. In the right triangle shown to the right:
   a. $\tan A = \frac{a}{b}$
   b. $\sin A = \frac{a}{c}$
   c. $\cos A = \frac{b}{c}$

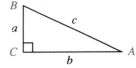

7. When an observer sights upward, the angle the line of sight makes with the horizontal is called the angle of elevation. When an observer sights downward, the angle the line of sight makes with the horizontal is called the angle of depression.

CHAPTER REVIEW

7-1

$\triangle ADC$ is a right triangle with altitude $\overline{DB}$.

1. If $AD = 6$ and $AB = 4$, find AC.
2. If $AB = 3$ and $BC = 8$, find BD.
3. If $BD = 6$ and $BC = 3$, find AC.
4. If $DC = 12$ and $BC = 6$, find AB.

7-2

∠U and ∠S are right angles.

5. If $RU = 4$ and $UT = 6$, find RT.
6. If $RS = 8$ and $RT = 17$, find ST.
7. If $RT = 9$ and $RU = 5$, find UT.

8. Find the length of the altitude to the base of an isosceles triangle if the legs are 10 in. long and the base is 12 in. long.

7-3

Determine whether each triangle with the given side lengths is acute, obtuse, or right.

9. 4, 5, 8
10. 11, 60, 61
11. $2\sqrt{3}$, $4\sqrt{2}$, 6

7-4

Find x, y, and/or z.

12.
13.
14.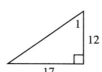

7-5

Use the table on page 636 or a calculator to complete each statement.

15. $\tan 23° \approx$ ___
16. $\tan 68° \approx$ ___
17. $\tan$ ___ ≈ 0.7421

18. Find x.
19. Find $m\angle 1$.

 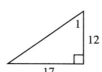

7-6

Write and solve an equation to find the value of x.

20.
21.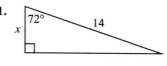
22.

7-7

23. A person on top of a 150-ft tower looked at a car below. If the angle of depression was 32°, find the distance from the car to the foot of the tower?

CHAPTER TEST

Complete each statement.

1. *BD* is the geometric mean between ___ and ___ .
2. *BC* is the geometric mean between ___ and ___ .
3. If *AD* = 3 and *DC* = 15, then *BD* = ___ .

△*ABC* is a right triangle with hypotenuse of length *c* and legs of length *a* and *b*. Complete each statement.

4. If *a* = 6 and *b* = 8, then *c* = ___ .
5. If *b* = 3 and *c* = 10, then *a* = ___ .
6. If *a* = 7 and *c* = $7\sqrt{2}$, then *b* = ___ .

State whether each triangle with the given side lengths is acute, right, or obtuse.

7. 2, 4, 5   8. 5, 12, 13   9. $2\sqrt{3}$, 5, 6

Find the value of *x* and *y*.

10.

11.

12.

Use the table on page 636 or a calculator to complete each statement.

13. tan 43° ≈ ___
14. tan ___ ≈ 3.0777

Use the table on page 636 or a calculator to find the indicated side lengths to the nearest hundredth and angles to the nearest degree.

15.

16.

17.

18.

19. Is the following statement true or false? As a plane flies toward an observer on the ground, its angle of elevation decreases.
20. The angle of elevation of the top of a tree from a point 21 m from its foot is 48°. Find the height of the tree.
21. A plane is flying at an altitude of 2,100 m. The angle of depression from the plane to a control tower is 36°. Find the distance from the control tower to the plane.

PROBLEM SOLVING

Simplify the Problem

Sometimes the numbers involved in a problem are so large that a direct
solution is difficult and/or time-consuming. In such situations, the strategy
Simplify the Problem is helpful. One method of simplifying a problem is to
find a solution using a small number. Then, using a larger number, find
another solution. After repeating the process several times, your results can
be organized in a table and a pattern can be found.

Example 1

In a soccer tournament, there were a total of 32 teams. When a team lost, it
was eliminated from the tournament and played no more games. To win the
tournament, a team could not lose any games. How many games were
needed to determine a champion?

Solution

Simplify the problem by considering a situation in which there were
only two teams. In this case, one game would be necessary. If there were
three teams, two games would be required (the winner of the first game
meeting the team that had not yet played). The table below shows the
pattern.

Number of teams	2	3	4	5	$\cdots$	32
Number of games	1	2	3	4	$\cdots$	31

31 games were needed.

Problem-Solving Strategies	
Draw a Diagram	Work Backward
Make a Table	Simplify the Problem
Look for a Pattern	

*The problem-solving strategies that
have been introduced up to this point
in the book are presented in the chart.*

Problems

Solve.

1. How many squares are in the figure below?

2. The figure below was made with 4 triangles,
   each having sides 1 m long. If a longer figure
   is made with 70 triangles, what will its
   perimeter be?

3. A warehouse has 16 identical desks to be
   distributed to 3 offices. Each office must
   receive at least 1 desk. In how many ways can
   the desks be distributed?

4. Ten houses are arranged in a circle. The phone
   company needs to connect each house. How
   many wires are needed if a separate wire is
   required for each pair?

8

Circles

A bicycle wheel has a radius of 14 in. Find the diameter and circumference of the wheel.

TANGENTS, ARCS, AND CHORDS

OBJECTIVE: *Apply basic definitions and concepts related to circles.*

8-1 Basic Terms

A **circle** is the set of all points in a plane that are a given distance from a given point in the plane called the **center.** A **radius** of the circle is a segment with one endpoint the center and the other endpoint on the circle. The length of the radius is called *the radius* of the circle. A circle is named by its center. The circle below may be referred to as circle *P* (⊙*P*). In ⊙*P*, $\overline{PA}$ is a radius and the radius is 5. All radii of a circle are congruent.

Congruent circles are circles that have congruent radii. So ⊙*P* and ⊙*Q* below are congruent.

The distance from the airport is shown on this map by a set of circles with center *A*. If the radius of each successive circle represents an additional 10 mi, about how far are *B* and *C* from the airport at *A*?

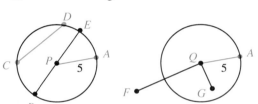

A **chord** is a segment that joins two points on the circle. A **diameter** is a chord through the center of the circle. For ⊙*P*, $\overline{CD}$ is a chord and $\overline{BE}$ is a diameter. Notice that a diameter is twice as long as a radius. Point *F* is *on the exterior of* the circle so $QF > 5$; point *G* is *on the interior of* the circle so $QG < 5$.

A line that contains a chord of the circle is a **secant.** A line in the plane of the circle that intersects the circle in exactly one point is a **tangent** to the circle. That point is the **point of tangency.** In the figure to the right, $\overleftrightarrow{RS}$ is a secant and $\overrightarrow{PQ}$ is a tangent with *A* the point of tangency for $\overrightarrow{PQ}$.

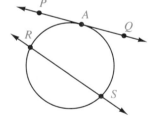

A polygon is **inscribed** in a circle if all its vertices are on the circle. A polygon is **circumscribed** about a circle if each of its sides is tangent to the circle. Two circles in the same plane with the same center are called **concentric** circles.

ABCD is an inscribed polygon.

EFGH is a circumscribed polygon.

concentric circles with center *O*

A **sphere** is the set of all points in space a given distance from a point called the *center* of the sphere. The given distance is called the radius of the sphere.

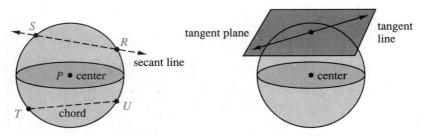

Chords, secants, and tangents of spheres are defined for spheres in a way similar to the way they are for circles. A plane is *tangent to the sphere* and is called a *tangent plane* if it contains exactly one point of the sphere.

Class Exercises

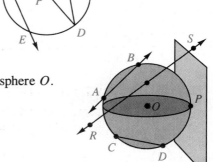

Short Answer

1. Find the length of the radius of $\odot P$.
2. Name two chords of $\odot P$ that are not diameters.
3. Name a diameter of $\odot P$.
4. Find the length of a diameter of $\odot P$.
5. Name a secant of $\odot P$.
6. Name a tangent of $\odot P$.
7. Name the point of tangency for the tangent plane to sphere O.
8. Name a secant of sphere O.
9. Name a chord of sphere O.
10. Name a line that is tangent to sphere O.

Sample Exercises

Complete each statement.

11. The diameter of a circle
    a. with radius 12 is ___ .   **b.** with radius $\sqrt{5}$ is ___ .   **c.** with radius $\frac{\sqrt{3}}{2}$ is ___ .
12. The radius of a circle
    a. with diameter 24 is ___ .   **b.** with diameter 15 is ___ .   **c.** with diameter $\frac{5}{2}$ is ___ .

The radius of $\odot C$ is 5 cm, the radius of $\odot A$ is 13 cm. Complete each statement.

13. $AB = $ ___   14. $AC = $ ___

Discussion

15. Is line m a tangent line? Why or why not?
16. Is point A a point of tangency? Why or why not?
17. Is line m a secant? Why or why not?
18. Is ray BC a tangent? Why or why not?
19. Explain why $ABCD$ is not a circumscribed polygon for the circle shown.

Exercises

A

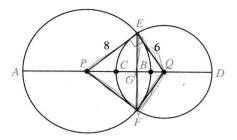

1. Name a radius of ⊙*P*. Find its length.
2. Find the length of a radius of ⊙*Q*.
3. *BQ* = _?_
4. *CP* = _?_
5. Name a segment that is a chord of both circles.
6. What kind of triangle is △*PEF*?
7. Explain why △*PEQ* ≅ △*PFQ*.
8. Explain why △*GEQ* ≅ △*GFQ*.

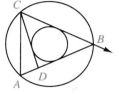

9. Name a triangle that is inscribed in a circle.
10. Name a triangle that is circumscribed about a circle.
11. Name a secant line and the circle for which it is a secant.
12. Name a tangent and the circle for which it is a tangent.

Point *P* lies outside ⊙*O*.

13. How many lines through *P* are tangents to ⊙*O*?
14. How many lines through *P* are secants for ⊙*O*?

Point *Q* lies inside ⊙*O*.

15. How many lines through *Q* are tangents of ⊙*O*?
16. How many lines through *Q* contain a diameter of ⊙*O*?

B

Draw a circle and then complete the figure as indicated.

17. Draw a segment in the interior of the circle that is not a chord.
18. Draw a segment that intersects the circle in two points, but is not a diameter, or chord.
19. Draw a line that is neither a secant nor a tangent line.
20. Draw a ray that intersects the circle in only one point but is not a tangent.
21. Draw a segment that has one endpoint on the circle but is not a chord.

Determine whether each statement is always, sometimes, or never true.

22. A chord is a diameter.
23. A secant to a circle is a tangent to the same circle.
24. A segment with one endpoint the center of a circle is a radius of the circle.
25. A line that passes through a point inside a circle is a secant for that circle.
26. A line that lies in a plane that is tangent to a sphere is a tangent line of the sphere.
27. A handle 0.41 cm in diameter is reduced to a diameter of 0.34 cm as shown to the right. Find the depth of cut.
28. Give a convincing argument that if a plane and a sphere intersect, the intersection is a single point, or a circle.

depth of cut

29. A washer with a listed size of $\frac{9}{16}$ in. has an inside diameter B of 0.562 in. and an outside diameter A of 1.156 in. Find the width C of the washer.

C

Use always, sometimes, or never to complete the statements below about a pair of concentric circles.

30. There ___ exists a line that is a tangent to one circle and a secant to the other circle.

31. There ___ exists a line that is a tangent to both circles.

32. A line that is a secant to one circle is ___ a secant for the other circle.

33. A line that intersects the inside of the small circle is ___ a secant for both circles.

Critical Thinking

Complete each statement to form a correct generalization.

34. A line that contains an interior point of a circle and is in the same plane as the circle is a ___ line.

35. Two circles can intersect each other in at most ___ points.

Mixed Review

ABCD is a parallelogram. Complete each statement.

1. $m\angle A =$ ___   **2.** $m\angle ABC =$ ___   **3.** $m\angle ABD =$ ___
4. $m\angle ADB =$ ___   **5.** $m\angle DBC =$ ___   **6.** $m\angle ADC =$ ___
7. $AD =$ ___   **8.** $AB =$ ___

CONNECTIONS ◇◇

Algebra and Geometry

A rectangular coordinate system of the plane allows you to connect geometry and algebra. See how a circle can be described using algebra.

The circle shown has radius 3 with center at the origin of a rectangular coordinate system. Point $P(x, y)$ is on the circle.
Point P and the origin are vertices of a right triangle with sides of length x, y, and 3. You can use the Pythagorean Theorem to obtain the equation $x^2 + y^2 = 3^2$.

Since the coordinates of each point on the circle satisfy this equation, it is called an equation of the circle.

Exercises

1. Write the equation of the circle with center $(0, 0)$ and radius 4.

2. Write the equation of the circle with center $(0, 0)$ and radius 8.

8-2 Tangent Lines

EXPLORE Use a compass and straightedge to construct a line ℓ perpendicular to a radius of a circle. What kind of line is line ℓ?

In the previous lesson, you learned that a line is tangent to a circle if it lies in the plane of the circle and intersects the circle in only one point. Theorem 8.1 and its converse Theorem 8.2 are about tangents to a circle.

◆ **THEOREM 8.1**

If a line is perpendicular to a radius of a circle at a point on the circle, then the line is tangent to the circle.

Given: Line m is $\perp PA$ at A.

Prove: Line m is a tangent to $\odot P$.

Proof Let B be any point on m other than A. Since $PA \perp m$, $\triangle PAB$ is a right triangle with hypotenuse PB. This means that $PB > PA$ and B must be on the exterior of the circle. Therefore B cannot lie on the circle and point A is the only point of m that is on the circle. It follows that m is tangent to the circle.

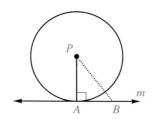

◆ **THEOREM 8.2**

If a line is tangent to a circle, then it is perpendicular to the radius at the point of tangency.

Given: Line m is tangent at point A.

Prove: Line m is $\perp \overline{OA}$.

Proof Use an indirect proof. So assume that the desired conclusion is not true. That is, suppose $\overline{OA}$ is not $\perp m$. Then there exists a segment $\overline{OB}$ which is $\perp m$. If so, $OB < OA$. But B lies exterior to the circle since m is a tangent line. This means that $OB > OA$. Statements $OB < OA$ and $OB > OA$ are contradictory. Therefore the supposition is false and m is $\perp \overline{OA}$.

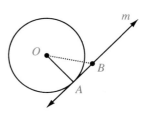

Many theorems in geometry have interesting relationships with one another. In Exercises 18 and 19 you may decide to apply Theorem 8.2 to prove Theorem 8.3 and its corollary.

◆ **THEOREM 8.3**

The two tangent segments from an exterior point of a circle are congruent.

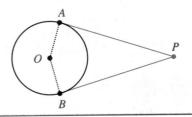

▶ **COROLLARY 8.3a**

The line through an external point and the center of a circle bisects the angle formed by the two tangents from the external point.

Example 1

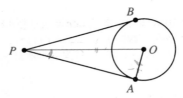

$\overline{PA}$ and $\overline{PB}$ are tangent segments from P.
$PO = 17$, $OA = 8$, $m\angle APO = 28$.
Find   **a.** $m\angle POA$ **b.** PB

Solution

Let $PA = x$

a. $m\angle POA = 90 - 28$ *Since PA is tangent, conclude*
$\qquad\qquad\quad = 62$ *from Theorem 8.2 that $\overline{PA} \perp \overline{AO}$.*

b. $8^2 + x^2 = 17^2$ *Use the Pythagorean Theorem.*
$\qquad\quad x^2 = 17^2 - 8^2$
$\qquad\quad\; x = 15$
$\qquad\; PA = 15$

Since $PB = PA$, $PB = 15$.

Try This

Find PO if $OA = 5$ and $PB = 12$.

Example 2

BC is tangent to $\odot A$ from B. $BC = 12$, $AC = 5$.   Find BD.

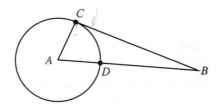

Solution

$AB^2 = 5^2 + 12^2$ *Apply the Pythagorean Theorem.*
$AB^2 = 25 + 144 = 169$ *From Theorem 8.2 we know that*
$\qquad\qquad\qquad\qquad\quad$ *$\triangle ACB$ is a right triangle.*

$AB = 13$, $BD = 13 - 5$ or $BD = 8$.

Try This

$BD = 8$ and the radius of the circle is 7.   Find BC.

Example 3

$\triangle ABC$ is a circumscribed triangle. Find $AB + BC + AC$.

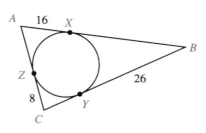

Solution

$AX = AZ = 16$
$BX = BY = 26$
$CY = CZ = 8$
These are tangent segments from exterior points.
$AB + BC + AC = (16 + 26) + (26 + 8) + (8 + 16)$
$= 100$

Try This

Find $AB + BC + AC$ if $BX = 21$, $CZ = 7$, and $AC = 22$.

Class Exercises

Short Answer

Consider the pair of concentric circles with center O and complete each statement.

1. Suppose that p is tangent to the circle. Then $m\angle OAD = $ ___ .
2. Suppose that $m\angle OCE = 90$. Then q is ___ to the circle at C.
3. Suppose that q is tangent to the circle at C and that $p \parallel q$. Then $m\angle CAD = $ ___ .

AB and *AD* are tangent segments from *A*.
Complete each statement.

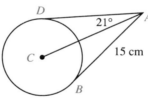

4. $AD = $ ___
5. $m\angle BAC = $ ___

Sample Exercises

6. If the radius of the circle to the right is 8 cm then $AC = \underline{}$.

AB is a tangent segment from *B*. **Complete each statement.**

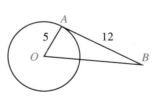

7. $m\angle OAB = $ ___
8. If $AB = 12$ and $OA = 5$, then $OB = $ ___ .
9. If $m\angle ABO = 25$, then $m\angle AOB = $ ___ .

Discussion

10. If r is tangent to both circles and if lines p and q pass through the centers of the circles and the points of tangency, give a convincing argument that p is parallel to q.
11. In the figure suppose that lines p and q pass through the centers of the circles and are perpendicular to line r at points A and B which are points on the circles. Give a convincing argument that r is tangent to both circles.

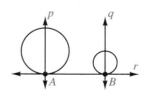

Exercises

A

$\overline{XA}$ and $\overline{XB}$ are tangent from the external point X.

1. If $OA = 7$ and $XO = 25$, find AX.
2. If $XA = 24$ and $XO = 26$, find the radius of the circle.
3. $m \angle AXO = 32$ Find $m \angle AXB$.
4. $m \angle AOX = 48$ Find $m \angle AXB$.
5. $m \angle AXB = 38$ Find $m \angle AOB$.

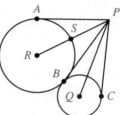

$\overline{PA}$, $\overline{PB}$, and $\overline{PC}$ are tangents to $\odot Q$ and $\odot R$ from an external point P.

6. If $PA = 10$, find PC.
7. If $PA = 15$ and $AR = 8$, find PS.
8. If $m \angle RPQ = 35$, find $m \angle APC$.

$ABCD$ is a circumscribed quadrilateral with $AD = 6$.

9. Find x.   10. Find y.
11. Find z.   12. Find CD.
13. Find the perimeter of $ABCD$.
14. **Given:** $m \angle QPR = 90$

   Prove: $PQBR$ is a square.

$\triangle ABC$ is a circumscribed triangle.

15. Prove that if $\angle 1 \cong \angle 2 \cong \angle 3$, then $\triangle ABC$ is an equilateral triangle.
16. Prove that $\triangle ABC$ is an isosceles triangle with base $\overline{BC}$, if and only if $\angle 1 \cong \angle 2$.

17. Suppose that a corner of a board is to be rounded off. An angle bisector $\overline{CO}$ is drawn, and A and B are points on the edge of the board so that $\overline{OA}$ and $\overline{OB}$ are perpendicular to the edges of the board. If a circle is drawn centered at O with radius $\overline{OA}$, why do you know that the two edges of the board are tangent to the drawn circle?

B

18. Prove Theorem 8.3.

   Given: $\overline{PA}$ and $\overline{PB}$ are tangent to $\odot O$.

   Prove: $PA = PB$

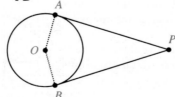

19. Prove Corollary 8.3a.

   Given: $\overline{PA}$ and $\overline{PB}$ are tangent to $\odot O$.

   Prove: OP bisects $\angle BPA$.

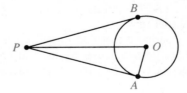

20. Construct a circle and a line tangent to it.
21. Construct two circles with a common tangent.
22. **Given:** $\overline{PA}$ and $\overline{PB}$ are tangents from external point P.

    Prove: $\angle 1 \cong \angle 2$
23. **Given:** $\overline{PA}$ and $\overline{PB}$ are tangents from external point P.

    Prove: $\angle 3 \cong \angle 4$

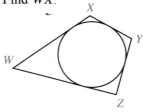

24. Given: circumscribed polygon $ABCD$
    $AB = 12$, $BC = 15$, $CD = 25$
    Find AD.

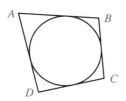

25. Given: circumscribed polygon $WXYZ$
    $XY = 8$, $YZ = 10$, $WZ = 21$
    Find WX.

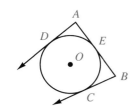

26. **Given:** $\overline{AD}$, $\overline{AB}$, and $\overline{BC}$ are tangents to $\odot O$.

    Prove: $AD + BC = AB$

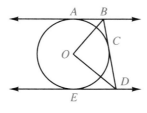

27. **Given:** $\overline{XU}$ and $\overline{XV}$ are tangents to $\odot O$.
    $XO = 17$, $OU = 8$, $ZW = WY$
    Find $XZ + YZ + XY$.

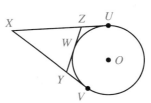

$\overline{AB}$, $\overline{BD}$, and $\overline{DE}$ **are tangents to** $\odot O$.

28. **Given:** $\overline{BO} \perp \overline{DO}$

    Prove: $\overline{AB} \parallel \overline{DE}$
29. **Given:** $\overline{AB} \parallel \overline{DE}$

    Prove: $\overline{BO} \perp \overline{DO}$

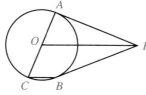

C

30. **Given:** $\overline{PA}$ and $\overline{PB}$ are tangents to $\odot O$.
    $\overline{AC}$ is a diameter.

    Prove: $\overline{BC} \parallel \overline{PO}$

31. Suppose that quadrilateral $WXYZ$ is circumscribed about a circle. Prove that $XY + WZ = WX + YZ$.
32. Quality control in the manufacturing of machine parts often requires unusual methods of measurement. For example, in order to check that the angles A and B are correct on a part called a dovetail, circular plugs are inserted as shown. Then the distance x is measured with a micrometer. For the dovetail shown here, what should this distance equal?

Critical Thinking

33. Suppose points A_1, A_2, . . . , A_n are arranged around a circle so that for each i, $i = 1, 2, . . . , n$, $m \angle A_i O A_{i+1} = \frac{360}{n}$ for all n. Suppose tangent lines are drawn at each point A_i intersecting at points P_1, P_2, . . . , P_n. State a generalization about the kind of polygon $P_1 P_2 . . . P_n$ is. Give a convincing argument that your answer is correct.

Mixed Review

$m \parallel n$ **Write a proportion involving each of the following.**

  1. u and v **2.** x and u **3.** x and y

Find y.

  4. $x = 2$ **5.** $x = 3$ **6.** $x = 1.8$

Career

Seismologist

An earthquake causes motions of the earth's surface, the site of which is the focus of the earthquake. The focus is centered in rocks that have broken and shifted position and most of the energy released in an earthquake travels from the focus in seismic waves.

A seismologist studies and interprets data about earthquakes in an effort to predict when and where they will take place. Seismologists locate earthquakes by studying the time intervals between which the seismic waves reach different seismographic stations. Circles are drawn on the map to show the distance of the earthquake from each station; the epicenter of the earthquake is located where the circles intersect.

8-3 Common Tangents and Tangent Circles

A line that is tangent to two coplanar circles is called a **common tangent** of the two circles. Common tangents are classified into two types. A common **external tangent** does not intersect the segment joining the centers of the two circles. A common **internal tangent** does intersect the segment joining the centers of the two circles.

A belt wrapped around two wheels transfers power from one wheel to the other. In this lesson you will learn how to calculate the length *AB* on such a belt linkage system.

In the figure to the right, line *MO* is a common external tangent to circles *P* and *Q*. Line *NO* is a common internal tangent to circles *P* and *Q*.

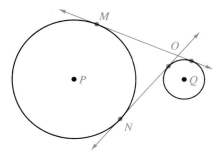

Two circles are called tangent circles if they intersect in exactly one point and they may be externally tangent or internally tangent.

In the figure below you can see that two tangent circles are called externally tangent if each lies in the exterior of the other. They are called internally tangent if one lies in the interior of the other.

 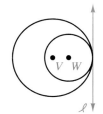

    Externally tangent circles   Internally tangent circles

The following example illustrates how similar triangles can be used to find unknown lengths in problems that involve common tangents.

Example 1

$\overline{RT}$ is a common tangent to $\odot P$ and $\odot Q$.
$QS = 7$, $ST = 24$, $RT = 48$
a. $x = PR = $ __?__   **b.** $y = QT = $ __?__

Solution

    $\triangle PRT \sim \triangle QST$ *Both are right triangles with a common acute angle and so are similar by AA Similarity.*

    a. $\frac{x}{48} = \frac{7}{24}$ or $x = PR = 14$ *Corresponding sides of similar triangles are proportional.*
    b. $y^2 = 7^2 + 24^2$ or $y = QT = 25$ *Apply the Pythagorean Theorem.*

Try This

$z = PT = $ __?__

Example 2

$\overline{AB}$ is a common external tangent to circles D and C and $DC = 13$. Find AB.

Solution

$13^2 = 5^2 + x^2$ *Draw $\overline{CE}$ to complete rectangle ABCE.*
                Apply the Pythagorean Theorem.

$x = AB = 12$

Try This

Suppose $\odot C$ is moved so that $DC = 15$. Find AB.

Class Exercises

Short Answer

State the number of external tangents and the number of internal tangents that exist for each pair of circles.

1.

Disjoint circles

2.

Externally tangent circles

3.

Internally tangent circles

4.

Intersecting circles

5.

Concentric circles

6.

One inside the other

Sample Exercises

$\overline{AB}$ is a common tangent to $\odot E$ and $\odot F$.

7. $EA = 10$, $FB = 3$, $CD = 12$ Find EF.
8. $EA = 10$, $FB = 3$, $CD = 12$ Find AB.
9. $EA = 10$, $FB = 2$, $CD = 5$ Find AB.

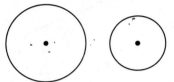

Complete each statement.

10. $ST = $ ___   **11.** $UV = $ ___

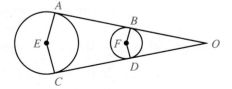

Discussion

12. $\overline{AB}$ is a common tangent between circles of equal radii. Give a convincing argument that $ABDC$ is a rectangle.

13. $\overline{AB}$ and $\overline{CD}$ are common tangents. Give a convincing argument that $\angle AEC \cong \angle BFD$.

Exercises

A

$\overline{AB}$ **is a common tangent.** $AE = 10$, $BD = 5$, $BC = 12$

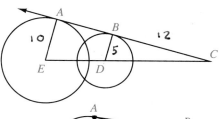

   1. Find AC.   **2.** Find AB.
   3. Find CD.   **4.** Find ED.
   5. If $AE = 9$, $BD = 3$, and $BC = 4$ find ED. Are the two
       circles tangent to each other?

$\overline{AB}$ **is a common tangent.** $AE = 15$, $BF = 6$, $CD = 20$.

   6. Find EF.
   7. Find AB.
   8. Find $AB + BF + EF + AE$.

$\overline{ST}$ **is a common tangent and the circles are tangent to each other.**

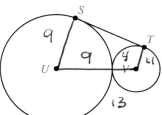

   9. If the radii are 9 and 4, find ST.
   10. If the radii are 8 and 5, find ST.
   11. If the radii are 9 and 3, find ST.
   12. If $ST = 15$, $UV = 17$, and $VT = \frac{9}{2}$, find US.
   13. If $ST = 24$, $UV = 25$, and $US = 16$, find VT. 9

$\overline{AB}$ **is a common tangent.** $CA = 8$, $CP = 17$, $AP = 15$, $BD = 5$

   14. Find PB.
   15. Find PD.
   16. Find AB.
   17. Prove that $\angle PCA \cong \angle PDB$.

   18. The centers of two circles with radii 4 and 9 are 17 units apart. Find the
       length of a common external tangent.
   19. The centers of two circles with radii 5 and 7 are 14 units apart. Find the
       length of a common external tangent.

B

   20. Given: $\overline{EF}$ and $\overline{GH}$ are common internal
          tangents.
       Prove: $\overline{EF} \cong \overline{GH}$

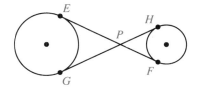

   21. Given: $\overline{AB}$ and $\overline{CD}$ are common external
          tangents that intersect each other at P.
       Prove: $\overline{AB} \cong \overline{CD}$

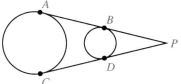

   22. Prove that in the figure for Exercise 21, $ABDC$ is a trapezoid.

   23. Given: $\overline{AB}$ is a common internal tangent of two disjoint congruent circles.
       Prove: $\overline{AB}$ and $\overline{CD}$ bisect each other.

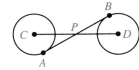

24. Three metal disks each with a radius of 10 cm are tangent to each other. The disks are enclosed by a metal frame that forms an equilateral triangle. What is the length of one side of the frame?

25. Suppose that four disks, each with radius 10 cm and arranged to form a square, are enclosed by a square metal frame similar to the figure. How does the length of a side of this square compare to the length of a side of the triangle in Exercise 24?

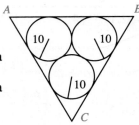

C

26. $\overline{DE}$ and $\overline{FG}$ are common tangents for the three circles. If the radii of the three circles are 8, 3, and 5 as shown, find BC.

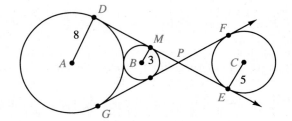

27. Construct $\odot O$ and $\odot P$ each with a radius of 2 such that $OP = 6$. Construct two circles that are tangent to both $\odot O$ and $\odot P$.

28. After completing the constructions in Exercise 27, construct as many additional circles as you can that are tangent to both $\odot O$ and $\odot P$.

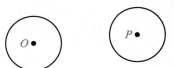

Critical Thinking

29. Construct $\odot A$, $\odot B$, and $\odot C$ with equal radii such that $\triangle ABC$ is an equilateral triangle as shown. Next construct at least four circles that are tangent to all three circles. How many other circles that are tangent to all three circles do you think exist?

Algebra Review

Multiply.

1. $5(x - 2)$
2. $4(x - 8)$
3. $-6(y - 4)$
4. $-12(y - 4)$
5. $6(2x - 3y - 8z)$
6. $-9(3x - 2y - 5z)$
7. $8(-2x - 6y + 7)$
8. $15(2a + 4b - 8)$

Math Contest Problem

$\overline{AB}$ is a common tangent of $\odot C$, $\odot D$, $\odot E$, and $\odot F$. Suppose that $AC = 12$, $DB = 9$, and $AE = BF = 3$. If the midpoint of $\overline{EF}$ is the center of a circle that is tangent to both $\odot E$ and $\odot F$, what are the possible values for its radius?

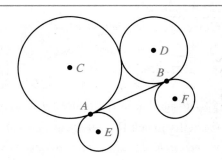

8-4 Arcs and Their Measure

An **arc** of a circle consists of two points and a continuous part of a circle between them. Notice that any two given points on a circle determine two different arcs.

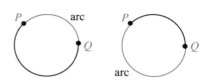

A **central angle** of a circle is an angle whose vertex is the center of the circle. $\angle ABC$ is a central angle of $\odot B$ in the figure shown.

The sides of a central angle separate the circle into two different arcs. The endpoints and all the points on both the circle and the interior of the central angle are called a **minor arc.** The arc in the exterior of the central angle is called a **major arc.** Note that three letters are usually used to name a major arc. If the endpoints are the endpoints of a diameter then the circle is divided into two arcs called **semicircles.**

minor arc $\overset{\frown}{AC}$ major arc $\overset{\frown}{AXC}$ semicircle $\overset{\frown}{AXC}$

An arc, like an angle, is measured in degrees.

The measure of a minor arc is the measure of its central angle. $m\overset{\frown}{AB} = x$
The measure of a major arc is $360 - m$, where m is the measure of the central angle of its minor arc. $m\overset{\frown}{ACB} = 360 - x$

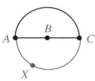

The measure of a semicircle is 180.

Congruent arcs are arcs with equal measure that lie in the same circle or in congruent circles. In the figure to the right $m\overset{\frown}{AB} = m\overset{\frown}{CD} = 50$. So two arcs with the same measure are not congruent unless they lie in congruent circles.

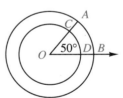

Example 1

Complete each statement.
a. $m\overset{\frown}{AB} = $ ___   b. $m\overset{\frown}{ACB} = $ ___

    Solution
    a. $m\overset{\frown}{AB} = 65$ b. $m\overset{\frown}{ACB} = 360 - 65 = 295$

Try This

Complete each statement.
a. $m\angle BOC = $ ___   b. $m\overset{\frown}{ADC} = $ ___

● POSTULATE 20   Arc Addition Postulate

The measure of adjacent nonoverlapping arcs is the sum of the measures of the two arcs. That is, if C is on $\overarc{AB}$, then $m\overarc{AC} + m\overarc{CB} = m\overarc{AB}$.

This postulate applies to both minor arcs and major arcs. For example,

$m\overarc{AC} = m\overarc{AB} + m\overarc{BC}$, and
$m\overarc{DAC} = m\overarc{DAB} + m\overarc{BC}$

A point B on $\overarc{AC}$ is the *midpoint* of $\overarc{AC}$, if $m\overarc{AB} = m\overarc{BC}$.

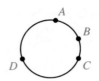

Example 2

Find each measure.   a. $m\overarc{AC}$ **b.** $m\overarc{AD}$

   Solution

   a. $m\overarc{AC} = 35 + 120$ **b.** $m\overarc{AD} = 360 - (35 + 120 + 42)$
               $= 155$ $= 163$

Try This

a. $m\overarc{BD} = \underline{\ ?\ }$ **b.** Show that D is the midpoint of $\overarc{CE}$.

Recall that a chord is a segment that joins two points on a circle. Theorem 8.4 and its converse, Theorem 8.5, describe a relationship between congruent chords and congruent minor arcs.

◆ THEOREM 8.4

In a circle or in congruent circles congruent chords have congruent minor arcs.

Given: $\overline{AB} \cong \overline{CD}$
Prove: $\overarc{AB} \cong \overarc{CD}$

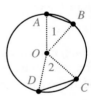

Proof Statements

Statements	Reasons
1. $\overline{AB} \cong \overline{CD}$	1. Given
2. Draw $\overline{OA}, \overline{OB}, \overline{OC}$, and $\overline{OD}$.	2. Two points determine a segment.
3. $\overline{OA} \cong \overline{OB} \cong \overline{OC} \cong \overline{OD}$	3. Radii of a circle are congruent.
4. $\triangle AOB \cong \triangle COD$	4. SSS Congruence Postulate
5. $\angle 1 \cong \angle 2$	5. Corr. parts of $\cong \triangle$'s are $\cong$.
6. $m\angle 1 = m\overarc{AB}$	6. Definition of measure of minor arc
7. $m\angle 2 = m\overarc{CD}$	7. Definition of measure of minor arc
8. $m\overarc{AB} = m\overarc{CD}$	8. Substitution

◆ THEOREM 8.5

In a circle or in congruent circles congruent minor arcs have congruent chords and congruent central angles.

Class Exercises

Short Answer

1. What is the radius of $\odot O$?
2. Name a minor arc.
3. Name a major arc.
4. Name a semicircle.
5. Name two congruent arcs.
6. Name the central angle of $\overarc{CD}$.
7. Name two arcs with endpoint E.

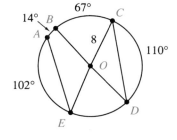

Sample Exercises

8. Find $m\overarc{BC}$. 9. Find $m\overarc{CD}$.
10. Find $m\overarc{AC}$. 11. Find $m\overarc{ACD}$.
12. Find $m\overarc{AEC}$. 13. Find $m\overarc{ADB}$.

14. Explain why $\overline{BD}$ is not a diameter.

Discussion Exercises

15. Suppose that A, B, and C are points on a circle. Give a convincing argument that $m\overarc{ACB} + m\overarc{AB} = 360$.
16. Suppose that $m\overarc{AB} = m\overarc{AC}$. Give a convincing argument that $\triangle ABC$ is isosceles.

Exercises

A

Find each measure.

1. $m\overarc{BC}$ 2. $m\overarc{AC}$
3. $m\overarc{BAD}$ 4. $m\overarc{ADC}$
5. $m\angle BOC$ 6. $m\overarc{AE}$

7. Name a pair of congruent arcs.

$\overline{DF}$ **is a tangent to $\odot O$ from the external point F and $m\angle OFD = 38$.**
Find each measure.

8. $m\overarc{AB}$ 9. $m\overarc{AD}$ 10. $m\overarc{AC}$
11. $m\overarc{BC}$ 12. $m\overarc{ADC}$ 13. $m\overarc{ACD}$
14. $m\angle DOF$ 15. $m\overarc{ED}$ 16. $m\overarc{AE}$

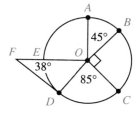

B

Find each measure.

17. $m\angle AOB$ 18. $m\angle BOC$
19. $m\angle COD$ 20. $m\angle AOD$

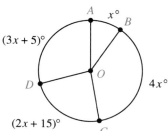

21. Given: $\widehat{AB} \cong \widehat{CD}$
   Prove: $\widehat{AC} \cong \widehat{BD}$
22. Given: $\widehat{AC} \cong \widehat{BD}$
   Prove: $\widehat{AB} \cong \widehat{CD}$

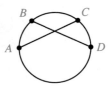

23. Given: $\odot O$ with tangents $\overline{CA}$ and $\overline{CB}$
   $m \angle ACB = x$
   Prove: $m\widehat{AB} = 180 - x$
24. Given: $\odot O$ with tangents $\overline{CA}$ and $\overline{CB}$
   $m \angle ACB = x$
   Prove: $m\widehat{ADB} = 180 + x$

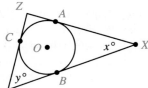

25. Find the coordinates of a point B above the x axis such that $m\widehat{AB} = 90$.
26. Find the coordinates of a point C below the x axis such that $m\widehat{AC} = 90$.
27. Find the coordinates of a point D in the quadrant I such that $m\widehat{AD} = 45$.
28. Find the coordinates of a point E in the quadrant III such that $m\widehat{AE} = 135$.

$A\,(2, 0)$

C

29. Given: $\triangle XYZ$ is a circumscribed triangle.
   $m \angle X = x$
   $m \angle Y = y$
   Prove: $m\widehat{AC} = x + y$

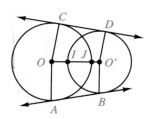

30. Given: $\overleftrightarrow{AB}$ is a tangent of $\odot O$ and $\odot O'$.
   I is the midpoint of $\overline{BID}$.
   J is the midpoint of $\overline{AC}$.
   $\overleftrightarrow{CD}$ is the tangent of $\odot O'$.
   Prove: $\overleftrightarrow{CD}$ is tangent to $\odot O$.

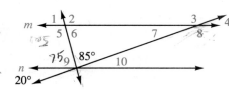

Critical Thinking

31. Complete the table below and discover a formula for the number of chords and arcs for n points on a circle.

number of points	2	3	4	5	$\cdots$	n
number of chords	1	3	6	___	$\cdots$	___
number of arcs	2	6	12	___	$\cdots$	___

Mixed Review

Lines m and n are parallel. Find each measure.

1. $m \angle 10$ 2. $m \angle 9$
3. $m \angle 2$ 4. $m \angle 6$
5. $m \angle 7$ 6. $m \angle 8$

Enrichment

The Earth as a Sphere

As you know, the earth is considered a sphere. This may seem strange since there are mountains on the earth's surface several miles high. However, if a scale model of the earth were made 8 ft in diameter it would be smoother than a finely polished bowling ball. The highest mountain would be represented by a projection of only 0.007 in. above the surface. The slight difference between the polar and equatorial diameters would also be negligible. Thus, for most purposes, the earth may be considered a sphere.

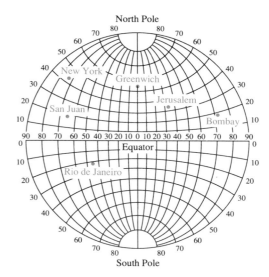

To locate a point on the earth, reference lines are needed (much like the grid used for locating points on a plane). Since the earth revolves from west to east on an axis through its poles, a series of circular arcs is drawn through the poles. These are called meridians.

The meridian through Greenwich, England, is arbitrarily chosen as the zero meridian. The other meridians are then defined in degrees both east and west from this meridian. New York City is near the meridian 74° W; Jerusalem is near the meridian 35° E. The degree measure associated with a point on the earth, along with the east or west designation, is called the longitude of the point.

To completely determine a point on the earth, another reference line is needed. This is the equator. A point is located by means of the arc, from the point to the equator, that is intercepted on the meridian passing through the point. Thus, if $m\widehat{PE} = 60$ ($m\angle POE = 60$) the point P is said to have latitude 60° N. The latitude of New York City is about 41° N as shown in the figure. The equator has latitude 0° and the north pole has latitude 90° N.

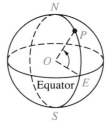

Longitude and latitude are used in many fields including astronomy, map making, and sailing. For example, to determine the location of a ship at sea, navigators first use an instrument called a sextant to calculate their latitude.

Exercises

Use the above figure to give the approximate latitude and longitude of each city.

1. Bombay
2. Rio de Janeiro
3. San Juan
4. Show that the radius of the circle of latitude 60° is half the radius of the earth.

8-5 Chords of Circles

Get a cardboard pizza platter from a pizza shop. Experiment and discover a way to find the center of the platter.

The midpoint of an arc bisects the arc. Any line or ray containing this midpoint is also said to bisect the arc. In this figure, point B and $\overrightarrow{OB}$ bisect $\overarc{AC}$.

◆ **THEOREM 8.6**

If a diameter is perpendicular to a chord, then it bisects the chord and its minor and major arcs.

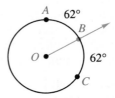

Given: ⊙P with diameter $\overline{CD}$ and chord $\overline{AB}$
  $\overline{AB} \perp \overline{CD}$
Prove: $\overline{AE} \cong \overline{BE}$, $\overarc{AD} \cong \overarc{BD}$, $\overarc{AC} \cong \overarc{BC}$
Plan Draw $\overline{PA}$ and $\overline{PB}$ and use HL congruence to conclude that $\triangle APE \cong \triangle BPE$. Then conclude that $\overline{AE} \cong \overline{BE}$ and $\angle APE \cong \angle BPE$. Consequently $\overarc{AD} \cong \overarc{BD}$ and $\overarc{AC} \cong \overarc{BC}$.

Compare the hypotheses of Theorems 8.6 and 8.7. The hypothesis of each is part of the conclusion of the other.

◆ **THEOREM 8.7**

If a diameter bisects a chord that is not a diameter, then it is perpendicular to the chord and bisects its major and minor arcs.

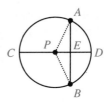

Given: ⊙P has diameter $\overline{CD}$ bisecting chord $\overline{AB}$.
Prove: $\overline{CD} \perp \overline{AB}$, $\overarc{AD} \cong \overarc{BD}$, $\overarc{AC} \cong \overarc{BC}$
Plan Use SSS congruence to prove $\triangle APE \cong \triangle BPE$. Then use corresponding parts of congruent triangles are congruent to draw the final conclusion.

Example 1

Refer to the figure to complete each statement.

a. $AD = $ ___   **b.** $OE = $ ___

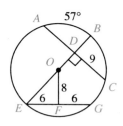

Solution

a. $AD = 9$ *EB ⊥ AC means that EB bisects AC.*
b. $OE^2 = 6^2 + 8^2$ *OF bisects EG and hence ⊥ it.*
    $= 100$ *Use the Pythagorean Theorem.*
    $OE = 10$

Try This

Find $m\widehat{AEC}$ in the figure to the right.

The proofs of the following theorems are completed in Exercises 30–32.

◆ **THEOREM 8.8**

The perpendicular bisector of a chord contains the center of the circle.

An electrician's drill bit has a shank end with six flat surfaces as shown to the right. These flat surfaces must be an equal distance from the rotating axis to ensure that the drill runs smoothly. How can a machinist determine that this is the case if the center of the drill is not known? To answer this question consider the distance from the center of a circle to a chord of the circle.

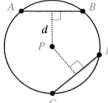

Recall that the distance from a point to a line is defined as the perpendicular distance from the point to the line. In this figure d is the perpendicular distance to $\overline{AB}$ from center P.

◆ **THEOREM 8.9**

In the same circle or in congruent circles congruent chords are equidistant from the center.

◆ **THEOREM 8.10**

In the same circle or in congruent circles, chords equidistant from the center are congruent.

Example 2

Refer to the figure to complete each statement:

a. $AB = $ ___   **b.** $x = $ ___

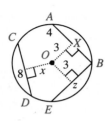

Solution

$AB = 8$ $\overline{OX} \perp \overline{AB}$ means that X is the midpoint of $\overline{AB}$.

$x = 3$ Since $\overline{AB}$ and $\overline{CD}$ are the same length, they are the same distance from the center.

Try This

Find z. Explain your answer.

Class Exercises

Short Answer

Complete each statement with a valid conclusion.

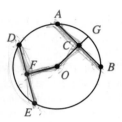

1. If $\overline{OC}$ is the perpendicular bisector of $\overline{AB}$, then ___ .
2. If $AB = DE$, then ___ .
3. If C is the midpoint of $\overline{AB}$ and G bisects $\widehat{AB}$, then ___ .
4. If $\overline{OF} \perp \overline{DE}$, then ___ .
5. If $\overline{OC} \perp \overline{AB}$, $\overline{OF} \perp \overline{DF}$, and $OC = OF$, then ___ .

Sample Exercises

    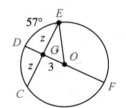

6. Find x.   7. Find y.   8. Find $m \angle EGO$.
9. Find $m \angle GEO$.   10. Find $m \widehat{CD}$.

Discussion

11. Explain how you can find the center of this circle in order to redraw a complete circle with a compass.

12. Would the following be the start of a proof of Theorem 8.9 or Theorem 8.10?

    Given: $OX = OY$
    Prove: $RS = TU$

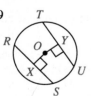

13. Give a convincing argument that Theorem 8.10 is true.

Exercises

A

Complete each of the following.

1. $y =$ ___
2. $x =$ ___
3. $m\,\widehat{AD} =$ ___
4. $m\,\widehat{ABD} =$ ___
5. $m\angle FIO =$ ___
6. $m\,\widehat{GH} =$ ___
7. $m\,\widehat{HE} =$ ___
8. $m\,\widehat{FEH} =$ ___

9. Find FH.
10. Find $m\,\widehat{GF}$.
11. Find OD.
12. Find $m\angle ODB$.
13. Find $m\angle OBD$.
14. Find $m\,\widehat{FE}$.
15. If $m\,\widehat{GC} = 137$, then $m\,\widehat{AE} =$ ___ .

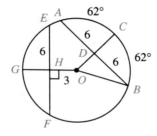

$m\,\widehat{AB} = m\,\widehat{CD} = 100,\ m\,\widehat{BD} = 40,\ \overline{OX} \perp \overline{AB},\ \overline{OY} \perp \overline{CD}$

Find each measure.

16. $m\,\widehat{EB}$
17. $m\angle YOB$
18. $m\angle OYX$
19. $m\angle YXB$
20. $m\angle AOC$

21. If $\overline{AB}$ is a diameter, $AB = 8$, and $m\angle ABC = 45$, how far is $\overline{BC}$ from the center of O?

B

22. Chords $\overline{PQ}$ and $\overline{RS}$ in a circle are equal in length. If $\overline{PQ}$ is distance $4x$ and $\overline{RS}$ is distance x^2 from the center, how far is each chord from the center?
23. $\overline{AB}$ and $\overline{CD}$ are both d units from the center of the circle. $AB = 2x + 7$ and $CD = 3x - 5$. What is the length of each chord?

24. Often machine parts like the one shown here will work properly only if the groove is "centered." Why does measuring $\overline{AB}$ and $\overline{CD}$ tell you whether or not the groove is centered?

25. Given: $\overline{AD} \perp \overline{BC}$, $\overline{AD}$ is a diameter.
   Prove: $\triangle ABC$ is isosceles.

26. Given: $\overline{OY} \perp \overline{AB}$, $\overline{OX} \perp \overline{CD}$, $OX = OY$
   Prove: $\widehat{AD} \cong \widehat{BC}$

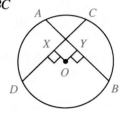

27. A chord is located 5 in. from the center of a circle with radius 13 in. Find the length of the chord.

28. An equilateral triangle with sides of length 10 is inscribed in a circle. Find the distance from the center of the circle to the side of the triangle.

29. Prove Theorem 8.7.
   Given: $\odot P$ has diameter $\overline{CD}$ bisecting chord $\overline{AB}$.
   Prove: $\overline{CD} \perp \overline{AB}$, $\widehat{DA} \cong \widehat{DB}$, $\widehat{AC} \cong \widehat{BC}$

30. Prove Theorem 8.8.
   Given: $\odot P$ with chord $\overline{AB}$
      $\overline{CD}$ is the $\perp$ bisector of $\overline{AB}$.
   Prove: $\overline{CD}$ contains the center of $\odot P$.

31. Prove Theorem 8.9.
   Given: $\overline{AB} \cong \overline{CD}$
   Prove: $OS = OT$

32. Prove Theorem 8.10.
   Given: $OS = OT$
   Prove: $\overline{AB} \cong \overline{CD}$

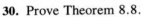

33. A part of an old wheel is found by an archeologist in a dig. The archeologist would like to determine how large the complete wheel was. How can she determine the radius of the complete wheel?

34. Given: $\overline{OX} \perp \overline{AB}$
      $\overline{OY} \perp \overline{CD}$
      $m \angle 1 = m \angle 2$
   Prove: $AB = CD$

35. Given: $\overline{OX} \perp \overline{AB}$
      $\overline{OY} \perp \overline{CD}$
      $AB = CD$
   Prove: $m \angle 1 = m \angle 2$

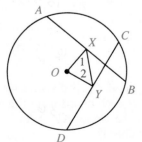

C

Circle O pictured is the set of all points in the coordinate plane whose coordinates satisfy the equation $x^2 + y^2 = 25$. The horizontal line consists of all points whose y-coordinate is 3.

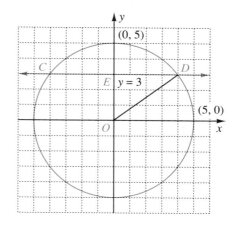

36. Use the Pythagorean Theorem to find the length ED. Then find the length CD.
37. Use the results of Exercise 36 to find the coordinates of points C and D.
38. Use the distance formula to find the length of CD.
39. Solve the system of equations $x^2 + y^2 = 25$ and $y = 3$ to find the coordinates of points C and D.

Critical Thinking

Complete each statement with the word *always*, *sometimes*, or *never*. Give a convincing argument to support each answer.

40. If AB and CD are parallel chords, then $ABCD$ is ___ a rectangle.
41. A line through the midpoint of a chord and its intercepted arc ___ passes through the center of the circle.
42. A line that is perpendicular to a chord ___ includes the center of the circle.

Algebra Review

Solve.

1. $4 + 3x = 28$
2. $5 + 4y = 37$
3. $5y - 9 = 21$
4. $4 - 3y = 13$
5. $10y - 7 = -12$
6. $6 - 8x = 18$
7. $8 - 2y = 22$
8. $3 - 6y = 15$

Quiz

Complete each statement with the most appropriate word.

1. A chord that contains the center of a circle is a ___ .
2. A ___ is a line that intersects the circle in exactly one point.

$\overline{AB}$ is tangent to $\odot E$.

3. If $AB = 8$ and $EB = 12$, find AE.
4. If $DC = 10$ and $AE = 13$, find EF.
5. If $m \angle ABE = 28$, find $m\widehat{AG}$.

6. Draw a pair of circles that have two common external tangents and no common internal tangents.

7. If $\overline{XY} \cong \overline{YZ}$ and $m\widehat{XY} = 105$, find $m \angle XTZ$.
8. Find $m\widehat{WX}$.   9. Find $m \angle XYZ$.

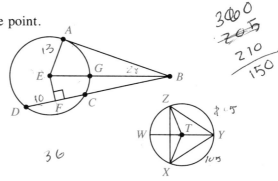

ANGLES AND SEGMENTS

OBJECTIVE: *State and apply theorems concerning measures of inscribed angles.*

8-6 Inscribed Angles

Construct a circle and an inscribed angle. Use a protractor to measure $\widehat{AC}$ and $\angle ABC$. What relationship do you discover?

An **inscribed angle** is an angle with vertex on a circle and sides that contain chords of the circle. In the figure, $\angle BAC$ is an inscribed angle and $\widehat{BC}$ is its **intercepted arc.**

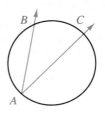

◆ **THEOREM 8.11**   Inscribed Angle Measure

The measure of an inscribed angle is half the measure of its intercepted arc.

Given: inscribed $\angle BAC$

Prove: $m\angle BAC = \frac{1}{2}m\widehat{BC}$

Plan   Consider these three cases. In Case 1 the center of the circle is on one side of the inscribed angle. In Case 2 the center is in the interior of the angle and in Case 3 the center of the circle is in the exterior of the angle.

Case 1

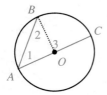

$m\widehat{BC} = m\angle 3$
$\quad\quad = m\angle 1 + m\angle 2 \text{ or}$
$m\widehat{BC} = 2m\angle 1$

Case 2

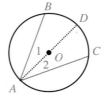

Use Case 1 for $\angle 1$ and $\angle 2$. Add angles and arcs.

Case 3

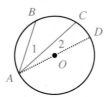

Use Case 1 for $\angle BAD$ and $\angle 2$. Subtract angles and arcs.

In Case 1, the conclusion follows from the fact that $\angle 3$ is an exterior angle of $\triangle ABO$. This proof will be completed in Exercises 25, 26, and 27.

Example 1

Find each measure.

a. $m \angle CAB$

b. $m \angle CDB$

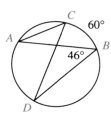

Solution

a. $m \angle CAB = 30$ *The measure of $\angle CAB$ is $\frac{1}{2}$ its intercepted arc BC.*

b. $m \angle CDB = 30$ *$\angle CDB$ has the same intercepted arc as $\angle CAB$.*

Try This

Find each measure.

a. $m \overset{\frown}{AD}$

b. $m \angle ACD$

Several corollaries to Theorem 8.11 are presented below. Their proofs follow directly from the theorem and you will be asked to prove them in Exercises 28, 29, and 30.

▶ COROLLARY 8.11a

If two inscribed angles intercept the same arc, then the angles are congruent.

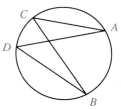

▶ COROLLARY 8.11b

If a quadrilateral is inscribed in a circle, then its opposite angles are supplementary.

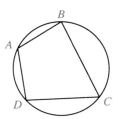

▶ COROLLARY 8.11c

An angle inscribed in a semicircle is a right angle. Also, if an inscribed angle is a right angle its intercepted arc is a semicircle.

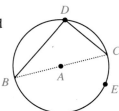

Think about point B moving along the circle toward point C. The inscribed angle measure theorem continues to be true as $\overline{CB}$ moves to form a tangent at C. A **tangent-chord angle** has its vertex on a circle with one side tangent to the circle at the vertex and the other side containing a chord. Figure **e** shows a tangent-chord angle with intercepted arc AC.

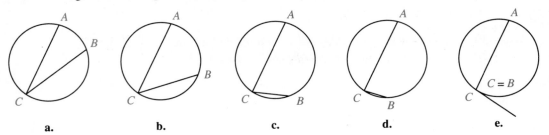

| a. | b. | c. | d. | e. |

In all five cases, $m \angle C = \frac{1}{2} m \overset{\frown}{AB}$.

This sequence of figures provides a convincing argument for the next theorem.

◆ **THEOREM 8.12**

The measure of a tangent-chord angle is half the measure of its intercepted arc.

Example 2

$\overleftrightarrow{BE}$ **is tangent at B. Find each measure.**
a. $m \angle ADC$
b. $m \angle BCD$

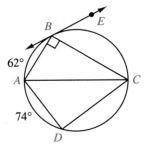

Solution

a. $m \angle ADC = 90$ *Opposite angles of an inscribed quadrilateral are supplementary.*

b. $m \angle BCD = m \angle DCA + m \angle BCA$
$= (\frac{1}{2})74 + (\frac{1}{2})62$
$= 37 + 31$
$= 68$

Try This

Find each measure.
a. $m \angle CBE$
b. $m \angle DAB$

Class Exercises

Short Answer

1. Name two congruent inscribed angles.
2. Name two inscribed angles that are not congruent.
3. Name an angle that is not an inscribed angle.
4. Name a tangent-chord angle.
5. Name two inscribed angles that have measure 45.
6. Name two inscribed angles whose intercepted arc is $\overset{\frown}{AD}$.

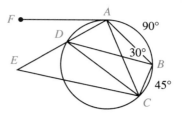

Sample Exercises

Find each measure.

7. $m \angle BDC$ 8. $m \angle BAC$ 9. $m \overset{\frown}{ADC}$
10. $m \angle ABC$ 11. $m \angle ADC$ 12. $m \angle FAD$

Discussion

$\overleftrightarrow{EC}$ is tangent at E.

13. Explain why $\angle BED$ is not an inscribed angle.
14. Explain why $\angle CED$ is not a tangent-chord angle.
15. Explain why $\angle BFE \cong \angle BEC$.

16. Complete the proof. State a theorem (in if-then form) that you have proven.

    Given: $\overleftrightarrow{AB} \parallel \overleftrightarrow{CD}$. (Draw auxiliary line BD.)

Statements	Reasons
1. $\overleftrightarrow{AB} \parallel \overleftrightarrow{CD}$	1. ___
2. $\angle ABD \cong \angle BDC$	2. ___
3. ___	3. ___

Exercises

A

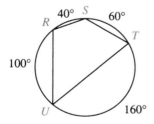

Find each measure.

1. $m \angle ADB$ 2. $m \overset{\frown}{BC}$ 3. $m \angle BDC$ 4. $m \overset{\frown}{AC}$
5. $m \angle R$ 6. $m \angle S$ 7. $m \angle T$ 8. $m \angle U$

$\overrightarrow{CD}$ is tangent at C. **Find each measure.**

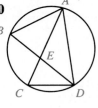

9. $m\angle CAB$
10. $m\angle ABC$
11. $m\angle ACB$

$\overrightarrow{AC}$ bisects $\angle BAD$. $m\widehat{CD} = 80$, $m\widehat{AD} = 160$
Find each measure.

12. $m\angle BAC$ 13. $m\angle BDC$
14. $m\angle AEB$ 15. $m\angle ADB$

16. Suppose that a harbor is too shallow for ships to enter inside the circular arc ACB, also known as the "danger circle." The navigator of a ship at location C measured $\angle ACB$ and discovered it was equal to a published "danger angle." How did the ship's navigator know that the ship was on the danger circle?

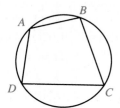

B

17. Suppose that $ABCD$ is a quadrilateral inscribed in a circle and that $\overline{AC}$ is a diameter of the circle. If $m\angle A$ is three times $m\angle C$, what are the measures of all four angles?
18. If $m\angle A = 4x + 35$, $m\angle B = 3x + 35$, and $m\angle D = 7x + 15$, find the measure of all four angles of quadrilateral $ABCD$.

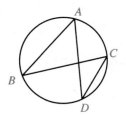

19. If $m\angle ABC = 3x + 5$ and $m\angle ADC = 5x - 21$, find the measure of these two angles.
20. If $m\angle BAD = 3x + 50$, $m\angle ABC = 4x + 25$, and $m\angle BCD = 7x + 30$, find $m\angle ADC$.

21. Prove that a trapezoid inscribed in a circle is an isosceles trapezoid.
22. Given $\odot A$ and a point P exterior to the circle, construct the circle with diameter $\overline{AP}$ and let B and C be the points at which the two circles intersect. Prove that $\overline{PB}$ and $\overline{PC}$ are tangent segments from the exterior point P.

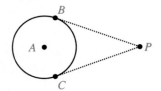

23. Given: $\overline{AB}$ and $\overline{BC}$ are diameters.
      $\odot X$ and $\odot Y$ are tangent at B.

Prove: $\angle 1 \cong \angle 2$

24. Given: $\overline{AB}$ and $\overline{BC}$ are diameters.
      $\odot X$ and $\odot Y$ are tangent at B.

Prove: $\frac{AE}{EB} = \frac{CD}{DB}$

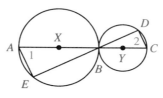

25. Prove Case 1 of Theorem 8.11.

  Given: inscribed $\angle BAC$

  Prove: $m \angle BAC = \frac{1}{2} m \overset{\frown}{BC}$

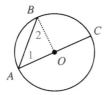

26. Use Case 1 to prove Case 2 of Theorem 8.11.

  Given: inscribed $\angle BAC$

  Prove: $m \angle BAC = \frac{1}{2} m \overset{\frown}{BC}$

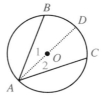

27. Use Case 1 to prove Case 3 of Theorem 8.11.

  Given: inscribed $\angle BAC$

  Prove: $m \angle BAC = \frac{1}{2} m \overset{\frown}{BC}$

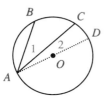

28. Prove Corollary 8.11a.

  Given: inscribed $\angle$s ACB and ADB

  Prove: $\angle ACB \cong \angle ADB$

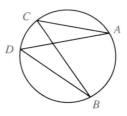

29. Prove Corollary 8.11b.

  Given: inscribed quadrilateral $ABCD$

  Prove: $\angle A$ and $\angle C$ are supplementary.

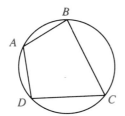

30. Prove Corollary 8.11c.

  Given: $\angle BDC$ is inscribed in semicircle $\overset{\frown}{BDC}$.

  Prove: $\angle D$ is a right angle.

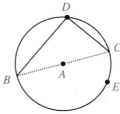

31. If $TV = 3$, $VS = 8$, $RV = 4$, find x.

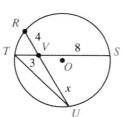

C

32. **Given:** $\overline{CD}$ is tangent to the circle at D and $\overline{AD}$ contains the center of the circle.

    Prove: $\frac{AD}{AC} = \frac{DB}{DC}$

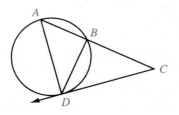

33. Suppose that a triangle is inscribed in each of two congruent circles. If a side and an adjacent angle of one is congruent to a side and an adjacent angle of the other prove that the two triangles are congruent.

Assume the two circles are tangent at *T*.

34. Prove that $\overline{AC} \parallel \overline{BD}$. (HINT: Draw the tangent line at point T.)
35. If $AB = 5$, $DT = 8$, and $CD = 6$, find BT.

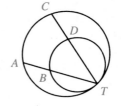

Critical Thinking

Complete each statement with the word *always*, *sometimes*, or *never*. Give a convincing argument that your answer is correct.

36. A quadrilateral that is inscribed in a circle with at least one diagonal a diameter is ____ a parallelogram.
37. A quadrilateral that is inscribed in a circle with both diagonals a diameter is ____ a rectangle.
38. If a triangle is inscribed in a circle to which a tangent line to the circle at one of the vertices forms a 60° tangent-chord angle with one side of the triangle, then the triangle is ____ an equilateral triangle.

Algebra Review

Find the LCM.

1. a^2b, ab^2
2. $3x^2$, $6xy$
3. $x + y$, $x - y$
4. $a + 1$, $a^2 - 1$
5. $8x^2y^2$, $12y^3$
6. $12xy^2$, $16x^3y$
7. $x^2 + 16$, $x - 2$
8. $x^2 - 2x + 1$, $1 - x^2$

Computer Activity

Use computer software to investigate the measure of an angle formed by two chords intersecting inside a circle.

Draw $\overline{BC}$ and $\overline{DE}$. Name the intersection of $\overline{BC}$ and $\overline{DE}$ point F.
Measure $\angle CFD$.
Measure $\angle CAD$ and $\angle BAE$.

What generalization can you make about the measure of angle formed by two chords intersecting inside a circle?

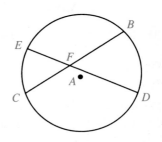

8-7 Angles of Chords, Secants, and Tangents

In the previous section you studied inscribed angles and tangent-chord angles. In both types of angles, the vertex of the angle is on the circle. In the angles formed by chords, secants, and tangents, vertices are either in the interior of the circle or on the exterior of the circle. Theorem 8.13 deals with the case in which the vertex is on the interior of the circle. This theorem also helps answer the question to the right.

If a ship's captain measures $\angle ACB$ and finds it to be greater than the published "danger angle" how would he know that he was located inside the "danger circle"?

◆ **THEOREM 8.13**

The measure of an angle formed by two chords intersecting inside a circle is one half the sum of the intercepted arcs.

Given: chords $\overline{AB}$ and $\overline{CD}$ intersecting at point X

Prove: $m\angle AXC = \frac{1}{2}(m\,\overset{\frown}{AC} + m\,\overset{\frown}{BD})$

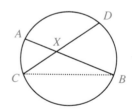

Proof Draw $\overline{BC}$. Then $\angle AXC$ is an exterior angle of $\triangle XCB$ and hence $m\angle AXC = m\angle XCB + m\angle XBC$. Furthermore, $m\angle XCB = \frac{1}{2}m\,\overset{\frown}{BD}$ and $m\angle XBC = \frac{1}{2}m\,\overset{\frown}{AC}$. Therefore, $m\angle AXC = \frac{1}{2}(m\,\overset{\frown}{AC} + m\,\overset{\frown}{BD})$.

Example 1

Find $m\angle 1$.

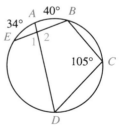

Solution

$m\angle 1 = \frac{1}{2}(m\,\overset{\frown}{AB} + m\,\overset{\frown}{ED})$ *Since $m\angle BCD = 105°$, you know*
$\quad\ = \frac{1}{2}(40 + 136)$ *that $m\,\overset{\frown}{BED} = 210$. So $m\,\overset{\frown}{ED} =$*
$\quad\ = 88$ *$210 - (34 + 40) = 136$.*

Try This

Find $m\angle 2$.

The next theorem deals with the measure of an angle whose vertex is outside the circle and whose sides intersect the circle. There are three cases. The sides are (1) both secants or (2) both tangents or (3) one secant and one tangent.

◆ THEOREM 8.14

The measure of an angle formed by two secants, two tangents, or a secant and a tangent drawn from a point in the exterior of a circle is equal to half the difference of the measures of the intercepted arcs.

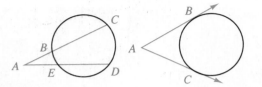

Example 2

Find

a. $m\angle CAE$ if $m\widehat{BD} = 10$ and $m\widehat{CE} = 50$.
b. $m\angle GAF$ if $m\widehat{GF} = 105$ and $m\widehat{GEF} = 255$.

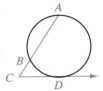

Solution

a. $m\angle CAE = \frac{1}{2}(m\widehat{CE} - m\widehat{BD})$
$= \frac{1}{2}(50 - 10)$
$= 20$

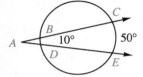

b. $m\angle GAF = \frac{1}{2}(m\widehat{GEF} - m\widehat{GF})$
$= \frac{1}{2}(255 - 105)$
$= \frac{1}{2}(150) = 75$

Try This

Find $m\angle GAE$ if $m\widehat{GE} = 166$ and $m\widehat{GD} = 62$.

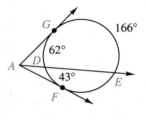

Example 3

$\overline{AD}$ is a diameter and $\overline{GD}$ is tangent at D.
$m\widehat{AB} = 25$, $m\widehat{CD} = 40$ Find $m\angle AFB$.

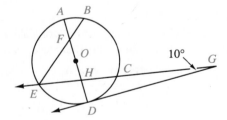

Solution

$m\angle EGD = \frac{1}{2}(m\widehat{ED} - m\widehat{CD})$ *Apply the tangent-secant form of Theorem 8.14.*
$10 = \frac{1}{2}(m\widehat{ED} - 40)$
$10 + 20 = \frac{1}{2}m\widehat{ED}$ *Use this fact in an application of Theorem 8.13*
$m\widehat{ED} = 60$ *to find $m\angle AFB$.*
$m\angle AFB = \frac{1}{2}(m\widehat{AB} + m\widehat{ED})$
$= \frac{1}{2}(25 + 60)$
$= 42.5$

Try This

Find $m\angle AHC$.

Class Exercises

Short Answer

Name an angle whose sides are as follows.

1. two secants of the circle
2. two tangents of the circle
3. a secant and a tangent of the circle
4. on intersecting chords of the circle

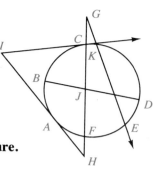

Tell what arc measures you would need to know to find each measure.

5. $m \angle BJF$ 6. $m \angle FGE$ 7. $m \angle AIC$ 8. $m \angle IHG$

Sample Exercises

Find the measure of each numbered angle.

9.

234°
126°
1

10.

2 58°
162°

11.

3 16° 88°

Discussion

12. This figure illustrates which one of the three cases of Theorem 8.14? Draw figures that illustrate the other two cases and give a convincing argument why each case is true.

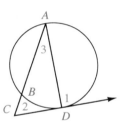

Exercises

A

Find the measure of each numbered angle.

1.

42°
1
124°

2.

32° 2 20°

3.

3
18° 66°

4. If $m\widehat{AC} = 39$ and $m\widehat{BD} = 73$, find $m \angle AED$.
5. If $m \angle AEC = 48$ and $m\widehat{AC} = 34$, find $m\widehat{BD}$.
6. If $m \angle BEC = 130$ and $m\widehat{AD} = 120$, find $m\widehat{BC}$.

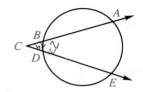

7. If $m\widehat{BD} = 15$ and $m\widehat{AE} = 85$, then find $m\angle ACE$.
8. If $m\angle ACE = 32$ and $m\widehat{BD} = 22$, find $m\widehat{AE}$.
9. If $m\angle ACE = 28$ and $m\widehat{AE} = 94$, find $m\widehat{BD}$.

$\vec{BA}$ and $\vec{BC}$ are tangent to $\odot X$.

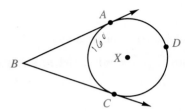

10. If $m\widehat{AC} = 160$, find $m\angle ABC$.
11. If $m\widehat{ADC} = 240$, find $m\angle ABC$.
12. If $m\widehat{AC} = b$ and $m\widehat{ADC} = 3b$, find $m\angle ABC$.

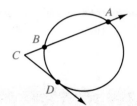

13. If $m\widehat{AD} = 165$ and $m\widehat{BD} = 63$, find $m\angle ACD$.
14. If $m\widehat{BD} = 55$ and $m\angle ACD = 43$, find $m\widehat{AD}$.
15. If $m\widehat{AD} = x$ and $m\widehat{BD} = y$, find $m\angle ACD$.

16. $\overleftrightarrow{AB}$ is tangent to $\odot O$. $m\widehat{AE} = 160$, $m\widehat{AD} = 50$, $m\widehat{DC} = 60$
Find $m\angle 1$ and $m\angle 2$.

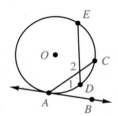

B

This design was drawn by using 16 points equally spaced around the circle. Find the measure of each angle.

17. $m\angle 1$ 18. $m\angle 2$
19. $m\angle 3$ 20. $m\angle 4$

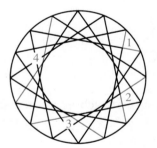

A diameter $\overline{AB}$ and a chord $\overline{CD}$ intersect inside $\odot O$ at X.
If $m\widehat{AD} = 128$ and $m\angle AXD = 74$, find each measure.

21. $m\widehat{AC}$ 22. $m\widehat{CB}$ 23. $m\widehat{BD}$

In $\odot O$, $\overline{AC}$ is a diameter and $\overline{AE}$ is a tangent. $m\widehat{DC} = 30$,
$m\angle AED = 30$ Find each measure.

24. $m\widehat{AB}$ 25. $m\widehat{BC}$ 26. $m\angle AXD$

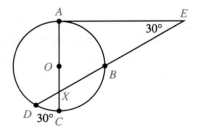

27. Prove Theorem 8.14 for the case of two secant lines.

Given: $\overrightarrow{PA}$ and $\overrightarrow{PD}$ secants

Prove: $m\angle P = \frac{1}{2}(m\overset{\frown}{AD} - m\overset{\frown}{BC})$.

(HINT: Use the auxiliary line BD.)

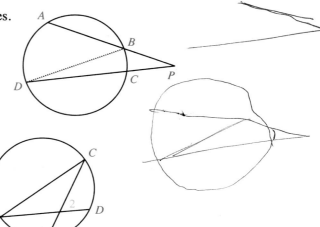

$m\overset{\frown}{AB} = 55$, $m\overset{\frown}{BD} = 40$, $\overline{AC}$ is a diameter and $\overrightarrow{PB}$ is tangent to the circle at B.

28. Find $m\angle P$.
29. Find $m\angle 2$.
30. Find $m\angle 1$.

31. Is $\overline{AD} \parallel \overline{PB}$? Explain.

C

32. Given $m\angle AXD = 72$, $m\angle AED = 28$
Find $m\overset{\frown}{AD}$ and $m\overset{\frown}{CB}$.

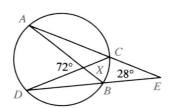

33. Given concentric circles centered at O. $\overline{AB}$ and $\overline{CD}$ are chords of the large circle that intersect at point E on the small circle. $m\overset{\frown}{EF} = 80$, $m\overset{\frown}{AC} = 20$ Find $m\overset{\frown}{BD}$.

$\odot O$ is tangent to $\odot B$ at point A. $\overline{GA}$ is tangent to both circles at A and $\overline{CD}$ is tangent to $\odot O$ at B. $\overline{GA} \parallel \overline{CD}$, $m\angle AGB = 42$

34. Find $m\overset{\frown}{AH}$.
35. Find $m\overset{\frown}{AF}$.
36. Find $m\overset{\frown}{AE}$.

$\odot O$ is tangent to the larger circle at A. Chords $\overline{AE}$ and $\overline{CD}$ intersect at F on $\odot O$ and $\overline{CD}$ is tangent to $\odot O$.

37. If $m\angle EAB = 25$, find $m\angle AHF$.
38. If $m\angle DFE = 65$, find $m\angle BAE$.
39. If $m\angle DFE = 65$, find $m\overset{\frown}{BE}$.

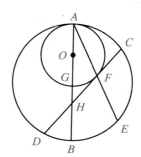

Critical Thinking

Complete the following statements by considering special cases and making generalizations.

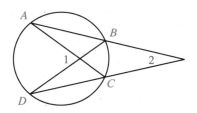

40. If $m\widehat{AD} = 2m\widehat{BC}$, then $m\angle 2 =$ ___ $m\widehat{BC}$.

41. If $m\widehat{AD} = 3m\widehat{BC}$, then $m\angle 1 =$ ___ $m\widehat{BC}$.

42. Reread the question asked in the caption under the map at the beginning of the lesson. Give a convincing argument that if $m\angle ACB$ is greater than the "danger angle," the captain will know that the ship was located inside the danger circle.

Mixed Review

Determine the values of x and y so that each figure is a parallelogram.

1. 116°, 4y°, 64°, 2x°

2. x°, 57°, y°

3. y, x°, 43°, 18

4. 24, 74°, 59°, x°, y

5. A tower 160 ft high casts a shadow 220 ft long. Find the angle of elevation of the sun.

6. A ramp is 100 ft long and rises vertically 12 ft. Find the angle of elevation of the ramp.

Biographical Note

Emmy Noether (1882–1935)

Emmy Noether has been recognized as the most creative abstract algebraist of modern times. At the age of 31 she began to lecture on mathematics, sometimes substituting for her father, a professor of mathematics at Erlangen University in Germany. After years of unsuccessful attempts to overcome the objections of those faculty members who wanted to exclude women from the faculty, she won formal admission as an academic lecturer in 1919.

From 1930 to 1933 she was at the center of the mathematical activity at Gottingen. When the Nazis came to power in 1933, Noether and many others were prohibited from taking part in any academic activities. Within a year she came to the United States and became professor of mathematics at Bryn Mawr College.

The extent and significance of Noether's work cannot be judged from only her writing. Many of her remarks and suggestions revealed her great insights and influenced the work of students and colleagues.

8-8 Segments of Chords, Secants, and Tangents

EXPLORE

Construct on paper or on a computer screen ⊙O with diameter $\overline{AB}$ of length 4 and construct $\overline{CD}$ perpendicular to $\overline{OB}$ at its midpoint. Find $AE \cdot BE$ and $CE \cdot DE$. What do you discover?

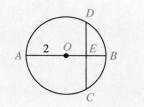

In the last lesson you studied how the measure of an angle formed (1) by chords intersecting in the interior of a circle, (2) by two secants from an external point, and (3) by a tangent and a secant from an external point are related to the measures of the intercepted arcs. In this lesson the same three situations are presented, but you will focus on lengths of chords and segments.

◆ THEOREM 8.15

If two chords intersect in a circle, then the product of the lengths of the segments of one chord equals the product of the lengths of the segments of the second chord.

Given: $\overline{AC}$ and $\overline{BD}$ are chords intersecting at P.

Prove: $AP \cdot PC = BP \cdot PD$

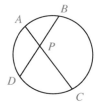

Plan You can prove that $\triangle ABP \sim \triangle DCP$ by the AA Similarity Theorem. Use the fact that ratios of lengths of corresponding sides in similar triangles are proportional to conclude $\frac{AP}{DP} = \frac{BP}{CP}$ and rewrite this equation.

Example 1

Find x if $RV = 3$, $TV = 7$, and $SV = 8$.

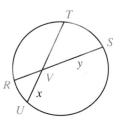

Solution

$RV \cdot VS = UV \cdot VT$

$3 \cdot 8 = x \cdot 7 \quad x = \frac{24}{7}$

Try This

Find y if $UV = 8$, $VT = 15$, and $RV = 7$.

The next theorem is about secants from an external point. The conclusion of the theorem is similar to that for Theorem 8.15.

Suppose that two secants from an external point P intersect a circle at points A, B, C, and D as shown to the right. $\overline{PA}$ and $\overline{PB}$ are called secant segments and $\overline{PC}$ and $\overline{PD}$ are called external segments.

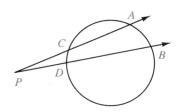

THEOREM 8.16

If two secant segments are drawn to a circle from an exterior point, then the product of the lengths of one secant segment and its external segment equals the product of the lengths of the other secant segment and its external segment.

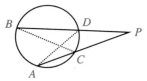

Given: $\overline{PA}$ and $\overline{PB}$ are secant segments from the external point P and intersect the circle at points C and D to form external segments $\overline{PC}$ and $\overline{PD}$.

Prove: $PA \cdot PC = PB \cdot PD$

Plan You can prove that $\triangle ADP \sim \triangle BCP$ by the AA Similarity Theorem. Ratios of corresponding sides in similar triangles are proportional so $\frac{PA}{PB} = \frac{PD}{PC}$. Rewrite this proportion to obtain the desired form.

Example 2

Find x in the figure to the right.

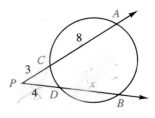

Solution

$$PA \cdot PC = PB \cdot PD$$
$$(8 + 3)3 = (x + 4)4$$
$$33 = 4x + 16$$
$$17 = 4x$$
$$x = \frac{17}{4}$$

Try This

If $PC = 7$, $PD = 9$, and $DB = 15$, find AC.

As the secant $\overline{PB}$ moves closer and closer to the position of tangent from P, the product $PB \cdot PD$ becomes $PB \cdot PB$. This result is stated in Theorem 8.17.

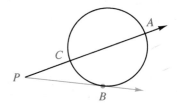

THEOREM 8.17

If a tangent segment and a secant segment are drawn to a circle from an exterior point, then the square of the length of the tangent segment equals the product of the lengths of the secant segment and its external secant segment.

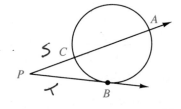

Example 3

Find x in the figure to the right.

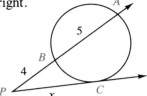

Solution

$$PA \cdot PB = PC^2$$
$$(5 + 4)4 = x^2$$
$$36 = x^2$$
$$x = 6$$

Try This

If $PC = 10$ and $PB = 6$, find AB.

Class Exercises

Short Answer

Complete each statement.

1.

$$AP \cdot PB = \underline{\quad}$$

2.

$$DP \cdot PC = \underline{\quad}$$

3.

$$AP \cdot PB = \underline{\quad}$$

Sample Exercises

4. $AP = 8$, $BP = 6$, $CP = 5$ Find DP.
5. $AB = 11$, $AP = 6$, $DP = 7$ Find CP.
6. $EQ = 8$, $FQ = 6$, $GQ = 5$ Find HQ.
7. $EQ = 7$, $HQ = 9$, $GH = 6$ Find FQ.

Discussion

8. Imagine that points A, C, and D are fixed and that point B is moving clockwise around the circle. When B is near D is the value of $AX \cdot XB$ almost 1 or almost 0? Explain. If $\overline{CD}$ is a diameter, where would point B be located if $AX \cdot XB$ were exactly equal to one?

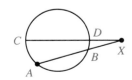

9. Give a convincing argument that for some locations of point B on the circles above $AX \cdot XB$ is greater than 10.

Exercises

A

Find x.

1.

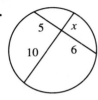

5   x

10   6

2.

7

4

x

3.

8

x

4

3

4.

3

9

4

x

5.

2

x   4

x + 4

6.

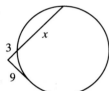

x

3

9

7. $AP = 12$, $PB = 7$, $PD = 11$ Find PC.
8. $AQ = 8$, $QC = 3$, $BQ = 5$ Find QD.
9. $AB = 9$, $BP = 10$, $PD = 18$ Find CD.
10. $AC = 12$, $AQ = 8$, $BQ = 5$ Find BD.
11. $AB = 8$, $AP = 17$, $CD = 7$ Find DP.
12. $BD = 18$, $AC = 14$, $CQ = 5$ Find BQ.
13. $AC = 15$, $BQ = 9$, $QD = 4$ Find AQ and CQ.

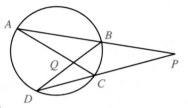

A   B   P   Q   C   D

B

Find each variable.

14.

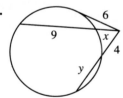

6

9   x

4

y

15.

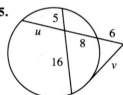

5

u

8   6

16   v

16.

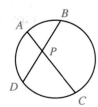

6

8   x

5

w   4

17. Is the triangle in Exercise 16 equilateral, isosceles, or scalene?
    Explain your reasoning.

18. Prove Theorem 8.15.

    Given: $\overline{AC}$ and $\overline{BD}$ are chords intersecting at P.

    Prove: $AP \cdot PC = BP \cdot PD$

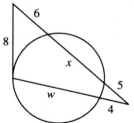

A   B   P   D   C

19. Find the lengths of chords $\overline{AB}$ and $\overline{CD}$.

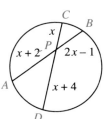

20. Suppose that $\overline{PA}$ and $\overline{PC}$ are both tangent to $\odot O$. Prove that $PC^2 = PB \cdot PD$.

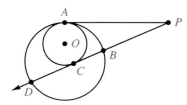

21. Suppose a radio tower T is 800 ft tall. Assuming that the diameter of the earth is 8000 mi, how far is it from the top of the tower to the horizon point A?

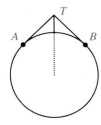

C

22. If $\overline{PB}$ and $\overline{PD}$ are secant segments and $PB = PD$, prove that $PA = PC$.

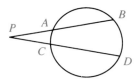

23. In the figure O is the center of two concentric circles. $\overline{RS}$ is tangent to the smaller circle. If $RX = 5$ and $RS = 30$, find XY.

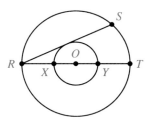

24. Suppose that two circles intersect at C and D and that point P is a point on $\overline{CD}$ exterior to both circles. $\overline{PA}$ and $\overline{PB}$ are tangent to the circles as shown. Prove that $\triangle APB$ is isosceles.

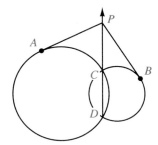

25. The two circles are tangent at E and $\overline{PE}$ is tangent to both circles at E. If $AP = 15$ and $PB = 6$, find $DP \cdot PC$. Explain your answer.

26. If $PF = 18$ and $PE = 5$, find $DP \cdot PC$. Explain your answer.

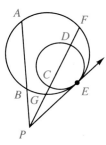

27. If $AG = 5$ and $BG = 7$, find $\frac{CG}{DG}$ and $\frac{EG}{FG}$.

28 If $m\angle BEF = 38$, find $m\angle BCI$.

29. Prove that $\overline{CD} \| \overline{EF}$.

30. Prove that $m\overset{\frown}{EH} = m\overset{\frown}{FI}$.

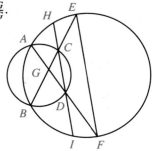

Critical Thinking

31. Suppose that $\overline{PD}$ and $\overline{PD}'$ are secants of all three circles. Decide whether or not each equation is always true, sometimes true, or never true. Give a convincing argument for each answer.

a. $PA \cdot PB = PA' \cdot PB'$

b. $PA \cdot PC = PA' \cdot PC'$

c. $PA \cdot PD = PA' \cdot PD'$

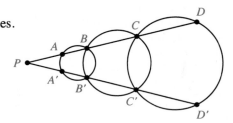

Algebra Review

Multiply.

1. $(x + 1)^2$ **2.** $(x - 3)^2$ **3.** $(a + 5)^2$ **4.** $(y - 5)^2$

5. $(m + 3)(m - 2)$ **6.** $(2a + 3)(a - 1)$ **7.** $(s + 3)(3s - 4)$ **8.** $(r - 5)(r + 5)$

Quiz

Determine whether each statement is true or false.

1. The measure of an inscribed angle is one half the measure of the intercepted arc.

2. If two inscribed angles in a circle are congruent, then they intercept the same arc.

3. If a right angle is inscribed in a circle, then its intercepted arc is a semicircle.

4. The measurement of an angle formed by two secants intersecting in the exterior of a circle is equal to one half the difference of the two intercepted arcs.

$\overline{DF}$ **is tangent to** $\odot T$.

5. If $m\angle B = 32$, find $m\overset{\frown}{EC}$.

6. If $m\overset{\frown}{AD} = 76$, find $m\angle ADF$.

7. If $m\overset{\frown}{AE} = 28$ and $m\overset{\frown}{BD} = 170$, find $m\angle l$.

8. If $CF = 3$ and $BC = 9$, find DF.

$\overline{WZ}$ **and** $\overline{WY}$ **are secants.**

9. If $m\overset{\frown}{ZY} = 88$ and $m\overset{\frown}{RX} = 26$, find $m\angle W$.

10. If $m\angle ZXY = 32$ and $m\angle W = 20$, find $m\overset{\frown}{RX}$.

11. If $WZ = 15$, $WR = 4$, and $WX = 3$, find XY.

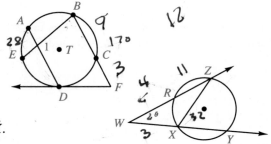

CRITICAL THINKING

Venn Diagrams and Reasoning Patterns

Venn diagrams (see page 38) can be used to test whether an argument is logically correct. An if-then statement can be represented in terms of circles, which help illustrate the validity of arguments based on the conditional. Consider the following examples.

Example 1

If a student is taking geometry, then she recognizes triangles. $p \rightarrow q$

Bonnie is taking geometry. p (premise)

Bonnie recognizes triangles. q (conclusion)

recognize triangle

taking geometry

Bonnie

The outer circle defines those students that recognize triangles. The inner circle indicates that all of the students taking geometry recognize triangles. Since Bonnie is in the inner circle, she is automatically among those students that recognize triangles.

Example 2 *Assuming the Converse*

If a figure is a parallelogram, then it is a quadrilateral. $p \rightarrow q$

Figure $ABCD$ is a quadrilateral. q

Figure $ABCD$ is a parallelogram. p

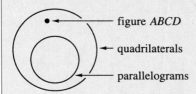

figure $ABCD$

quadrilaterals

parallelograms

The Venn diagram shows that a point representing figure $ABCD$ can be outside the parallelogram circle, so the reasoning pattern is invalid. Here, the converse of the original conditional is assumed.

Example 3 *Assuming the Inverse*

If a student worked hard, then he passed the course. $p \rightarrow q$

Matthew did not work hard. $\sim p$

Matthew did not pass the course. $\sim q$

Matthew

passed course

worked hard

The Venn diagram shows that although Matthew did not work hard, the point representing him could still be inside the circle representing those who passed the course. The error in this case is assuming the inverse of the original conditional.

Exercises

Draw Venn diagrams to show each reasoning pattern and decide whether it is valid.

1. If you are over 21, then you can vote.

   Marika cannot vote.

   Marika is not over 21.

2. If you do not pay taxes, then you will go to jail.

   Peter paid his taxes.

   Peter went to jail.

3. If you have enough, then you must share.

   Theresa has enough.

   Theresa must share.

4. If you are a citizen, then you want power.

   If you want power, then you must vote.

   If you are a citizen, then you must vote.

5. If you are a doctor, then you have gone to college.

   Pat is not a doctor.

   Pat did not go to college.

6. If x is divisible by 4, then x is even.

   10 is even.

   10 is divisible by 4.

CHAPTER SUMMARY

Vocabulary

arc (8-4)
center (8-1)
central angle (8-4)
chord (8-1)
circle (8-1)
circumscribed polygon (8-1)
common tangents (8-3)

concentric circles (8-1)
congruent arcs (8-4)
congruent circles (8-1)
diameter (8-1)
inscribed angle (8-6)
inscribed polygon (8-1)
intercepted arc (8-6)

major arc (8-4)
minor arc (8-4)
radius (8-1)
secant (8-1)
semicircle (8-4)
sphere (8-1)
tangent (8-1)
tangent-chord angle (8-6)

Key Ideas

1. If a line is perpendicular to a radius of a circle at a point on the circle, then the line is tangent to the circle.
2. If a line is tangent to a circle, then it is perpendicular to the radius at the point of tangency.
3. In the same circle or congruent circles
   a. congruent chords have congruent minor arcs.
   b. congruent minor arcs have congruent chords and congruent central angles.
   c. congruent chords are equidistant from the center.
   d. chords equidistant from the center are congruent.
4. If a diameter is perpendicular to a chord, then it bisects the chord and its minor and major arcs.
5. If two inscribed angles intercept the same arc, then the angles are congruent.
6. The following are angle-arc relationships.

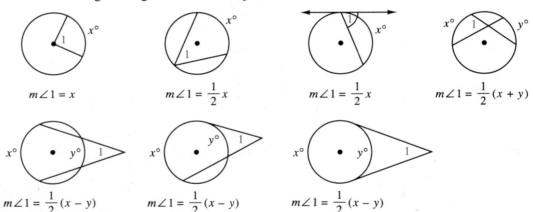

$m\angle 1 = x$ $\qquad$ $m\angle 1 = \dfrac{1}{2}x$ $\qquad$ $m\angle 1 = \dfrac{1}{2}x$ $\qquad$ $m\angle 1 = \dfrac{1}{2}(x + y)$

$m\angle 1 = \dfrac{1}{2}(x - y)$ $\qquad$ $m\angle 1 = \dfrac{1}{2}(x - y)$ $\qquad$ $m\angle 1 = \dfrac{1}{2}(x - y)$

7. The following are chord, secant, and tangent relationships.

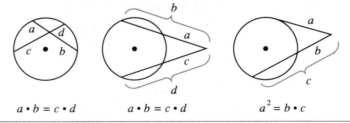

$a \cdot b = c \cdot d$ $\qquad$ $a \cdot b = c \cdot d$ $\qquad$ $a^2 = b \cdot c$

CHAPTER REVIEW

8-1

Determine whether each statement is true or false.

1. $\overline{BD}$ is a chord.
2. $\overline{BC}$ is a secant.
3. $\overline{CD}$ is a radius.
4. $\angle ACD$ is inscribed in $\odot A$.

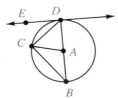

8-2

$\overline{XW}$ and $\overline{XY}$ are tangent to $\odot P$ at W and Y.

5. Find $m\angle PYX$.
6. If $XW = 10$, find XY.
7. If $m\angle WXY = 60$ and $XY = 6\sqrt{3}$, find PY.

8-3

8. If $WL = 6$, $LM = 8$, and $MY = 4$, find XM.
9. If $m\angle Y = 30$, $WL = 7$, and $WX = 8$, find XM.
10. Draw a pair of circles that have only one common internal tangent.

8-4

In $\odot I$, HF is a diameter.

11. If $m\angle 1 = 43$, find $m\widehat{FG}$.
12. If $m\widehat{EF} = 53$, find $m\angle 3$.
13. If $m\widehat{HG} = 140$ and $\angle 1 = \angle 2$, find $m\widehat{HE}$.

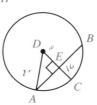

8-5

In $\odot D$, $AB \perp DC$ and $\overline{AE} \cong \overline{EB}$.

14. If $AD = 26$ and $DE = 10$, find AB.
15. If $m\widehat{BC} = 45$ and $AE = 7$, find AD.
16. If $AB = 16$ and $AD = 9$, find DE.

8-6

$\overline{SW}$ is tangent at S. **Determine whether each statement is true or false.**

17. If $m\angle U = 103$, then $m\widehat{VRS} = 206$.
18. If $m\widehat{RU} = 150$, then $m\angle S = 150$.
19. If $m\angle WSR = 44$, then $m\widehat{RS} = 22$.

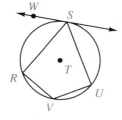

8-7

$\overline{AB}$ and $\overline{AE}$ are tangent at B and E. $m\widehat{CB} = 50$, $m\widehat{CD} = 30$, $m\widehat{DE} = 116$

20. Find $m\angle 1$.
21. Find $m\widehat{BE}$.
22. Find $m\angle A$.
23. Find $m\angle 2$.

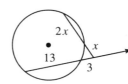

8-8

24. Find x in the figure on the right.
25. Find x in the figure on the left.

CHAPTER TEST

Determine whether each statement is true or false.

1. A radius is a segment that joins two points on a circle.
2. Concentric circles have the same center.
3. Two circles are congruent if their radii are congruent.
4. If a line is perpendicular to a radius of a circle at a point on the circle, then the line is tangent to the circle.
5. If the measure of an arc in one circle is equal to the measure of an arc in another circle, the chords of these arcs are congruent.
6. If a quadrilateral is inscribed in a circle, then its opposite angles are complementary.

$\overline{AB}$ is tangent at A.

7. If $m\widehat{ED} = 48$, find $m\angle 3$.
8. If $m\widehat{DC} = 42$ and $m\angle 4 = 100$, find $m\widehat{EG}$.
9. If $m\widehat{ED} = 74$ and $m\widehat{GC} = 38$, find $m\angle 1$.
10. If $m\widehat{DEA} = 210$ and $m\widehat{AC} = 70$, find $m\angle ABD$.
11. If $m\angle 2 = 28$ and $m\angle 3 = 34$, find $m\angle 4$.

$\overline{LM}$ is a common tangent.

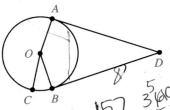

12. If $QM = 6$, $MN = 8$ and $LN = 20$, find PL.
13. If $PL = 5$ and $LN = 10$, find PN.
14. If $PL = 10$, $QM = 2$, and $LM = 20$, find LN.

$\overline{AD}$ and $\overline{BD}$ are tangent to $\odot O$.

15. Find $m\angle OAD$.
16. If $BD = 8$, find AD.
17. If $m\angle BOC = 37$ and $m\angle AOB = 120$, find $m\widehat{AC}$.
18. If $\angle AOB$ is supplementary to $\angle ADB$ and $m\widehat{AB} = 100$, find $m\angle ADB$.

Complete each statement.

19. The perpendicular bisector of a chord contains the ____ of the circle.
20. In a circle, chords equidistant from the center are ____ .
21. If a diameter bisects a chord that is not a diameter, then it is ____ to the chord.

Find x in each figure.

22.

23.

24.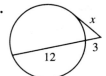

PREPARING FOR COLLEGE ENTRANCE EXAMS

Give the one correct answer for each question.

1. If $m = x + 7$ and $n = x - 12$, then $m - n$ is equal to which of the following?

(A) 5   (B) 19   (C) -5

(D) -19 (E) $2x - 5$

2. If $z < 0$, which of the following must be negative?

(A) z^2 (B) $-2z$ (C) $z + 1$

(D) $|z| - z$ (E) $\frac{z}{2}$

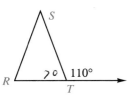

3. In the figure above, if $\overline{RS} \cong \overline{ST}$, then $m \angle RST =$

(A) 40   (B) 140   (C) 70

(D) 110   (E) 60

4. A long string of colored lanterns is prepared for a party. The colors of the lanterns form a repeating pattern starting with red, yellow, green, blue, white; red, yellow, green, blue, white, and so on. What color is the 37th lantern?

(A) red   (B) yellow   (C) green

(D) blue   (E) white

5. If the perimeter of a rectangular yard is 200 ft, which of the following could be the length of one of its sides?

I. 40 ft

II. 51 ft

III. 100 ft

(A) I only   (B) II only   (C) III only

(D) I and II only   (E) I, II, and III

6. If the sum of five consecutive integers is 50, what is the largest of these integers?

(A) 16   (B) 12   (C) 10

(D) 9   (E) Cannot be determined from the information given.

7. A florist sells b bouquets of roses at d dollars per bouquet in h hours. Which of the following represents the amount of money received in two hours from the sale of roses?

(A) $\frac{2bd}{h}$ (B) $\frac{bd}{2h}$ (C) $2bdh$

(D) $\frac{2bh}{d}$ (E) $\frac{bh}{2d}$

8. In the figure above, if $p \parallel q$, then $y - x =$

(A) 180   (B) 90   (C) 45

(D) 0   (E) Cannot be determined from the information given.

9. If M is odd, which of the following CANNOT be a whole number?

(A) $\sqrt{M}$ (B) $\frac{M - 1}{2}$ (C) $\frac{M^2}{2}$

(D) M^2 (E) $\frac{M}{5}$

$KLMN$ is a parallelogram.

10. In the figure above, what is the value of y?

(A) 36   (B) 60   (C) 72

(D) 108   (E) 45

11. If $x - y > 0$, which of the following MUST be true?

(A) $|x| > y$ (B) $-x > -y$

(C) $x > 0$ (D) $x^2 > y^2$ (E) $y < 0$

12. If 12 liters of pure alcohol are mixed with 8 liters of pure water, what percent of the resulting mixture is alcohol?

(A) $66\frac{2}{3}\%$ (B) 80%   (C) 40%

(D) 75%   (E) 60%

9

Constructions
and Loci

A contractor wants to construct the perpendicular bisector of a beam shown on a blueprint. How can this be done using only a compass and straightedge?

BASIC CONSTRUCTIONS

OBJECTIVE: *Construct congruent segments, congruent angles, perpendicular bisectors, and angle bisectors.*

9-1 Segments, Angles, and Bisectors

In geometry, a **construction** is a geometric figure produced by using only a *compass* and *straightedge*. A compass is used to draw arcs and circles. A straightedge, which unlike a ruler has no measurement marks, is used to draw a line segment between two points. Basic constructions are used as a basis for more involved constructions.

CONSTRUCTION 1

Given a segment, construct a segment congruent to the given segment.

Given: $\overline{AB}$

Construct: a segment congruent to $\overline{AB}$

Procedure 1. Use a straightedge to draw $\overrightarrow{CE}$.
2. Open your compass to radius AB.
3. Placing the point of the compass at C, mark an arc intersecting $\overrightarrow{CE}$ at D.
4. $\overline{CD}$ is congruent to $\overline{AB}$.

Proof $\overline{CD} \cong \overline{AB}$ since they are radii of congruent circles.

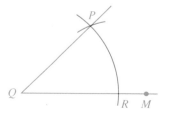

CONSTRUCTION 2

Given an angle, construct an angle congruent to the given angle.

Given: $\angle BAC$

Construct: an angle congruent to $\angle BAC$

Procedure 1. Draw ray $\overrightarrow{QM}$.
2. Using A as center and any radius, mark an arc intersecting the sides of $\angle BAC$ at D and E.
3. Using Q as center and radius $\overline{AD}$, mark an arc intersecting $\overrightarrow{QM}$ at R.
4. Using R as center and $\overline{DE}$ as radius mark an arc intersecting the first arc at P.
5. Draw $\overrightarrow{QP}$.
6. $\angle PQR$ is congruent to $\angle BAC$.

Proof By construction $\overline{QR} \cong \overline{AE} \cong \overline{QP} \cong \overline{AD}$ and $\overline{DE} \cong \overline{PR}$. Therefore $\triangle QPR \cong \triangle ADE$ by the SSS Postulate and $\angle PQR \cong BAC$ since corresponding parts of congruent triangles are congruent.

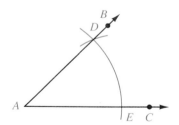

CONSTRUCTION 3

Given a segment, construct the perpendicular bisector of the given segment.

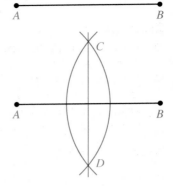

Given: $\overline{AB}$

Construct: the perpendicular bisector of $\overline{AB}$

Procedure 1. Using A as center and a radius greater than $\frac{1}{2} AB$, mark an arc.

2. Using B as center and the same radius, mark a second arc intersecting the first arc at points C and D.

3. Draw $\overline{CD}$ intersecting $\overline{AB}$.

4. $\overline{CD}$ is the perpendicular bisector of $\overline{AB}$.

Proof Points C and D are equidistant from A and B. It follows that $\overline{CD}$ is the perpendicular bisector of $\overline{AB}$ from Theorem 4.7.

CONSTRUCTION 4

Given an angle, construct the bisector of the given angle.

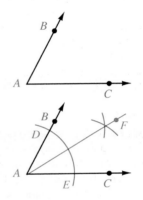

Given: $\angle BAC$

Construct: the bisector of $\angle BAC$

Procedure 1. Using A as center and any radius, mark arcs intersecting the sides of $\angle BAC$ at points D and E.

2. Using D and E as centers and the same (or larger) radius, mark arcs intersecting at F.

3. Draw $\overline{AF}$.

4. $\overline{AF}$ bisects $\angle BAC$.

Proof Draw $\overline{DF}$ and $\overline{EF}$. Then $\triangle ADF \cong \triangle AEF$ by SSS. Thus $\angle DAF \cong \angle EAF$ since they are corresponding parts of congruent triangles.

Example 1

Given $\overline{AB}$ and $\overline{CD}$, construct a segment equal in length to $AB + CD$.

Solution

Use Construction 1 twice to construct a segment of length $AB + CD$.

$AB + CD$

Try This

Construct a segment equal in length to $\frac{1}{2}(AB + CD)$.

Example 2

Construct an isosceles triangle with base $\overline{BC}$ and congruent sides $\overline{AB}$.

Solution

1. Draw $\overrightarrow{DX}$.
2. Construct $DE = BC$.
3. Using D as center and $\overline{AB}$ as radius, draw an arc.
4. Using E as center and $\overline{AB}$ as radius, draw an arc intersecting the first arc at F.
5. Draw sides $\overline{DF}$ and $\overline{EF}$.

Class Exercises

Short Answer

1. Which construction would you use to construct a segment equal in length to the perimeter of a given triangle?
2. Which construction would you use to construct an angle equal in measure to the sum of the measures of the acute angles of a given obtuse triangle?
3. Which two constructions would you use to construct an angle equal in measure to the average measure of two given angles?

Sample Exercises

4. Use a ruler to draw a segment of length 2 cm. Construct an equilateral triangle with each side 2 cm long. What is the measure of each angle?
5. Use the triangle constructed in Exercise 4 to construct a 30° angle.
6. Use a ruler to draw segments of lengths 3 cm, 5 cm, and 6 cm. Construct a triangle using these three segments.
7. Draw two segments a and b of unequal length. Construct a segment of length $\frac{(a + b)}{2}$.
8. Draw an acute angle ($\angle 1$) and an obtuse angle ($\angle 2$). Construct an angle with a measure of $\frac{m\angle 1 + m\angle 2}{2}$.

Discussion

9. Try to construct a triangle with sides of lengths 3 cm, 5 cm, and 8 cm. What happens? Why?
10. Using only the construction for bisecting a segment, can you divide a segment into 4 equal parts? 6 equal parts? 8 equal parts? 12 equal parts? 16 equal parts? Explain.
11. Given $\triangle ABC$, suppose you constructed $\angle D \cong \angle A$, $\overline{DE} \cong \overline{AB}$, and $\overline{DF} \cong \overline{AC}$, then drew $\overline{EF}$. Would you have a triangle congruent to $\triangle ABC$? Explain.
12. Given $\triangle RST$, suppose you constructed $\overline{MN} \cong \overline{ST}$. Then, using M as center and RS as radius, suppose you drew an arc. Suppose next, using N as center and RT as radius, you drew an arc intersecting the first arc at P, then drew $\overline{PM}$ and $\overline{PN}$. Would you have constructed a triangle congruent to $\triangle RST$? Explain.

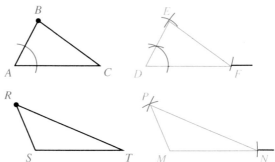

Exercises

A

Draw segments of length m and n and construct a segment of the given length. Label the constructed segment $\overline{AB}$.

1. $m + n$ 2. $2m + n$ 3. $2n - m$ 4. $\frac{m + n}{2}$

Trace angles 1 and 2 and construct an angle with the given measure. Label the constructed angle ∠ABC.

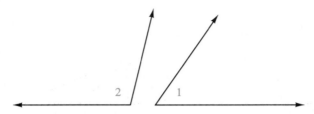

5. $m \angle 1 + m \angle 2$ 6. $m \angle 2 - m \angle 1$
7. $180 - m \angle 2$ 8. $\frac{m \angle 1 + m \angle 2}{2}$

9. Draw three segments of lengths 4.5 cm, 6 cm, and 7.5 cm. Construct a triangle with sides of these three lengths. What kind of triangle is it?
10. Draw three segments of lengths 3 cm, 4 cm, and 6 cm. Construct a triangle with sides these three lengths. What kind of triangle is it?

Trace △ABC.

11. Use the SAS Postulate to construct △DEF congruent to △ABC.
12. Use the ASA Postulate to construct △XYZ congruent to △ABC.

13. Consider your solutions to Exercises 11 and 12. Is it easier to construct congruent triangles using the SAS Postulate or the ASA Postulate? Why?
14. Draw a segment $\overline{EF}$ approximately 8 cm long. Construct a segment $\overline{XY}$ whose length is $\frac{1}{4}EF$.
15. Draw an obtuse angle ABC. Construct an angle DBC with a measure that is $\frac{1}{4}m \angle ABC$.
16. Construct an equilateral triangle with each side 4 cm long.
17. Use the triangle constructed in Exercise 16 to construct a 30° angle.
18. Construct a 15° angle.

B

19. Draw a triangle ABC. Construct a triangle XYZ with sides twice the length of the sides of △ABC.
20. Draw a triangle DEF. Construct a triangle PQR with sides half the length of the sides of △DEF.

Construct an angle with the given measure.

21. 120° 22. 105°
23. 75° 24. 150°

25. Construct an isosceles triangle with base $\overline{AB}$ and vertex ∠C.
26. Construct an isosceles triangle ABC given segments representing the perimeter and the base $\overline{BC}$.

27. Draw an obtuse triangle ABC and use the ASA Postulate to construct a triangle DEF congruent to △ABC.

C

28. Construct a triangle ABC given $\angle A$, $\angle B$, and a segment representing the perimeter.
(HINT: Study the figure. Find the length of each side.)

AB + BC + CA   AB + BC + CA

29. Construct an isosceles trapezoid $BCFE$ given $\angle B$ and the bases $\overline{BC}$ and $\overline{EF}$.

Critical Thinking

30. Draw three different triangles and label each triangle ABC. In the first triangle make $\angle A$ acute, in the second triangle make $\angle A$ a right angle, and in the third triangle make $\angle A$ obtuse. In each triangle construct the angle bisector $\overline{AD}$ (D is on $\overline{BC}$) and the median $\overline{AM}$. Compare the lengths of $\overline{AD}$ and $\overline{AM}$. State a generalization. Test your generalization by drawing other triangles and comparing the lengths of the angle bisector and the median from the same vertex.

Algebra Review

Solve each inequality.

1. $3(y + 6) < 2y + 12$ **2.** $8 - \frac{3b}{5} \leq -8$ **3.** $2(y + 5) > 4 + 15$

4. $5(n + 6) < 3n - 6$ **5.** $3x - \frac{4}{2} \geq \frac{2x}{4}$ **6.** $\frac{4x}{3} + \frac{2}{5} > 0$

Historical Note

Impossible Constructions

The geometricians of ancient Greece investigated what figures could be constructed with straightedge and compass. One of the construction problems they were not able to solve is the angle trisection problem, given below.

Given $\angle BAC$, you want to construct rays AD and AE (with points D and E in the interior of $\angle BAC$) so that $\angle BAD \cong \angle DAE \cong \angle EAC$.

It was not until more recent times that proofs using modern abstract algebra eventually verified the impossibility of this construction and other constructions that had perplexed mathematicians over the centuries.

9-2 Perpendicular and Parallel Lines

EXPLORE You can use paper folding to form a perpendicular from a point P to a line m by folding the paper so that line m is folded onto itself and the crease contains point P as shown below.

On three different pieces of paper, draw lines r, s, and t and mark a point P, as positioned in the figures below.

Fold the papers to form lines through P that are perpendicular to the lines r, s, and t. Label each perpendicular (crease) as horizontal, vertical, or neither.

The three constructions presented in this section apply definitions and theorems about perpendicular and parallel lines from previous chapters. The first construction is similar to bisecting an angle.

CONSTRUCTION 5

Given a point on a line, construct the perpendicular to the line at the given point.

Given: point P on m

Construct: the perpendicular to m at P

Procedure 1. Using P as center and any radius, draw arcs intersecting m at A and B.

2. Using A as center and any radius longer than $\overline{AP}$, draw an arc. Using B as center and the same radius draw an arc intersecting the first arc at C.

3. Draw $\overline{PC}$.

4. $\overline{PC}$ is perpendicular to m at P.

Proof   By construction $\overline{PA} \cong \overline{PB}$ and $\overline{AC} \cong \overline{BC}$. Hence $\triangle CAP \cong \triangle CBP$ by SSS. Therefore, $\angle BPC$ is a right angle and $\overline{PC} \perp m$.

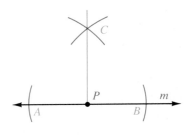

CONSTRUCTION 6

Given a point not on a line, construct the perpendicular to the line from the given point.

Given: point P not on m

Construct: the perpendicular to m from P

Procedure 1. Using P as center, draw an arc intersecting m at A and B.

   2. Using A as center and a radius greater than $\frac{1}{2}AB$, draw an arc. Using B as center and the same radius, draw an arc intersecting the first arc at X.

   3. Draw $\overleftrightarrow{PX}$.

   4. $\overleftrightarrow{PX}$ is perpendicular to m.

Proof   Since P and X are equidistant from A and B, $\overleftrightarrow{PX}$ is the perpendicular bisector of $\overline{AB}$. Therefore, $\overleftrightarrow{PX}$ is perpendicular to m.

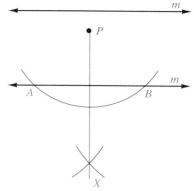

Example 1

Construct a 45° angle.

Solution

Construct a 90° angle by constructing a perpendicular. Bisect the 90° angle.

Try This

Construct a $22\frac{1}{2}°$ angle.

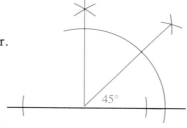

CONSTRUCTION 7

Given a point not on a line, construct the parallel to the given line through the given point.

Given: point P not on line m

Construct: the line through P parallel to m

Procedure 1. Draw any line through P intersecting m at A.

   2. At P use Construction 2 to construct $\angle 2$ congruent to $\angle 1$. Label the line containing the ray (just constructed) n.

   3. The line n contains P and is parallel to m.

Proof   Since $\angle 1$ and $\angle 2$ are congruent corresponding angles, the lines are parallel.

Example 2

Construct a line through the midpoint of $\overline{AB}$ that is parallel to $\overline{BC}$.

Solution

Use Construction 3 to find the midpoint of side $\overline{AB}$. Use Construction 7 to construct the line through the midpoint D parallel to $\overline{BC}$. Line ℓ contains D and is parallel to $\overline{BC}$.

Class Exercises

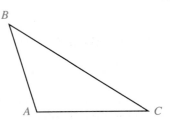

1. Which construction(s) would you use to construct the altitude from A to $\overline{BC}$?
2. Which construction(s) would you use to construct the altitude from B to $\overline{AC}$?
3. Which construction(s) would you use to construct a line through A parallel to $\overline{BC}$?

Sample Exercises

Construct each figure.

4. an isosceles right triangle with legs approximately 2 cm long
5. a square with perimeter equal to approximately 8 cm
6. a triangle with sides in the ratio of $1 : 1 : \sqrt{2}$
7. a rectangle with sides approximately 3 cm and 5 cm long
8. an isosceles right triangle with a hypotenuse approximately 5 cm long
9. a square with a diagonal approximately 4 cm long

Draw a line m and mark a point P positioned approximately as shown. Construct the perpendicular to m through P.

10.   11.

$P \bullet$

12. Draw a line m and mark a point P positioned approximately as shown. Construct the parallel to m through P.

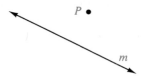

$P \bullet$

Discussion

13. Kris constructed the perpendicular from a point P not on m to m. She drew an arc intersecting m at points A and B. Kris said she could construct the perpendicular by increasing the radius and marking arcs above m rather than below m. Is she correct?
Explain your reasoning.
14. Could Construction 7 be done using alternate interior angles rather than corresponding angles?
Explain your reasoning.

Exercises

A

Draw line *m* and point *P* as shown. Construct the perpendicular to *m* from *P*.

1.   P •

2.

3. P •

Draw line *m* and point *P* as shown. Construct the perpendicular to *m* at *P*.

4.

5.

6.

Draw line *m* and point *P* as shown. Construct the parallel to *m* through *P*.

7.   P •

8.

9.

• P

10. Construct a 135° angle.   **11.** Construct a $157\frac{1}{2}°$ angle.

12. Draw a triangle *RST* with an obtuse angle at vertex *R*. Construct an altitude from *R* to $\overline{ST}$.

13. Draw a triangle *MNP*. Construct a line through *M* parallel to $\overline{NP}$.

14. Construct a right triangle *ABC* with $m\angle A = 90$. Construct the midpoint of the hypotenuse and label it *M*. Construct a line through *M* parallel to $\overline{AC}$.

P •

15. Draw a segment $\overline{AB}$ and mark a point *P* positioned approximately as shown to the right. Construct a parallelogram with side $\overline{AB}$ and a vertex at *P*.

A ———————————— B

Use segments approximately the length of m and n.

16. Construct a right triangle with legs of lengths *m* and *n*.

17. Construct a square given a side of length *n*.

18. Construct a rectangle with length *m* and width *n*.

B

Use segments approximately the length of *m* and *n* above.

19. Construct a square with the diagonal of length *m*.

20. Construct a right triangle with leg length *n*.

21. Construct a square with perimeter equal to the given length.

•————————————————————————•

perimeter

22. Construct a rhombus *ABCD* with perimeter equal to the length shown in Exercise 21 and $m\angle A = 45$.

23. Construct an isosceles right triangle given the sum of the lengths of the legs.

●————————————————————————●

sum of the lengths of legs

C

List your procedure for each construction and explain why it works.

24. Construct a rhombus *ABCD* given lengths of diagonals $\overline{BD}$ and $\overline{AC}$.

●—————————————————● ●————————————————●
B   D   A   C

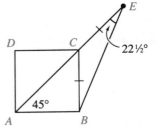

25. Construct a square *ABCD* given the sum of the lengths of the diagonal $\overline{AC}$ and side $\overline{BC}$. (HINT: Study the figure to the right.)

26. Construct a square *ABCD* given the sum and difference of the lengths of the diagonal $\overline{AC}$ and side $\overline{BC}$.

●————————————————————● ●——————————————————●
       AC + BC   *AC − BC*

Critical Thinking

27. Draw a line *m* and a point *P* not on *m*. Using a compass, *not* a straightedge, construct another point *A* such that $\overleftrightarrow{PA}$ is parallel to *m*.

Mixed Review

1. *JP* = 9, *PK* = 4, *PL* = 12   Find *PM*.
2. *JQ* = 5, *QM* = 4, *KQ* = 2   Find *QL*.
3. *JK* = 5, *KP* = 3, *PL* = 6   Find *ML*.
4. *JM* = 9, *JQ* = 6, *KQ* = 2   Find *KL*.

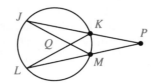

Study Skills

Solving Construction Problems

The following procedures can be of help in solving construction problems that require a series of basic constructions.

1. Draw the "given" segments and angles.
2. Sketch the figure as it should appear when completed. Identify given parts.
3. Analyze the figure you have sketched to determine the sequence of constructions needed to complete the figure.
4. Construct the figure. Write out the sequence of steps you used.

9-3 Circles

EXPLORE

Draw a circle with center O and radius r. For each of the three cases given below, state the relationship between $\overline{OP}$ and r.

1. From point P there exists only one tangent to circle O through P.
2. From point P there exist two tangents to circle O through P.
3. From point P there exist no tangents to circle O through P.

The following two constructions involve the first two cases in the Explore.

CONSTRUCTION 8

Given a point on a circle with center O, construct the tangent to the circle at the given point.

Given: point P on $\odot O$

Construct: the tangent to $\odot O$ at P

Procedure 1. Draw $\overrightarrow{OP}$.

      2. Construct the perpendicular to $\overrightarrow{OP}$ at P. Label the line m.

      3. Line m is the tangent to O at P.

Proof   Since m is perpendicular to radius $\overline{OP}$ at point P on $\odot O$, m is tangent to the circle.

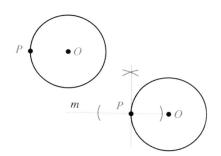

CONSTRUCTION 9

Given a point outside a circle, construct a tangent to the circle from the given point.

Given: point P outside $\odot O$

Construct: a tangent to $\odot O$ from P

Procedure 1. Draw $\overline{OP}$.

      2. Bisect $\overline{OP}$. Label the midpoint Q.

      3. Using Q as center and $\overline{QP}$ as radius, draw circle Q. Label the points of intersection of $\odot Q$ and $\odot O$, X and Y.

      4. Draw $\overrightarrow{PX}$.

      5. $\overrightarrow{PX}$ is a tangent to $\odot O$ from P. The other tangent to $\odot O$ from P, which is not drawn, is $\overrightarrow{PY}$.

Proof   Draw $\overline{OX}$. Since $\angle OXP$ is inscribed in a semicircle, it is a right angle. Therefore, $\overrightarrow{PX}$ is a tangent since it is perpendicular to radius $\overline{OX}$ at a point on the circle.

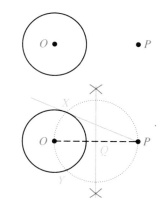

CONSTRUCTION 10

Given a circle, construct the center of the circle.

Given: circle with unknown center

Construct: X so that X is the center of the circle

Procedure 1. Draw nonparallel chords $\overline{AB}$ and $\overline{CD}$.
2. Construct perpendicular bisectors of $\overline{AB}$ and $\overline{CD}$. Label them p and q. Label the point of intersection of p and q point X.
3. X is the center of the circle.

Proof Since the perpendicular bisector of a chord contains the center of the circle, lines p and q both contain the center. Two lines intersect in only one point. Thus the center of the circle must be X, the point of intersection of the perpendicular bisectors of chords $\overline{AB}$ and $\overline{CD}$.

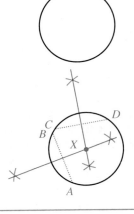

Example

Given arcs m and n of the same circle, find the center of the circle.

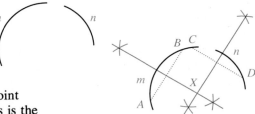

Solution

Draw chords $\overline{AB}$ and $\overline{CD}$. Construct the perpendicular bisector of each chord. The point of intersection of the perpendicular bisectors is the center of the arcs. X is the center of the arcs.

Class Exercises

Short Answer

1. Which construction would you use to construct a tangent to $\odot O$ at point X on $\odot O$?
2. Which construction would you use to construct a tangent to $\odot O$ from a point Y outside $\odot O$?
3. Which construction would you use to construct the center of $\overset{\frown}{ABC}$?

Sample Exercises

Draw each figure approximately the same as the one shown and complete the construction.

4. Construct a line that is parallel to $\overline{AB}$ and tangent to $\odot O$.
5. Construct tangents to $\odot O$ at points A and B.
6. Draw a circle with center M and a radius of 1 in. Mark a point P that is 2 in. from M. Construct a tangent from P to circle M.

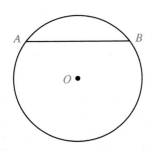

Discussion

7. If $\overrightarrow{PA}$ and $\overrightarrow{PB}$ are tangents to $\odot O$ with A and B on $\odot O$, is it possible for $\overline{AB}$ to contain the center of the circle? Explain your reasoning.

Exercises

A

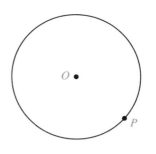

1. Draw a circle and mark a point P on the circle as shown to the right. Construct a tangent to the circle at P.
2. Draw a circle and mark a point Q outside the circle as shown to the right. Construct two tangents to the circle from Q.
3. Draw a circle with diameter $\overline{AB}$. Construct tangents to the circle at A and B.
4. Draw a circle and mark points P and Q on the circle. Construct $\triangle MPQ$ so that $\overline{MP}$ and $\overline{MQ}$ are tangent to the circle.
5. Draw a circle with a radius of 2 cm and mark a point P, 5 cm from the center. Construct two tangents from P to the circle.
6. Trace around a circular object such as a cup. Find the center of the circle.
7. Trace three arcs on the circumference of a circular object. Find the center of the arcs. Then use a compass to complete the circle.
8. Use a circular object to draw an arc that is about one third the circumference of the entire circle. Find the center of the arc. Then use a compass to complete the circle.
9. Draw a circle. Circumscribe a square about the circle.
10. Draw a circle with diameter $\overline{AB}$. Construct a tangent parallel to $\overline{AB}$.

B

11. Draw a circle and a point P outside it. Construct isosceles triangle PAB with P as the vertex such that $\overline{PA}$, $\overline{PB}$, and $\overline{AB}$ are tangent to the circle. (HINT: Draw $\overline{OP}$ to determine the point of tangency for $\overline{AB}$.)

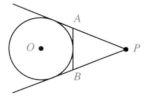

12. Draw a circle. Construct two tangents to the circle parallel to each other.
13. Draw a circle. Construct two tangents to the circle perpendicular to each other.
14. Mark three points on your paper that are not collinear. Construct a circle containing the three points.
15. Construct a rectangle with a length of approximately 5 cm and a width of approximately 3 cm. Circumscribe a circle about the rectangle.

Draw a circle and a line p approximately as shown.

16. Construct a line tangent to the circle that is parallel to p.
17. Construct a line tangent to the circle that is perpendicular to p.

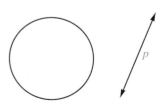

18. Draw a circle. Construct an equilateral triangle circumscribed about it.
19. Draw a circle. Construct a quadrilateral circumscribed about it.

C

Write a procedure for each construction and prove that it works.

20. Construct three congruent circles that are tangent to one another.
21. Draw an angle and mark a point P on the angle. Construct a circle tangent to the sides of the angle and containing P.
22. Draw two parallel lines and mark a point P between the lines as shown. Construct a circle that contains P and is tangent to the two lines.

Critical Thinking

23. Consider circles Q and P with radii r_1 and r_2 respectively, as shown below. The dotted circle has radius $r_1 - r_2$. Study the figure and create a method for constructing a common external tangent $\overline{BC}$ to circles Q and P. (HINT: Begin by constructing a tangent from P to the dotted circle. Consider how to construct rectangle $BAPC$.)

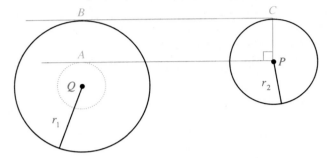

24. Create a method for constructing a common internal tangent to circles Q and P. (HINT: Begin by constructing a dotted circle with radius $r_1 + r_2$. Consider the method you devised in Exercise 23.)

Mixed Review

Complete each proportion and find x, y, and z.

1. $\frac{2}{?} = \frac{?}{3}$ 2. $\frac{?}{y} = \frac{y}{3}$ 3. $\frac{5}{?} = \frac{?}{2}$

4. $\frac{2}{z} = \frac{z}{?}$ 5. $\frac{2}{x} = \frac{x}{?}$ 6. $\frac{3}{?} = \frac{?}{5}$

Computer Activity

Triangle Ratios

Use computer software to complete the following construction.

1. Draw a triangle ABC.
2. Select a point D on $\triangle ABC$ so that AD is equal to $\frac{1}{3}AB$.
3. Select a point E on $\triangle ABC$ so that BE is equal to $\frac{1}{3}BC$.
4. Select a point F on $\triangle ABC$ so that CF is equal to $\frac{1}{3}CA$.
5. Draw $\overline{CD}$, $\overline{AE}$, and $\overline{BF}$.
6. Label the points of intersection R, S, and T.
7. Find the area of $\triangle ABC$.
8. Find the area of $\triangle RST$.
9. Find the ratio of the area of $\triangle RST$ to $\triangle ABC$.

Draw another triangle and repeat the steps above to see if the ratio of the areas is the same.

9-4 Special Segments

EXPLORE

Construct the triangle in *Figure 1* and determine the length of *x*. Extend *Figure 1* so it represents *Figure 2* and determine the length of *y*. Extend *Figure 2* to represent *Figure 3* and determine the length of *z*. If you were to extend the figure one more time, what would the length of the new hypotenuse be?

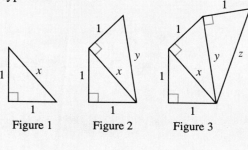

Figure 1   Figure 2   Figure 3

One question considered by mathematicians is, "Can a line segment of a given length be constructed?" Given the length of a single unit, for example, it is easy to construct a segment of length 5 units. The first construction in this section involves dividing a line segment into *n* congruent parts.

CONSTRUCTION 11

Given a segment, divide the segment into *n* congruent parts.

Given: segment *AB*

Construct: $\overline{AB}$ divided into three congruent segments

Procedure 1. Draw any ray $\overrightarrow{AC}$.
   2. Using any radius, construct segments $\overline{AM}$, $\overline{MN}$, and $\overline{NP}$ such that $\overline{AM} \cong \overline{MN} \cong \overline{NP}$.
   3. Draw $\overline{PB}$.
   4. Construct lines through *N* and *M* that are parallel to $\overrightarrow{PB}$ and intersect $\overline{AB}$.
   5. $\overline{AD} \cong \overline{DE} \cong \overline{EB}$ and points *D* and *E* divide $\overline{AB}$ into three congruent segments. To divide $\overline{AB}$ into *n* congruent parts, mark *n* congruent segments on $\overrightarrow{AC}$ and construct the parallel lines as described in the above procedure.

Proof   Consider a line through *A* parallel to the other parallel lines. Since the lines constructed parallel to $\overline{PB}$ cut off congruent segments on transversal $\overline{AP}$, they cut off congruent segments on transversal $\overline{AB}$. Therefore, $\overline{AD} \cong \overline{DE} \cong \overline{EB}$.

The proof can be generalized to dividing a segment into *n* congruent parts.

CONSTRUCTION 12

Given three segments, construct a fourth segment so that the four segments are proportional.

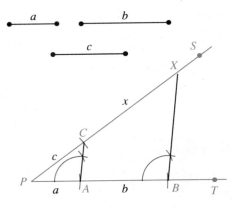

Given: segments of lengths a, b, and c

Construct: a segment of length x such that $\frac{a}{b} = \frac{c}{x}$

Procedure 1. Draw an angle SPT.
           2. Copy segments a and b on $\overrightarrow{PT}$ so that $PA = a$ and $AB = b$. Copy c on $\overrightarrow{PS}$ so that $PC = c$.
           3. Draw $\overline{AC}$.
           4. Construct a line through B parallel to $\overline{AC}$. Label the point of intersection with $\overrightarrow{PS}$ as X.
           5. $\overline{CX}$ has length x such that $\frac{a}{b} = \frac{c}{x}$.

Proof $\overline{BX} \parallel \overline{AC}$ in $\triangle PBX$, so by the Triangle Proportional Segment Theorem, $\frac{PA}{AB} = \frac{PC}{CX}$ or $\frac{a}{b} = \frac{c}{x}$.

Example 1

Given segments of lengths a, b, and c, construct a segment of length x such that $\frac{a}{b} = \frac{x}{c}$.

Solution

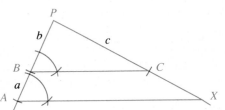

Rewrite the proportion as $\frac{b}{a} = \frac{c}{x}$.
Using Construction 12, mark off segments of lengths b and a on $\overrightarrow{PA}$ and a segment of length c on $\overrightarrow{PX}$. Construct a line through A parallel to $\overline{BC}$. $\overline{CX}$ has length x.

A procedure for constructing a segment that is the geometric mean between two given segments is based on properties of both circles and right triangles, as shown in Construction 13 below.

CONSTRUCTION 13

Given two segments, construct their geometric mean.

Given: segments a and b

Construct: geometric mean between a and b

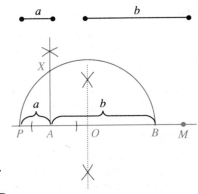

Procedure 1. Draw $\overrightarrow{PM}$ and mark off $PA = a$ and $AB = b$.
           2. Construct the perpendicular bisector of $\overline{PB}$. Label the midpoint of $\overline{PB}$ as point O.
           3. Draw a semicircle using O as center and OB as radius.
           4. Construct the perpendicular to $\overline{PB}$ at A. Label the intersection with the semicircle point X.
           5. AX is the geometric mean between a and b.

Proof $\angle PXB$ is a right angle since it is inscribed in a semicircle. Therefore, $\overline{XA}$ is the altitude to the hypotenuse of a right triangle and XA is the geometric mean between PA and PB.

Example 2

Given the unit segment shown, construct a segment with length $\sqrt{3}$.

Solution

Use Construction 13, marking off segments representing one and three units.
$\frac{1}{x} = \frac{x}{3}$. Thus $x = \sqrt{3}$.

Class Exercises

Short Answer

1. Given a segment that represents the perimeter of an equilateral triangle, which construction(s) would you use to construct a segment the length of one side of the equilateral triangle?
2. Given a segment that represents the perimeter of a regular pentagon, which construction(s) would you use to construct a segment the length of one side of the regular pentagon?
3. Which construction(s) would you use to divide a 9-in. segment into four congruent segments?
4. Given a segment representing one unit, which construction(s) would you use to construct a segment of length $\sqrt{5}$?

Sample Exercises

5. Given segments of lengths 2 cm, 3 cm, and 5 cm, construct a segment of length x so that $\frac{2}{3} = \frac{5}{x}$.
6. Given segments of length a and b, construct a segment $x = \sqrt{ab}$.

Use the unit segment shown to the right.

7. Given the unit segment shown, construct a segment of length $\frac{\sqrt{3}}{2}$.
8. Given the unit segment shown, construct a segment of length $2\frac{1}{3}$ units.

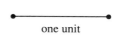

one unit

9. Draw segments of lengths 2 cm and 8 cm. Construct the geometric mean of the two segments.

Discussion

10. Given segments with lengths a and b, discuss how you could use Construction 13 to find a segment of length x so that $\frac{a}{b} = \frac{b}{x}$.
11. Explain what would happen if you were to use an obtuse angle in completing Construction 11.

Exercises

A

1. Draw a segment 10 cm long. Use Construction 11 to trisect the segment.
2. Draw a segment 13 cm long. Use Construction 11 to divide the segment into five congruent segments.

Given three segments and a stated proportion, construct a segment of length x.

3. $\frac{a}{b} = \frac{c}{x}$

4. $\frac{a}{b} = \frac{c}{x}$

5. $\frac{x}{a} = \frac{b}{c}$

6. $\frac{a}{x} = \frac{b}{c}$

7. Draw segments of lengths 2 in. and 4.5 in. and construct the geometric mean.

Use the unit segment to the right to construct a segment of the indicated length.

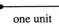
one unit

8. $\sqrt{2}$ 9. $\frac{\sqrt{2}}{2}$ 10. $\sqrt{5}$ 11. $2\sqrt{2}$

B

12. Use the unit segment and the segments constructed in Exercises 8 and 11 to find the missing segment in the proportion $\frac{\sqrt{2}}{\sqrt{8}} = \frac{1}{x}$. Solve the proportion for x and compare x with the length of the segment you constructed.
13. Draw a segment 10 cm long and divide it into two segments with lengths in the ratio $1:2$.
14. Draw a segment 7 in. long. Divide it into two segments such that one segment is twice as long as the other.
15. Draw a triangle ABC with base $\overline{AC}$. Divide $\overline{AC}$ into two segments having the ratio of the adjacent sides, $\frac{AB}{BC}$.
16. Draw a segment 6 cm long and divide it into two segments with lengths in the ratio $2:3$.

a

Use segments a and b to construct the required segment c.

17. $c = \frac{b^2}{a}$ 18. $c = \sqrt{ab}$ 19. $c = \sqrt{2ab}$

b

C

20. Given a unit segment and a segment m, construct a segment that represents $\frac{1}{m}$.

one unit

m

21. Draw a line ℓ and two points P and Q, as shown below. Construct a circle that is tangent to ℓ and contains P and Q. (HINT: Consider the figure on the right and use Construction 13.)

$Q \bullet$

Critical Thinking

To find geometric solutions to an equation of the form $ax = b$ you can use Construction 12 and convert $ax = b$ to $\frac{a}{b} = \frac{1}{x}$. Using the unit segment shown to the right, construct a segment having a length that is a whole number greater than one. Then construct a segment that would represent the solution to the given equation. Use algebra to see if your constructed segment seems like a reasonable solution.

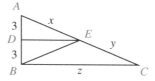

one unit

22. $2x = 3$ **23.** $3x = 10$ **24.** $4x = 3$

Mixed Review

$\overline{BE}$ bisects $\angle B$. $\overline{DE} \parallel \overline{BC}$

1. Complete the proportion $\frac{x}{y} = \frac{?}{?}$ in two different ways.
2. Find z.

CONNECTIONS ◇

Geometric Constructions and Algebra

Geometric constructions played an important role in the history of algebra. As the early Arab mathematicians developed symbolic ways of solving algebra problems, they verified the results via constructions to make sure the results were really valid. Consider this equation.

$$x + 1 = 3$$

The mathematician can approach the solution of this equation algebraically by adding (-1) to each side of the equation and then adding to get $x = 2$. To find the solution geometrically the mathematician could start with a unit segment, copy it to get a segment three units long, and then mark off one unit on it so that the length of x, or 2 units, is the remaining portion of the segment.

Consider using geometric construction to solve the problem involving the system of equations $x + y = a$ and $xy = b^2$ where $b \le \frac{a}{2}$.

The values of a and b are given.
The first step is to draw a semicircle of radius $\frac{a}{2}$.
Next construct a line that is parallel to the diameter of the semicircle and b units from it. Since $b \le \frac{a}{2}$, b is either tangent to the circle or intersects it in two places. Construct the perpendicular from each of the points of intersection to the diameter. Either one of these points will divide the diameter into two segments with lengths x and y.

Explain why this construction solves the system of equations given above.

9-5 Concurrency Theorems for Triangles

EXPLORE

Draw a large acute triangle on a sheet of paper. Fold the paper to form creases representing the perpendicular bisector of each side of the triangle. What conclusion can you reach regarding the three perpendicular bisectors of the sides of the triangle?

In this lesson you will use inductive reasoning to investigate properties that involve these lines. Consider the perpendicular bisectors below.

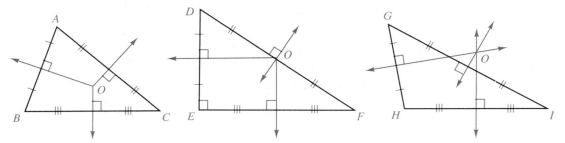

Three or more coplanar lines that have a point in common are called **concurrent lines.** In each triangle above, the three perpendicular bisectors are concurrent (at point *C*).

◆ **THEOREM 9.1**

The perpendicular bisectors of the sides of a triangle are concurrent in a point that is equidistant from the three vertices of the triangle.

The point that is equidistant from the vertices of a triangle is called the **circumcenter** of the triangle. It is the point of concurrency of the perpendicular bisectors of the sides of the triangle. *O* is the circumcenter of △*ABC* since *OA* = *OB* = *OC*. Circle *O* is circumscribed about △*ABC*.

The next theorem involves the bisectors of the angles of a triangle. You can see in the figure to the right that the angle bisectors are concurrent at *I*. If you were to measure the distances from *I* to the sides of the triangle ($\overline{ID}$, $\overline{IF}$, $\overline{IE}$), you would discover the relationship stated in the following theorem.

◆ THEOREM 9.2

The bisectors of the angles of a triangle are concurrent in a point that is equidistant from the three sides of the triangles.

You will be asked to prove Theorems 9.1 and 9.2 in Exercises 23, 24 and 26.

The point of concurrency of the angle bisectors of a triangle is called the **incenter** of the triangle and is the center of the inscribed circle of the triangle. In the diagram to the right, I is the incenter of $\triangle ABC$ and $IF = IE = ID$.

Example 1

Inscribe a circle in $\triangle ABC$.

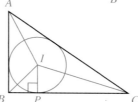

Solution

Bisect the angles to find the incenter I.
Construct $\overline{IP}$ perpendicular to side $\overline{BC}$.
Draw the inscribed circle with center I and radius $\overline{IP}$.

The medians of a triangle also have a special relationship. Study the medians of $\triangle ABC$. By using measurement to determine the ratios $\frac{AG}{AD}$, $\frac{CG}{CF}$, and $\frac{BG}{BE}$, you will discover the following theorem.

◆ THEOREM 9.3

The medians of a triangle are concurrent in a point that is two thirds of the distance from each vertex to the midpoint of the opposite side.

You will be asked for part of the proof of Theorem 9.3 in Exercise 25.

The point of intersection of the medians of a triangle is called the **centroid.** The centroid is the "center of gravity" of a triangle. That is, if you were to cut a triangle out of a firm substance, such as cardboard, the centroid would be the point at which you could balance the triangle.

Example 2

If G is the centroid of $\triangle ABC$ and $AG = 4$ cm, find AD and GD.

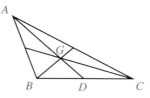

Solution

$AG = \frac{2}{3}AD$ *Theorem 9.3*
$4 = \frac{2}{3}AD$
$AD = 6$
$GD = 6 - 4 = 2$

Try This

Find the length of the median $\overline{AD}$ of $\triangle ABC$ if $GD = 15$.

Consider the altitudes of the acute, right, and obtuse triangles below.

Observe that the three altitudes in each triangle are concurrent. This leads to Theorem 9.4, which you will be asked to prove in Exercise 27. The point of intersection of the lines containing the altitudes is the **orthocenter.**

◆ **THEOREM 9.4**

The lines that contain the altitudes of a triangle are concurrent.

Class Exercises

Short Answer

1. Name an altitude, an angle bisector, and a median of $\triangle ABC$ if $AZ = ZC$.

2. The lines p and q are perpendicular bisectors of sides $\overline{AB}$ and $\overline{AC}$ of $\triangle ABC$. If $OA = 5$, find OB and OC.

3. What is the name of the center of the circle containing the vertices of a triangle?
4. What is the name of the center of the circle to which the sides of a triangle are tangent?
5. Name the point of concurrency of (a) the angle bisectors, (b) the medians, (c) the perpendicular bisectors of the sides, and (d) the altitudes of a triangle.

Sample Exercises

In $\triangle ABC$, $\overline{AX}$, $\overline{BY}$, and $\overline{CZ}$ are medians. Complete each statement.

6. If $AZ = 3$, $ZB = $ ___ .   7. If $CG = 4$, $GZ = $ ___ .
8. If $AB = BY$, $BG = $ ___ .   9. If $CZ = BC$, $BX = $ ___ .

10. Draw an obtuse triangle. Construct the orthocenter of the triangle.
11. Draw a right triangle. Construct the circumcenter of the triangle.
12. Use a compass to circumscribe a circle about the triangle in Exercise 11.

Discussion

13. If you have an acute-triangle-shaped metal plate, which theorem will help you decide where to drill a hole in which to place a rod to balance the plate?
14. To circumscribe a circle about a triangle, which theorem can you use?

Exercises

A

1. Draw an acute triangle. Construct the centroid and label it G.
2. Draw a right triangle. Construct the orthocenter and label it H.
3. Draw an obtuse triangle. Construct the orthocenter and label it M.
4. Draw an obtuse triangle. Construct the circumcenter and the circumscribed circle.
5. Draw a right triangle. Construct the circumcenter and the circumscribed circle.
6. Draw an acute triangle. Construct the incenter and the inscribed circle.

Use your answers to Exercises 1–6. Draw sketches to indicate whether the point named is *inside*, *on*, or *outside* the triangle.

	acute $\triangle$	right $\triangle$	obtuse $\triangle$
7. circumcenter	___	___	___
8. incenter	___	___	___
9. centroid	___	___	___
10. orthocenter	___	___	___

Assume G is the centroid of $\triangle ABC$. Complete each statement.

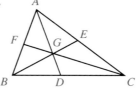

11. If $BE = 9$, $BG =$ ___ . 12. If $GC = 3$, $FC =$ ___ .
13. If $GE = 8$, $BE =$ ___ . 14. If $AD = 24$, $GD =$ ___ .
15. If $BE = 12$, $BG =$ ___ . 16. If $AG = 10$, $GD =$ ___ .
17. If $AG = x$, $GD =$ ___ . 18. If $BE = x$, $BG =$ ___ .

B

19. Prove that the median from the vertex angle of an isosceles triangle is also the angle bisector.
20. Prove that an altitude of an equilateral triangle is also a median.
21. If $\triangle ABC$ is an equilateral triangle with each side having length 5, find the length of the radius of the inscribed circle.
22. If $\triangle DEF$ is an isosceles right triangle with the legs having lengths 3, find the radius of the circumscribed circle.
23. Write a two-column proof for part of Theorem 9.1.

    Given: Lines r, s, and t are perpendicular bisectors of the sides of $\triangle ABC$ and are concurrent at point O.

    Prove: $OA = OB = OC$

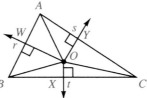

24. Write a two-column proof for part of Theorem 9.2.

    Given: $\overline{AI}$, $\overline{BI}$, and $\overline{CI}$ are angle bisectors concurrent at I.
    $\overline{DI}$, $\overline{EI}$, and $\overline{FI}$ are perpendicular to the sides of $\triangle ABC$.

    Prove: $DI = EI = FI$

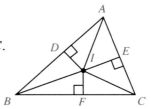

c

Italian mathematician Giovanni Ceva (1647–1736) stated the following condition for concurrency of lines, part of what is known as Ceva's Theorem. If $\frac{AD}{DB} \cdot \frac{BF}{FC} \cdot \frac{CE}{EA} = 1$, then $\overline{AF}$, $\overline{CD}$, and $\overline{BE}$ are concurrent. Use this part of Ceva's Theorem, the figure to the right, and the given information.

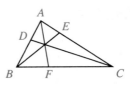

25. Prove the concurrency part of Theorem 9.3 (HINT: Use definition of median.)

   Given: $\overline{DX}$, $\overline{EY}$, and $\overline{FZ}$ are medians.

   Prove: $\overline{DX}$, $\overline{EY}$, and $\overline{FZ}$ are concurrent.

26. Prove the concurrency part of Theorem 9.2 (HINT: Use Theorem 6.9.)

   Given: $\overline{DX}$, $\overline{EY}$, and $\overline{FZ}$ are angle bisectors.

   Prove: $\overline{DX}$, $\overline{EY}$, and $\overline{FZ}$ are concurrent.

27. Prove Theorem 9.4 (HINT: Use similar triangles.)

   Given: $\overline{DX}$, $\overline{EY}$, and $\overline{FZ}$ are altitudes.

   Prove: $\overline{DX}$, $\overline{EY}$, and $\overline{FZ}$ are concurrent.

Critical Thinking

28. Draw a large acute triangle. Construct the circumcenter and label it O. Construct the centroid and label it G. Construct the orthocenter and label it H. Are O, G, and H collinear? What fraction of OH is OG? Is the same true for a right triangle? an obtuse triangle? State a generalization.

Algebra Review

Simplify. Assume all variables are nonnegative.

1. $\sqrt{8a^2}$ 2. $\sqrt{120}$ 3. $-\sqrt{144x}$ 4. $\sqrt{27} + \sqrt{3}$
5. $\sqrt{75} - \sqrt{12}$ 6. $\sqrt{45x^3y}$ 7. $\sqrt{z^6}$ 8. $\sqrt{1600r^3}$

Quiz

1. Draw a 5-in. segment. Construct the perpendicular bisector of the segment.
2. Draw an obtuse angle. Construct the angle bisector.
3. Draw a right triangle. Construct the altitude from the right angle to the hypotenuse.
4. Draw a line t and a point K not on line t. Construct $\overleftrightarrow{KL} \parallel t$.
5. Draw a 4-in. segment. Divide it into three equal parts by construction.
6. Draw $\odot T$ and a point X outside $\odot T$. Construct the tangents to $\odot T$ through X.

Indicate whether each statement is true or false.

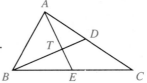

7. The three altitudes of a triangle are concurrent at the circumcenter.
8. The three medians of a triangle are concurrent at its center of gravity.
9. The angle bisectors of the triangle are concurrent at the incenter.
10. In $\triangle ABC$, if $\overline{BD}$ and $\overline{AE}$ are medians, then $TE = \frac{2}{3}AE$.

LOCUS

9-6 Simple Locus

A **locus** of points is a set of points and only those points that satisfy one or more conditions. The plural of locus is *loci*.

The set of points equidistant from the banks of a river can be described as a locus of points.

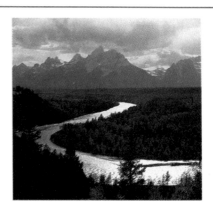

In geometry, the solution to a locus problem requires the drawing of a figure that satisfies specific conditions.

Consider the following problem.

Example 1

Determine the locus of points in the plane that are equidistant from points *A* and *B*.

Solution

Find a point that is equidistant from *A* and *B*.
Find other points equidistant from *A* and *B* and determine if the points form a familiar geometric figure. Draw the figure and write a description of it.

The locus of points in the plane equidistant from points *A* and *B* is the perpendicular bisector of the segment *AB*.

Try This

Determine the locus of points in space that are equidistant from points *A* and *B*.

To solve a locus problem, you will need to find the set of points defined by given conditions. You may find it helpful to use the strategy for solving locus problems outlined below.

Steps for Solving Locus Problems

1. Find a point that satisfies the given condition(s).
2. Find other points that satisfy the given condition(s).
3. Draw a figure that contains the points and, if possible, describe the figure in terms of a common geometric figure.
4. **a.** Make sure that every point in the described figure satisfies the given condition(s).
   b. Make sure that points not in the figure do not satisfy the given condition(s).

The solution to a locus problem consists of the figure and the description, as outlined in Step 3 of the steps for solving locus problems. Unless otherwise stated, the solution to a locus problem involves points that are coplanar only.

The following example illustrates how to use these four steps.

Example 2

Determine the locus of points that are 1 in. from a given point P.

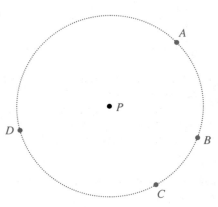

Solution

Step 1 Find a point that is 1 in. from P.
(point A)

Step 2 Find three other points that are 1 in. from P.
(points B, C, and D)

Step 3 Draw the figure and write a description of it.
The locus of points 1 in. from P is a circle with center P and a radius of 1 in.

Step 4 a. Is every point on the circle 1 in. from P?
(yes)
b. Are there any points that are 1 in. from P that are not on the circle?
(no)

Try This

Determine the locus of points in space that are 3 in. from a given point P.

The following example presents only the solution to the locus problem.

Example 3

Determine the locus of points that are 1 cm from a given line m.

Solution

The locus of points consists of two lines parallel to m and 1 cm from m.

Try This

Determine the locus of points in space that are 1 cm from a given line m.

Class Exercises

Short Answer

Determine whether the locus of points is best described by a point, a line, or a plane.

1. set of points equidistant from the ceiling and floor of a room
2. set of points of $\overline{AB}$ that are equidistant from A and B

3. set of points in a plane that are equidistant from sides $\overline{AB}$ and $\overline{CD}$ of rectangle $ABCD$

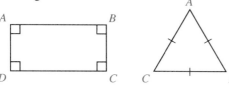

4. set of points in a plane that are equidistant from vertices A, B, and C of equilateral triangle ABC

5. set of points in space that are equidistant from vertices A, B, and C of equilateral triangle ABC

6. set of points that are equidistant from the front wall and the back wall of a room

Sample Exercises

7. Draw an angle.

  a. Find a point that is equidistant from the sides of the angle.
  b. Find three other points that are equidistant from the sides of the angle.
  c. Describe the set of points that are equidistant from the sides of the angle.
  d. Are there any points other than the figure you described that are equidistant from the sides of the angle?

8. Draw two parallel lines.

  a. Find a point that is equidistant from the two parallel lines.
  b. Find three other points that are equidistant from the two parallel lines.
  c. Describe the set of points that are equidistant from the two lines.
  d. Are there any points other than the figure you described that are equidistant from the parallel lines?

Determine the locus of points that satisfy the given conditions.

9. the locus of points that are equidistant from the vertices of a square

10. the locus of points that are equidistant from the bases of a parallelogram

11. the locus of points that are 5 cm from a circle with center P and a radius of 3 cm

12. the locus of the midpoints of congruent chords of a given circle

Discussion

Determine whether each statement is true or false. Explain your answer.

13. The locus of points 5 cm from a given line s is a line above s and a distance of 5 cm from s.

14. The locus of points equidistant from two intersecting lines is a line that bisects one of the angles formed by the intersecting lines.

15. The locus of points equidistant from two parallel lines is a line parallel to both.

16. Describe a line in space that is equidistant from all points on a circle.

Exercises

A

Determine the locus of points that satisfy the given conditions.

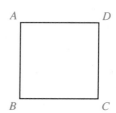

1. the locus of points that are equidistant from the goal lines of a football field
2. the locus of points that are 3 cm from a circle with center P and a radius of 5 cm
3. the locus of the vertex of a right triangle with a given hypotenuse
4. the locus of the midpoints of all chords parallel to a given chord
5. the locus of the midpoints of radii of a given circle
6. the locus of the midpoints of chords drawn from a given point on a given circle
7. the locus of all cities that are 4 mi from a given railroad track that is straight

Determine the locus of points that satisfy the given conditions with respect to square *ABCD*.

8. the locus of points that are equidistant from sides $\overline{AB}$ and $\overline{CD}$
9. the locus of points that are equidistant from sides $\overline{AB}$ and $\overline{BC}$
10. the locus of points that are equidistant from the diagonals $\overline{AC}$ and $\overline{BD}$
11. the locus of points that are half the length of the diagonal $\overline{AC}$ from the intersection of the diagonals $\overline{AC}$ and $\overline{BD}$

Determine the locus of points in space that satisfy the given conditions.

12. the locus of points that are 3 cm from a point P
13. the locus of points that are equidistant from two parallel planes
14. the locus of points that are equidistant from two given points
15. the locus of lines that are perpendicular to a given line at a given point on the line

B

Determine the locus of points that satisfy the given conditions.

16. the locus of points that are a distance equal to the radius of a given circle from the circle
17. the locus of the centers of circles that are tangent to a given circle O at a given point P on circle O
18. the locus of the centers of all circles that have a given radius and that contain a given point P
19. the locus of midpoints of all possible segments $\overline{AD}$ of a $\triangle ABC$, given point D on side $\overline{BC}$

20. Describe the locus of the center of a ball bearing that rolls inside a circular plate.
21. Describe the locus of a doorknob as the door is opened and closed.
22. Describe the locus of points in space that are equidistant from the four vertices of a square.

Refer to the graph to the right.

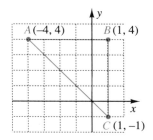

23. Write an equation that describes the locus of points that are equidistant from A and B.
24. Write an equation that describes the locus of points that are equidistant from B and C.
25. Write an equation that describes the locus of points that are equidistant from A and C.
26. Determine the coordinates of the locus of points that are equidistant from A, B, and C.

c

27. What is the locus of the midpoints of all chords formed by secants drawn to a circle from a given external point?
28. In rectangle $ABCD$, $\overline{AB}$ is twice as long as $\overline{BC}$. E is the midpoint of $\overline{CD}$. Describe the locus of midpoints of segments that have their endpoints on the sides of the rectangle and that are parallel to $\overline{AE}$.

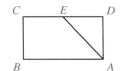

29. Describe the locus of the vertices of a 60° angle having rays that contain two given points A and B.

Critical Thinking

30. Suppose A and B are two points that are 4 in. apart. What is the locus of points P such that $AP + PB = 5$ in.? What happens to the figure if A and B are moved farther apart? What kind of figure is approximated as points A and B get closer and closer together?

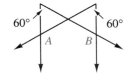

Mixed Review

Classify the triangle with the given side lengths as acute, right, or obtuse.

1. 5, 7, 9   2. 7, 10, 12
3. 3, 4, 7   4. 8, 15, 17
5. 2, 4, 5   6. 5, 12, 13

Enrichment
The Nine-Point Circle

Construct a triangle with sides of lengths 8 cm, 11 cm, and 15 cm. Then construct the following points.

a. Construct the midpoint s of the three sides of the triangle
b. Construct the points at which the three altitudes join the sides of the triangle Label the point of intersection of the three altitudes H.
c. Construct the midpoints of the segments joining H with the vertices of the triangle

How do the nine points you constructed in parts **a**, **b**, and **c** appear to be related?

9-7 Compound Locus

A locus problem that involves more than one set of conditions for defining a set of points is called a compound locus problem. The situation described in the caption under the photograph presents two sets of conditions for determining the locus of points of the area where most of the shots hit. The solution to a compound locus problem involves the identification of the points that satisfy all the given conditions. The following example presents a compound locus problem and its solution.

In a tennis match most of the shots were hit 3 ft from the base line and 5 ft from the side line. In what area were most of the shots hit?

Example 1

Determine the locus of points equidistant from points A and B and a given distance from line s.

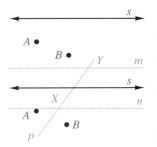

Solution

Determine the locus of points equidistant from A and B. (line p)
Determine the locus of points a given distance from line s. (lines m and n)
Points X and Y satisfy both of the given conditions

The solution to the problem is points X and Y.

The following steps can be used to solve compound locus problems.

Steps for Solving Compound Locus Problems

1. Determine the locus of points for the first condition.
2. Determine the locus of points for the second condition.
3. Determine the points that satisfy both conditions.

Example 2 uses the steps given above to solve a compound locus problem.

Example 2

Determine the locus of points equidistant from two concentric circles and equidistant from two secants that intersect at the center of the circles.

Solution

Step 1 Determine the points equidistant from lines m and n. (lines p and q)

Step 2 Determine the points equidistant from the two concenteric circles. (dotted circle)

Step 3 Determine the intersection of the loci. (points A, B, C, and D)

The solution to the problem is points A, B, C, and D.

Try This

Determine the locus of points equidistant from two concentric circles and equidistant from two parallel tangents to the smaller circle.

Example 3

Determine the locus of points equidistant from two parallel lines and equidistant from two points on one of the lines.

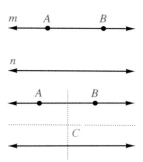

Solution

The solution consists of point C.

Try This

Determine the locus of points in space equidistant from two parallel lines and equidistant from two points on one of the lines.

Class Exercises

Short Answer

Determine whether each statement is true or false.

1. A circle and a line can intersect in zero, one, or two points.
2. A circle and a pair of intersecting lines must intersect in at least one point.
3. A circle and a pair of intersecting lines cannot intersect in more than four points.

State the number of points of intersection possible for the locus of points.

4. a line and a pair of intersecting lines
5. a line and a pair of parallel lines
6. a pair of intersecting lines and a pair of parallel lines

Sample Exercises

7. Consider the lines m and n and point P that is 1 cm from m and 2 cm from the intersection of m and n. Describe each locus.

   a. points equidistant from lines m and n
   b. points 3 cm from P
   c. points equidistant from lines m and n and 3 cm from P

Draw a figure and describe the locus of points.

8. the locus of points 3 cm from circle Q and 1 cm from a line containing the center of the circle
9. the locus of points equidistant from two parallel lines that are 4 cm apart and 5 cm from a point P on one of the lines
10. the locus of points equidistant from the congruent sides of an isosceles triangle that are 5 cm long and form a 60° angle, and that are 1 cm from the base of the triangle

Discussion

Consider a circle Q with a radius of 5 cm and two lines m and n that are tangent to the circle from a point X that is 10 cm from Q. Circle P is concentric with circle Q and has a radius s.

11. For what values of s will circle P intersect lines m and n in four points?
12. For what values of s will circle P not intersect lines m and n?
13. For what values of s will circle P intersect lines m and n in two points?

Exercises

A

Describe each of the following.

1. the locus of points equidistant from the diameters $\overline{AC}$ and $\overline{BD}$, that are 6 cm long, and intersect at P
2. the locus of points 2 cm from circle P
3. the locus of points equidistant from the diameters $\overline{AC}$ and $\overline{BD}$ and 2 cm from circle P
4. the locus of points equidistant from points A and B
5. the locus of points equidistant from lines m and n that intersect at A
6. the locus of points equidistant from lines m and n and equidistant from points A and B

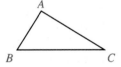

Draw a figure and describe the locus of points.

7. the locus of points 2 cm from a given line $\overleftrightarrow{AB}$ and equidistant from A and point C not on $\overleftrightarrow{AB}$
8. the locus of points 3 cm from $\overleftrightarrow{AB}$ and equidistant from parallel lines $\overleftrightarrow{BC}$ and $\overleftrightarrow{AD}$
9. the locus of points 4 cm from a point P and equidistant from two parallel lines each 1 cm from P
10. the locus of points 3 cm from P, equidistant from points P and A
11. the locus of points 3 cm from the vertex of a given angle and equidistant from the sides of the angle

12. Given equilateral triangle ABC, determine the locus of points which are distance BC from B and distance AC from C.

13. Given scalene triangle ABC, determine the locus of points equidistant from B and C and distance AD from $\overline{BC}$ where $\overline{AD}$ is an altitude of $\triangle ABC$.

14. Given rectangle $ABCD$, determine the locus of points equidistant from B and C and equidistant from sides $\overline{CB}$ and $\overline{CD}$ (extended).

Draw a diagram to represent each of the different solutions possible.

15. Describe the locus of points equidistant from two given parallel lines and a given distance from a transversal intersecting the two lines.
16. Describe the locus of points a given distance from a given point and equidistant from two parallel secants.
17. Describe the locus of points a given distance from a given circle and equidistant from two intersecting chords.
18. Describe the locus of points equidistant from two concentric circles and equidistant from two parallel lines.

B

19. If the locus of points equidistant from M and N is the same as the locus of points equidistant from $\overrightarrow{PM}$ and $\overrightarrow{PN}$, what kind of triangle is PMN?
20. If the locus of points equidistant from vertices A, B, and C of $\triangle ABC$ is at the midpoint of side $\overline{AB}$, what kind of triangle is ABC?

21. The intersection of the set of points a given distance x from a given circle with a radius r and the set of points equidistant from two intersecting diameters of the given circle is four points. Is $x < r$, $r < x$ or $x = r$? Draw a diagram to illustrate your answer.
22. Draw a figure in which the intersection of the locus of points equidistant from two parallel lines, m and n, and the locus of points equidistant from two intersecting lines, p and q, is two points, A and B.

Describe the locus of points in space that satisfy the given conditions.

23. the locus of points 10 cm from P and 2 cm from a plane containing P
24. the locus of points equidistant from a ceiling and floor of a room and equidistant from two opposite walls of the room

C

25. How many points on the earth's surface are equidistant from New York and San Francisco and 1000 miles from the equator?
26. Write the equation of the line that represents the locus of points equidistant from the lines $y = 2x - 3$ and $y = 2x + 1$.
27. Write the equation of the lines that represent the locus of points equidistant from the lines $y = 4x + 1$ and $y = -4x + 1$.
28. Describe the locus of points in space such that for a given segment AB, every point P forms an angle APB such that $m \angle APB = 90$.

Critical Thinking

29. Consider line m and a point P located 4 cm from m. Find a point A such that A is 2 cm from m and 2 cm from P. Find a point B such that B is 3 cm from m and 3 cm from P. Find a second point that is 3 cm from m and 3 cm from P. Find two points that are 4 cm from m and 4 cm from P. Find two points that are 5 cm from both m and P.

Draw a smooth curve through all the points you determined. These points can be described as the locus of points that are equidistant from a given line m and a given point P. Such points form a parabola.

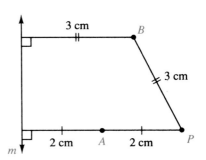

Algebra Review

Solve each inequality.

1. $3(y + 6) < 2y + 12$ 2. $2(y + 5) > y + 15$ 3. $5(n + 6) < 3n - 6$

Math Contest Problem

Draw a circle O with a diameter $\overline{AC}$. Extend $\overline{AC}$ to point D. As a point E on the circle moves from A to C, it traverses an arc of $x°$. Find an expression for $m \angle ECD$ in terms of x.

9-8 Constructions and Loci

A construction problem requires the construction of a figure given the measures of parts of the figure. To solve the problem you must construct a locus of points based on the given information. The solution consists of the steps in the construction process together with the construction. Study the examples below.

Example 1

Construct right triangle ABC given the length of the hypotenuse $\overline{AB}$ and the measure of $\angle A$, an acute angle.

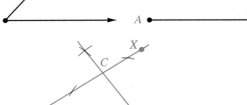

Solution

1. Copy $\angle A$.
2. Mark off $\overline{AB}$ on one ray of the angle.
3. Construct the perpendicular from B to $\overrightarrow{AX}$. Label the point of intersection of the perpendicular and $\overrightarrow{AX}$ point C.

Triangle ABC has right angle C, hypotenuse of length AB, and $\angle A$ the measure of the given acute angle. Therefore $\triangle ABC$ is the required triangle.

Try This

Construct a right triangle ABC with hypotenuse $\overline{AB}$ and side $\overline{BC}$.

Example 2

Construct rhombus $ABCD$ given the measure of $\angle A$ and the length of diagonal $\overline{AC}$.

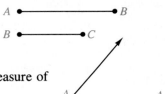

Solution

1. Copy $\angle A$ and bisect it.
2. Mark off $\overline{AC}$ on the bisector of $\angle A$.
3. Construct $\angle 2$ congruent to $\angle 1$ at C. Label the intersection with $\overrightarrow{AX}$ point D.
4. Construct $\overline{AB} \cong \overline{AD}$.

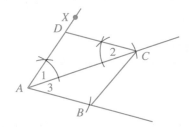

Figure $ABCD$ is a parallelogram since $\overline{AB} \parallel \overline{CD}$ ($\angle 2 \cong \angle 3$) and $\overline{CD} \cong \overline{AB}$.
Since $\overline{AB} \cong \overline{AD}$, $ABCD$ is a rhombus.

Try This

Construct a rhombus $ABCD$ given $\angle A$ and side AB = 3 cm.

Class Exercises

Short Answer

Give the steps needed to complete each construction.

1. Construct an isosceles triangle given the vertex angle and one of the equal sides.
2. Construct an isosceles triangle given the base and the altitude to the base.
3. Construct a square given a diagonal.
4. Construct a rhombus given both diagonals.

Sample Exercises

Use $\angle 1$ and $\overline{AB}$ and $\overline{CD}$.

5. Construct an isosceles triangle with a base $\overline{CD}$ and an altitude $\overline{AB}$.
6. Construct an isosceles triangle with $\angle 1$ as the vertex angle and congruent sides of length AB.
7. Construct a rectangle $RSTV$ with $\overline{RS} \cong \overline{AB}$ and $\overline{ST} \cong \overline{CD}$.
8. Construct an isosceles triangle KLM with base $\overline{KL} \cong \overline{CD}$ and $\angle K \cong \angle L \cong \angle 1$.
9. Construct a square with the diagonal having length CD.

Discussion

10. Suppose you are constructing an equilateral triangle given the altitude $\overline{AP}$ and you have completed the first three steps in the construction process as follows.

    1. Construct a perpendicular to m at P.
    2. Mark off $\overline{PA}$ equal in length to the given altitude.
    3. Construct a 30° angle at point A.

    Describe two different methods you could use to complete the construction.

Exercises

A

1. Draw a line p. Construct the locus of points 2 cm from p.
2. Draw a segment $\overline{BC}$. Construct the locus of the vertices A of $\triangle ABC$ such that the altitudes from A to $\overline{BC}$ are each 3 cm in length.
3. Draw an angle A of approximately 60°. Construct a circle with a radius of 2 cm that is tangent to the sides of $\angle A$.

Use ∠1 and the three segments given.

4. Construct a rhombus $ABCD$ with $m\angle A = m\angle 1$ and $AB = p$.
5. Construct a parallelogram $ABCD$ with $m\angle A = m\angle 1$, $AB = r$, and $BD = q$.
6. Construct an isosceles trapezoid $ABCD$ with the longer base $AB = r$, $m\angle A = m\angle 1$, and altitude p.
7. Construct an isosceles triangle ABC with $\angle A$ the vertex angle, altitude $AD = q$, and $m\angle B = m\angle 1$.
8. Construct a right triangle ABC with $m\angle A = 90$, the altitude $AD = q$, and $m\angle B = m\angle 1$.
9. Construct an isosceles triangle ABC with congruent sides $\overline{AB}$ and $\overline{AC}$ having length r and the altitude $\overline{CD}$ to the side $\overline{AB}$ having length p.
10. Construct a circle O with tangents $\overline{PA}$ and $\overline{PB}$ having length r and $m\angle APB = m\angle 1$. A and B are points of tangency.

B

Use ∠1 and the three segments given above.

11. Construct an isosceles trapezoid $ABCD$ with the longer base $AB = q$, diagonal $AC = r$, and $m\angle CAB = m\angle 1$.
12. Construct a right triangle ABC with $m\angle B = 90$, leg $BC = q$, and the altitude $BD = p$.
13. Construct a right triangle ABC with $m\angle A = 90$, altitude $AD = p$, and median $AM = q$.
14. Construct a triangle ABC with base $BC = r$, side $AB = q$, and altitude $AD = p$.
15. Construct a triangle ABC with base $BC = r$, altitude $AD = p$, and median $AM = q$.
16. Construct a circle with radius q that is tangent to two congruent intersecting circles with radius p.
17. Construct an equilateral triangle given the radius p of its inscribed circle.

C

18. Construct a right triangle ABC given the sum of the legs $\overline{AB}$ and $\overline{AC}$ and acute angle B.
19. Construct a circle with radius r that is tangent to two congruent nonintersecting circles with a radius s.
20. Construct a circle that is tangent to a given circle at point P and contains a point Q outside the given circle.

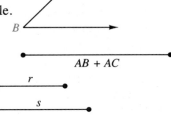

Critical Thinking

A rusty compass is one that is stuck and always has the same opening (radius). You can use your compass as a rusty compass by not changing its radius during the construction process. A collapsible compass is one that springs back together as soon as it is lifted from the paper.

You can use your compass as a collapsible compass by not using the same radius once you have drawn an arc.

21. Copy $\overline{AB}$ and bisect it using
   a. a collapsible compass
   b. a rusty compass with opening from C to D

22. Draw an acute angle and bisect it using
   a. a collapsible compass
   b. a rusty compass

Indicate whether each of the following constructions can be done with (a) a rusty compass, (b) a collapsible compass, (c) both a rusty compass and a collapsible compass, or (d) neither.

23. Construct the perpendicular to a line through a point on the line.
24. Construct the perpendicular to a line from a point not on the line.
25. Construct a parallel to a line through a given point not on the line.

Mixed Review

1. What is the measure of each interior angle of a regular 10-sided polygon?
2. If four angles of a pentagon have measures of 100°, 160°, 90°, and 150°, find the measure of the fifth angle.

Determine whether each statement is true or false.

3. If a parallelogram is inscribed in a circle, it is a rectangle.
4. If $ABCD$ is a parallelogram, then its diagonals are congruent.
5. If $m\angle A = 40$ in right triangle ABC and $m\angle D = 50$ in right triangle DEF, then the triangles are similar.

Quiz

Describe the locus of points that satisfy the given conditions.

1. Given parallel lines t and w that are 6 cm apart, describe the locus of points equidistant from t and w.
2. Given $\triangle ABC$, describe the locus of points equidistant from A and B.
3. Given two distinct points R and S that are 4 in. apart, describe the locus of points 3 in. from R and 2 in. from S.
4. Given $\angle M$, what is the locus of points equidistant from the sides of $\angle M$ and 3 m from the vertex M?

Complete the construction.

5. Draw a segment having length t and an acute angle $\angle 1$. Construct a rhombus $ABCD$ with $\angle A \cong \angle 1$ and $AC = t$.
6. Draw two segments, a and b, having unequal lengths. Construct a right triangle with legs of lengths a and b.

DISCRETE MATH

Tree Diagrams and Counting

A **tree diagram** is used to count the possibilities for an event. Consider how many different outfits are possible with 2 pairs of slacks and 3 shirts.

Slacks	Shirts	Outfits
black	white	black slacks and white shirt
	yellow	black slacks and yellow shirt
	red	black slacks and red shirt
blue	white	blue slacks and white shirt
	yellow	blue slacks and yellow shirt
	red	blue slacks and red shirt

For each of the 2 pairs of slacks you have 3 choices of shirts, so there are $2 \cdot 3$ or 6 possible choices. This illustrates the *Multiplication Principle:* If the first step can be done in n_1 ways, the second in n_2 ways, and the kth step in n_k ways—the number of different ways the entire procedure can be done is $n_1 \cdot n_2 \cdot n_3 \cdot \ldots \cdot n_k$. Tree diagrams are helpful if the counting of possibilities is complicated and the Multiplication Principle does not apply.

Example

In how many different ways can the Special Olympics series be played out if the A and B teams involved play until one of the teams has won two games?

Solution

Game 1	Game 2	Game 3	Winner
A	A		A
	B	A	A
		B	B
B	A	A	A
		B	B
	B		B

There are 6 different ways in which the series of games can be played out.

Exercises

Use the Multiplication Principle.

1. There are 12 flights from Chicago to New York and 8 flights from New York to Miami. How many different routings from Chicago to New York to Miami are possible?

2. There are 5 different routes from school to the stadium and 4 routes from there to the store. How many different routes can one take to the store via the stadium?

Make a tree diagram for each situation.

3. a five-game series in which one team must win three games to be called the champion

4. a seven-game World Series in which the first of the two teams with 4 wins is the champion

CRITICAL THINKING

Inductive Reasoning

Critical thinking is based on the consideration of evidence, patterns and relationships. **Inductive reasoning**, which plays an important role, involves forming a conclusion by working from a sequence of specific examples.

Consider the diagrams showing circles with interior regions formed by segments connecting points on the circles. What is the maximal number of regions formed in the interior of the circles by a given number of points? Counting in the first four circles the pattern of regions 1, 2, 4, and 8—you might guess that 5 points will result in 10 regions. You might form the conjecture that n lines cut the interior of a circle into $2n - 1$ regions. An extension of the drawings to the case with 5 points shows that the conjecture appears to hold. With 5 points, 16 regions are formed. However the extension to the case with 6 points shows that only 31 regions are formed. This case gives a counterexample which shows that the pattern formed by inductive reasoning was not valid for all cases.

1 point
1 region

2 points
2 regions

3 points
4 regions

4 points
8 regions

Consider the pattern in the sums to the right. What conjecture is appropriate?

The sum for each series of odd numbers appears to be a square number. Thus, one might conjecture: The sum of the first n odd numbers is n^2 or

$$\underbrace{1 + 3 + 5 + 7 + \ldots + (2n - 1)}_{n \text{ numbers}} = n^2$$

$$1 = 1$$
$$1 + 3 = 4$$
$$1 + 3 + 5 = 9$$
$$1 + 3 + 5 + 7 = 16$$
$$1 + 3 + 5 + 7 + 9 = 25$$

This conjecture is valid and can be proved using a method known as mathematical induction. In this case, it led to a valid result. Inductive reasoning is a powerful form of critical reasoning but the validity of the conjectures must be tested. It is not enough to form a conjecture on the basis of a few cases. If conjectures are to give us a useful generalization, they must be true for all cases.

Exercises

Make a 10 × 10 grid of numbers from 1 to 100 to form conjectures and test if they are valid. If a conjecture is not valid, give a counterexample.

1. Select any 3 × 3 array of numbers from the grid. What can you say about the sum of the numbers on the diagonals?
2. Select any 3 × 3 array of numbers from the grid. What can you say about the relationship of the number in the center to the sum of the numbers on the diagonal?
3. Select any 3 × 3 array of numbers from the grid. What can you say about the sums of numbers in the first row and numbers in the last row?
4. Select any 3 × 3 array of numbers from the grid. What can you say about the sums of numbers from opposite corners?
5. Select any 3 × 3 array of numbers from the grid. What can you say about the sum of the middle column and the sum of the middle row?

CHAPTER SUMMARY

Vocabulary

construction (9-1)   concurrent lines (9-5)   orthocenter (9-5)
centroid (9-5)   incenter (9-5)
circumcenter (9-5)   locus (9-6)

Key Ideas

1. A construction is a geometric figure produced by using only a compass and straightedge.
2. Every triangle has the following concurrency properties.
   a. The perpendicular bisectors of the sides of the triangle intersect at a point that is equidistant from the vertices of the triangle.
   b. The bisectors of the angles of the triangle intersect at a point that is equidistant from the sides of the triangle.
   c. The medians of the triangle intersect at a point that is two thirds of the way from each vertex to the opposite side.
   d. The lines that contain the altitudes of the triangle are concurrent.
3. A locus of points is a set of points, and only those points, that satisfy one or more conditions.
4. When a locus of points must satisfy more than one condition, its location can be found from the intersection of the loci for each separate condition.

CHAPTER REVIEW

9-1

1. Draw a segment $\overline{AB}$ approximately 4 in. long. Construct a segment $\overline{CD}$ such that $\overline{AB} \cong \overline{CD}$.
2. Draw $\angle B$ whose measure is approximately 70°. Construct $\angle T$ such that $m \angle T = \frac{1}{2} m \angle B$.
3. Draw an obtuse angle. Construct an angle congruent to the obtuse angle.
4. Draw a segment $\overline{RS}$ approximately 8 in. long. Construct a segment $\overline{WY}$ whose length is $\frac{1}{4} RS$.

9-2

Copy the diagram to the right.

5. Construct a line through O perpendicular to $\overline{LN}$.
6. Construct a line through M perpendicular to $\overline{PO}$.
7. Construct a line through P parallel to $\overline{LN}$.
8. Construct a square with a diagonal approximately 5 cm long.
9. Construct a rectangle with sides approximately 4 cm and 6 cm long.

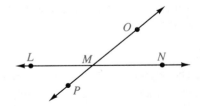

9-3

Draw a large ⊙T. Label a point _U_ on ⊙T and a point _X_ outside ⊙T.

10. Construct tangents to ⊙T from a point _X_.
11. Construct a tangent to ⊙T at a point _U_.
12. Draw a large ⊙A. Locate its center by construction.

9-4

13. Draw a segment that is approximately 9 in. long. By construction, divide this segment into five equal parts.
14. Construct the segment of length _x_ given the segments of lengths _a_, _b_, and _c_ and the proportion $\frac{a}{x} = \frac{b}{c}$.

15. Draw two segments that are approximately 3 in. and 5 in. long. Construct their geometric mean.

9-5

Choose the correct word to complete each statement.

16. The three altitudes of a triangle concur at a point called the ___ .
    a. circumcenter   **b.** incenter   **c.** orthocenter   **d.** centroid
17. The three angle bisectors concur at a point called the ___ .
    a. circumcenter   **b.** incenter   **c.** orthocenter   **d.** centroid
18. The point equidistant from the vertices of a triangle is called the ___ .
    a. circumcenter   **b.** incenter   **c.** orthocenter   **d.** centroid

19. In △_ABC_, medians $\overline{AD}$ and $\overline{CE}$ concur at point _T_. If _AT_ = 6, then _AD_ = __?__ .

9-6

Describe the locus of points that satisfy the given condition.

20. the locus of the centers of circles with radii 2 cm and passing through a given point _T_
21. the locus of points equidistant from sides $\overline{AB}$ and $\overline{CD}$ in rectangle _ABCD_

9-7

22. Point _R_ is on line ℓ. What is the locus of points that are 3 cm from ℓ and 4 cm from _R_?
23. Points _X_ and _Y_ are 5 m apart. What is the locus of points 3 m from both _X_ and _Y_?

9-8

Use the segments shown to the right.

24. Construct a rectangle with width _a_ and length _b_.
25. Construct isosceles triangle _RST_ with _RS_ = _RT_ = _a_ and _ST_ = _b_.

CHAPTER TEST

Draw segments and an angle like those shown to the right.

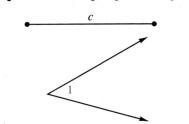

1. Construct an angle congruent to ∠1.
2. Construct $\overline{XY}$ such that $XY = 2a$.
3. Construct the geometric mean between a and b.
4. Construct a segment of length x such that $\frac{x}{a} = \frac{b}{c}$.
5. Construct an isosceles triangle with vertex angle congruent to ∠1 and legs of length b.

6. Draw a segment approximately 8 cm long. Bisect the segment.
7. Draw line m and point P as shown. Construct the parallel to m through P.
8. Draw a line ℓ with point W on line ℓ. Construct a line perpendicular to ℓ through W.

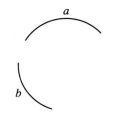

9. Draw $\odot A$ with point B on $\odot A$. Construct the tangent through B.
10. Draw $\odot Q$. Locate a point P not on $\odot Q$. Construct a tangent to $\odot Q$ from P.
11. Trace arcs a and b. Construct the center of the circle containing the arcs.
12. Draw a segment. Divide it into three equal parts by construction.
13. Construct a 45° angle.
14. Draw an angle ABC. Construct circle Q having radius x and tangent to $\overline{BA}$ and $\overline{BC}$.

State the name for the point described.

15. the point of concurrency of the angle bisectors of a triangle
16. the point that is equidistant from the vertices of a triangle

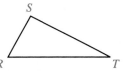

17. Which of the following are used to construct the orthocenter of △RST?
    a. perpendicular bisectors   **b.** angle bisectors
    c. medians   **d.** altitudes
18. Draw a triangle like △RST. Construct the altitude from point S.

Draw each locus of points in a plane and write its description.

19. the locus of points 3 cm from line t
20. the locus of the midpoints of all radii of a given circle
21. the locus of points within a circle that are equidistant from the ends of a chord
22. the locus of points equidistant from points A and B and 1.5 cm from point P
23. Lines ℓ and m intersect at W. Describe the locus of points equidistant from ℓ and m and 3 in. from W.
24. Describe the locus of points in a room equidistant from the ceiling and floor and equidistant from the front wall and back wall.

PROBLEM SOLVING

Make an Accurate Drawing

In some cases the answer to a problem can be found by making an accurate drawing or scale drawing. Study the example below in which a scale drawing is used to solve a problem.

Example 1

An 8-ft by 12-ft pool table has a ball in the corner. Suppose the ball is struck and travels at a 45° angle with a side until it hits the side. The ball then rebounds off that side and travels at a 45° angle until it hits and rebounds off another side. How many times will the ball hit a side before it reaches a corner?

Scale: $\frac{1}{2}$ cm = 1 ft

Solution

The scale drawing shows it will have three hits.

Problem-Solving Strategies	
Draw a Diagram	Work Backward
Make a Table	Simplify the Problem
Look for a Pattern	Make an Accurate Drawing

The problem-solving strategies that have been introduced up to this point in the book are presented in the chart.

Problems

Use an accurate drawing or scale drawing to solve the problems below.

1. Suppose a ball travels as described in the example above on an 8-ft by 10-ft table. How many times will the ball hit a side before it reaches a corner?

2. Suppose a ball travels as described in the example above on a 6-ft by 8-ft table. How many times will the ball hit a side before it reaches a corner?

3. A pilot in a small plane maintains a constant ground speed of 120 mph. She travels due north for 30 min, then northeast for 10 min, then southeast for 45 min, and then southwest for 30 min. At that point how long will it take to fly straight home?

4. O is the intersection of the perpendicular bisectors of the sides of $\triangle ABC$, G is the intersection of the medians, and H is the intersection of the altitudes. Observe that O, G, and H are collinear. What fraction of OH is OG? Try several triangles.

Chapters 1–9

1. Line PQ is __?__ .

   a. a subset of plane J
   b. perpendicular to plane J
   c. coplanar with plane J
   d. both a. and c.

2. Two names for the same angle are __?__ .
   a. $\angle ABC$, $\angle CAB$ b. $\angle CBA$, $\angle BAC$
   c. $\angle ACB$, $\angle BCA$ d. $\angle BCA$, $\angle ABC$

3. An acute angle has a measure __?__ .
   a. greater than 90   b. less than 90
   c. equal to 90   d. both a. and c.

4. If E is the midpoint of $\overline{BD}$, then __?__ .

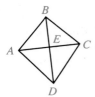

   a. $\overline{AE} \cong \overline{EC}$ b. $\overline{BE} \cong \overline{ED}$
   c. $\overline{AD} \cong \overline{CD}$ d. $\overline{AB} \cong \overline{BC}$

5. A triangle with no congruent sides is __?__ .
   a. equiangular   b. obtuse
   c. scalene   d. isosceles

6. Whenever $p \rightarrow q$ is true and p is true, what can you conclude?
   a. $q \rightarrow p$ is true   b. q is true
   c. $\sim q$ is true   d. both a. and c. are true

7. What is a conclusion arrived at through inductive reasoning?
   a. postulate   b. theorem
   c. generalization   d. deduction

8. Vertical angles are always __?__ .
   a. congruent   b. supplementary
   c. acute   d. obtuse

9. What type of angles are $\angle AOC$ and $\angle COB$?

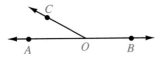

   a. complementary   b. supplementary
   c. a linear pair   d. both b. and c.

10. Two lines intersecting to form congruent right angles are __?__ .
    a. bisectors   b. vertical
    c. perpendicular   d. segment bisectors

11. Name a pair of alternate interior angles.

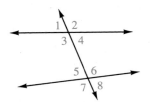

    a. 3 and 5   b. 2 and 3
    c. 5 and 4   d. 2 and 7

12. In $\triangle MKR$, find the measure of $\angle 1$.

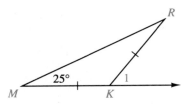

    a. 25   b. 50   c. 130   d. 60

13. $\triangle DKR$ is isosceles. If $m\angle K = 50$, find $m\angle D$.
    a. 50
    b. 55
    c. 65
    d. 60

14. Given that $\triangle STU \cong \triangle VWX$, then __?__ .
    a. $\angle S \cong \angle W$ b. $\angle T \cong \angle W$
    c. $\overline{TU} \cong \overline{VX}$ d. $\overline{US} \cong \overline{WX}$

Area and Perimeter of Polygons

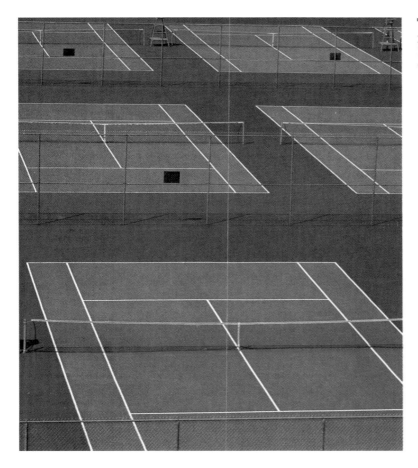

The area of a tennis court is 2808 sq ft. Its length is 78 ft. Find the width and perimeter of the tennis court.

15. These two triangles are congruent by __?__ .

   a. ASA   **b.** SSS   **c.** SAS
   d. not enough information to tell

16. Given that $PR = PS$ and PQ bisects RS, you could prove $\triangle PRQ \cong \triangle PSQ$ by __?__ .

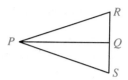

   a. SSS   **b.** ASA   **c.** AAS
   d. not enough information to tell

17. In a parallelogram opposite angles are __?__ .
   a. supplementary   **b.** congruent
   c. complementary   **d.** acute

18. In parallelogram $ABCD$, find $m\angle A + m\angle B$.
   a. 90   **b.** 180   **c.** 270   **d.** 360

19. The diagonals of a rhombus __?__ .
   a. bisect opposite angles
   b. are congruent
   c. intersect, forming a pair of acute angles
   d. all of the above

20. $\angle B \cong \angle C \cong \angle D \cong \angle E$ What is $BCDE$?
   a. trapezoid   **b.** rectangle
   c. square   **d.** rhombus

21. If the scale on a map indicates that 5 cm = 2 km, what would the actual length of a line segment shown on the map as 24 cm be?
   a. 9.6 km   **b.** 0.42 km
   c. 8 km   **d.** 60 km

22. If $\frac{p}{q} = \frac{x}{y}$, find $\frac{y}{q}$.
   a. $\frac{x}{p}$ **b.** $\frac{p}{x}$ **c.** $\frac{y}{x}$ **d.** $\frac{q}{y}$

23. Which of these polygons must be similar?
   a. two isosceles triangles
   b. two rectangles
   c. two parallelograms with 75° angles
   d. two regular octagons

24. The hypotenuse and one leg of a right triangle are 29 and 21. Find the length of the other leg.
   a. 1282   **b.** 36   **c.** 20   **d.** $15\sqrt{2}$

25. A triangle whose sides are 5, 10, and 13 is a(n) __?__ .
   a. obtuse triangle   **b.** acute triangle
   c. right triangle   **d.** impossibility

26. The shorter leg in a 30°–60°–90° triangle is 12. Find the length of the hypotenuse.
   a. $6\sqrt{3}$ **b.** 24   **c.** $12\sqrt{3}$ **d.** $2\sqrt{6}$

27. Find the measure of $\overset{\frown}{PQR}$.

   a. 220   **b.** 290   **c.** 325   **d.** 140

28. If L and M are points on a circle, what is $\overline{LM}$?
   a. secant   **b.** radius
   c. chord   **d.** tangent

29. $\overline{LM}$ is tangent to $\odot R$ at M. If $m\angle MRS = 80$, find $m\overset{\frown}{MTS}$.

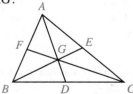

   a. 280   **b.** 220   **c.** 320   **d.** 40

30. G is the centroid of $\triangle ABC$. If $AD = 12$, find AG.

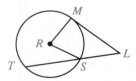

   a. 6   **b.** 8   **c.** 12   **d.** 24

31. Name the points of concurrency where the medians of a triangle meet.
   a. incenter   **b.** centroid
   c. orthocenter   **d.** circumcenter

OBJECTIVE: *Apply formulas for the perimeter and area of rectangles.*

10-1 Perimeter and Area of Rectangles

A geometric figure, such as rectangle *EFGH* below, consists of the points that make up its sides, or boundary. The **perimeter** (*p*) of a polygon is the sum of the lengths of its sides. For a rectangle, perimeter $= 2\ell + 2w$.

The perimeter and area of rectangular regions are important when building a wall or laying out a playing field.

A **region** includes the figure and its interior, as indicated by the shaded part inside rectangle *EFGH* above. The **area** (*A*) of a region is the number of square units contained in the region. By counting the number of square units in the rectangle above, you can see that the area of *EFGH* is 8 square units.

The following postulate ensures that a given region has exactly one area.

● **POSTULATE 21**

Every closed region has an area, which is a unique positive number.

The length of rectangle *EFGH* above gives the number of square units in each row. The width gives the number of rows of square units. You can use multiplication to find the total number of square units, as stated in the following postulate.

● **POSTULATE 22**

The area *A* of a rectangle is the product of its length ℓ and its width *w*.
$A = \ell w$

Since a square is a rectangle, the formula $A = \ell w$ can be used to find the area of a square. The length and width of a square are the same, so $A = s^2$.

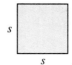

In the future, a specific unit of measure, such as square meters (m²), will not always be stated. In such cases, it is understood that "units" are used for length and "square units" are used for area.

Example 1

Find the width of rectangle $ABCD$, if it has area 54 sq. units.

Solution

$9(x + 2) = 54$ $A = \ell w$
$9x + 18 = 54$
$9x = 36$
$x = 4$ The width is $4 + 2$, or 6.

Try This

Find the perimeter of $ABCD$ if the area is not given and $x = 11$.

The following two postulates give additional properties of area.

● **POSTULATE 23**

If two closed figures are congruent, then they have equal areas.

● **POSTULATE 24**

The area of a region is the sum of the areas of all its nonoverlapping parts.

Example 2

Find the area of $ABCDEF$.

Solution

area $AGEF = 14 \cdot 4 = 56$
area $GBCD = 11 \cdot 10 = 110$
area $ABCDEF = 56 + 110 = 166$ square units   *Postulate 24*

Try This

Find the area of $ABCDEF$ if $BC = 13$ and $FE = 15$.

Example 3

Find the area of $GHIJKL$.

Solution

area $GHIM = (12.4)(4.6) = 57.04$ cm²
$LK = 12.4 - 9.3 = 3.1$ cm
$LM = 4.6 - 2.8 = 1.8$ cm
area $LKJM = (3.1)(1.8) = 5.58$ cm²
area $GHIJKL = 57.04 - 5.58 = 51.46$ cm²

Try This

Use a different method to find the area of $GHIJKL$.

Class Exercises

Short Answer

Complete each statement.

1. The perimeter of a rectangle with length a and width b is ____ .
2. The area of a rectangle with length a and width b is ____ .
3. The perimeter of a square with side length y is ____ .
4. The area of a square with side length y is ____ .
5. When the side length of a square is given in centimeters, the area is given in ____ .
6. Region C is made up of nonoverlapping regions A and B. If the area of region A is x and the area of region B is y, then the area of region C is ____ .
7. The area and perimeter of a rectangle with length 8 cm and width 6 cm are ____ and ____ .
8. Four rows of six squares each are put together to form a rectangle. Its area is ____ .

Sample Exercises

Find each missing value.

9.

A = ____

Rectangle

10.

A = 81   s = ____

Square

11.

w = ____

$\ell = 9$ A = 54   perimeter = ____

Rectangle

12. Find the area of *ABCDEFGH*.
    Assume adjacent sides are perpendicular.

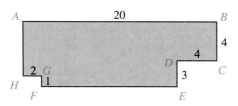

13. Use variables to express the area of a rectangle that has length x and width $x - 3$.
14. Use variables to express the length of the sides of a square that has area z.
15. Use variables to express the width of a rectangle that has area A and length ℓ.
16. It costs $150 per sq ft to build a house. A planned rectangular house now has dimensions 70 ft by 40 ft. If the plan is changed to extend the dimensions to 72 ft by 42 ft, how much will the cost increase?

Discussion

17. Describe or draw as many rectangles as you can that have lengths and widths that are whole numbers and area 36 cm^2.
18. Describe or draw at least five different rectangles that have lengths and widths that are whole numbers and equal perimeters. How do the areas of the rectangles compare?
19. Do you think there is a rectangle with whole-number length and width that has the same number for its area as for its perimeter?

Exercises

A

Refer to rectangle *ABCD* to complete the table.

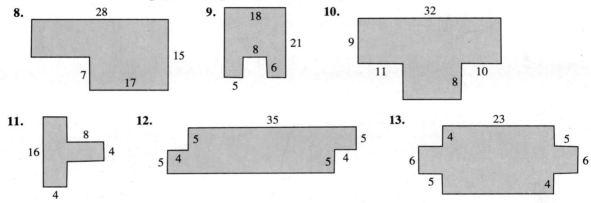

	Length	Width	Area	Perimeter
1.	13	9	——	——
2.	12	12	——	——
3.	$5\sqrt{2}$	$3\sqrt{2}$	——	——
4.	——	7	63	——
5.	——	10	——	56
6.	$x + 5$	x	——	——
7.	y	——	$y^2 - 5y$	——

Find the area of each figure. All adjacent sides are perpendicular.

8. 28, 15, 7, 17

9. 18, 21, 8, 6, 5

10. 32, 9, 11, 8, 10

11. 8, 16, 4, 4

12. 35, 5, 5, 4, 5, 4

13. 23, 4, 5, 6, 5, 4, 6

State a postulate that supports each statement.

14. You can find the area of a rectangular region by multiplying its length by its width.

15. You know that every closed region has one and only one positive number that can be called its area.

16. You can add the areas of regions that have only boundaries in common to find the total area of the combined region.

17. When you see two regions that have the same size and shape, you know they have the same area.

18. Jim needs to fertilize his rectangular yard which measures 10 m by 37 m. If one bag of fertilizer covers 180 m², approximately how many bags are needed to cover the yard?

B

Find the area of each rectangle.

19. 26, 10

20. 45°, 10

21. 60°, 24

240

$144\sqrt{3}$

Determine whether each statement is always, sometimes, or never true.

22. Two squares with the same area have the same perimeter.
23. Two squares with the same perimeter have the same area.
24. The perimeter and the area of a given square are the same number.
25. Two rectangles with the same area have the same perimeter.
26. Two rectangles with the same perimeter have the same area.

Find the area of each shaded region. Assume adjacent lines are perpendicular.

27.

28.

29.

30. The dimensions of one lot for building a house are twice the dimensions of a second lot. How do the areas of the lots compare?
31. The width of a rectangular playing field is 60 yd. The area of the field is 7200 sq yd. How far is it diagonally across the field?
32. The ratio of the height of a wall to the length of the wall is $2:3$. The area of the wall is 384 sq ft. What are the height and length of the wall?
33. Find the area of the roof of the building shown to the right. If you assume that 10% of the materials ordered are wasted in cutting, how many 4 ft by 8 ft plywood sheets should be ordered for this roof?

34. A fence was relocated to change the area of a rectangular field. The new length of the field is the old length, ℓ, increased by 6. The new width is 6 less than the old length. If the area of the new field is 108, what is its length and width?

C

35. *ADCB* and *MBNX* are rectangles. The area of *MBNX* is one third the area of *ABCD* and *M* is the midpoint of $\overline{AB}$. How does *BN* compare to *BC*?

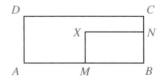

36. In this window pane, the vertices of the shaded square are the midpoints of the sides of the large square. Show that the area of the large square is twice the area of the shaded square.

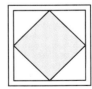

37. A homeowner has 64 ft of fence that can be used to make a pen for rabbits. He wants to make a rectangular pen that gives the rabbits as much grass area as possible. What dimensions should he use for the pen?
38. The coordinates of the vertices of a rectangle are (3, 1), (1, 3), (5, 7), and (7, 5). Find the area and the perimeter of the rectangle.

39. Give the dimensions of a rectangle that has perimeter 20 cm and area 21 cm². What do you think is the *greatest* possible area for a rectangle with perimeter 20 cm?

Critical Thinking

40. A student claimed it is possible to keep the area of a rectangle the same and change the perimeter and vice versa. Do you agree? Support your conclusion.

41. *ABCD*, *IBHF*, and *EFGD* are all rectangles. Give a convincing argument that regions *X* and *Y* have equal area no matter where *F* is located on diagonal $\overline{BD}$.

42. In the figure to the right, *D* is the center of the smaller of the two squares. The larger square overlaps the smaller square in quadrilateral *ABDE*. Find the area of *ABDE*. Give a convincing argument that this area would be the same whether *B* trisects $\overline{AC}$ or not.

Mixed Review

Find each of the following.

1. *EF* = 6, *EG* = 8   Find *FG*.
2. *FG* = 3, *GH* = 7   Find *FH*.
3. *GH* = 10, *FH* = 13   Find *FG*.
4. *FG* = 8, *EG* = 5   Find *FE*.
5. *FE* = 4, *EH* = 16   Find *EG*.
6. *FE* = 3, *EH* = 12   Find *EG*.
7. *FE* = 5, *EH* = 15   Find *FG*.
8. *FE* = 5, *EH* = 15   Find *GH*.
9. *FH* = 30, *EH* = 18   Find *EG*.
10. *FH* = 12, *FE* = 4   Find *GH*.

Biographical Note

Benjamin Banneker

Benjamin Banneker, a free black American born in 1731, was probably the best-known black in early American history. He was a mathematician, an astronomer, a surveyor, and a farmer.

Largely self-taught, Banneker, at an early age, built a remarkable clock that kept almost perfect time for more than fifty years. President George Washington was so impressed by Banneker's mathematical and engineering abilities that he appointed Banneker to the Capital Committee in Washington where he helped draw up plans that determined the borders of the District of Columbia.

As an astronomer, Banneker published almanacs that were later used by opponents of slavery as evidence of the abilities of blacks.

10-2 Areas of Parallelograms and Triangles

EXPLORE

On lined paper, draw and cut three different parallelograms. Can you make one straight cut that will separate a parallelogram into two pieces that can be fitted together to form a rectangle? How do the areas of the parallelogram and rectangle compare?

The idea in the Explore suggests a way to develop a formula for finding the area of a parallelogram. To understand and use such a formula, you first need to be able to identify the base and altitude of a parallelogram. Any side of a parallelogram can be called a **base.** The length of this side is also called the base (b). For each base, a segment perpendicular to the line containing the base with endpoints on this line and the side opposite the base is called the **altitude.** The length of the altitude is called the **height** (h). Sometimes, as long as no confusion results, the height is also described as "the altitude."

The diagram below shows region R being moved from the left side of the parallelogram to the right side.

You can use this procedure to give a convincing argument that the area of a parallelogram is the same as the area of a rectangle with the same base and height. This idea is the basis of Theorem 10.1.

◆ **THEOREM 10.1**

The area of a parallelogram equals the product of the base b and the height h. $A = bh$

Given: $\square ABCD$ with base b and altitude h
Prove: $A = bh$
Plan Draw altitudes $\overline{AE}$ and $\overline{DF}$, forming right triangles ABE and DCF. Prove $\triangle ABE \cong \triangle DCF$ (area I = area III) using the HL Congruence Theorem. area $ABCD$ = area II + area III (Postulate 24). By substitution, area $ABCD$ = area II + area I = area rectangle $ADFE$ = bh.

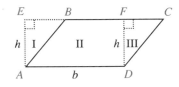

Theorem 10.1 can be used to prove that parallelograms with equal bases and equal altitudes have equal areas. You will be asked to complete this proof in Exercise 36.

Example 1

Find each area.

a. $\square TWXY$
b. $\square PQRS$

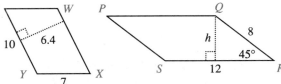

Solution

a. $A = bh = (10)(6.4) = 64$
b. $h = \frac{8}{2}\sqrt{2} = 4\sqrt{2}$
   $A = bh = (12)(4\sqrt{2}) = 48\sqrt{2}$

In a 45°–45°–90° triangle with hypotenuse x, a leg has length $\frac{x}{2}\sqrt{2}$.

Try This

Find the area of a parallelogram with base 15, side 10, and a 30° angle.

The following diagram demonstrates that two congruent triangles can be combined to form a parallelogram.

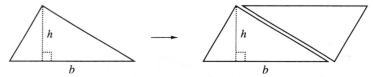

You can use this procedure to give a convincing argument that the area of the triangle is half the area of the parallelogram. This idea is summarized in Theorem 10.2.

◆ **THEOREM 10.2**

The area of a triangle equals half the product of the base b and the height h. $A = \frac{1}{2}bh$

Given: $\triangle ABC$ with base b and altitude h
Prove: $A = \frac{1}{2}bh$

Plan Draw $\overline{BD} \parallel \overline{AC}$ and $\overline{BD} \cong \overline{AC}$, producing $\square ABDC$. Prove that $\triangle ABC \cong \triangle DCB$ and that these triangles have equal areas. Then show that area $\triangle ABC = \frac{1}{2}$ area $\square ABDC = \frac{1}{2}bh$.

Theorem 10.2 can be used to prove that triangles with equal bases and equal altitudes have equal areas.

Example 2

Find each area.

a. $\triangle GHI$
b. $\triangle DEF$

Solution

a. $A = \frac{1}{2}bh = \frac{1}{2}(6)(12) = 36$

b. $A = \frac{1}{2}bh$

$b = \frac{1}{2}(12) = 6$

$h = \frac{12}{2}\sqrt{3} = 6\sqrt{3}$

$A = \frac{1}{2}(6)(6\sqrt{3}) = 18\sqrt{3}$

In a 30°–60°–90° triangle, the side opposite the 30° angle is one half the hypotenuse. The side opposite the 60° angle is one half the hypotenuse times $\sqrt{3}$.

Try This

Find the area of a 45°–45°–90° triangle with hypotenuse 12.

Class Exercises

Short Answer

1. Name each base of $\triangle ABC$ and give its corresponding altitude.
2. Give three different pairs of segment lengths that can be multiplied to find area $\triangle ABC$.
3. Find the area of a parallelogram with base 10 cm and height twice the base.
4. Find the area of a triangle with base 8 and height half the base.

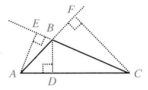

Sample Exercises

Find the area of each figure.

5.

6.

7.

8. A service station operator bought the parallelogram-shaped lot A and the adjoining lot B for $6 per square foot. What was the total cost?

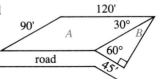

Discussion

9. Lines ℓ and m are parallel. Give a convincing argument that triangles EAF, EBF, and ECF all have the same area.
10. Do you think that if two parallelograms have the same area, they necessarily have equal bases and equal heights? If they have equal bases and equal heights, must they have equal areas? Explain.

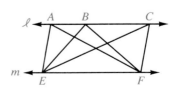

Exercises

A

Use ▱ JKLM to find each missing value.

	b	h	A
1.	24 m	6.3 m	___
2.	$7\sqrt{2}$	$5\sqrt{2}$	___
3.	9 cm	___	54 cm²
4.	x	___	$x^2 + 4x$
5.	$y + 2$	$y + 3$	___

Use △PQR to find each missing value.

	b	h	A
6.	12.4 m	5.4 m	___
7.	10 cm	___	35 cm²
8.	t	$2t$	___
9.	___	y	$2xy$

Find the area of each figure.

10.

11.

12.

13. Find the area of a parallelogram with base 24, another side 8, and height 6.4.

14. Find the height of a parallelogram that has a base of 12 and an area of 84.

15. Find the base of a triangle that has a height of 12 and an area of 96.

16. A triangle and a parallelogram each have an area of 64 and a height of 4. How do their bases compare?

17. A surveyor was able to find the area of the quadrilateral-shaped plot of land using the following information: $\overline{FG} \parallel \overline{CD}$, $\overline{FC} \parallel \overline{BG}$, $\overline{CD}$ is the perpendicular bisector of $\overline{AB}$, $CD = AB = 168$ m. Find the area of $FGBC$.

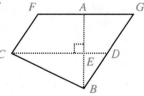

18. Find the cost of putting siding on the triangular region of the house to the right if siding costs 90 cents per square foot.

B

Find the area of each figure.

19.

20.

21.

Find *AB*. Each quadrilateral is a parallelogram.

22.

23.

24.

25. If area $\square ABCD$ = area $\square EFGH$ and $AB = 2EF$, how does this altitude to $\overline{AB}$ compare to the altitude to $\overline{EF}$?

26. The bases of two triangles are the same length. The altitude of the first triangle is 5 cm and the area of the second triangle is three times the area of the first. What is the altitude of the second triangle?

27. If the base and altitude of a triangle are doubled, what happens to the area of the triangle?

28. A triangle and a parallelogram have the same area. Give two possible descriptions of how their bases and altitudes might compare.

29. *M* is the midpoint of $\overline{RS}$. *N* is the midpoint of $\overline{MS}$. What is the area of the unshaded region? What is the ratio of the area of the shaded region to the area of $\triangle RST$?

30. Draw a triangle and a median. Show that the median divides the triangle into two regions with equal areas.

31. Draw a triangle and its three medians. Show that the six regions formed have equal areas.

32. A developer wanted to blacktop the shaded portion of this corner building site. How much will it cost if blacktopping costs $5 per square meter?

33. Find the area of a 30°–60°–90° right triangle if the hypotenuse has length 16.

34. Find the area of an equilateral triangle with side length 6.

35. Draw the triangle with coordinates $(2, 2)$, $(8, 4)$, and $(3, 9)$ on a coordinate grid. Use the altitude with endpoints $(2, 2)$ and $(6, 6)$ to find the area of the triangle.

36. Prove that parallelograms with equal bases and equal heights have equal areas.

37. What is the area of this sail in terms of the length *k* of the keel? If 1 sq ft of sail is needed to support 1 lb of total weight, what length keel would be used for a 125-lb person and a 35-lb glider? What length keel is needed to support you and a 35-lb glider?

C

38. Prove that the area of an equilateral triangle with sides of length *s* is $A = s^2\frac{\sqrt{3}}{4}$.

39. *ABCD* is a parallelogram and *X* is any point inside. Prove that the area of the shaded region is one half the area of the parallelogram.

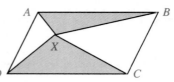

40. If triangles are cut off the corners of square *JKLM*, an octagon results.

a. If *JK* = *s*, prove that when a regular octagon results, $x = \frac{s}{2}(2 - \sqrt{2})$.

b. Use the figure and formula to find the area of a regular octagon whose side length is 2.

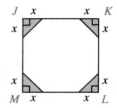

41. The length of an edge of the cube is 1.

a. Find the length of $\overline{BE}$ and $\overline{BH}$.

b. Find the area of △*BEG*.

c. Find the area of rectangle *BCHE*.

d. Find the area of △*BIC*.

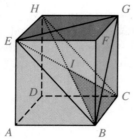

Critical Thinking

42. The ancient Babylonians used the formula $\frac{(a + c)(b + d)}{4}$ to find the area of a quadrilateral with side lengths *a*, *b*, *c*, and *d*. Does it work for rectangles? parallelograms? Explain.

43. How could you use the areas of triangles *LMN*, *LFM*, *MFN*, and *NFL* to prove that your hypothesis in Exercise 35 on page 79 is correct?

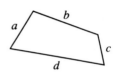

Mixed Review

Find each of the following.

1. *DE* = 5 Find *CE*.

2. *QR* = 10 Find *PR*.

3. *CE* = $8\sqrt{2}$ Find *CD*.

4. *QR* = 7 Find *PQ*.

5. *PR* = $12\sqrt{2}$ Find QR.

6. *CE* = 32 Find *DE*.

Enrichment

Heron's Formula

Heron of Alexandria (A.D. 75) is said to have discovered a formula that can be used to find the area of any triangle when its side lengths are known. In the formula, *a*, *b*, and *c*, are the lengths of the sides and $s = \frac{1}{2}(a + b + c)$.

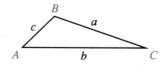

Heron's Formula

1. Use Heron's Formula to find the area of a right triangle with sides of lengths 5, 12, and 13.

2. Develop a formula for the area of an equilateral triangle with side length *t*.

area △*ABC* = $\sqrt{s(s-a)(s-b)(s-c)}$

OBJECTIVE: *Apply the formulas for the area of trapezoids and other quadrilaterals.*

10-3 Areas of Trapezoids and Other Quadrilaterals

EXPLORE

On lined paper, draw and cut out a trapezoid. Label its parallel segments and height as shown. Make a second trapezoid identical to the first. Can you put the trapezoids together to make a parallelogram? What is the area of the parallelogram? of the trapezoid?

You have seen that many area applications involve finding the area of a rectangle, a triangle, or a parallelogram. In this lesson you will see that the formula for finding the area of a trapezoid is also used in real-world situations.

In the Explore you may have discovered the formula for the area of a trapezoid. This formula, stated below, can also be found by dividing the trapezoid into two triangles.

◆ **THEOREM 10.3**

The area of a trapezoid equals half the product of the height h and the sum of the bases b_1 and b_2. $A = \frac{1}{2}h(b_1 + b_2)$

Given: trapezoid $ABCD$ with bases b_1 and b_2 and height h
Prove: $A = \frac{1}{2}h(b_1 + b_2)$

Proof Since $\overline{BC} \parallel \overline{AD}$, h is the height of both $\triangle ABC$ and $\triangle ACD$.
area of trapezoid $ABCD$ = area $\triangle ABC$ + area $\triangle ACD$
$= \frac{1}{2}b_1h + \frac{1}{2}b_2h$
$= \frac{1}{2}h(b_1 + b_2)$

Example 1

Find the area of the trapezoid.

Solution
$A = \frac{1}{2}h(b_1 + b_2) = \frac{1}{2}(16)(42 + 24) = 8(66) = 528$

Try This
Find the area of a trapezoid with height 8.5 and bases 13.4 and 9.2.

You can use formulas to find the areas of certain other quadrilaterals. A rhombus and a square have perpendicular diagonals. A figure with two distinct pairs of congruent, adjacent sides, often called a **kite,** also has perpendicular diagonals.

kite

The area of any quadrilateral with perpendicular diagonals can be found as follows.

$$\text{area } PQRS = \text{area } \triangle PQS + \text{area } \triangle RSQ$$
$$= \tfrac{1}{2} SQ \cdot PT + \tfrac{1}{2} SQ \cdot TR$$
$$= \tfrac{1}{2} SQ (PT + TR) = \tfrac{1}{2} SQ \cdot PR$$

This procedure is summarized in Theorem 10.4, where $d_1 = SQ$ and $d_2 = PR$.

 THEOREM 10.4

The area of any quadrilateral with perpendicular diagonals d_1 and d_2 is half the product of the lengths of its diagonals. $A = \tfrac{1}{2} d_1 d_2$

Class Exercises

Short Answer

1. The area of a trapezoid is its __?__ times the average of its bases.
2. The area of a square is its diagonal squared and then divided by __?__ .
3. The area of a kite is __?__ the product of the lengths of its diagonals.
4. The area of a trapezoid is the same as the sum of the areas of two __?__ .

Sample Exercises

Find the area of each figure.

5.
trapezoid

6.

7.

8. Find the area of a square with diagonal of length 6.

Discussion

9. A student claimed that the area of a trapezoid could be found simply by finding the product of the length of its median and its height. Do you think this is correct? Discuss how to give a convincing argument to support your conclusion.
(HINT: Consider Theorem 5.17.)

10. Any trapezoid $ABCD$ can be placed next to a trapezoid $CDFE$ congruent to it to form a parallelogram $ABEF$. How could you use this idea to give a convincing argument that the formula for the area of a trapezoid is correct?

Exercises

A

Find the area of each figure. The figures in Exercises 1–4 are trapezoids.

1.

2.

3.

4.

5.
kite

6.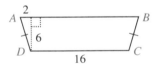
rhombus

7. A trapezoid has bases 15 and 9 and height 7. Find its median and its area.

8. Find the area of a trapezoid if the sum of its bases is 36 and its altitude is 17.

9. A trapezoid has bases 12 and 8 and area 384. Find its height.

10. A trapezoid has median 16 and height 4.8. Find its area.

11. The lengths of the diagonals of a rhombus are 24 and 18. Find its area.

12. Find the area of a quadrilateral that has perpendicular diagonals with lengths 15.4 and 9.7.

Is enough information given in each diagram to find the area of trapezoid *ABCD*? If so, find the area. If not, tell what information you need to find the area.

13.

14.
named
140ª

18

15.
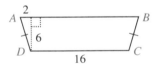

16. The diagonals of a quadrilateral are perpendicular. What is the area of the quadrilateral if one diagonal has length 54 m and the other has length 72 m?

17. Find the area of the trapezoidal cross section of a dam if it is 180 m tall and has bases 20 m and 60 m long.

18. Find the length of the side of a square that has area equal to that of a rhombus with diagonals 9 and 8.

19. Ms. Gray pays 15 cents per square foot each month to lease space in a shopping center. Each store front is 50 ft wide.

a. Find the monthly cost for her to lease store C.

b. How much does the owner receive each month if all the stores are leased at this rate?

20. Find the length of the long diagonal of a kite with short diagonal 16 cm and area 144 cm².

Find the area of each trapezoid. Theorems 7.7 and 7.8 about special triangles may be helpful.

21.

22.

B

23. Find the longer base of a trapezoid with shorter base 12, height 8, and area 128.

24. Find the height of a trapezoid with bases 16 and 21 and area 129.5.

25. One diagonal of a rhombus is 12 cm long and its area is 120 cm². Find the length of a side of the rhombus.

26. $BD = 10$ and $AB = 13$ in rhombus $ABCD$. Find its area.

27. Suppose the perimeter of rhombus $ABCD$ is 20 and $AC = 8$. Find the area of the rhombus.

28. Suppose $m \angle BAD = 60$ and $AB = 16$ in rhombus $ABCD$. Find the area of the rhombus.

29. $FGHI$ is a parallelogram and $IJ = FG$. Find GJ.

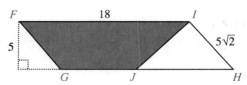

30. The ratio of the base to the height to the other base of a trapezoid is $2 : 3 : 4$. The area of the trapezoid is 117. Find the bases and the height.

Exercises 31–33 refer to these figures.

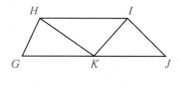

31. $\overline{AB}$, $\overline{DC}$, and $\overline{EF}$ are parallel. Find the area of hexagon $ABCFED$.

32. Find the area of rhombus $QSRT$ if $m \angle QSR = 50$ and the length of the shorter diagonal is 6. Use the table on page 636 or a calculator.

33. $GHIJ$ is a trapezoid and K is the midpoint of $\overline{GJ}$. Explain why the area of $GHIK$ is equal to the area of $HIJK$.

34. What is the effect on the area of a trapezoid if a base is doubled? a height is doubled? a median is doubled? both bases are doubled?

35. If *PQRS* is a trapezoid with bases $\overline{PQ}$ and $\overline{RS}$ and *X* is a point on $\overline{PQ}$, what is the ratio of the area of $\triangle RXS$ to the area of trapezoid *PQRS*?

36. Find the height of an isosceles trapezoid with 45° base angles and bases 8 and 14.

37. One base of a trapezoid is twice the other. The height is equal to the longer base and the area is 60. Find the height of the trapezoid.

38. A real estate agent estimated the area of a plot of land formed by regions *A*, *B*, *C*, and *D* between the road and the shore. What is the approximate area of this land?

39. A city planner measured the distances shown from the old oak, the big rock, and the flag to the east-west line. Other distances along the line are shown. What is the area of the city park?

C

40. Find the length of the diagonals of a rhombus that has area 120 and perimeter 52.

41. Prove that the two trapezoids formed by the segment joining the midpoints of the bases of a given trapezoid have equal areas.

42. *RSTU* is a trapezoid and *M* is the midpoint of $\overline{ST}$. Prove that the area of the shaded region is one half the area of *RSTU*.

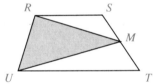

43. Suppose *NP* = 4 *LM*. How does the area of trapezoid *NLMP* compare to the area of triangle *LMO*?
Show that your answer is correct.

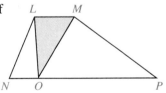

44. It is often necessary to find the area between a curve and the *x*-axis. Sometimes this area can be approximated by trapezoids. Find and add the areas of the shaded regions to estimate the area between this curve and the *x*-axis.

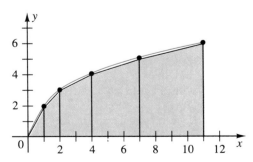

Critical Thinking

45. The following is a formula for finding the area of any quadrilateral that has all its vertices lying on a circle.

Area $= \sqrt{(s - a)(s - b)(s - c)(s - d)}$, where s is half the perimeter of the quadrilateral and a, b, c, and d are the lengths of its sides.

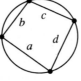

a. Explain how you could use measurement to see if the formula probably works.

b. Show that the formula works for the quadrilateral on the coordinate plane to the right.

c. Give a convincing argument that the formula does not work for a quadrilateral whose vertices are not all on a circle.

d. Show that the formula works when the quadrilateral is a square or a rectangle.

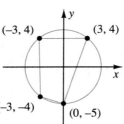

Mixed Review

$\overline{BD}$ and $\overline{CD}$ are tangents to $\odot O$. Complete each statement.

1. $m \angle OBD =$ ___
2. If $OD = 12$ and $AD = 7$, then the radius of the circle is ___ .
3. If $BD = 5$, then $CD =$ ___ .
4. If $BD = 8$ and $OB = 6$, then $AD =$ ___ .
5. $ED \cdot$ ___ $= CD^2$.

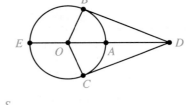

Find each of the following.

6. $m\,\widehat{RS} = 30$, $m\,\widehat{TQ} = 70$ Find $m \angle RPS$.
7. $m\,\widehat{RT} = 170$, $m\,\widehat{SQ} = 130$ Find $m \angle SPQ$.
8. $TP = 8$, $PS = 5$, $RP = 4$ Find PQ.
9. $TS = 16$, $PS = 6$, $PQ = 12$ Find RP.
10. $PS = 2$, $TP = x$, $RP = 5$, $PQ = x - 3$ Find PQ.

Calculator Investigation

It has been claimed that the formula $A = \frac{1}{4}\sqrt{4p^2q^2 - (b^2 + d^2 - a^2 - c^2)^2}$ gives the area of any quadrilateral with side lengths a, b, c, d and diagonal lengths p, q.

1. Test the formula by using a calculator. Check to see if the formula works for
  a. a rectangle with width 3 cm and length 4 cm
  b. an isosceles trapezoid with one base 25 cm, another base 15 cm, height 5 cm, and sides $5\sqrt{2}$ cm
  c. a kite with diagonals 8 cm and 11 cm, a pair of sides 5 cm, and a pair of sides $4\sqrt{5}$ cm

2. Show how the formula can be simplified to give the standard formula for the area of a square. Do the same for a rhombus.

10-4 Area of Regular Polygons

Use a compass to construct a regular hexagon. Cut the hexagon into six equilateral triangles. Can you place the triangles together to form two trapezoids? a parallelogram? Suppose the height of each triangle is a and the length of each side is s. Use the formulas for the areas of a triangle, a trapezoid, and a parallelogram to describe three different ways of showing that the area of the hexagon is $3as$.

You learned in Chapter 3 that a regular polygon is both equiangular and equilateral. A circle can be inscribed in any regular polygon, such as *ABCDE*. Also, a circle can be circumscribed about any regular polygon.

The **center** of a regular polygon is the center of its circumscribed circle. The **apothem** of a regular polygon is the distance from the center of the polygon to a side. It is also the radius of a circle inscribed in the polygon. The **radius** of a regular polygon is the distance from the center of the polygon to a vertex. It is also the radius of the circumscribed circle.

Recall from Lesson 10-1 that the perimeter of a polygon is the sum of the lengths of the sides of the polygon. To find the area of a regular polygon with side length s, it seems reasonable to break it up into triangles. In the case of a regular pentagon, there are five congruent triangles with height a and area $\frac{1}{2}sa$, so the area of a pentagon $= 5(\frac{1}{2}sa) = \frac{1}{2}a(5s)$. But $5s$ is the perimeter, so the area of a pentagon $= \frac{1}{2}ap$.

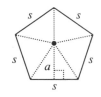

◆ **THEOREM 10.5**

The area of a regular polygon equals half the product of its apothem a and its perimeter p. $A = \frac{1}{2}ap$

Given: an n-sided regular polygon *ABCD* . . .
  with apothem a, sides s, and perimeter p

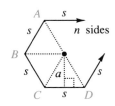

Prove: area of *ABCD* $= \frac{1}{2}ap$

Proof Consider the congruent triangles formed by drawing all the radii. For each of these, $A = \frac{1}{2}sa$. Since there are n such triangles, the area of *ABCD* . . . $= n(\frac{1}{2}sa)$ or $\frac{1}{2}a(ns)$. Since $ns = p$, the area of *ABCD* . . . $= \frac{1}{2}ap$.

The following example uses right triangle properties to find the apothem.

Example

Find the apothem and the area of this regular hexagon.

Solution

$m\angle AOC = 60$, so $m\angle AOB = 30$ *A central angle of a regular n-gon measures $\frac{360}{n}$.*

$a = 2\sqrt{3}$, $p = 6(4) = 24$ $\triangle AOB$ *is a 30°–60°–90° triangle.*

$A = \frac{1}{2}ap = \frac{1}{2}(2\sqrt{3})(24) = 24\sqrt{3}$

Try This

Find the apothem and area of a regular hexagon with 6-cm sides.

Class Exercises

Short Answer

Complete each statement.

1. The apothem of a regular polygon is the radius of its ___ circle.
2. The radius of a regular polygon is the radius of its ___ circle.
3. The perimeter of a regular hexagon with side length 8 is ___ .
4. The perimeter of a regular polygon with n sides, each of length s, is ___ .
5. The area of a regular octagon with perimeter 40 and apothem 6 is ___ .

Sample Exercises

6. Find the area of a regular pentagon with side 10 and apothem 6.9.
7. Find the area of a regular hexagon with side 5 and apothem $\frac{13}{3}$.

PQRSTU is a regular hexagon.

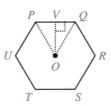

8. What is the measure of $\angle POQ$? How do you know?
9. What is the measure of $\angle VOQ$? Why?
10. What kind of triangle is $\triangle POV$?
11. Suppose $PO = 10$. Find PV and VO.
12. Suppose PQ is 16. Find PO, PV, and VO.

Discussion

13. Consider a polygon with an inscribed circle of radius r. As the number of sides of the polygon increases, give a convincing argument that the area of the polygon approaches $\frac{1}{2}rc$, where c is the circumference of the inscribed circle.

Exercises

A

Find the area of each regular polygon.

1.

2
$4\sqrt{3}$

2.

11
16

3.

9.5   11

4.

$4\sqrt{2}$

696

5.

14.5
12

6.

$8\sqrt{3}$ 16

Find the measure of $\angle 1$ and $\angle 2$ in each regular polygon.

7.

1 2

8.

1
2

9.

1
2

Complete the table for the regular polygons to the right.

Figure	r	s	p	a	A
10. triangle	12	___	___	___	___
11. triangle	___	$10\sqrt{3}$	___	___	___
12. triangle	___	___	$24\sqrt{3}$	___	___
13. square	___	16	___	___	___
14. square	$8\sqrt{2}$	___	___	___	___
15. square	___	___	___	$5\sqrt{2}$	___
16. hexagon	10	___	___	___	___
17. hexagon	___	___	___	$9\sqrt{3}$	___
18. hexagon	___	6	___	___	___

Determine whether each statement is true or false. If false, tell why.

19. An apothem of a regular polygon is a perpendicular bisector of a side.

20. An apothem of a regular polygon is the radius of the circumscribed circle.

21. A radius of a regular polygon bisects an angle of the polygon.

22. A radius of a regular polygon is a radius of the inscribed circle.

23. A radius of a regular polygon is always longer than an apothem.

24. Only regular polygons have apothems.

B

25. Find the area of a regular hexagon with apothem $3\sqrt{3}$.

26. Find the area of a regular hexagon with radius 8.

27. If the area of a regular hexagon is $36\sqrt{3}$ cm², find its apothem and the length of its side.

28. If the apothem of a regular hexagon is 5 m, find its perimeter and area.

29. An equilateral triangle and a regular hexagon are both inscribed in a circle with radius 6. Find the difference in their areas.

30. A side of a regular hexagon is s units long. Find the area of the hexagon.

31. A side of a regular hexagon is twice the square root of its apothem. Find the length of the apothem and the side.

32. The apothem of a regular pentagon is 13 cm. Find the area of the pentagon.

33. The perimeter of a regular pentagon is three more than seven times the approximate value of the apothem. The area of the pentagon is 440. Find the length of a side and an approximation for the apothem. You may wish to use a calculator.

34. A regular hexagon and a square are circumscribed about a circle with radius 10. How much more area does the square have?

35. A flower garden is to be made with a decorative brick border as shown by the shaded part of this figure. The inner square planting area is formed by connecting the midpoints of the 12-ft sides of the outer regular octagon. Find the area of the brick border.

36. If each side of a five-pointed star measures 5 in., find the area of the star. (HINT: Connect some of the vertices of the star to form a pentagon.)

37. Approximately how much would it cost to replace this hexagonal window if glass costs $2 per square foot?

2 ft

C

38. If a square building and a regular hexagonal building have the same perimeter, how do the areas of their floors compare?

39. If an equilateral triangle and a regular hexagon have equal perimeters, prove that the ratio of their areas is 2 to 3.

40. The area of a regular hexagon is $50\sqrt{3}$ sq ft. Find its perimeter and apothem.

41. A side of a regular octagon is 2 units long. How long is its apothem?

a

2

42. Find the difference in area between an inscribed and a circumscribed octagon if the radius of the circle is 6.

43. If the radius of a circle is doubled, what is the effect on the area of an octagon circumscribed about the circle?

44. The figure to the right shows the intersection of a cube and the plane that is the perpendicular bisector of the segment joining one pair of opposite vertices of the cube. This plane contains the midpoints of the six sides of the cube. Find the area of this regular hexagonal region if the length of each side of the cube is 3 cm.

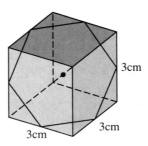

3cm

3cm

3cm

Critical Thinking

45. On a grid like those shown below, a "side" is a segment connecting a pair of dots. If one straight segment goes through more than two dots, it is still just one side. As shown below, four sides are the most possible for a convex polygon drawn on a 2×2 grid. Six sides are the most possible for a convex polygon on a 3×3 grid.

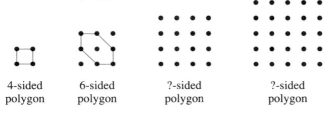

4-sided polygon   6-sided polygon   ?-sided polygon   ?-sided polygon

Is it reasonable to use this information to predict the maximum number of sides possible on a 4×4 and a 5×5 grid? Explain. Then find the maximum number of sides for a convex polygon on a 4×4 and a 5×5 grid. Find the perimeter and area of each polygon. What patterns, if any, do you discover?

46. Devise a formula for finding the area of any *n*-sided regular polygon with radius 1 unit and show why it works.
(HINT: You may want to consider trigonometric ratios.)

Algebra Review

Write an equation to solve each of the following.

1. Two trains leave town at the same time and travel in opposite directions. One travels 55 mph and the other travels 48 mph. In how many hours will the trains be 206 mi apart?

2. It takes Melissa 3 h to paint a certain area of a house. It takes Gayle 5 h to do the same job. How long would it take them, working together, to do the painting job?

3. Luis received grades of 85, 87, 91, and 89 on his chemistry tests. What must his grade be on the next exam if his average is to be at least 90?

4. There were 203 tickets sold for a school wrestling match. The price for students was $1.25. For nonstudents, the price was $2. The total amount of money collected was $310. How many of each type of ticket were sold?

Careers

Carpenter

Carpentry is the craft of cutting, joining, and finishing wood. A carpenter's work includes the design and assembly of cabinets, doors, wood floors, and other household items.

Carpenters often specialize in one of two broad areas. *Rough carpentry* involves working with frameworks for buildings and other large structures for which strength and stability are important. *Finish carpentry* includes the fitting of doors, window frames, and wood floors. A carpenter who has expertise in all areas of the field may want to go into business as a contractor and oversee work on a large project.

Because of the precision required in designing and assembling wood structures, carpenters must be able to read technical literature and blueprints. A thorough knowledge of geometry is important to carpenters as they interpret scale drawings, design structures with right angles, and construct wood floors to cover a specified area.

In the Middle Ages, apprentices worked with master craftsmen to learn the trade. In recent times, a combination of on-the-job training and courses of study at vocational schools provides training for many carpenters.

10-5 Ratios of Areas and Perimeters of Similar Polygons

An engineer who wants to decide whether it is more economical to put in two small heating ducts or one large one in a new building must compare the areas as well as the perimeters of two similar polygons.

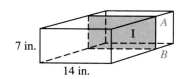

7 in.

14 in.

$$\frac{\text{perimeter of rectangle I}}{\text{perimeter of rectangle II}} = \frac{2 \cdot 7 + 2 \cdot 14}{2 \cdot 5 + 2 \cdot 10} = \frac{42}{30} = \frac{7}{5}$$

$$\frac{\text{area of rectangle I}}{\text{area of rectangle II}} = \frac{7 \cdot 14}{5 \cdot 10} = \frac{98}{50} = \frac{49}{25} = \left(\frac{7}{5}\right)^2$$

5 in.

10 in.

The cross-sectional area, which determines the amount of air moved, is about twice as large for the larger duct. But the perimeter of the larger duct, which determines the amount of material needed, is only $\frac{7}{5}$ that of the smaller duct. Since twice as much air is moved for only $\frac{7}{5}$ the cost, one large duct would be more economical than the two small ones.

Notice that in this example, the ratio of the perimeters is the same as the ratio of the sides, while the ratio of the areas is the *square* of the ratio of the sides.

◆ **THEOREM 10.6**

If two polygons are similar, then the ratio of their perimeters equals the ratio of the lengths of any pair of corresponding segments.

◆ **THEOREM 10.7**

If two polygons are similar, then the ratio of their areas equals the square of the ratio of the lengths of any pair of corresponding segments.

It is easy to show that the "segments" in the above theorems can be sides, radii, apothems, altitudes, medians, or diagonals.

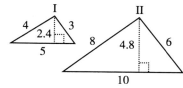

Example

Find the ratio of the areas of these similar triangles by
a. computing areas   **b.** using Theorem 10.7.

Solution

a. area of $\triangle I = \frac{1}{2}(5)(2.4) = 6$ area of $\triangle II = \frac{1}{2}(10)(4.8) = 24$

$\frac{\text{area of } \triangle I}{\text{area of } \triangle II} = \frac{6}{24} = \frac{1}{4}$

b. The scale factor of $\triangle I$ to $\triangle II$ is $1:2$.

$\frac{\text{area of } \triangle I}{\text{area of } \triangle II} = \left(\frac{1}{2}\right)^2 = \frac{1}{4}$

Try This

Find the ratio of the perimeters of the above triangles by computation and by using Theorem 10.6.

Class Exercises

Short Answer

1. The ratio of a pair of corresponding sides of two similar triangles is $3:2$. Find the ratio of the perimeters of these triangles.
2. The ratio of a pair of corresponding sides of two similar quadrilaterals is $2:1$. Find the ratio of the areas of these quadrilaterals.
3. The ratio of the corresponding altitudes of a pair of similar triangles is $2:3$. Find the ratio of the areas of the two triangles.
4. The ratio of the areas of two similar triangles is $16:1$. Find the ratio of the perimeters of the two triangles.

Sample Exercises

Find the ratio of the areas and perimeters of similar figures I and II.

5.

6.
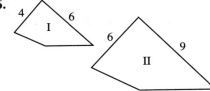

7. The ratio of the length of the hypotenuse of triangular sail I to the length of the hypotenuse of similar triangular sail II is $3:2$. The area of sail I is 24 sq ft. Find the area of sail II.
8. The ratio of the height of $\triangle CDE$ to the height of similar triangle $\triangle FGH$ is $3:5$. The perimeter of $\triangle FGH$ is 25 cm. Find the perimeter of $\triangle CDE$.

9. The areas of two regular hexagons are in the ratio $144:64$. Find the ratio of the side lengths of these polygons. Find the ratio of the perimeters of the polygons.
10. Find the length of the side and the apothem of pentagon II. How did you find these lengths.

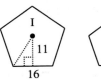

area of I: area of II = 12:9

Determine whether each statement is true or false. Explain your answers.

11. The ratio of the areas of two similar triangles is $9:4$, so the ratio of the lengths of corresponding sides of the triangles is $36:16$.
12. The ratio of the perimeters of any two regular polygons is the same as the ratio of the apothems of the polygons.
13. The ratio of the radii of two regular polygons with the same number of sides is $2:1$, so the ratio of the areas of these polygons is $4:1$.
14. A diagonal of one of two similar rectangles is three times the length of a diagonal of the other, so the area of the first rectangle is nine times the area of the other.
15. If you know that the perimeter of a figure is three times that of a second figure similar to it, then you know that any side of the first figure is three times the corresponding side in the second figure.

In each figure, $\overline{DE} \parallel \overline{CB}$. Find the ratio of the perimeters and areas of $\triangle ABC$ to $\triangle ADE$. How do you know?

16.

17.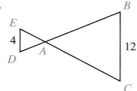

Discussion

18. Can you use Theorem 10.6 to conclude that the ratio of the perimeter of triangle I to the perimeter of triangle II is 15 to 10? Explain.

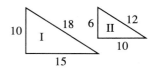

19. Suppose you have proved that Theorem 10.7 is true for similar triangles. Give a convincing argument that the theorem is also true for similar regular polygons.

Exercises

A

1. Find the ratio of the perimeters of these polygons using Theorem 10.6. Then check the ratio by computing perimeters.
2. Find the ratio of the areas of these polygons using Theorem 10.7. Then check the ratio by computing the areas.

Complete the table for a pair of similar figures.

Scale factor	Ratio of perimeters	Ratio of areas
3. $1:2$	___	___
4. $4:3$	___	___
5. $a:b$	___	___
6. ___	$2:5$	___
7. ___	$1:4$	___
8. ___	$x:y$	___
9. ___	___ $3:4$	$9:16$
10. ___	___ $2:\sqrt{5}$	$4:5$
11. ___	___ $\sqrt{p} \ \sqrt{q}$	$p:q$

12. The lengths of the sides of two squares are 4 and 8. Find the ratio of their perimeters.

13. Find the ratio of the areas for the squares in Exercise 12.
14. Two regular pentagons have side lengths in the ratio $13:20$. Find the ratio of their perimeters.
15. Find the ratio of the areas of the pentagons in Exercise 14.
16. $\overline{BD} \parallel \overline{AE}$, $AC:BC = 3:2$
Find the ratios of the areas and perimeters of $\triangle ACE$ and $\triangle BCD$.

17. The ratio of the areas of two regular pentagons is 25 : 36. Find the ratio of their
    a. sides   b. apothems   c. radii
    d. diagonals   e. perimeters
18. Two regular hexagons have apothems of 6 cm and 15 cm. The area of the smaller hexagon is 126 cm². Find the area of the larger hexagon.

B

19. A billboard that is 6 ft by 10 ft costs $100 per week to rent. If the cost is the same per square foot, how much should a 9 ft by 15 ft billboard cost?
20. A box manufacturer makes cubical boxes 1 ft on a side. If he doubles the dimensions, how much new material does he need to make the larger cubical box?
21. Suppose $\triangle ABC$ is a right triangle and $\overline{CD} \perp \overline{AB}$. If $CD = 8$, $AD = 16$, and $BD = 4$, find these ratios.

   a. $\dfrac{\text{area of } \triangle ACD}{\text{area of } \triangle CDB}$ b. $\dfrac{\text{area of } \triangle ACD}{\text{area of } \triangle ABC}$

22. Suppose points X, Y, and Z are the midpoints of the sides of $\triangle ABC$. Find the ratio area of $\triangle XYZ$: area of $\triangle ABC$.

23. Two radii of similar regular polygons are in the ratio 5 : 4. The sum of their perimeters is 20. Find the perimeters of these polygons.
24. The apothems of two similar regular polygons are in the ratio 3 : 5. If the area of the larger polygon is 35 square units, find the area of the smaller polygon.
25. A builder has a small tract of land valued at $45,000 and wants to lay out a similarly shaped tract of land that is $2\frac{1}{2}$ times as large. If the large tract costs the same amount per acre as the small tract, what would you expect the large tract to cost?
26. The area of a rectangular TV screen with a 7-in. diagonal is 25 sq in. How long, to the nearest inch, would the diagonal be for a TV screen with an area of 121 sq in.?
27. A small carpet is 1 m long. A larger, similarly shaped carpet is 3 m long. The small carpet sold for $65. If the price of a carpet is directly proportional to its area, what would you expect the large carpet to cost?
28. A solar panel is 3 m long and 2 m wide. Find the dimensions of a similarly shaped panel that has four times the area of this panel.
29. A scale drawing of the rectangular floor of a gym shows dimensions 9 cm by 24 cm. The scale factor is 1 cm : 6 m. Find the area of the gym floor. You may want to use a calculator.
30. A is the right triangular region and B is the trapezoidal region adjacent to A. Find the ratio of the areas of regions A and B.

C

31. A square-based pyramid is "sliced" by a plane that intersects edge $\overline{PR}$ at point Q and is parallel to base A. The result is the square cross section B. If $PQ:QR = 1:3$, find the ratio area of B:area of A.

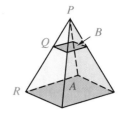

32. Suppose $\triangle ABC$ is a right triangle with hypotenuse c and legs a and b. Consider equilateral triangles on the sides of $\triangle ABC$ as shown. If the areas of these triangles are A_1, A_2, and A_3 as shown, show that $\frac{A_2}{A_1} + \frac{A_3}{A_1} = 1$.

33. Points W, X, Y, and Z are the midpoints of the sides of square $KLMN$. Find $\frac{\text{area of } KLMN}{\text{area of } WXYZ}$.

34. Points R, S, T, U, V, and W are the midpoints of the sides of regular hexagon $ABCDEF$. Find $\frac{\text{area of } ABCDEF}{\text{area of } RSTUVW}$.

35. Given a circle, find the ratio of the perimeter of a circumscribed square to the perimeter of an inscribed square. Find the ratio of their areas.

36. Determine x so that the area of $\triangle ADE = \frac{1}{2}$ area of $\triangle ABC$.

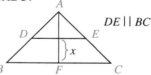

$DE \parallel BC$

37. A heating contractor made a duct with a square cross section with 12-in. sides. How long should one side of square duct be in order to have a cross section that carries twice as much air?

12 in.

12 in.

38. If the amount of air carried by a 10-in. square duct is to be increased by 30%, what size square duct should be used? (Round to the nearest half inch.)

Critical Thinking

39. How could you divide a triangle into three parts of equal area by drawing two lines parallel to a base? Trace this triangle, mark points on the altitude that make segments of selected lengths, and draw lines through them parallel to base $\overline{AC}$. Adjust your choices as needed to divide the triangle correctly. Generalize the procedure.

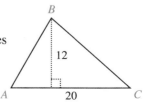

40. Points A', B', and C' are points of trisection of the sides of $\triangle ABC$. What fraction of the area of $\triangle ABC$ is the area of the shaded region? Make a conjecture. Then devise a way of testing your conjecture to see if it might be true. (HINT: Consider computer software for geometry or small-grid graph paper.)

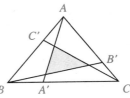

Mixed Review

$\overleftrightarrow{AC} \parallel \overleftrightarrow{DG}$ **Complete each statement.**

1. $\angle ABF$ and $\angle BFG$ are ___ angles.
2. $\angle DEH$ and ___ are corresponding angles.
3. $m \angle ABF + m \angle BFE = $ ___
4. If $m \angle BFG = 100$ and $m \angle FBE = 35$, then $m \angle ABE = $ ___.
5. If $m \angle BEG = 47$ and $m \angle CBF = 82$, then $m \angle EBF = $ ___.

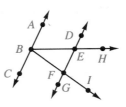

Determine whether each statement is true or false.

6. If two lines are cut by a transversal and a pair of alternate interior angles are supplementary, then the lines are parallel.
7. In a plane, two lines perpendicular to the same line are always parallel.
8. Two nonintersecting noncoplanar lines are called skew lines.

Quiz

Find the area of each figure.

1. rectangle

2. square

3. parallelogram

4. trapezoid

5. regular hexagon

6. rhombus

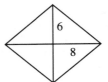

7. A trapezoid with area 42 has bases 4 and 10. Find its height.
8. Two similar polygons have sides in the ratio $4:7$. What is the ratio of their areas?
9. Two similar regular polygons have apothems 4 and 5. If the perimeter of the smaller polygon is 16, find the perimeter of the larger polygon.

OBJECTIVE: *Apply formulas for the circumference and arc length of a circle.*

10-6 Circumference and Arc Length

EXPLORE

The perimeter of a regular polygon with n sides that is inscribed in a circle with diameter d can be found by using this formula. perimeter $= nd\sin(\frac{180}{n})°$

Use a calculator or a computer to show what happens to the perimeter as larger and larger values of n are used.

When a computer graphics plotter draws "curved lines," the pen of the plotter really draws many short connected line segments that only appear to be curved.

As the number of sides of a regular polygon inscribed in a circle with diameter 1 increases, the perimeter of the polygon gets closer and closer to the length of the boundary or **circumference,** of its circumscribed circle. It approaches this as a limit, as suggested below.

5 sides

8 sides

10 sides

To look at this numerically, suppose the formula in the Explore is used to calculate the perimeter of regular polygons inscribed in a circle with diameter 1.

A Regular Polygon with Diameter 1

Number of sides	5	8	10	25	50	100
Perimeter	2.939	3.061	3.090	3.133	3.139	3.141

Notice that the perimeters seem to be approaching a limiting value. The following perimeters of 100-sided regular polygons inscribed in circles with different diameters were also calculated using the formula in the Explore.

Approximate Perimeters for 100-Sided Regular Polygons

Diameter of circumscribed circle	1	2	3	4	5
Perimeter	3.14	6.28	9.42	12.56	15.70
Ratio of perimeter to diameter	3.14	3.14	3.14	3.14	3.14

As you can see in the table, the ratio of the perimeter of the regular polygon to the diameter of its circumscribed circle, $3.14 : 1$, is always the same. This is also true for the ratio of the circumference of a circle to its diameter, as indicated in the following theorem.

◆ THEOREM 10.8

The ratio $\frac{C}{d}$ of the circumference C to the diameter d is the same for all circles.

The ratio $\frac{C}{d}$, which is the same for any circle, is denoted by π (the Greek letter pi). π is an irrational number, which means it cannot be written as an exact decimal. Note that π is the limiting value for the perimeter of regular polygons inscribed in circles with diameter 1. (See the first table.)

Some approximations of π are 3.14, $3\frac{1}{7}$ and 3.14159.

Since $\frac{C}{d} = \pi$ no matter what size the circle is, you can use this equation to derive the formula for finding the circumference of any circle. $\frac{C}{d} = \pi$, so $C = \pi d = 2\pi r$.

The circumference of a circle with radius r and diameter d is given by the formula $C = \pi d = 2\pi r$.

Example 1

Find the circumference of a circle with radius 8 cm.

> #### Solution
> $d = 2r$, so $d = 2 \cdot 8 = 16$
> $C = \pi d$
> $C = \pi \cdot 16$ or 16π cm   *Leave the answer in terms of π unless asked to give an approximate answer.*

Try This

Use $\pi \approx 3.14$ to find the approximate circumference of a circle with diameter 10 cm.

The **length of an arc** of a circle, ℓ, is a fractional part of the circumference of the circle. In this circle, $60°$ out of a possible $360°$ are cut by the angle, so ℓ is $\frac{60}{360}$ or $\frac{1}{6}$ of the circumference. You can describe the length of any arc using a ratio as in the following theorem.

◆ THEOREM 10.9

The ratio of the length of an arc of a circle, ℓ, to the circumference c equals the ratio of the degree measure of the arc, m, to 360.

$\frac{\ell}{C} = \frac{m}{360}$ or $\frac{\ell}{2\pi r} = \frac{m}{360}$

Example 2

Find the length of a 30° arc of a circle with a 10-cm radius.

Solution

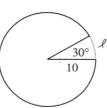

$$\frac{\ell}{2\pi r} = \frac{m}{360}$$

$$\frac{\ell}{2\pi \cdot 10} = \frac{30}{360} \quad \text{Replace } r \text{ with 10 and } m \text{ with 30.}$$

$$\frac{\ell}{20\pi} = \frac{1}{12}, \text{ so } \ell = \frac{5}{3}\pi \text{ cm}$$

Try This

Find the degree measure of an arc of length 6π of a circle with radius 9.

Class Exercises

Short Answer

Determine whether each statement is true or false.

1. The circumference of a circle circumscribed about a regular polygon can be approximated by the perimeter of the polygon as the number of its sides increases.
2. The ratio of the circumference to the diameter of a circle gets larger if the radius of the circle is increased.
3. The value of π is found by dividing the circumference of a circle by its radius.
4. π is represented exactly by the decimal 3.14.
5. The length of an arc and the degree measure of an arc are the same.
6. A formula for the circumference of a circle is $C = \pi d$.

Sample Exercises

7. Find the circumference of a circle with diameter 10.
8. Find the circumference of a circle with radius 8.
9. The diameter of a bike gear is 21 cm. Choose the more useful approximation for π, $\frac{22}{7}$ or 3.14, and find the circumference of the gear.
10. Find the length of an arc with measure 62 in a circle with diameter 14.
11. $\triangle ABC$ is an equilateral triangle and A is the center of a circle with radius 5. Find the length of $\overarc{EF}$ and $\overarc{ED}$.

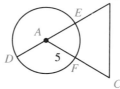

Discussion

12. Do you think a regular polygon with 1000 sides has perimeter equal to the circumference of its circumscribed circle? Explain your reasoning.
13. The diameter of two circles may differ and the circumferences may differ. Discuss what property of the circles is always the same and why.
14. Without using any formulas, give a convincing argument that the information given about this figure cannot be correct.

Exercises

A

Complete the table. Where appropriate, leave answers in terms of π.

	Radius	Diameter	Circumference
1.	4	—	—
2.	—	6	—
3.	—	—	8π
4.	—	—	16

5. Give an approximation to the circumference of a circle with radius 28 cm. Use $\frac{22}{7}$ for π.
6. Give an approximation to the circumference of a circle with radius 5 cm. Use 3.14 for π.
7. A circle has circumference 31.4 cm. Find its approximate diameter.

Complete the table.

	Radius	Degree measure of arc	Length of arc
8.	5	60	—
9.	8	—	4π
10.	$\frac{10}{\pi}$	—	2
11.	—	20	2π

12. A satellite is in orbit at a constant altitude of 300 mi. It is tracked by a ground station through an angle of 45°. How far, in miles, did the satellite travel?
13. The diameter of a bike wheel is 63 cm. How far does the bike move with one revolution of the wheel?

Find the perimeter of each figure. All arcs are arcs of circles.

14.

15.

B

Find the circumference of each circle.

16.

Square

17.

Equilateral triangle

18.

Regular hexagon

19. If a gallon of paint covers 400 sq ft, how many gallons are required to paint a silo (excluding the roof) that is 10 ft in diameter and 50 ft high?

20. A round tower with a 10-m circumference is surrounded by a fence that is 2 m from the tower all around. How long is the fence?

21. On a large machine, the centers of two pulleys are 16 ft apart and the radius of each pulley is 24 in. How long a belt is needed to wrap around both pulleys?

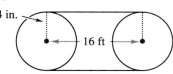

22. The large sprocket on the pedals of a bicycle has 50 teeth and the small sprocket on the wheel has 20 teeth. When the pedals make two complete revolutions, how many revolutions does the wheel make?

23. diameter $AB = 24$, $m \angle BAC = 18$
Find the length of $\overset{\frown}{BC}$.

24. If the radius of the circle is 6, find the length of $\overset{\frown}{UV}$.

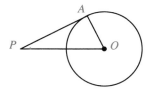

25. diameter $AD = 16$, measure of $\overset{\frown}{AC} = x$, measure of $\overset{\frown}{BD} = 2x$
Find the lengths of $\overset{\frown}{AC}$ and $\overset{\frown}{BD}$.

26. $PA = 12$, $PO = 13$
PA is tangent to $\odot O$ at A.
Find the circumference of the circle.

27. The proportion $\frac{\ell}{C} = \frac{m}{360}$ was given in Theorem 10.9. Use it to derive a formula for (a) finding ℓ when m and C are known and (b) finding m when ℓ and C are known.

28. Give a formula for finding the length of a semicircular arc of a circle with radius r.

29. Give a formula for finding the length of an arc intercepted by an angle of 90°.

C

30. Assume that the earth's equator is a perfect circle with radius 4000 mi and that a wire hoop is fitted tightly around it. Suppose a 40-ft piece of wire has been spliced into the hoop and the hoop is held equidistant from the earth's surface. What would be the distance between the hoop and the earth?

31. Four posts with 3-in. radii are bound together with a wire. Find the length of the shortest wire that will go around them.

3 in.

Critical Thinking

32. Suppose the curve AB is drawn on a graphics screen of a computer. Circles and segments of selected sizes can be moved around the screen. The circle diameters and segment lengths can be automatically determined at any time. Describe how you would estimate the length of the curve (a) using segments and (b) using circles. Include drawings of your procedures.

Algebra Review

Factor completely.

1. $10x^3 - 90x$
2. $m^4 - 625$
3. $8t^4 - 8$
4. $16y^2 + 16$
5. $5x^2 - 10x - 15$
6. $y^2x + 5yx + 6x$
7. $18 - 2x^2$
8. $st^2 - 64s$
9. $2x^2 + 5x - 12$

Computer Activity

The following is a program for calculating perimeters for regular polygons inscribed in a circle with diameter 1. It uses the formula given in the Explore.

Computer languages usually require angle or arc measures to be given in special units called *radians*, instead of degrees. A 180° arc of a circle with radius 1 has a measure of π radians. Note that this idea is used in line 30.

```
10 PRINT "HOW MANY SIDES FOR THE POLYGON?"
20 INPUT N
30 LET P = N*SIN(3.1415926/N)
40 PRINT "SIDES: "; N, "PERIMETER: "; P
50 LET N = N+1
60 IF N < 200 THEN 30
70 END
```

Exercises

1. Run the program. What can you say about the perimeters of polygons with greater and greater numbers of sides? Why is this true?
2. How can you change the program so that the perimeters produced are even closer to the circumference of the circumscribed circle?
3. How large must N be to produce a perimeter so close to the circumference of the circumscribed circle that it is correct to the hundred thousandth's place?

10-7 Areas of Circles, Sectors, and Segments

You have seen that, as the number of sides of a regular polygon inscribed in a circle increases, the perimeter of the polygon gets closer and closer to a fixed number called the circumference of the circle. In a similar way, as the number of sides of a regular polygon inscribed in a circle increases, its *area* gets closer and closer to a limiting value called the area of the circle. The apothem *a* of the regular polygon gets closer and closer to the radius *r* of the circle and the perimeter *p* of the polygon gets closer and closer to the circumference *C* of the circle.

A farmer might need to find the area of the circular field to calculate irrigation costs.

The variables in the formula for the area of a regular polygon can be replaced by their limiting values to produce a formula for the area of a circle.

area of polygon $= \frac{1}{2}ap$

area of circle $= \frac{1}{2}rc$ *Replace "polygon" with "circle," a with r, and p with c.*
area of circle $= \frac{1}{2}r(2\pi r)$ *Replace C with $2\pi r$.*
area of circle $= \pi r^2$

◆ **THEOREM 10.10**

     The area of a circle with radius *r* is given by the formula $A = \pi r^2$.

Example 1
Find the area of a circle with radius $5\sqrt{2}$.

$$A = radius^2 (\pi)$$

Solution
$A = \pi r^2$
$A = \pi(5\sqrt{2})^2$
$A = 50\pi$ The area of the circle is 50π square units.

Try This
Find the radius of a circle that has area 64π.

A **sector** of a circle is a region formed by two radii and an arc of a circle. The region *HOJ* shaded in this circle is a sector. The region bounded by the radii and major arc *HIJ* is also a sector.

The area of sector *HOJ* is $\frac{60}{360}$ of the area of the whole circle, or $\frac{60}{360}(36\pi)$ square units. This suggests the following theorem.

◆ THEOREM 10.11

The area of a sector, with arc degree measure m, of a circle with radius r is given by the formula $A = \frac{m}{360}(\pi r^2)$.

The formula can be rewritten as the proportion $\frac{A}{\pi r^2} = \frac{m}{360}$.

Example 2

Find the area of sector AOB.

Solution

$A = \frac{m}{360}(\pi r^2)$

$A = \frac{45}{360}(\pi\, 10^2)$

$A = \frac{100\pi}{8} = \frac{25\pi}{2}$

The area of sector AOB is $\frac{25\pi}{2}$ square units.

Try This

Find the area of the unshaded sector of circle O.

Example 3

Find the area of the blue region if $m\angle MON = 60$.

Solution

area of sector $MON = \frac{60}{360}(\pi\, 6^2) = 6\pi$

area of sector $POQ = \frac{60}{360}(\pi\, 3^2) = \frac{3}{2}\pi$

area of blue region $= 6\pi - \frac{3}{2}\pi = \frac{9}{2}\pi$

Try This

Find the area of the green region.

A **segment of a circle** is a region formed by an arc and its chord, as shown by the shaded area in the circle below. The area of the segment can be found by subtracting the area of $\triangle DOF$ from the area of sector DOF.

Example 4

Find the area of the shaded segment of circle O.

Solution

area of sector $DOF = \frac{60}{360}(64\pi)$

area of $\triangle DOF = \frac{1}{2}8(4\sqrt{3}) = 16\sqrt{3}$ $\triangle OEF$ is a $30°$–$60°$–$90°$ triangle, so $EF = 4$ and $EO = 4\sqrt{3}$.

area of segment $= \frac{60}{360}(64\pi) - 16\sqrt{3}$ area of shaded segment $=$

$= \frac{32\pi}{3} - 16\sqrt{3}$ area of sector DOF − area of $\triangle DOF$

Try This

Find the area of the shaded segment if $\angle DOF$ is a right angle.

Class Exercises

Short Answer

Complete each statement.

1. To find the area of a circle, square its radius and multiply by ___ .
2. The area of a sector of a circle with a 90° arc is ___ (fraction) of the area of the whole circle.
3. To find the area of a segment of a circle, you can subtract the area of a triangle from the area of a ___ .
4. The ratio of the area of a sector to the area of the whole circle equals the ratio of the measure of the arc of the sector to ___ .

Sample Exercises

5. Find the area of a circle with radius 5.
6. A circle has radius 9. Find the area of a sector of the circle with arc measure 30°.
7. Find the area of a circle with diameter 12.
8. Find the area of a sector of a circle with radius $\sqrt{7}$. The central angle of the sector is 120°.
9. Find the area of circle with radius 2. Find the area of a circle with radius twice as long. How does the area of the second circle compare with that of the first?

Discussion

10. When given the radius, a student concluded that the area of the circle was 12 square units and the area of the sector was 2 square units. Use only the information in the figure to give a convincing argument that the student's conclusion is incorrect.

11. A student concluded that the area of the shaded segment was less than 4 square units. Without finding its exact area, give a convincing argument that this conclusion is incorrect.

Exercises

A

Find the area of each circle with the given radius. Give your answers in terms of π.

1. 4   2. 6.5   3. 7   4. π 5. $\sqrt{5}$

Find the area of each circle with the given diameter.

6. 8   7. 9.5   8. 4π 9. $4\sqrt{2}$ 10. 98

Find the radius of each circle with the given area.

11. 121π 12. 289π 13. 8π 14. 100   15. 1.6π

Find the area of each circle with the given circumference.

16. 4π **17.** 8π **18.** $\sqrt{5}\pi$ **19.** 20   **20.** 3.5π

Find the area of each shaded sector. Give your answer in terms of π.

21.
     22.
     23.

Find the approximate area of each sector. Use 3.14 for π.

24. central angle 45°, radius 3 cm
25. central angle 15°, radius 10 cm
26. central angle 160°, diameter 6 cm
27. central angle 50°, diameter 14 cm

Find the area of each shaded segment.

28.
     29.
     30.

B

31. If the area of a sector is one tenth the area of the circle, find the measure of the central angle of the sector. If the area of the sector is $\frac{1}{n}$ the area of the circle, find the measure of the central angle of the sector.

32. Two circles have radii 3 cm and 5 cm. Find the ratio of their areas.

33. The areas of two circles are in the ratio 16 to 9. Find the ratio of their radii.

34. Find the area of both the inscribed and circumscribed circles of a square whose sides are 4 cm.

35. Find the degree measure of the arc of a sector with area 36π if the area of the circle is 144π.

Find the area of the shaded regions in each square.

36.
     37.
     38.

39. A pipe 12 in. in diameter carries how many times as much water as a pipe 10 in. in diameter?

40. Write a formula for the area of a circle in terms of the diameter d of the circle.

41. The figure to the right represents the cross section of pipe $\frac{1}{4}$ in. thick that has an inside diameter of 3 in. Find the area of the shaded region.

C

42. Circles of equal radii are packed in a rectangle as shown. If you threw darts at this "target," what percent of the time would you expect to hit the shaded region? (Assume all darts hit the target.)

43. If $BC = 2AB$, what fraction of the circle is shaded?

44. A goat is tied to the corner of a house on a 33-m rope. There is a fence as shown. What is the total grazing area for the goat?

45. Given a right $\triangle ABC$, its circumscribed circle, and semicircles on the two legs, show that the sum of the areas of the two shaded regions is equal to the area of $\triangle ABC$.

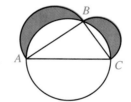

46. Given point G between E and F, and semicircles on $\overline{EG}$, $\overline{GF}$, and $\overline{EF}$ as shown, if $\overline{GH} \perp \overline{EF}$, show that the area of the shaded region is equal to the area of the circle with $\overline{GH}$ as diameter. (HINT: Consider the right triangle $\triangle EHF$.)

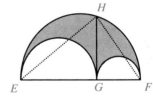

47. If $\triangle ABC$ is an equilateral triangle, what fraction of the triangle is shaded?

48. In the figure the small circle is tangent to four circular arcs. What fraction of the large circle is shaded?

49. Conduit for telephone cable is sized so that it carries three cables (each circular and tangent to the conduit and to each other) that are each 1 cm in radius. What fraction of the conduit is filled?

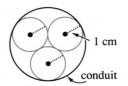

1 cm

conduit

Critical Thinking

50. An official archery tournament target has four concentric rings and a center bull's eye. Each ring is 4.8 in. wide and the diameter of the bull's eye is 9.6 in. Draw a picture, analyze this situation, and estimate the probability of hitting the bull's eye. Then figure out the probability and compare it with your estimate. You may assume that every arrow shot hits the target.

51. The Pythagorean Theorem states that the sum of the areas of squares on the two legs of a right triangle equals the area of the square on the hypotenuse. What if figures other than squares were considered? Would the relationship still be true? Investigate this situation and support your conclusion. Try it with more than one type of figure.

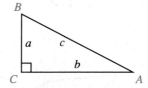

Mixed Review

Determine whether each statement is true or false.

1. If *ABDC* is a rectangle, then $\overline{AD}$ is perpendicular to $\overline{CB}$.
2. If $\overline{AD} \cong \overline{CB}$, then *ABDC* is a rhombus.
3. If $\overline{AD}$ is perpendicular to $\overline{CB}$, then *ABDC* is a rhombus.
4. If *ABDC* is a square, then $\angle ADC \cong \angle ADB$.
5. $\overline{AD} \cong \overline{CB}$ if $\overline{AB} \cong \overline{CD}$ and $\overline{AC} \cong \overline{BD}$

CRITICAL THINKING

Recognizing the Role of Propaganda

Propaganda is any systematic promotion of ideas to further a cause. The term comes from the Latin word meaning "propagate." Sometimes we make incorrect decisions because we react to propaganda that someone uses to persuade us to a point of view. Consider the following examples.

Example 1 *Jumping on the Bandwagon*
Ben saw this advertisement in a magazine.

"Olympic athletes choose Panther running shoes."

He felt that if Olympic athletes liked Panthers the best, they must be good running shoes. Ben bought two pairs of Panthers and later decided that he did not really like them.

Analysis

This form of propaganda tries to convince individuals that they will take on characteristics of others if they imitate their behavior.

Example 2 *Appealing to Authority or Testimony*
A television ad shows Bert Medico, an actor who plays a doctor on a soap opera, reading a report issued by the National Medical Doctors Association (NMDA). It describes the medical value of the pain reliever NoAche. A viewer likes Bert Medico, respects the NMDA, and goes to the store to buy NoAche. Later, she finds it upsets her stomach.

Analysis

In this situation, the fact that Bert plays a doctor on a soap opera carries over, as the viewer evaluates what Bert says during the ad. So it appears that the NMDA report on NoAche is accepted by a well-known doctor.

Example 3 *Avoiding the Question*
A congressman is asked if he is in favor of a plan to build a controversial highway. He responds, "I'm sure the people of this county will use wise judgement as they decide how to vote on this plan. I have always had great confidence in the decision-making process at our state and local levels."

Analysis

Listeners would think the congressman favors their view, as everyone likes to feel he or she uses good judgement in making decisions. The congressman did not actually state his position on the planned highway.

Example 4 *Transferring a Feeling*
A television ad for a sportscar shows a beautiful horse racing across a lush pasture as it shows the automobile. Marla watches the ad and tells a friend, "That car is a beauty—it can really fly."

Analysis

Marla equated the speed of the horse with the speed of the car in the advertisement. That is, she transferred her feelings about the horse to the car.

Exercises

1. Give another example of each of the above forms of propaganda.

Identify the type of propaganda involved in each situation.

2. Singh chose to buy a baseball because it had Babe Ruth's name on it.
3. Kara wanted to stay out later on weekends because, "All my friends get to stay out later."
4. When a store clerk was asked if an item had a guarantee, she said, "I have never had anyone bring one of those back because it did not work properly."
5. Think of another form of propaganda and give an example of its use.

CHAPTER SUMMARY

Vocabulary

altitude (10-2)	boundary (10-1)	radius of a regular polygon (10-4)
apothem (10-4)	circumference (10-6)	region (10-1)
area (10-1)	kite (10-3)	sector of a circle (10-7)
base (10-2)	perimeter (10-1)	segment of a circle (10-7)

Key Ideas

1. Every closed region has an area which is a unique positive number.
2. If two closed figures are congruent, then they have equal areas.
3. The area of a region is the sum of all of its nonoverlapping parts.
4. The following is a list of area formulas for polygonal and circular regions.

   Rectangle $A = \ell w$ Triangle $A = \frac{1}{2}bh$ Regular polygon $A = \frac{1}{2}ap$

   Square $A = s^2$ Trapezoid $A = \frac{1}{2}h(b_1 + b_2)$ Circle $A = \pi r^2$

   Parallelogram $A = bh$ Rhombus $A = \frac{1}{2}d_1 d_2$ Sector $A = \frac{m}{360}(\pi r^2)$

5. The area of any quadrilateral with perpendicular diagonals is half the product of the length of its diagonals.
6. If two polygons are similar, then the ratio of their perimeters equals the ratio of any pair of corresponding sides.
7. If two polygons are similar, then the ratio of their areas equals the square of the ratio of the lengths of any pair of corresponding sides.
8. In a circle with radius r, length of an arc ℓ, and measure of the arc m, $\frac{\ell}{2\pi r} = \frac{m}{360}$.
9. The area of a segment of a circle can be found by subtracting the area of a triangle from the area of a sector.

CHAPTER REVIEW

10-1

1. If the area of a square is 64, find its perimeter.
2. Find the area of a rectangle with length 6 and diagonal 10.
3. Find the perimeter of a rectangle with width 3.2 and area 22.4.

10-2

4. Find the perimeter and area of a 30°–60°–90° triangle if the hypotenuse has a length of 20.
5. Find the area of a parallelogram with base 8 and height 4.2.

Find the area of each figure.

6.

$3\sqrt{2}$

3   4

7.

9   6

10

8.

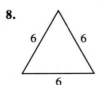

6   6

6

10-3

9. A trapezoid has an area of 28 cm² and bases 3 cm and 11 cm. Find its height.
10. Find the area of a rhombus with diagonals 4 and 10.
11. One diagonal of a kite is 4.3 cm long. The area is 13.33 cm. Find the length of the other diagonal.

10-4

Find the area of each regular polygon.

12.

13.
5 m

14.
10

10-5

Two similar polygons have apothems of length 9 and 25. Determine whether each statement is true or false.

15. The ratio of their sides is 9 : 25.
16. The ratio of their areas is 3 : 5.
17. The ratio of their perimeters is 9 : 25.

18. Two similar polygons have perimeters 7 and 5. If the area of the smaller polygon is 75, find the area of the larger polygon.

10-6

19. Find the circumference of circle O.

12

20. A square with area 36 is inscribed in a circle. Find the circumference of the circle.
21. Find the length of a 70° arc of a circle with radius 10.

10-7

Find the area of each shaded region.

22.
6
80°

23.
120°
8

Summary & Review   481

CHAPTER TEST

Find the area of each figure.

1. a rectangle with length 6 and width $4\sqrt{2}$
2. a rectangle with length 12 and diagonal 13
3. a rhombus with one diagonal 12 and perimeter 40
4. a parallelogram with sides 8 and 10 and an included angle of 60°
5. a 45°–45°–90° triangle with hypotenuse $6\sqrt{2}$
6. a regular hexagon with apothem $5\sqrt{3}$
7. an isosceles trapezoid with bases 4 and 12 and legs 5
8. a sector of a circle with circumference 10π and central angle 40°

Find the area of each figure.

9.

16

9

Parallelogram

10.

8·12

6

8

Rhombus

11.

10

Regular hexagon

Find the area of each shaded region.

12.

2

Regular hexagon

13.

90°

4

4

14.

100°

5

Two similar polygons have perimeters 40 and 50. Find each of the following.

15. the ratio of their sides
16. the ratio of their apothems
17. the ratio of their areas

18. Find the perimeter of a square if its area is 20 cm².

Find x.

19.

x

60°

10

20.

10π

x

21.

3

circumference = x

DISCRETE MATH

Geometric Probability

Geometry plays a role in many probability problems. Recall that the probability of an event that can occur in m ways out of n equally possible ways is the ratio $\frac{m}{n}$. For example, in rolling a die, the probability of the event that an even digit occurs is $\frac{3}{6}$. This is because there are three even digits (2, 4, 6) out of six possible outcomes (1, 2, 3, 4, 5, 6).

In the above example, the possibilities were finite and the problem could be solved by counting the desired outcomes. In other cases, we must measure the outcomes and compare the measures associated with the events.

Example 1

Consider the event of a number being chosen at random on the segment $\overline{AB}$ below. Find the probability that the number is between C and D.

Solution

Since $AB = 9$ and $CD = 1$, the probability is $\frac{1}{9}$.

In other situations, the probability is determined by comparing the area of two regions.

Example 2

Find the probability that a dart hitting the dartboard below lands in one of the shaded areas.

All horizontal and vertical segments measure 1 ft.

Solution

The dartboard has an area of 7 sq ft. The shaded areas cover 2 sq ft. Thus, the probability that the dart lands in a shaded area is $\frac{2}{7}$.

Exercises

1. A point is chosen at random on $\overline{AE}$. Find the probability that the point is between C and D.

2. A point is chosen at random on $\overline{RS}$. Find the probability that the point is between T and U.

3. A point is chosen at random inside square $EFGH$. Find the probability that the point lies inside the shaded region.

4. Suppose a dart is thrown at a regular hexagonal dartboard with the design shown below. Find the probability that the dart hits one of the shaded regions.

5. If a point is chosen at random inside trapezoid $ABCD$, find the probability that it lies inside trapezoid $ABEF$. Find the probability that the point lies inside trapezoid $EFDC$.

Surface Area and Volume

A cylindrical storage tank has a diameter of 10 m and a height of 30 m. Find the volume of the tank.

PRISMS AND PYRAMIDS

OBJECTIVE: *Identify the bases, lateral faces, and edges of a prism and determine its lateral area and surface area.*

11-1 Surface Area of Prisms

Fold a piece of paper into fourths. Unfold and tape the edges together as shown to construct a model of the lateral faces of a square-based prism.

1. By varying the number of folds, construct models with triangular, pentagonal, hexagonal, and octagonal bases.
2. How many pairs of parallel faces does each have?
3. Form a generalization.

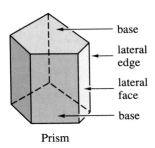

The models that you constructed in the Explore are examples of three-dimensional solids. A **polyhedron** is a solid made up of polygonal regions called **faces.** The sides and vertices of the faces are called, respectively, **edges** and **vertices** of the polyhedron. A **prism** is a polyhedron with a pair of identical faces, called **bases,** that lie in parallel planes. The vertices of these bases are joined to form parallelogram-shaped regions called **lateral faces.** Adjacent lateral faces share a common edge called a **lateral edge.** An **altitude** of a prism is a segment that is perpendicular to both bases with endpoints in the planes of the bases. The length of an altitude is called the **height**(h) of the prism.

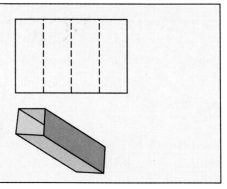

base
lateral edge
lateral face
base

Prism

As shown below, a prism is named by the shape of its bases. If the lateral edges of a prism are perpendicular to its bases, the prism is called a **right prism.** If the lateral edges are not perpendicular to the bases, the prism is an **oblique prism.**

Right triangular prism

Oblique pentagonal prism

Right trapezoidal prism

Imagine cutting a cube apart and laying its surface flat. The area of these six squares is called the surface area of the cube. This gives an idea of what is meant, in general, by the **surface area** of a solid.

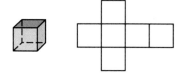

The sum of the areas of the lateral faces of a prism is called the **lateral area** (*LA*) of the prism. When you add the area of the two bases to the lateral area, you obtain the **surface area** (*SA*) of the prism. For example, in this right prism the lateral area can be calculated by adding together the areas of the lateral faces.

$LA = e_1h + e_2h + e_3h + e_4h + e_5h$
$LA = (e_1 + e_2 + e_3 + e_4 + e_5)h$
$LA = ph$ (The sum of the edge-lengths of one base is the perimeter, *p*.)

◆ **THEOREM 11.1**

The lateral area of a right prism is equal to the perimeter *p* of a base times the height *h* of the prism. $LA = ph$

The surface area is the sum of the lateral area and twice the area of a base *B*. $SA = ph + 2B$

Example 1

Find the lateral area and the surface area of the right triangular prism shown.

Solution

$LA = ph$
$ = (3 + 4 + 5) \cdot 7$
$ = 12 \cdot 7$
$ = 84 \text{ cm}^2$

$SA = LA + 2B$
$ = 84 + 2\left(\tfrac{1}{2} \cdot 3 \cdot 4\right)$ *The 3–4–5 triangular bases are right triangles.*
$ = 96 \text{ cm}^2$

Try This

Find the lateral area and the surface area of a right triangular prism whose base edges have lengths 5, 12, and 13 and whose height is 18.

Example 2

Find the lateral area and the surface area of the right equilateral triangular-based prism shown, if $AB = 14$ and $AD = 20$.

Solution

$LA = ph$
$ = (14 + 14 + 14) \cdot 20$
$ = 42 \cdot 20 = 840$

$SA = ph + 2B$
$ = 840 + 2\left(\tfrac{1}{2} \cdot 14 \cdot 7\sqrt{3}\right)$
$ = (840 + 98\sqrt{3})$

Try This

Find the lateral area and the surface area of a right regular hexagonal-based prism whose height is 12 cm and whose base edge-length is 5 cm.

Class Exercises

Short Answer

Name the bases and the lateral edges of each polyhedron that appears to be a prism. If it is not a prism, tell why.

1.

2.

3.

Determine whether each statement is true or false.

4. The lateral faces of a prism are always rectangles.
5. The least number of faces a prism can have is five.
6. An octagonal prism has six lateral faces and six lateral edges.
7. For any prism, the ratio of the number of base edges to the number of lateral edges is $2:1$.
8. The surface area of a prism is equal to the perimeter of a base times the height of the prism.
9. The base of a right triangular prism will always be a right triangle.
10. A lateral edge of an oblique prism is an altitude of the prism.
11. Since all lateral faces of a prism are parallelograms, each lateral face of a right prism is a rectangle.
12. Each lateral face of a prism is a rectangular region.
13. A prism must have at least six base edges.

Sample Exercises

ABCD is a base of this right rectangular prism.

14. Find the height of the prism.
15. Find the perimeter of the base.
16. Find the lateral area of the prism.
17. Find the surface area of the prism.

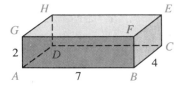

A right prism whose bases are regular hexagons has base edges 3 m long and a height of 6 m.

18. Find the lateral area of the hexagonal prism.
19. Find the surface area of the hexagonal prism.

20. Sketch a prism with a square base.
21. Sketch a prism with a hexagonal base.

Discussion

22. Explain why face *BCEF* can be viewed as a base in the right rectangular prism above. What is the height if *BCEF* is the base?
23. Explain why, in the right rectangular prism above, you can correctly claim that its height is 4. What is the base relative to a height of 4?

Exercises

A

Find the surface area of each right rectangular prism.

1.

2.

3.

Complete the table. Refer to the right rectangular prism with dimensions ℓ, w, and h denoting length, width, and height respectively.

	ℓ	w	h	LA	SA
4.	26	5	20	—	—
5.	6	$2\frac{1}{2}$	$5\frac{2}{3}$	—	—
6.	6	—	2	40	—
7.	$5\sqrt{2}$	$4\sqrt{2}$	$3\sqrt{2}$	—	—
8.	2.5	3.8	—	—	44.2
9.	$10x$	$7x$	$4x$	—	—

Find the lateral area and the surface area of each right prism.

10.

Equilateral–triangular bases

11.

Isoceles right–
triangular bases

12.

Trapezoidal bases

Decide whether each statement is always, sometimes, or never true.

13. The two bases of a prism can differ in their total number of edges.

14. A prism can have lateral faces that are hexagonal regions.

15. The bases of a right prism are isosceles trapezoids.

16. The altitude of a prism is longer than a lateral edge.

17. The altitude of a prism is shorter than a base edge.

18. If two prisms have equal surface areas, then the bases of the two prisms have equal areas.

19. Square cake pans 20 cm on an edge and 6 cm deep are to be coated on the inside with a non-stick material. If the amount of non-stick material available covers 100 m², how many pans can be coated?

B

20. Find the surface area of a right prism with equilateral triangular bases if all edges are two units long.

21. The perimeter of a base of a right prism is 37 cm and a lateral edge is 22 cm. Find the lateral area of the prism.

22. In a right hexagonal prism, one edge of a regular hexagonal base is 3 cm. If the height of the prism is 5 cm, find the lateral area of the prism.
23. The lateral faces of a cube are squares. Find the lateral area and the surface area of a cube whose base-edge length is 5 cm.
24. Find the lateral area of a right prism with pentagonal bases if its height is 10 cm and the sides of the bases are 2 cm, 3 cm, 4 cm, 5 cm, and 7 cm.
25. The length of a lateral edge of a right prism is 10 cm and its lateral area is 52 cm². Find the perimeter of the base.
26. The height of a right square-based prism is twice the length of a base edge. If the surface area is 490 square units, find the lengths of the edges of the prism.
27. If the lateral area of a right rectangular prism is 384 cm², its length is twice its width, and its height is twice its length, find the width of the prism.
28. An equilateral triangular-based prism 12 cm high has rectangular lateral faces and a lateral area of 288 cm². Find the surface area of the prism.
29. A right prism with a regular hexagonal base has a surface area of $96\sqrt{3}$ cm². Find the height of the prism if its base-edge length is 4 cm.

The figure to the right shows a prism in which all faces are parallelograms. Point O is the intersection of diagonals $\overline{AG}$ and $\overline{BH}$.

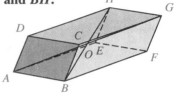

30. Prove that O is the midpoint of $\overline{AG}$ and $\overline{BH}$.
31. Explain why point O is also the midpoint of $\overline{DF}$.

32. A commercial walk-in refrigerator with outside dimensions 8 ft by 24 ft by 7 ft is to be painted. Its walls, floor, and ceiling are each 3 in. thick. Inside, all four walls, the floor, and the ceiling are to be painted. Outside, only the four walls are to be painted. How many gallons of paint are needed if one gallon of paint covers 300 sq ft?

C

33. A school hall 12 ft high and 12 ft wide turns a 90° corner as shown in this top view. If $\overline{AB} \parallel \overline{CD}$, find CD.
34. In Exercise 33, can a pole 34 ft long be carried horizontally down the hall and around the corner? Explain.

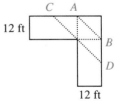

35. Suppose that the length of diagonal $\overline{AF}$ of a face of the cube to the right is 3 cm. Find the surface area of the cube.
36. Suppose that the length of diagonal $\overline{AG}$ of the cube is 5. Find the surface area of the cube.

Critical Thinking

Give a counterexample by sketching a figure to show that each statement is false.

37. A solid with a pair of square faces that lie in parallel planes must be a prism.

38. A solid with a pair of congruent polygonal faces that lie in parallel planes must be a prism.

39. The solid to the right is made from 14 cubes glued together.

    a. Each square in this figure is one square unit. What is the surface area of the solid?

    b. How can you move one block and increase the surface area by two square units?

    c. How can you move one block and decrease the surface area by two square units?

Mixed Review

Use the table on page 636 or a calculator to find each of the following.

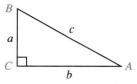

1. If $m \angle A = 37$ and $c = 12$, find b to the nearest hundredth.
2. If $m \angle B = 69$ and $a = 5$, find b to the nearest hundredth.
3. If $a = 3$ and $b = 9$, find $m \angle A$ to the nearest degree.
4. If $a = 2$ and $c = 4$, find $m \angle B$ to the nearest degree.
5. If $m \angle B = 50$ and $b = 7$, find c to the nearest hundredth.
6. If $a = b = 13$, find $m \angle B$ to the nearest degree.

Careers

Geologist

Geology is the study of the earth. Geologists are scientists who try to explain the beginnings of the earth and its changes through time by studying soil, rocks, mountains, and other landforms. Subjects as diverse as fossils, glaciers, and volcanoes are included in the work of geologists.

There are several subfields of geology. Physical geology deals with the present condition of the earth. Dynamical geology deals with the processes that cause changes in the earth's composition and structure. Historical geology is the study of the events by which the earth achieved its current state. Economic geology includes such applications as the construction of dams and the preservation of the environment.

Geologists hold a variety of positions, most connected to companies that explore for oil, gas, or other minerals. Because geometry is so useful in the study of rock formations and mineral crystals, mathematics plays an important role in the training of many geologists.

11-2 Surface Area of Pyramids

The Great Pyramid was built in Egypt over two thousand years ago. With an original height of about 480 ft, the base of the pyramid covers an area greater than ten football fields. In this lesson, you will learn how to find the lateral area and surface area of pyramids.

A **pyramid** is a polyhedron in which all faces but one have a vertex in common. The common vertex is called the *vertex* of the pyramid, and the face that does not contain the vertex is called the *base* of the pyramid. The remaining faces are called *lateral faces* and are always triangles. The segment from the vertex of the pyramid perpendicular to the base is called the *altitude* of the pyramid.

The length of the altitude is the *height* of the pyramid. Like a prism, a pyramid is named by its base. For example, a pyramid with a pentagonal base is called a pentagonal pyramid. If the base is a regular polygon and all lateral edges are congruent, the pyramid is called a **regular pyramid.** Most of the pyramids in this book are regular pyramids.

In a regular pyramid, all of the lateral faces are congruent isosceles triangles. The **slant height** of a regular pyramid is the height of any one of the lateral faces.

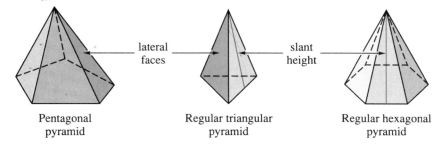

Pentagonal pyramid   Regular triangular pyramid   Regular hexagonal pyramid

A pyramid may be named by specifying its vertex and the vertices of its base. For example, the pyramid to the right is *V-PQRS*.

The lateral area (*LA*) of a regular pyramid, like a prism, is equal to the sum of the areas of its lateral faces. The surface area (*SA*) is the sum of the lateral area and the area of its one base.

Consider a regular pyramid with a pentagonal base, slant height ℓ, and base edge e. The area of each lateral face is $\frac{1}{2}e\ell$. Therefore, the lateral area is

$$LA = 5 \cdot \tfrac{1}{2}e\ell$$
$$= \tfrac{1}{2}(5e)\ell$$
$$= \tfrac{1}{2}p\ell \quad \text{(since the perimeter of the base is } 5e\text{)}$$

◆ THEOREM 11.2

The lateral area of a regular pyramid is equal to half the product of the perimeter of the base p and the slant height ℓ. $LA = \tfrac{1}{2}p\ell$

The surface area of a regular pyramid is the sum of the lateral area and the area of the base B. $SA = \tfrac{1}{2}p\ell + B$

Example 1

Find the lateral area and surface area of the regular square pyramid to the right.

Solution

$$LA = \tfrac{1}{2}p\ell$$
$$= \tfrac{1}{2} \cdot 40 \cdot 13$$
$$= 260 \text{ square units}$$
$$SA = 260 + 100 = 360 \text{ square units}$$

Try This

Find the lateral area and surface area of a regular square pyramid with base edge 6 and lateral edge $\sqrt{34}$.

Example 2

Find the lateral area and surface area of a regular hexagonal pyramid with slant height 11 cm and base edge 8 cm.

Solution

$$LA = \tfrac{1}{2}p\ell$$
$$= \tfrac{1}{2} \cdot 48 \cdot 11$$
$$= 264 \text{ cm}^2$$
$$SA = LA + B$$
$$= \tfrac{1}{2}p\ell + \tfrac{1}{2}ap \qquad \textit{The apothem of a regular hexagon}$$
$$= 264 + \tfrac{1}{2} \cdot 4\sqrt{3} \cdot 48 \qquad \textit{with side length 8 is } 4\sqrt{3}.$$
$$= 264 + 96\sqrt{3} \text{ cm}^2$$

Try This

Find the lateral area and surface area of a regular hexagonal pyramid if its slant height is 8 cm and the apothem of the base is 5 cm.

Class Exercises

Which of the following polyhedra are pyramids? For those that are, name the base and the lateral edges.

1.

2.

3.

Determine whether each statement is true or false.

4. The least number of faces of a pyramid is five.
5. A pentagonal pyramid has five triangular faces.
6. The slant height of a regular pyramid is the height of one of its lateral faces.
7. The vertex of a pyramid is a vertex of each face of the pyramid.
8. The base of a pyramid is always a regular polygon.

Complete each statement.

9. The sum of the areas of the lateral faces of a regular pyramid is called the ___ of the pyramid.
10. All of the lateral faces of a regular pyramid form congruent ___ triangles.

The figure to the right is a regular square pyramid. Give a special name for each indicated segment.

11. $\overline{EF}$ 12. $\overline{EG}$
13. $\overline{AE}$ 14. $\overline{FG}$

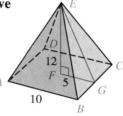

Sample Exercises

Use pyramid E-$ABCD$ to complete each statement.

15. The perimeter of the base is ___ .
16. The slant height is ___ .
17. $LA = $ ___
18. $SA = $ ___

19. Sketch a pyramid with a triangular base.
20. Sketch a pyramid with a square base.
21. Find the surface area of a regular square pyramid with base diagonal 4 cm and slant height 3 cm.

Discussion

22. Can a pyramid have an isosceles trapezoid as its base? If not, why? If so, is the slant height of such a pyramid defined?
23. Give a convincing argument that the lateral area of a pyramid is always greater than the base area of the pyramid.

Exercises

A

Find the lateral area and surface area of each regular pyramid.

1.
5

2.
9
4

3.
8
3

Complete the table below. The terms across the top of the table refer to the regular square pyramid shown to the right.

	altitude (*h*)	slant height (ℓ)	base edge (*e*)	*LA*	*SA*
4.	4	5	6	___	___
5.	24	___	14	___	___
6.	3	5	8	___	___
7.	12*x*	13*x*	10*x*	___	___
8.	___	*x*	*x*	___	___

9. Find the surface area of a regular triangular pyramid whose base-edge length is 5 in. and whose slant height is 8 in.
10. Find the surface area of a regular hexagonal pyramid whose base-edge length is 4 cm and whose slant height is 7 cm.

B

11. Find the slant height of a regular square pyramid with base-edge length 4 cm if its lateral area is 72 cm².
12. Find the surface area of a regular square pyramid with slant height 7 in. if its lateral area is 70 sq in.
13. Find the slant height of a regular hexagonal pyramid with base-edge length 6 cm and lateral area 198 cm².
14. Find the surface area of a regular hexagonal pyramid with slant height 6 m and lateral area 54 m².

A-BCD is a regular pyramid whose base is the equilateral triangle BCD. Point E is the midpoint of side $\overline{CD}$ so that $\overline{BE}$ is an altitude of the base.

15. Find the surface area of the pyramid if each edge of the pyramid is 8 cm.
16. Find the surface area of the pyramid if $BC = 8$ in. and $AC = 5$ in.
17. Find the surface area of the pyramid if $BE = 12$ and $AE = 5$.
18. Find the surface area of the pyramid if $CD = 4\sqrt{3}$ and $AO = 4$. (HINT: Point *O* is the point of concurrency of the three altitudes of △BCD.)

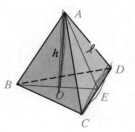

19. The surface area of a regular square pyramid is 48 cm². If the slant height is equal to the base-edge length, find the area of the base.
20. Find the slant height of a regular pyramid with base perimeter 20 cm and lateral area 70 cm².

21. A regular triangular pyramid with equilateral triangular lateral faces has edge length x. Find the surface area of this pyramid in terms of x.

c

22. A large container shaped like a regular hexagonal pyramid has an open top. If one hundred of these containers are to be painted, both inside and out, with a paint that covers 450 sq ft per gallon, how many gallons of paint must be purchased?

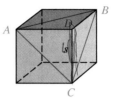

23. Suppose that a cube is sliced by a plane through points A, B, and C. Find the lateral area and surface area of pyramid D-ABC.
24. Find the surface area of pyramid D-ABC if $CD = 4$.

Critical Thinking
25. The pyramid to the right has a square base and two $45°$–$45°$–$90°$ triangular faces. Use a model or careful drawings to give a convincing argument that a cube can be divided into three identical pyramids like this one.
26. If the edges of the square face are one unit long, find the surface area of the pyramid described in Exercise 25. What assumptions are you making in doing this?

Algebra Review

Find the equation of the line through each pair of points.

1. $(1, 1)$ and $(2, 5)$ **2.** $(0, 9)$ and $(3, 3)$ **3.** $(6, 8)$ and $(-1, 8)$
4. $(-6, -7)$ and $(6, 7)$ **5.** $(-4, 1)$ and $(6, -2)$ **6.** $(1, 4)$ and $(1, -7)$

Enrichment

Euler's Formula

Use a sealed envelope to make the following model.

1. Construct an equilateral triangle ABC.
2. Cut along $\overline{DE}$, through C, parallel to $\overline{AB}$.
3. Fold back and forth along $\overline{AC}$ and $\overline{BC}$.
4. Let C' be the point on the reverse side corresponding to point C.
5. Open and pinch the envelope so that points D and E are joined and C and C' are separated. Tape along segment CC'.

How many faces (F), edges (E), and vertices (V) does this polyhedron have? The equation $F - E + V = 2$ is called Euler's Formula. Verify that the polyhedron you have constructed satisfies this formula. How many other polyhedra can you find that satisfy the formula?

11-3 Volume of Prisms

The **volume** of a solid is the number of cubic units contained in the solid. The right rectangular prism to the right is 8 cm long, 4 cm wide, and 2 cm high. It contains 64 cubic units, so its volume is 64 cm³.

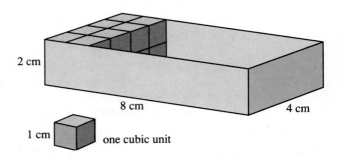

Notice that the volume of this rectangular solid can be calculated by multiplying the length by the width by the height. When calculating volume, always use the same unit of length for all three dimensions.

Imagine a prism with many thin layers of the polygonal base of the prism. You can see that the volume of the prism remains the same when the stack of layers slides as shown below.

This observation suggests a postulate which can be applied to develop volume formulas.

● **POSTULATE 25**   Cavalieri's Principle

Let S and T be two solids and let X be a plane. If every plane parallel to X that intersects S or T intersects both S and T in a cross section having the same area, then

volume of S = volume of T.

Cavalieri's Principle leads to this theorem and its corollary.

◆ **THEOREM 11.3**

The volume of any prism is the product of its height h and the area of its base B. $V = Bh$

▶ **COROLLARY 11.3a**

The volume of a right rectangular prism is the product of its length ℓ, its width w, and its height h. $V = \ell w h$

Example 1

Find the volume of the rectangular prism shown.

Solution

$V = \ell wh$

$\quad = 7 \cdot 2.5 \cdot 9 \quad$ *Convert 25 mm to 2.5 cm.*

$\quad = 157.5 \text{ cm}^3$

9 cm

7 cm

25 mm

Try This

Find the volume of a rectangular prism 4 ft long, 3 ft wide, and 18 in. high.

Example 2

Find the volume of the regular hexagonal prism shown.

Solution

$B = \frac{1}{2} \cdot 3\sqrt{3} \cdot 36 \quad$ *First find the area of the base. The apothem of*

$\quad = 54\sqrt{3} \text{ cm}^2 \quad$ *a regular hexagon with side length 6 is $3\sqrt{3}$.*

$V = Bh$

$\quad = 54\sqrt{3} \cdot 5$

$\quad = 270\sqrt{3} \text{ cm}^3$

5 cm

6 cm

Try This

Find the volume of an equilateral triangular prism with base edge of length 4 cm and height 7 cm.

Class Exercises

Short Answer

Determine whether each statement is true or false.

1. The volume of any prism can be found with the formula $V = \ell wh$.
2. The volume of any prism can be found with the formula $V = Bh$.
3. A unit of volume is a cube one unit on a side.
4. The cubic inch and the cubic centimeter are two units of volume.
5. There are 27 cu ft in 1 cu yd.

Sample Exercises

Find the volume of each rectangular prism with the given dimensions.

6. $\ell = 9$ cm   7. $\ell = 4$ in.   8. $\ell = 12$ cm
   $w = 5$ cm $w = 3$ in. $w = 50$ mm
   $h = 3$ cm $h = 8$ in. $h = 2$ cm

Discussion

9. If planes P and Q are parallel and the four triangular bases of these prisms are congruent, discuss how the volumes of these prisms compare. Explain your answer.

Exercises

A

Find the volume of each prism. (Exercises 1—5 show right prisms.)

1.
5 cm 8 cm 7 cm

2.
5 cm 2 cm 12 cm

3.
7 cm

Cube

4.
5 8 3

5.
5 9 4

6.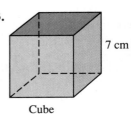
4 8

Regular hexagonal base

7. The base of a right prism is an equilateral triangle with sides of length 4 cm. The height of the prism is 9 cm. Find the volume of the prism.

8. A right regular prism has a hexagonal base. All sides of the prism are 5 cm long. Find the volume of the prism.

9. A right rectangular prism is 2 ft wide, 5 ft long and 18 in. high. Find the volume of the prism in cubic feet.

10. Find the volume of a prism whose base has an area of 14 cm^2 and whose height is 15 mm.

11. If the length of each side of a right rectangular prism is doubled, how does the volume change?

12. If each edge of the base of a regular hexagonal prism is doubled but the height stays the same, how does the volume change?

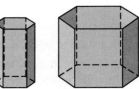

13. A landscape design specifies that topsoil to a depth of 4 in. be spread over a field that is 76 yd by 32 yd. How many cubic yards of topsoil should be ordered?

B

14. A silver ingot is molded into a bar shaped as shown. The ends are parallel isosceles trapezoids. Find the volume of the ingot.

2 cm 2 cm 4 cm 10 cm

15. A right rectangular container is 5 cm wide and 12 cm long and contains water to a depth of 7 cm. A stone is placed in the water and the water rises 1.7 cm. Find the volume of the stone.

16. A box mold as shown in the illustration can be used for making bricks. If the walls of the mold are $\frac{1}{2}$ in. thick and the bottom is $\frac{3}{4}$ in. thick, what is the volume of a brick made with this mold?

3.75 in.
5 in.
9 in.

17. A heating engineer needs to find the volume of a building in order to design its heating system. Find the volume of the building shown to the right.

15 m
8 m
15 m
20 m

18. A right prism with a square base has a height of 8 cm and a volume of 128 cm³. Find the length of each edge of the base.

19. A prism with an isosceles right triangular base has a volume of 40 cu in. and a height of 5 in. Find the lengths of the edges of the base.

20. A prism with a regular hexagonal base and a height of 3 in. has a volume of $288\sqrt{3}$ cu in. Find the length of each edge of the base.

21. All edges of a right prism with a regular hexagonal base are equal in length. If the volume of the prism is $27\sqrt{3}$ cm³, find the length of each side.

C

22. A concrete retaining wall is 80 ft long and has a cross section as shown. How many cubic yards of concrete are used in constructing this wall?

2 ft | 2 ft
2 ft
7 ft
2 ft
6 ft

23. An engineer's plan shows a canal with a trapezoidal cross section that is 8 ft deep and 14 ft across at the bottom with walls sloping outward at an angle of 45°. The canal is 620 ft long. A contractor bidding for the job estimates the cost to excavate the canal at $1.75 per cu yd. If the contractor adds 10% profit, what should the bid be?

24. If a square-based right prism has base edges a units long and a height of b units, find the volume of the prism.

b

a

25. If all edges of an equilateral triangular based right prism are s units long, find the volume of the prism.

26. Use the definition of a prism to explain whether or not you think these concrete steps with the landing at the top form a prism. What assumptions do you need to make to calculate the number of cubic yards of concrete needed for these steps? If you can order only a whole number of cubic yards of concrete, how much should you order?

Mixed Review

Find the area of each quadrilateral.

1.

16

11

Parallelogram

2.

8

12

20

Trapezoid

3.

4

3

3

4

4. The diagonal of a square is 6 in. long. Find its area.

Calculator Investigation

A box manufacturer wants to produce an open box with the following characteristics: the volume must be 2 m³ and the length must be twice the width. What dimensions will minimize the amount of material required?

If x represents the width of the box, then $2x$ represents the length. If h represents the height of the box, then

$$V = \ell w h$$
$$2 = 2x \cdot x \cdot h = 2x^2 h$$
$$\text{so } h = \frac{1}{x^2}.$$

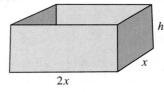

To minimize the amount of material needed, the manufacturer must consider the surface area of the box.

$$SA = \text{area of base} + 2(\text{area of front}) + 2(\text{area of side})$$
$$= 2x^2 + 2 \cdot 2xh + 2xh = 2x^2 + 4x\frac{1}{x^2} + 2x\frac{1}{x^2} = 2x^2 + \frac{6}{x}$$

Given any width x this formula can be used to calculate the surface area of the box.

1. Use a calculator to find the surface area of the box when $x = 0.25$ m, 0.5 m, 0.75 m, 1 m, 1.25 m, 1.5 m, 1.75 m, and 2 m. Make a table showing these widths and the corresponding surface areas.
2. Which of these widths corresponds to the least surface area?
3. Prepare another table, this time calculating the surface area of the box using widths from 0.2 m to 2 m in increments of 0.2 m.
4. Which width corresponds to the least surface area now? What dimensions do you think will minimize the surface area of the box?

11-4 Volume of Pyramids

How would you find the volume of the solid the right? You could find the volume of each of the six small pyramids and add these volumes to that of the shaded cube. The goal of this lesson is to develop a method for finding the volume of a pyramid.

It can be shown that pyramids with congruent bases and equal heights have equal volumes. Using this fact, you can conclude that the pyramids below have equal volumes — each has one third the volume of the prism in the middle.

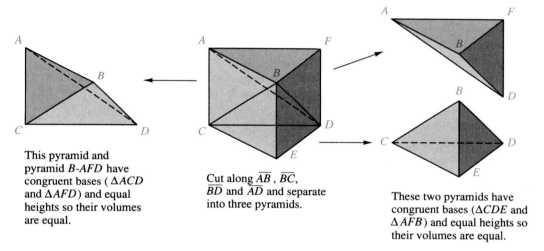

This pyramid and pyramid *B-AFD* have congruent bases ($\triangle ACD$ and $\triangle AFD$) and equal heights so their volumes are equal.

Cut along $\overline{AB}$, $\overline{BC}$, $\overline{BD}$ and $\overline{AD}$ and separate into three pyramids.

These two pyramids have congruent bases ($\triangle CDE$ and $\triangle AFB$) and equal heights so their volumes are equal.

The above figures suggest the following theorem.

◆ THEOREM 11.4

The volume of a pyramid is one third the product of the area of the base *B* and the length of the altitude *h*. $V = \frac{1}{3}Bh$

Example 1
Find the volume of the regular pyramid shown to the right.

Solution

$V = \frac{1}{3}Bh$

$= \frac{1}{3} \cdot 64 \cdot 11$ *Since the base is a square, B = 8^2 = 64.*

$= \frac{704}{3}$ cm^3

Try This
Find the volume of a square pyramid with 8.5 cm base edges and height 9 cm.

Example 2

Find the volume of the regular pyramid shown to the right.

12 cm

8 cm

Solution

$V = \frac{1}{3}Bh$

$= \frac{1}{3}\left(\frac{1}{2} \cdot 48 \cdot 4\sqrt{3}\right) \cdot 12$

$= 384\sqrt{3}$ cm³

The area of the base can be found using the formula $A = \frac{1}{2}ap$.

Try This

Find the volume of a pyramid with a height of 8 cm and an equilateral triangular base with base edges of 5 cm.

Class Exercises

Short Answer

Determine whether each statement is true or false.

1. Pyramids with congruent bases and equal altitudes have equal volumes.
2. The volume of a pyramid with a square base cannot be equal to the volume of a pyramid with a triangular base.
3. Two pyramids with equal volumes have equal altitudes.
4. If two pyramids have equal volumes and bases equal in area, then their altitudes are equal.

Sample Exercises

Find the volume of each pyramid.

5.

18

area of base = 51

6.

5

4

square base

7.

15

area of base = 65

8. A square pyramid has a volume of 135 cm³ and a height of 5 cm. Find the length of an edge of its base.

Discussion

9. A polygon with area B lies in plane M. Line p is parallel to and 4 in. above M and line q is parallel to and 8 in. above M. If P is any point on p and Q is any point on q, explain how the volumes of the pyramids with the polygonal base and vertices P and Q compare.

Exercises

A

1. Find the height of the pyramid to the right.
2. Find the area of the base of the pyramid.
3. Find the volume of the pyramid.
4. Find the surface area of the pyramid assuming opposite faces are congruent.

Find the volume of each regular pyramid.

5.

6.

7.

8. The area of the base of a pyramid is 62 sq in. and the height of the pyramid is 42 in. Find its volume.
9. A pyramid has a base with area 27 cm^2 and a height of 12 cm. Find its volume.
10. A pyramid has a right triangular base with legs 3 cm and 7 cm long. If the height of the pyramid is 10.3 cm, find its volume.
11. The height of a pyramid is 14 cm and the base is a right triangle having a hypotenuse of 13 cm and a leg of 12 cm. Find its volume.
12. A pyramid has a base area of 288 sq in. and a height of 2 ft. Find its volume.
13. The regular pyramid to the right with square base has base edges of length 10 and a slant height of 13. Find the height of the pyramid.
14. Find the volume of the pyramid described in Exercise 13.

B

15. A regular pyramid with a square base 16 cm on a side has a slant height of 17 cm. What is the volume of the pyramid?
16. A pyramid has a volume of 48 cm^3 and a base area of 14 cm^2. Find its height.
17. Find the height of a pyramid if its volume is 2500 cm^3 and the base is an equilateral triangle 15 cm on a side.
18. The volume of a pyramid is 336 cu in. and its base is a right triangle having one leg 0.5 ft long and another leg 1 ft long. Find its height.
19. The bases of the two pyramids to the right have equal area. How do their volumes compare?
20. Two square pyramids have equal heights. The edge of a side of one base is 3 and of the other base is 2. How do their volumes compare?
21. Find the volume of a pyramid whose height is 14 cm and whose base is a rhombus with diagonals 6 cm and 8 cm.
22. Prove that if the base of a pyramid is a parallelogram, then the plane determined by the vertex of the pyramid and a diagonal of the base will divide the pyramid into two pyramids that have the same volume.

23. The base of one pyramid is a rectangle with sides 5 cm and 8 cm long and the base of another pyramid is a square with sides 6 cm long. If the volumes of the two pyramids are equal, compare their heights.

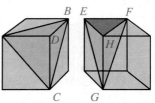

24. If the length of each side of the cubes to the right is 3 cm, find the volume of pyramid *D-ABC*.
25. Find the volume of pyramid *H-EFG* shown to the right.
26. Find the lengths of all six edges of both pyramids shown in the cubes to the right to verify that these are not identical pyramids.

C

27. All edges of a square pyramid are 8 cm long. Find the volume of the pyramid.
28. A right square-based pyramid is cut by a plane parallel to the base to form a second square-based pyramid. The heights of the two pyramids are *h* and *k* and the edges of the bases are $2x$ and $2y$. Prove that $\left(\frac{h}{k}\right)^2 = \frac{B_1}{B_2}$.

Critical Thinking

29. How do the volumes of these solids seem to compare? What assumptions do you make in arriving at your conclusion?

30. Why is it not possible for a regular hexagonal pyramid to have equilateral triangular faces?

Algebra Review

Solve each system of equations.

1. $x + y = 4$
   $y = 2x + 1$

2. $x + y = 5$
   $5x - 3y = 17$

3. $7p + 5q = 2$
   $8p - 9q = 17$

Quiz

Find the lateral area, surface area, and volume of each solid.

1. a right rectangular prism with length 9, width 3, and height 7
2. a cube with edges 2.6
3. a square pyramid with base area 144 and height 8
4. a regular hexagonal prism with height 6 and base apothem $4\sqrt{3}$

Determine whether each statement is true or false.

5. In a prism, the lateral faces are parallelograms.
6. A pentagonal pyramid has 15 edges.
7. A triangular prism has six vertices.

DISCRETE MATH

Levels of Tolerance

In manufacturing processes, companies are interested in producing products that satisfy a certain standard. The standard could be a fixed diameter for a car axle, the number of raisins in a box or the width of a 1 × 8 piece of lumber. In reality, the specified number is not always achieved; but rather the actual value is the specified target number plus or minus an acceptable amount, the tolerance.

Suppose an individual on an assembly line in a factory producing bulldozers is supposed to make 15 rock guards per day. The tolerance that has been set for this target number is 2 rock guards. That is, actual production between 13 and 17 rock guards is acceptable for a given day. Look at the production graphs for three individuals at the plant.

The first worker A always keeps production within the target (red line) plus or minus the tolerance levels shown by the parallel dotted lines (blue). Worker B occasionally overproduces, but never falls under the target number. Worker C always stays within the band of expectation indicated by the tolerance lines.

Such methods of production supervision allow factories to monitor the amount and quality of production, and also have applications in other situations.

Exercises

1. What are the positive and negative aspects of each of the three different production patterns shown above?
2. If all other factors were equal, which of the workers would you hire? Explain your reasoning.
3. The graph to the right shows the average speed on a state highway where the speed limit is 55 mph. The tolerance lines show the possible error rates for a radar gun set at 55 mph. What decisions would you make if you were a policeman who had to determine which day to set up a radar trap? if you were a motorist? if you were a person who studied human behavior?
4. The graph to the right shows the production of boats in a boat factory where the target number is 8 boats and the tolerance level is 2. What can you say about production in this factory? What factors might lead to this pattern of production?
5. Select a situation similar to the ones above where it is possible for you to obtain information. Collect some data and determine an acceptable target number and tolerance level. Then collect more data and graph your results on a production chart. Explain any special features you notice.

CYLINDERS, CONES, AND SPHERES

OBJECTIVE: *Find the surface area and volume of cylinders.*

11-5 Surface Area and Volume of Cylinders

 EXPLORE

Examine a can of fruit or vegetables. Estimate the area of the paper label that wraps the can.

Check your estimate by cutting the label with a single cut, laying it flat to form a rectangle, and measuring the rectangle.

A **cylinder,** like a prism, has congruent bases in a pair of parallel planes. But the bases of a cylinder are circular regions, rather than polygons. The segment joining the centers of the bases is called the axis of the cylinder. When the axis of a cylinder is perpendicular to the bases, the cylinder is called a **right cylinder.** Otherwise it is called an **oblique cylinder.** A segment joining the planes of the bases and perpendicular to both is an altitude of the cylinder and the length of an altitude is the height of the cylinder.

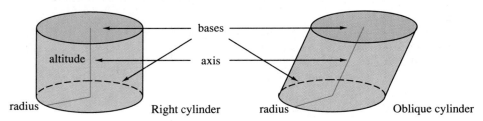

When a cylinder (without the top and bottom) is cut and laid flat you obtain a rectangle whose height is the height of the cylinder and whose length is the circumference of the circular bases. The area of this rectangle is the *lateral area* of the cylinder. By adding the area of the bases to the lateral area we obtain the *surface area* of the cylinder.

◆ THEOREM 11.5

The lateral area of a right cylinder is equal to the circumference of the base ($2\pi r$) times the height h. $LA = 2\pi rh$

The surface area of a right cylinder is equal to the lateral area ($2\pi rh$) plus the area of the bases ($2\pi r^2$). $SA = 2\pi rh + 2\pi r^2$

Example 1

Find the lateral area and the surface area of a cylinder with height 35 cm and diameter 18 cm.

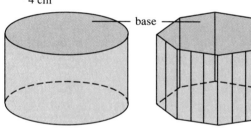

Solution

$LA = 2\pi rh$
$\quad = 2\pi\, 9 \cdot 35 \qquad$ *With diameter 18 cm, the radius is 9 cm.*
$\quad = 630\ \pi\ \text{cm}^2 \qquad$ *Substitute 9 for r and 35 for h.*

The lateral area is 630 cm².

$SA = 2\pi rh + 2\pi r^2$
$\quad = 2\pi \cdot 9 \cdot 35 + 2\pi \cdot 9^2 \qquad$ *Substitute 9 for r and 35 for h.*
$\quad = 630\pi + 162\pi$
$\quad = 792\pi\ \text{cm}^2$

The surface area is 792π cm².

Try This

Find the lateral area and the surface area of the cylinder to the right.

The shape of a prism with many sides approximates the shape of a cylinder. The greater the number of sides to the prism, the closer the approximation. Based on this comparison, you could conclude that the volume of a cylinder, like a prism, is found by multiplying the area of the base by the height.

◆ **THEOREM 11.6**

The volume of a right cylinder is the product of π, the radius r squared, and the height h. $V = \pi r^2 h$

Example 2

Find the volume of a cylinder with diameter 12 cm and altitude 5 cm.

Solution

$V = \pi r^2 h$
$\quad = \pi\, 6^2 \cdot 5 \qquad$ *Substitute 6 for r and 5 for h.*
$\quad = 180\pi\ \text{cm}^3$

The volume of the cylinder is 180π cm³.

Try This

Find the radius of a cylinder with altitude 4 cm and volume 100π cm³.

Class Exercises

Short Answer

Complete each statement.

1. The bases of a cylinder are ____ .
2. The perpendicular distance between the bases of a cylinder is called the ____ .
3. A cylinder is a right cylinder if its axis is ____ to the bases.
4. The altitude of the cylinder to the right is ____ .
5. The radius of the cylinder is ____ .

Sample Exercises

6. Find the lateral area of the cylinder to the right.
7. Find the area of one base of the cylinder.
8. Find the surface area of the cylinder.
9. Find the volume of the cylinder.
10. Sketch a cylinder.

Discussion

11. Is an axis of a cylinder never, sometimes, or always also an altitude of the cylinder? Explain.
12. If the altitude of a right cylinder is doubled, how does the volume of the cylinder change? Explain.
13. If the radius of the base of a right cylinder is doubled how does the volume of the cylinder change? Explain.

Exercises

A

Find the lateral area, the surface area, and the volume of each right cylinder.

1.
2.
3.

Complete the table.

	r	h	LA	SA	V
4.	8	6	___	___	___
5.	10	7	___	___	___
6.	5	___	___	___	100π
7.	___	4	___	___	64π

8. A cylindrical tank is 17 ft high and has a base radius of 10 ft. How many cubic feet are contained in the tank?

9. How many cubic yards are contained in the tank in Exercise 8?

10. What is the altitude of a right cylinder with radius 4 cm and volume 64π cm³?

11. What is the total surface area of a cylinder of altitude 8 cm and volume 200π cm³?

12. What is the lateral area of a cylinder of radius 5 cm and volume 100π cm³?

B

13. A right cylindrical water tank 18 ft in diameter contains water to a depth of 8 ft. What volume of water must be added to raise the water level to 12 ft?

14. A right cylindrical tank is 8 ft in diameter and 20 ft tall. How many gallons of paint are needed to paint the tank if one gallon covers 200 sq ft?

15. Find the surface area and the volume of a right cylinder that is 20 in. in diameter and 3 ft high.

16. A marble column in the shape of a right cylinder is 9 m high and 80 cm in diameter. If 1 m³ of marble weighs 300 kg, find the weight of the column.

17. Water is running into a right cylindrical tank at the rate of 5 cu ft per min. How long will it take to fill a tank 8 ft in diameter and 5 ft high?

18. A cylindrical hole with diameter 8 in. is cut through a cube 10 in. on a side. Find the surface area of this solid, shown to the right.

19. Find the volume of the solid in Exercise 18.

20. A copper pipe 8 in. long has an inside diameter of 0.5 in. and an outside diameter of 0.65 in. Find the volume of the copper in this piece of pipe.

0.65 in.   0.5 in.

21. If the radius of a right cylinder is doubled, is its volume doubled? Explain why or why not.

22. If the altitude of a right cylinder is doubled is its surface area doubled? Explain why or why not.

C

23. A 4×7 rectangle can be rotated about the long side to generate a cylinder. It also can be rotated about the short side to generate a cylinder. Find the ratio of the volumes of these cylinders.

24. A case is tightly packed with six cylindrical tin cans. Find the ratio of the volume of the box to the combined volumes of the tin cans.

25. Find the surface area and volume of this solid casting.

8 cm

dia. = 2 cm

2 cm   2 cm

4 cm

1 cm   1 cm

26. Find the surface area and volume of this bearing washer.

1½" core

¼"

¾"

⅜"

6" dia.

3" dia.

Critical Thinking

27. Isabella claimed that if the radius and the altitude of one of these cylindrical tanks are each doubled the surface area of the tank is quadrupled but the volume is eight times greater. Verify that Isabella is correct.

28. Given that surface quadruples but volume is eight times greater if all the dimensions are doubled, does it seem more efficient to build one large tank or several smaller tanks? Explain.

Algebra Review

Graph the lines containing these points and find each slope.

1. $(4, 0), (5, 7)$ **2.** $(3, 2), (-1, 2)$ **3.** $(-4, 2), (2, -3)$ **4.** $(3, 0), (6, 2)$
5. $(0, 5), (-4, -3)$ **6.** $(0, 0), (-2, -4)$ **7.** $(0, 2), (4, -3)$ **8.** $(1, 6), (-2, 0)$

Math Contest Problem

Find the volume of the cylinder cut on a slant.

4"

6"

5"

11-6 Surface Area and Volume of Cones

Take a circular piece of construction paper and cut from it a pie-shaped piece as shown. Join the two free edges and tape them together to form a cone-shaped hat. Is the radius of the base of the hat less than, equal to, or greater than the radius of the original disk?

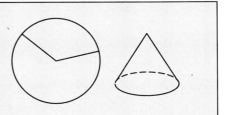

A **cone,** like a pyramid, has a vertex and a base. However its base is a circle instead of a polygon. The axis of a cone is the segment joining the vertex and the center of the base. If the axis of a cone is perpendicular to the base, the cone is called a **right cone.** Otherwise, it is called an **oblique cone.** The axis of a right cone is also its altitude. The length of the altitude is the height of the cone.

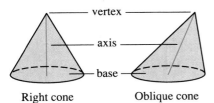

Right cone   Oblique cone

In a right cone, the distance from the vertex to the base along the surface of the cone is called the **slant height** (ℓ). The surface of the cone excluding the base is called the **lateral surface.**

slant height
ℓ

The Explore demonstrates that a cone can be cut along a line on the lateral surface and laid flat on a plane to form a sector of a circle. The radius of this sector is ℓ—the slant height of the cone. Also, the arc length of the sector is $2\pi r$—the circumference of the base of the original cone.

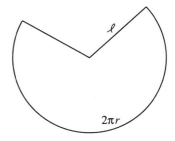

Based on this demonstration, you obtain the following proportion.

(area of sector) : (area of circle) = (circumference of base) : (circumference of circle of radius ℓ)

$$\frac{A}{\text{area of circle of radius } \ell} = \frac{2\pi r}{2\pi \ell} \text{ or } \frac{A}{\pi \ell^2} = \frac{r}{\ell}$$

You can solve this proportion to obtain the equation $A = \pi r \ell$ for the area of the lateral surface.

◆ **THEOREM 11.7**

The lateral area of a right cone is equal to the product of π, the radius r, and the slant height ℓ. $LA = \pi r \ell$

The surface area of a right cone is equal to the sum of the lateral area ($\pi r \ell$) and the area of the base (πr^2). $SA = \pi r \ell + \pi r^2$

Example 1

Find the lateral area and surface area for the cone to the right.

Solution

$LA = \pi r \ell$
$\quad = \pi \cdot 5 \cdot 13 \qquad$ *Substitute values for r and ℓ.*
$\quad = 65\pi$

$SA = \pi r \ell + \pi r^2$
$\quad = \pi \cdot 5 \cdot 13 + \pi 5^2$
$\quad = 65\pi + 25\pi$
$\quad = 90\pi$

Try This

If the surface area of a cone with base radius 5 cm is 100π cm², find the slant height.

You will recall that a pyramid and a prism with congruent bases and congruent altitudes have volumes that are related by the fraction $\frac{1}{3}$. The same relationship holds between the volume of a cone and a cylinder with congruent bases and congruent altitudes.

◆ **THEOREM 11.8**

The volume of a right cone is one third the product of π, the radius r squared, and the height h. $V = \frac{1}{3}\pi r^2 h$

Example 2

Find the volume of the cone to the right.

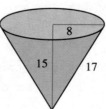

Solution

$V = \frac{1}{3}\pi r^2 h$
$\quad = \frac{1}{3}\pi \, 8^2 \cdot 15 \qquad$ *Substitute values for r and h.*
$\quad = 320\pi$

Try This

If the base radius is doubled and the altitude is divided in half, how does the volume of the cone change?

Class Exercises

Short Answer

Complete each statement.

1. The base of a right cone is a ____ .
2. The ____ of a cone is the segment from the vertex to the center of the base.
3. The height of a right cone is the length of its ____ .
4. If a sector of a circle is cut from a piece of poster board and taped together to form a hat, the assembled hat is a model of the ____ surface of a cone.
5. Given a right cone and a right cylinder with equal heights and congruent bases, the ____ of a right cone is $\frac{1}{3}$ the ____ of a right cylinder.
6. The lateral area of a right cone is always $\underline{(> \text{ or } <)}$ the area of its base.

Sample Exercises

7. Find the height of the cone to the right.
8. Find the radius of the cone.
9. Find the slant height of the cone.
10. Find the lateral area of the cone.
11. Find the surface area of the cone.
12. Find the volume of the cone.
13. Sketch a cone.

Discussion

14. Given a right cone with base radius r and slant height ℓ, does there always exist a right cone with base radius $2r$ and slant height $\frac{\ell}{2}$? Explain.
15. Suppose a pie-shaped wedge is cut from a circular piece of construction paper with edges brought together to form a cone-shaped hat. Suppose the angle of the cut is increased. Give a convincing argument that explains the effect on **a.** the radius, **b.** the altitude, and **c.** the slant height of the resulting cone.

Exercises

A

Find the lateral area (LA), the surface area (SA), and the volume (V) of each cone.

1.

2.

Complete the table.

	r	h	ℓ	LA	SA	V
3.	8	6	—	—	—	—
4.	10	7	—	—	—	—
5.	5	—	—	50π	—	—
6.	—	4	—	—	—	100π

7. If the volume of a right cone is 72π, find its surface area if its height and radius are equal.
8. If the base radius of a cone is 5 cm and its height is 12 cm, find the surface area and volume of the cone.
9. Which holds more, a cone-shaped drinking cup with a 6-in. base diameter or a cylindrical drinking cup of the same height with a 4-in. diameter? Explain.
10. What would the diameter of the cone-shaped cup be if it held an amount equal to the cylindrical-shaped cup?

11. Find the lateral area of a cone that has a base radius of 5 cm and a volume of 100π cm³.
12. If the radius and height of a cone are doubled, how does the volume change?
13. If the radius of a cone is doubled and its height is halved, how does the volume change?

B

14. How many gallons of paint are needed to paint an open conical shaped tank that has an 8-ft base radius and is 15 ft tall if one gallon covers 200 sq ft?
15. A container consists of a right cylinder of diameter 4 cm and height 8 cm topped by a right cone of height 6 cm. Find the volume of this container.
16. Find the surface area of the container pictured to the right.

17. Find the volume of the toy top pictured to the right.
18. Find the surface area of the top.

19. A cone-shaped tank with base diameter 10 ft and altitude 8 ft is being filled with water at the rate of 18 cu ft per min. How long will it take to fill the tank?

20. How many cubic inches of graphite are there in the wood pencil?

0.125" diameter

3"
0.25"

c

21. This solid is formed by cutting a cone with a slice parallel to the base of the cone. Find its volume and surface area. (HINT: Use similar triangles to find the height of the original cone.)

45°
$5\sqrt{2}$
$8\sqrt{2}$

22. The legs of a right triangle have lengths of 2 and 3. Cones are formed by revolving the triangles about the shorter and longer sides. Find the ratio of volumes and the ratio of surface areas of these two solids.

3
2

2
3

23. This solid is formed by cutting a cone with a plane parallel to the base, and then boring a cone-shaped cut into the resulting solid. If the height of the original cone is 37 units, the height of the resulting solid is 13 units, and the height of the cone that has been bored out is 5 units, how many cubic units of volume does the resulting solid have?

37
13
10
16

Critical Thinking

24. Suppose you have a cylindrical container and a conical container with the same base diameter and height. Suppose you fill the cylindrical container with water and then you insert the cone like a lid, forcing some of the water to be displaced. After removing the conical-shaped lid, how full would the cylindrical tank be?

25. The following implication is true. If a cone and a cylinder have the same base diameter and same altitude, then the volume of the cone is $\frac{1}{3}$ the volume of the cylinder.
State the converse of this implication. Do you think that the converse is true? Give a convincing argument that your answer is correct.

Mixed Review

1. Find the length of the diagonal of a square if each side has a length of $5\sqrt{2}$ cm.

2. Tell whether 3, 18, and 22 could be the lengths of the sides of a triangle.

3. How many diagonals does a six-sided convex polygon have?

4. The measures of two vertical angles are $6x$ and $4x + 20$. Find the measures

Computer Activity

The BASIC program below can be used to approximate the volume of a cone. For simplicity, consider a right circular cone of radius 1 and height 10.

One way to approximate its volume is with a stack of 10 cylindrical discs, each of equal height.

one disc
$V = \pi r^2 h$
$= \pi x^2 \cdot 1$
$= \pi x^2$

To determine the volume of one of these discs, look at a disc y units above the base of the cone. As shown above, $V = \pi x^2$. x can be found in terms of y using similar triangles.

$$\frac{10 - y}{x} = \frac{10}{1}$$

$$x = \frac{10 - y}{10}$$

so, $V = \pi(\frac{10 - y}{10})^2$.

Substituting $y = 0, 1, 2, \ldots, 9$ and adding the corresponding volumes gives an approximation of the volume of the cone.

More generally, if n discs are used instead of 10, each will have a height of $\frac{10}{n}$ and a volume of $\pi(\frac{10 - y}{10})^2 \cdot \frac{10}{n}$. In the program below, 3.14159 is used for π.

```
10 LET Y = 0
20 LET V = 0
30 PRINT "HOW MANY DISCS ARE TO BE USED?";
40 INPUT N
50 FOR I = 0 TO N − 1
60 LET Y = I * 10/N
70 LET V = V + 3.14159 * ((10 − Y)/10) ↑ 2 * (10/N)
80 NEXT I
90 PRINT "THE VOLUME OF THE DISCS IS"; V
100 END
```

Exercises

1. Use the formula $V = \frac{1}{3}\pi r^2 h$ to find the volume of the cone described above.
2. Run the program with N = 10 to find an approximation to the volume of the cone.
3. How does the approximation compare to the actual volume of the cone?
4. Run the program with other values for N. What happens as N gets larger and larger?
5. Change the program to approximate the volume of a cone with radius 1 and height 15.

11-7 Surface Area and Volume of Spheres

From basketballs to marbles to the earth itself, spherical shapes are found all around us. A **sphere** is a set of points in space that are a given distance, called the **radius,** from a given point, called the **center.**

The next theorem states the formula for both the surface area and volume of a sphere.

◆ **THEOREM 11.9**

The volume of a sphere is $\frac{4}{3}$ the product of π and the radius r cubed.
$V = \frac{4}{3}\pi r^3$

The surface area of a sphere is four times the product of π and the radius r squared. $SA = 4\pi r^2$

The Cavalieri Principle can be used to explain the volume formula for a sphere. To understand the volume formula for a sphere, consider a sphere of radius r and a cylinder with base radius r and height $2r$ with a double cone carved from it as shown below. Consider a cross section of both the sphere and the carved out cylinder that is a distance b from the center of the sphere.

A

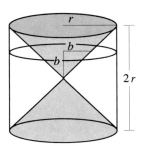

B

Use the Pythagorean Theorem to show that distance a in the figure is
$a^2 = r^2 - b^2$.

Compare the areas of the two cross sections.

 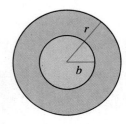

area of cross section A $= \pi a^2$ area of cross section B $= \pi r^2 - \pi b^2$
$$= \pi(r^2 - b^2)$$
$$= \pi a^2$$

The cross section areas of sphere A and solid B are equal. Thus the Cavalieri Principle indicates that the volume of solids A and B are equal. The volume of solid B, and therefore of sphere A, is

volume of sphere $= \pi r^2 (2r) - 2(\frac{1}{3} \pi r^2)r$
$$= 2\pi r^3 - \frac{2}{3} \pi r^3$$
$$= \frac{4}{3} \pi r^3$$

Example 1

Find the volume and surface area of a sphere of radius 4 cm.

Solution

$V = \frac{4}{3}\pi r^3$

$\quad = \frac{4}{3}\pi 4^3$ *Substitute 4 for r in each formula.*

$\quad = \frac{256}{3}\pi$ cm^3

$SA = 4\pi r^2$

$\quad\ = 4\pi 4^2$

$\quad\ = 64\pi$ cm^2

Try This

Find the volume and surface area of a sphere of radius 5 cm.

Example 2

If the surface area of a sphere is 36π cm^2, find its volume.

Solution

$SA = 4\pi r^2$ *Use the formula for SA and solve for r.*

$36\pi = 4\pi r^2$

$\quad 9 = r^2$

$\quad 3 = r$

$V = \frac{4}{3}\pi r^3$

$\quad = \frac{4}{3}\pi 3^3$ *Substitute 3 for r.*

$\quad = 36\pi$ cm^3

Try This

If the volume of a sphere is 972π cm^3, find its surface area.

Class Exercises

Short Answer

Determine whether each statement is true or false.

1. A sphere is contained in a plane.
2. A sphere is to space as a circle is to a plane.
3. A sphere with center O and radius 4 consists of all points that are a distance less than or equal to 4 units from O.

Sample Exercises

4. Find the volume of a sphere with radius 2 cm.
5. Find the surface area of a sphere with radius 6 cm.
6. Find the surface area of a sphere with radius $\frac{9}{2}$ ft.
7. Find the volume of a sphere with radius $\frac{3}{4}$ yd.
8. If the volume of a sphere is 12π, find the radius of the sphere.
9. If the surface area of a sphere is 64π, find its volume.

Discussion

10. For a sphere, can the number of square units of surface area ever be greater than the number of cubic units of volume? Explain.

Exercises

A

Find the surface area and volume of each sphere.

1.   2.

$SA = 4\pi r^2$ $V = \frac{4}{3}\pi r^3$
$4 \quad 100$ 1000
400π

Complete the table.

r	SA	V
3. 2	—	—
4. 6	—	—
5. 8	—	—
6. —	9π	—
7. —	—	288π

$SA = 4\pi r^2$
$4 \quad 36$
144π

$\dfrac{16\pi}{\pi} = \dfrac{4\pi r^2}{\pi}$

8. Find the surface area of a sphere of radius 9 cm.
9. Find the volume of a sphere of radius $\frac{3}{2}$ cm.
10. Find the volume of a sphere of radius 2π.
11. Find the radius of a sphere whose surface area is 16π cm^2.
12. Find the volume of a sphere whose surface area is 16π cm^2.

13. Find the volume of a sphere whose surface area is 176π cm^2.

14. Find the radius of a sphere whose volume is $\frac{9}{16}\pi$.

15. Find the surface area of a sphere whose volume is $4\pi\sqrt{3}$.

A cube whose edge length is 8 cm on a side is circumscribed about a sphere.

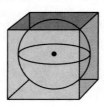

16. Find the surface area of the sphere.

17. Find the volume of the sphere.

18. Find the ratio of the volume of the cube to the volume of the sphere.

B

A plane that passes through the center of a sphere divides the sphere into two identical sets, each called a hemisphere.

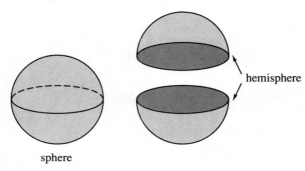

hemisphere

sphere

Assume that the solid is a right cylinder capped by two hemispheres.

19. Find the volume of the solid shown.

20. Find the surface area of the solid shown.

21. Find the ratio of the volume of the hemispheres to the volume of the cylinder portion.

22. If the radius of the solid is doubled find the ratio of the volume of the hemispheres to the volume of the cylinder portion.

23. If the radius of the above solid is doubled, is the surface area increased by a factor of 2, 4, 8, or none of these?

24. If the number of square feet of surface area of a sphere is equal to the number of cubic feet of volume of the sphere, find the radius of the sphere.

25. A sphere is inscribed in a cylinder. Show that the surface area of the sphere is equal to the lateral area of the cylinder.

C

26. A spherical tank whose radius to the outer surface is 15 ft is made of steel $\frac{1}{2}$ in. thick. How many cubic feet of steel are used in the construction of this tank?

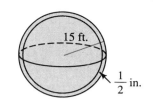
15 ft.
$\frac{1}{2}$ in.

27. A can of tennis balls contains three balls. Find the ratio of the volume of the can to the volume of the three balls.

Critical Thinking

28. If a hole is drilled through the center of a sphere the volume of the resulting solid, shown to the right, appears less than the volume of the original sphere. However the surface area of the resulting solid seems to increase. Is that always or sometimes true? Explain.

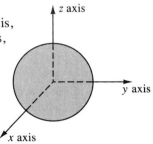

29. Visualize a sphere centered at the origin of a three-dimensional coordinate system. If holes are drilled into the sphere along the x axis, y axis, and z axis, will the sphere be cut into two pieces, four pieces, eight pieces, or will it remain as one solid? Explain.

z axis
y axis
x axis

Algebra Review

Solve and graph.

1. $3 < x$ and $x < 7$
2. $-2 < x$ and $x < -1$
3. $-3x - 6 > 4$ or $x + 3 > 8$
4. $-4x + 2 > 16$ or $x - 7 > 2$
5. $3 < x + 2 < 5$
6. $-4 \leq x - 3 < 1$
7. $-6 < 4x - 6 \leq 18$
8. $-17 \leq 5x + 6 < -3$

Historical Note

A Greek mathematician named Apollonius (225 B.C.) observed that if a right cone is cut by a plane as shown, the cross section that results is an ellipse. His work made it possible for Kepler (1609) to show that the orbits of the earth and other planets are approximately ellipses.

11-8 Volume and Surface Area of Similar Solids

A small scale model is usually prepared for large construction projects. These models may be constructed with cardboard and light balsa wood, even though the full-size structure could not be completed with these light materials. As an object is enlarged, the linear dimensions, area, and volume of the object increase at different rates. This explains why the materials used must change as objects get larger.

Consider the case of the cubes below.

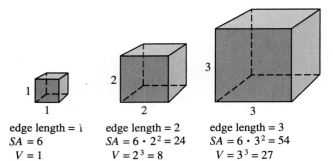

edge length = 1
$SA = 6$
$V = 1$

edge length = 2
$SA = 6 \cdot 2^2 = 24$
$V = 2^3 = 8$

edge length = 3
$SA = 6 \cdot 3^2 = 54$
$V = 3^3 = 27$

The ratios of edge lengths, surface areas, and volumes of the cubes above can be recorded in a table so that you can formulate a generalization.

edge length	surface area	volume
$2:1$	$4:1$	$8:1$
$3:1$	$9:1$	$27:1$
$3:2$	$9:4$	$27:8$
$a:b$	$a^2:b^2$	$a^3:b^3$

The generalization reached is that surface area increases at a rate proportional to the square of the length and volume increases at a rate proportional to the cube of the length.

These observations are true not only for cubes but for any solids that are identical in shape, that is, *similar solids*.

These observations can be summarized in the following theorem.

◆ THEOREM 11.10

If the lengths of two corresponding parts of two similar solids are in a ratio of $a:b$, then

a. the ratio of any corresponding lengths is $a:b$,
b. the ratio of corresponding surface areas is $a^2:b^2$,
c. the ratio of corresponding volumes is $a^3:b^3$.

Example 1

Two cylinders are similar with diameters 6 units and 9 units respectively.

a. Find the ratio of the circumference of their bases.
b. Find the ratio of their lateral areas.
c. Find the ratio of their volumes.

Solution

a. $6:9$ or $2:3$ *Circumferences are corresponding lengths.*
b. $6^2:9^2$ or $36:81$ or $4:9$ *Lateral areas are corresponding areas.*
c. $6^3:9^3$ or $216:729$ or $8:27$

Try This

If the height of the smaller cylinder is 8, find the surface area of the larger cylinder. Assume that the cylinders are similar.

The following example illustrates Theorem 11.10.

Example 2

Two similar prisms have edge lengths in a ratio of 2 to 5. The volume of the smaller prism is 40 cm³. Find the volume of the larger prism.

Solution

$$\text{ratio of volumes} = \frac{8}{125}$$
$$\frac{8}{125} = \frac{40}{x}$$
$$8x = 125 \cdot 40$$
$$x = 625$$

Thus, the volume of the larger prism is 625 cm³.

Try This

If the surface area of the larger prism is 825 cm², find the surface area of the smaller prism. Assume that the prisms are similar.

Class Exercises

Determine whether each statement is true or false.

1. If the edge length of a cube doubles, then the surface area of the cube doubles.
2. If the radius of a sphere triples, then its surface area becomes nine times greater.
3. If the edge length of a cube triples, then its volume becomes 27 times greater.
4. If the edge length of a cube doubles then its volume becomes four times greater.
5. If the linear dimensions of a solid are doubled then its surface area becomes four times greater.

Complete each statement.

6. If the linear dimensions of a solid are ___ its volume becomes eight times greater.
7. If two similar solids have corresponding lengths in a ratio of 2 to 3, then the ratio of their surface areas is ___ to ___ .
8. If two similar solids have corresponding lengths in a ratio of 2 to 5, then the ratio of their volumes is ___ to ___ .
9. If two similar cylinders have radii in a ratio of 9 to 16, then the ratio of their heights is ___ to ___ .

Sample Exercises

10. The diameters of two similar cylinders are in a ratio of 2 to 3 and the volume of the smaller cylinder is 1600π cm^3. Find the volume of the larger cylinder.
11. The altitudes of two similar cones are in a ratio of 3 to 5 and the surface area of the larger cone is 500π cm^2. Find the surface area of the smaller cone.
12. Suppose the ratio of the radii of two spheres is 2 to 7 and the volume of the smaller sphere is 48π cm^3. What is the volume of the larger sphere?

Discussion

13. Suppose that one apple is twice the diameter of another. The volume, and therefore the weight, of the larger apple is _?_ times that of the smaller apple. The cross-sectional area of the stem, and hence the strength, of the larger apple is _?_ times that of the smaller apple. Why does this explain the fact that when an apple gets to a certain size it falls off the tree?

14. A company manufactures bars of soap in two sizes that are similar in shape. The edges of the larger bar are twice as long as the corresponding edges of the smaller bar. If the smaller bar costs $0.39 per bar and the larger bar costs $1.89 per bar, which one is the better buy?

Exercises

Suppose that the cylinders to the right are similar.

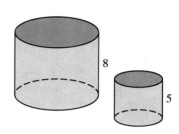

1. Find the ratio of the diameters of the cylinders.
2. Find the ratio of the surface areas of the cylinders.
3. Find the ratio of the volumes of the cylinders.
4. If the area of a base of the small cylinder is 50 cm², find the area of a base of the larger cylinder.
5. If the volume of the large cylinder is 512 cm³, find the volume of the small cylinder.

Suppose the two right rectangular prisms to the right are similar.

6. Find the ratio of the base perimeters of the two prisms.
7. Find the ratio of the surface areas of the prisms.
8. If the volume of the large prism is 54 cm³, find the volume of the small prism.
9. If the surface area of the small prism is 100 cm², find the surface area of the large prism.

10. A trough is made similar to the one to the right but 60 units long. What will the height of the larger trough be?
11. What will the ratio of the volumes of these two troughs be?
12. How much more paint will be needed to paint the larger trough, if both troughs are painted inside and outside?
13. Find the ratio of the weights of the two troughs.
14. If the surface area of the larger trough is 18 sq ft, find the surface area of the smaller trough.

15. Given two similar cylinders, the smaller with radius a and height h and the larger with radius $3a$, find the height of the larger cylinder.
16. Verify that Theorem 11.10 holds for the cylinders in Exercise 15.
17. Spherical fuel tanks of two different sizes are available. The diameter of the larger one is 1.5 times the diameter of the smaller one. If the cost of construction of the larger tank is 2.5 times the cost of the smaller one, which tank is the better buy? Explain.
18. The larger tank in Exercise 17 should have supporting legs how much larger in diameter than the smaller tank in order to have the strength rating of the smaller tank? (Assume that the strength of a post is proportional to its cross-sectional area.)

19. A certain filter system is packed with spherical particles that absorb unwanted materials from liquids that are drained through the filter. The effectiveness of the filter depends on how much surface area of these particles is exposed. The particles come in two sizes—1 cm in diameter (or 1 per cubic centimeter) and 0.5 cm in diameter (or 8 per cubic centimeter). Which size is more effective? Explain.

1 cm   1 cm

20. A brand of cereal comes in boxes of two sizes that are similar in shape and have a ratio of edge lengths as shown to the right. Suppose the two boxes are filled with an equal density. If the small box costs $0.73 and the large box costs $2.12, which one is the better buy?

Critical Thinking

21. A long piece of grass will bend under its own weight. On the other hand, lumber 2 in. by 4 in. by 8 ft, called a stud, is used for support in building a house. The support does not bend under its own weight. But suppose that each dimension of a stud increases continuously at the same rate. Explain how we know that a support increased in size will eventually bend under its own weight.

22. Explain why large, heavy animals like elephants and rhinos have short stubby legs.

Mixed Review

Find each of the following.

1. $TO = 9$, $OU = 10$, $OV = 15$ Find OW.
2. $TO = x$, $OU = 2x$, $OV = 4$, $OW = 8$ Find TO.
3. $m\widehat{TW} = 38$, $m\widehat{VU} = 72$ Find $m\angle TOV$.
4. $m\angle TOW = 40$, $m\widehat{VU} = 65$ Find $m\widehat{TW}$.

$\overline{SR}$ **and** $\overline{TR}$ **are tangents to** $\odot P$.

5. Find $m\angle PSR$.
6. If $SP = 6$ and $PR = 8$, find SR.
7. If $m\widehat{SQ} = 75$, find $m\angle SRP$.
8. If $PR = 9$ and $QR = 4$, find SR.
9. If $PR = 8$ and $TR = 4$, find PQ.

Quiz

1. Find the lateral area, surface area, and volume of a right circular cylinder with radius 5 and height 9.
2. Find the lateral area, surface area, and volume of a right circular cone with base area 144π and height 5.
3. Find the surface area and volume of a sphere with diameter 6.
4. A right circular cone has lateral area 35π and slant height 5. Find the area of the base.

A cone has radius 4 and height 6. A similar cone has radius 10.

5. Find the height of the larger cone.
6. Find the ratio of the areas of the cones.
7. Find the ratio of the volumes of the cones.

CRITICAL THINKING

Making and Supporting Decisions

In previous Critical Thinking lessons, the focus has been on individual topics, such as the following.

• Understanding the situation
• Dealing with assumptions
• Checking logic
• Understanding different patterns of reasoning

Now, consider all of these skills relative to the following situation.

A shipment of eight identical boxes, each assumed to contain the same top secret equipment, was delivered to Sonia, the manager of the secret equipment warehouse. They were marked, "TOP SECRET Do not open under any circumstances." As she was loading them to be taken to their destination, Sonia received a message that one box was missing a very small, but vital, part. Since she could not open the boxes, how could Sonia best determine which box had the missing part?

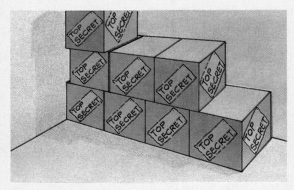

Answer the questions in each step below to use the process of critical reasoning.

1. Understand the situation.

a. What is the situation about?
b. What conclusion, decision, or solution is required?
c. Are there any questions you could ask to clarify the problem?

2. Deal with the data/evidence/assumptions.

a. Make a list of the most important evidence and data. Is other data needed?
b. Which evidence is opinion, not fact? Which is not relevant?
c. What assumptions are made? What other assumptions could be made?

3. Go beyond the data/evidence/assumptions.

Sonia decided to use the precision balances at a nearby aerospace laboratory. The scale operator allowed two free weighings and then charged $50 per weighing thereafter. Furthermore, Sonia did not have any funds at her disposal.

4. State and support your conclusion/decision/solution.

Write a paragraph detailing your solution to Sonia's problem. Describe one process she could have used to find the desired box without spending any money.

5. Apply the conclusion/decision/solution.

Two weeks after the above situation occurred, Sonia received a shipment of 12 boxes containing top secret equipment. Again, one box was missing a very small part. Sonia needed to use the precision balances to determine which box had the missing part. What is the least number of weighings necessary in this case?

CHAPTER SUMMARY

Vocabulary

altitude (11-1)	lateral face (11-1)	right cone (11-6)
cone (11-6)	oblique cone (11-6)	right cylinder (11-5)
cylinder (11-5)	oblique cylinder (11-5)	right prism (11-1)
edges (11-1)	oblique prism (11-1)	slant height (11-2)
faces (11-1)	polyhedron (11-1)	sphere (11-7)
height (11-1)	prism (11-1)	surface area (11-1)
lateral area (11-1)	pyramid (11-2)	vertices (11-1)
lateral edge (11-1)	regular pyramid (11-2)	volume (11-3)

Key Ideas

1. A polyhedron is a solid made up of polygonal regions called faces. The sides and vertices of the faces are called the edges and vertices of the polyhedron.

2. The following chart summarizes formulas for lateral area, surface area, and volume.

Solid	LA	SA	V
Right prism	ph	$ph + 2B$	Bh
Regular pyramid	$\frac{1}{2}pl$	$\frac{1}{2}pl + B$	$\frac{1}{3}Bh$
Right cylinder	$2\pi rh$	$2\pi rh + 2\pi r^2$	$\pi r^2 h$
Right cone	πrl	$\pi rl + \pi r^2$	$\frac{1}{3}\pi r^2 h$
Sphere	—	$4\pi r^2$	$\frac{4}{3}\pi r^3$

3. The volume of a right rectangular prism is the product of its length, width, and height.

4. If two similar solids have lengths of sides in a ratio of $a:b$, then the following statements are true.
   - The ratio of any corresponding lengths is $a:b$.
   - The ratio of corresponding surface areas is $a^2:b^2$.
   - The ratio of corresponding volumes is $a^3:b^3$.

CHAPTER REVIEW

11-1

1. How many vertices, edges, and faces does a hexagonal prism have?
2. Find the lateral area and surface area of a right rectangular prism with length 3 cm, width 6 cm, and height 2 cm.
3. Find the lateral area and surface area of a right regular hexagonal prism with base edges of length 6 and a height of 5.

11-2

4. Find the lateral area and surface area of a regular triangular pyramid with a slant height of 6 and base edges of length 5.
5. A regular pentagonal pyramid has a lateral area of 60 cm and a slant height of 4 cm. Find the length of an edge of the pyramid's base.

11-3

6. Find the volume of a right pentagonal prism with a base area of 30 and a lateral edge of length 7.
7. Find the volume of a right triangular prism whose height is 9 and whose base is a right triangle with legs 12 and 5.
8. The volume of a cube is 64 cu in. Find the surface area of the cube.

11-4

9. Find the volume of a regular hexagonal pyramid if the perimeter of the base is 48 in. and the altitude is 5 in.
10. Find the volume of a regular square pyramid with slant height 10 and base edges of length 12.
11. The volume of a regular pentagonal pyramid is 126 cm^3. If its base area is 42 cm^2, find the height of the pyramid.

11-5

12. Find the volume of the right cylinder to the right.

5

16

13. The area of the base of a right cylinder is 49π and its height is 4.2. Find the lateral area, surface area, and volume of the cylinder.
14. Find the volume of a right cylinder if it has a height of 3 and a lateral area of 30π.

11-6

15. A right cone has a height of 8 and a slant height of 17. Find the lateral area, surface area, and volume of the cone.
16. Find the volume of a right cone if the circumference of the base is 6π and the altitude is 7.

11-7

17. Find the surface area of a sphere with radius 7.
18. Find the volume of a sphere with diameter 4.
19. Find the surface area of a sphere if its volume is 36π.

11-8

Two similar cylinders have heights in a ratio of 3 to 4.

20. Find the ratio of the circumferences of their bases.
21. Find the ratio of their lateral surface areas.
22. Find the ratio of the diameters of their bases.
23. Find the ratio of their volumes.

24. Two similar prisms have surface areas in a ratio of 4 to 9. If the volume of the smaller prism is 40, find the volume of the larger prism.

CHAPTER TEST

Determine whether each statement is true or false.

1. The lateral faces of a pyramid are triangles.
2. The volume of any prism can be found with the formula $V = \ell wh$.
3. The surface area of a prism is the sum of its lateral area and twice the area of a base.
4. The lateral area of a pyramid with height 4 and base perimeter 6 is 24.
5. If the ratio of the diameters of two similar cylinders is 3 to 5, the ratio of their volumes is 9 to 25.

Find the surface area of each solid.

6. a regular square pyramid with height 5 and base edges of length 4
7. a right triangular prism with base edges of lengths 6, 8, and 10 and height 2
8. a cube with edge length 4 cm
9. a cylinder with height 20 in. and diameter 10 in.
10. a sphere with diameter 6

Find the volume of each solid.

11. a right rectangular prism with length 4, width 3, and height 8
12. a regular pentagonal pyramid with base area 26 and height 9
13. a right cone with slant height 26 and base circumference 48π
14. a sphere with radius 2 m
15. a triangular prism with base area 10 and height 6

48π ⚬ 26

$V = \frac{1}{3}\pi r^2 h$

16. A sphere has a surface area of 100π. Find its volume.
17. Two similar solids have heights in a ratio of 5 to 8. Find the ratio of their volumes.
18. Two similar cones have volumes in a ratio of 8 to 27. If the surface area of the smaller cone is 72, find the surface area of the larger cone.

Find the volume of each solid.

19.
   Square base

20.

21.
   9
   diameter = 8

22.
   Regular pyramid height = 10

23. 6

   lateral area = 48π

24.
   3
   diameter = 2

PROBLEM SOLVING

Guess, Check, Revise

Some problems can be solved by guessing a solution, checking the guess, and, if necessary, using information gained to revise the guess.

Example

A company received an electric bill of $108 for one month. The bill showed that 1440 kilowatt hours (kWh) were used. The manager of the company wanted to cut the electric bill exactly in half the next month. How many kilowatt hours could the company use to have a bill only half as large?

Electric Bill

$$\text{1st 600 kWh @ 4¢ each} = \$\ 24$$
$$\text{next 840 kWh @ 10¢ each} = \$\ 84$$
$$\text{Total} = \$108$$

Solution

The desired number of kilowatt hours must be greater than 600, since $24 is less than half of $108.

Guess: 800 kWh

$$\text{600 kWh @ \ 4¢ each} = \$24$$
$$\text{200 kWh @ 10¢ each} = \$20$$
$$\text{Total} = \$44$$

Since $44 is less than $54 (half of $108), the guess of 800 kWh was too low. The next guess should be higher.

Guess: 900 kWh

$$\text{600 kWh @ \ 4¢ each} = \$24$$
$$\text{300 kWh @ 10¢ each} = \$30$$
$$\text{Total} = \$54$$

900 kWh results in a bill of $54–the amount of electricity that could be used.

Problem-Solving Strategies	
Draw a Diagram	Simplify the Problem
Make a Table	Make an Accurate Drawing
Look for a Pattern	Guess, Check, Revise
Work Backward	

The problem-solving strategies that have been introduced up to this point in the book are presented in the chart.

Problems

1. At a banquet in a Chinese restaurant, 65 dishes were served. Every two guests shared a dish of rice between them; every three guests shared a dish of noodles; and every four guests shared a dish of meat. How many people were at the banquet if there were no extra dishes?

2. Renee accidentally hit the button on her clock radio that makes it go on and off repeatedly. The buzzer went on at exactly 7:00 AM. Then it went on and off at regular intervals. At 7:09 AM the buzzer was off, at 7:17 AM it was on, and at 7:58 AM it was on. Was the buzzer on or off at 9:00 AM?

3. Roosevelt's and Central High's bands have a combined total of 385 students. Roosevelt's and Riverside High's bands have a combined total of 320 students. Central's band has 65 more members than Riverside's. Roosevelt's band has 70 more members than Riverside's. How many members are in each school's band?

4. Is there a cube with whole-number side lengths that has the same volume as surface area? If so, what is the length of each side?

Coordinate Geometry

An air-traffic control screen shows two jets with coordinates (17, 42) and (71, 100). Find the coordinates of a helicopter located at the midpoint of the segment between the two jets.

SEGMENTS AND LINES

OBJECTIVES: *Graph a point given its coordinates and determine the coordinates of a point given its graph. Apply the midpoint formula.*

12-1 Coordinates and Midpoints

EXPLORE

Draw a coordinate system and graph the points A, B, C, and D as shown on the right. On a second paper trace the axes and mark the same four points. Flip the tracing paper over the x-axis and mark the traced points on your original graph. Label these points A', B', C', and D'. Compare the coordinates of A', B', C', and D' with the coordinates of A, B, C, and D. What conclusion can you draw? Repeat the process, this time flipping the tracing paper over the y-axis.

Recall that the plane containing a **rectangular coordinate system** is called the **coordinate plane.** The coordinate system consists of a horizontal number line, the **x-axis,** and a vertical number line, the **y-axis.** The intersection of the axes is called the **origin.** The x- and y-axes divide the coordinate plane into four **quadrants,** identified as quadrants I, II, III, and IV.

Points in the coordinate plane are determined by ordered pairs of numbers. The first number in an ordered pair, the **x-coordinate,** is called the **abscissa;** the second number, the **y-coordinate,** is called the **ordinate.** In the graph shown, the point M has an x-coordinate of 2 and a y-coordinate of 1. The notation $P(x, y)$ names the point P with coordinates (x, y).

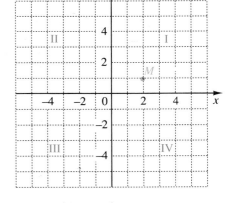

Example 1
a. Name the coordinates for each point.
   1. point A   **2.** point B   **3.** point F

b. Name the point for each pair of coordinates.
   1. $(3, 2)$ **2.** $(-1, 4)$ **3.** $(1, -2)$

   Solution
   a. 1. $(2, 4)$ **2.** $(0, 4)$ **3.** $(-4, 1)$
   b. 1. point P   **2.** point C   **3.** point L

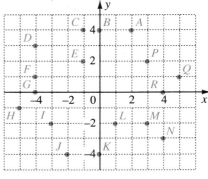

Try This
Name the coordinates of a point halfway between the given points.
a. the origin and point B   **b.** the origin and point G

In a rectangular coordinate system, the midpoint of a segment can be determined when the coordinates of the endpoints of the segment are known. In the graph to the right, observe that for the horizontal segment $\overline{MN}$, the x-coordinate of the midpoint is half the sum of the x-coordinates of the endpoints. For the vertical segment $\overline{PQ}$, the y-coordinate of the midpoint is half the sum of the y-coordinates of the endpoints.

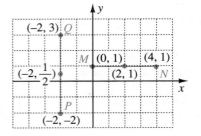

This idea can be used to find the midpoint of a segment that is oblique to the x- and y-axes, as is the case with segment $\overline{AB}$ in the graph to the right. The midpoint of segment $\overline{AB}$ with coordinates $A(-3, -2)$ and $B(5, 3)$ is M, which has coordinates $M\left(1, \frac{1}{2}\right)$.

This leads to the following theorem, which you will be asked to prove in Exercise 36.

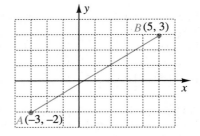

◆ **THEOREM 12.1**

If the coordinates of the endpoints of the segment $P_1 P_2$ are $P_1(x_1, y_1)$ and $P_2(x_2, y_2)$, then the coordinates of the midpoint of $\overline{P_1 P_2}$ are $\left(\frac{x_1 + x_2}{2}, \frac{y_1 + y_2}{2}\right)$.

Example 2

Find the coordinates of the midpoint M of $\overline{AB}$ if A has coordinates $(-4, -2)$ and B has coordinates $(8, 4)$.

Solution

$x = \frac{-4 + 8}{2} = 2 \quad y = \frac{-2 + 4}{2} = 1 \quad$ *Theorem 12.1*
$x = 2 \qquad\qquad y = 1$
The coordinates of M are $(2, 1)$.

Try This

Find the coordinates of the midpoint M of $\overline{AB}$ if A has coordinates $(5, -1)$ and B has coordinates $(-3, 5)$.

Example 3

M is the midpoint of $\overline{AB}$. Find the coordinates of A if M has coordinates $(2, 1)$ and B has coordinates $(10, 5)$.

Solution

$2 = \frac{x_1 + 10}{2} \qquad 1 = \frac{y_1 + 5}{2} \qquad$ *Theorem 12.1*
$4 = x_1 + 10 \qquad 2 = y_1 + 5$
$x_1 = -6 \qquad\quad y_1 = -3$
The coordinates of A are $(-6, -3)$.

Try This

M is the midpoint of $\overline{AB}$. Find the coordinates of B if M has coordinates $(-3, 1)$ and A has coordinates $(-5, 3)$.

Class Exercises

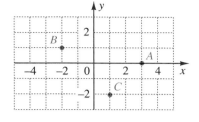

Short Answer

Name the coordinates of each point.

1. point A 2. point B 3. point C

Name the quadrant in which each point lies.

4. $(-4, 9)$ 5. $(8, -1)$ 6. $(-3, -5)$

7. Find the coordinates of a point one unit directly "above" a point with coordinates $(4, 7)$.
8. Find the coordinates of a point one unit directly "below" a point with coordinates $(-2, -5)$.
9. If the y-axis is the perpendicular bisector of $\overline{AB}$ and A has coordinates $(-4, 2)$, what are the coordinates of B?
10. If the x-axis is the perpendicular bisector of $\overline{AC}$ and A has coordinates $(-4, 2)$, what are the coordinates of C?
11. What is the x-coordinate of every point on the y-axis?
12. What is the y-coordinate of every point on the x-axis?

Sample Exercises

Find the midpoint of each segment with the following endpoints.

13. $A(6, 2), B(4, 10)$ 14. $C(1, 6), D(4, -3)$
15. $M(-3, 6), N(-1, -9)$ 16. $X(1, 5), Y(-5, -1)$

Discussion

17. The midpoint of $\overline{AB}$ has coordinates $(2, 3)$ and A is at the origin. How can you find the coordinates of B? Give the coordinates of B.
18. Points B and C trisect $\overline{AD}$ such that $AB = BC = CD$, A is at the origin, and B has coordinates $(1, 3)$. How can you find the coordinates of point D? Give the coordinates of D.

Exercises

A

Complete the table by finding the missing point or coordinates.

Point	Coordinates
1. A	___
2. C	___
3. ___	$(-1, 3)$
4. ___	$(5, 2)$

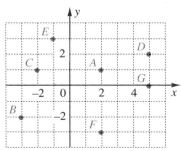

Name the quadrant that contains each point.

5. point A 6. point B 7. point C
8. point D 9. point E 10. point F

Determine the coordinates of the midpoint of each segment.

11.

12.

13.

14.

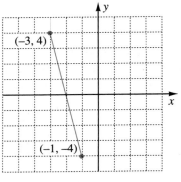

Determine the coordinates of the midpoint of the segment with the given endpoints.

15. $A(-3, 2)$, $B(7, 10)$ **16.** $M(-7, 4)$, $N(9, -4)$ **17.** $K(-1, -2)$, $L(5, 4)$

18. $R(-3, -5)$, $S(-7, -2)$ **19.** $E(-4, 2)$, $F(5, -3)$ **20.** $P(7, -3)$, $Q(0, 0)$

21. $X(a, b)$, $Q(0, 0)$ **22.** $Y\left(\frac{a}{2}, \frac{b}{2}\right)$, $Q(0, 0)$

23. Graph the points $A(-2, 5)$, $B(6, 1)$, and $C(-4, -3)$. Draw $\triangle ABC$. Find the midpoints of $\overline{AB}$, $\overline{BC}$, and $\overline{AC}$.

M is the midpoint of $\overline{AB}$. Find the coordinates of each point.

24. $A(1, 1)$, $M(5, 1)$ Find B.   **25.** $A(-2, -6)$, $M(-2, 1)$ Find B.

26. $A(-5, -3)$, $M(2, 1)$ Find B.   **27.** $M(0, 0)$, $B(-4, 3)$ Find A.

B

28. A soccer field is 100 yd long and 60 yd wide. Suppose coordinates are assigned to the corners of the field as pictured to the right. Find the coordinates of the center of the field.

29. A baseball player is halfway between first base and second base. Suppose home plate is the origin, first base has coordinates (90, 0) and second base has coordinates (90, 90). Find the coordinates of the player's position.

30. A baseball player is halfway between second base and third base. Refer to the coordinates given in Exercise 29 and determine the coordinates of the player's position.
(HINT: Find the coordinates of third base.)

31. Graph the points $A(1, 6)$, $B(6, 2)$ $C(8, -3)$, and $D(-5, 2)$. Find the midpoints of $\overline{AB}$, $\overline{BC}$, $\overline{CD}$, and $\overline{DA}$. Connect the midpoints to form a quadrilateral. What kind of quadrilateral does it appear to be?

32. Triangle ABC has vertices $A(-4, -3)$, $B(8, 0)$, and $C(6, 12)$. A line is drawn parallel to base $\overline{AB}$ and bisecting $\overline{AC}$. Find the coordinates of the point where the line intersects $\overline{BC}$.

33. Triangle MNP has vertices $M(6, -2)$, $N(-8, 4)$, and $P(-2, -3)$. A line is drawn parallel to base $\overline{MN}$ and bisecting $\overline{NP}$. Find the coordinates of the point where the line intersects $\overline{MP}$.

34. Suppose the coordinates of A and B are $(-4, 6)$ and $(6, -2)$. Find the coordinates of X on $\overline{AB}$ such that $AX = \frac{1}{4}AB$.

35. Suppose the coordinates of A and B are $(-7, -2)$ and $(5, -1)$. Find the coordinates of a point C on $\overline{AB}$ such that $AC = \frac{1}{2}AB$.

C

36. Prove Theorem 12.1.

Given: $P_1(x_1, y_1)$, $P_2(x_2, y_2)$, $P_1M = P_2M$

Prove: The coordinates of M are $\left(\frac{x_1 + x_2}{2}, \frac{y_1 + y_2}{2}\right)$.

(HINT: Draw the auxiliary lines indicated in the figure.)

37. Consider the points $P_1(x_1, y_1)$ and $P_2(x_2, y_2)$. Find the coordinates of the points that trisect $\overline{P_1P_2}$.

Critical Thinking

38. Consider a three-dimensional coordinate system with an x-axis, a y-axis, and a z-axis. Suppose that a cube with each edge 4 units long is placed as shown in the diagram. Find the coordinates of points A, B, C, and D. Find the coordinates of the center of the cube.

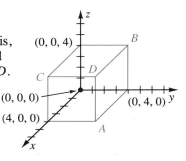

Algebra Review

Simplify.

1. $(3x^2yz^4)^2$ **2.** $(-2x^6y^2)^3$ **3.** $[(-n)^{15}]^2$

Solve.

4. $-25 = \frac{4x}{5} + 3x$ **5.** $\frac{3}{4x} + \frac{1}{4} = 8$ **6.** $\frac{1}{2}(4x - 6) = 6x + 5$

12-2 Slope of a Line

The degree of steepness, or **slope,** of each roof pictured is different.

The slope of a line or a segment depends on its steepness, or the rate at which it rises or falls. Consider the examples below.

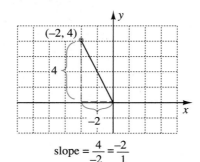

$$\text{slope} = \frac{2}{5}$$

$$\text{slope} = \frac{4}{-2} = \frac{-2}{1}$$

The slope of a line is determined by the change in the vertical distance $(y_2 - y_1)$ divided by the change in the horizontal distance $(x_2 - x_1)$.

■ DEFINITION

If P_1 and P_2 have coordinates (x_1, y_1), (x_2, y_2) respectively and $x_2 - x_1 \neq 0$, then the slope m of a line containing $\overline{P_1P_2}$ is $m = \frac{y_2 - y_1}{x_2 - x_1}$

There are two special cases of slope: the slope of a horizontal line and the slope of a vertical line.

Observe that for the segment in the graph to the right
$m = \frac{-2 - (-2)}{5 - (-3)} = \frac{0}{8} = 0$
If a line is horizontal, then $y_2 = y_1$ and
$m = \frac{y_2 - y_1}{x_2 - x_1} = \frac{0}{x_2 - x_1} = 0$
The slope of a horizontal line is zero.

Observe that for the segment in the graph to the right

$$m = \frac{3 - (-1)}{2 - 2} = \frac{4}{0}$$

If a line is vertical, then $x_2 = x_1$.

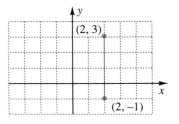

Since the denominator of m is 0, the slope is undefined. The slope of a vertical line is undefined. This is why the definition of slope includes the condition that $x_2 - x_1 \neq 0$.

Example

Find the slope of each segment. State whether the slope is positive, negative, zero, or undefined.

a. $\overline{AB}$ **b.** $\overline{BC}$ **c.** $\overline{AC}$

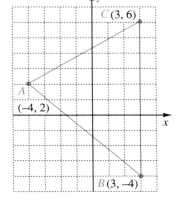

Solution

a. $m = \frac{-4 - 2}{3 - (-4)} = \frac{-6}{7}$

The slope of $\overline{AB}$ is negative.

b. $m = \frac{6 - (-4)}{3 - 3} = \frac{10}{0}$

The slope of $\overline{BC}$ is undefined.

c. $m = \frac{6 - 2}{3 - (-4)} = \frac{4}{7}$

The slope of $\overline{AC}$ is positive.

Try This

Find the slope of each of the medians of $\triangle ABC$.

Class Exercises

Short Answer

Indicate if the slope of each line is positive, negative, zero, or undefined.

1. The line rises to the right.
2. The line is parallel to the x-axis.
3. The rise of the line is zero.
4. The line falls to the right.
5. The line is perpendicular to the x-axis.
6. For changes in the vertical distance there is no change in the horizontal distance.

Sample Exercises

Find the slope of the line containing the given points.

7. $A(1, 2)$, $B(3, 7)$
8. $C(-2, 5)$, $D(7, 5)$
9. $S(-2, 6)$, $T(4, -2)$
10. $X(-4, -3)$, $Y(-4, -8)$

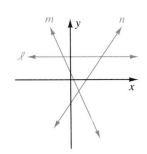

Discussion

11. Explain how you would estimate the slope for each of the lines ℓ, m, and n. What general guidelines would you give for estimating the slope of a line?

Exercises

A

Find the slope of each segment.

1. $\overline{AB}$ 2. $\overline{HN}$ 3. $\overline{AC}$
4. $\overline{MC}$ 5. $\overline{GJ}$ 6. $\overline{LQ}$
7. $\overline{HG}$ 8. $\overline{MB}$ 9. $\overline{MG}$

Find the slope of the line containing the given points.

10. $(0, 0)$, $(4, 6)$ 11. $(3, 5)$, $(9, 2)$
12. $(-7, 2)$, $(5, 2)$ 13. $(4, -2)$, $(-6, -5)$
14. $(-2, 5)$, $(6, -3)$ 15. $(-2, 10)$, $(-6, -4)$
16. $(0, 2)$, $(4, 1)$ 17. $(5, 0)$, $(0, -5)$
18. $(4\frac{1}{2}, -2)$, $(-2\frac{1}{4}, 1\frac{1}{3})$ 19. $(a, -b)$, $(b, -a)$

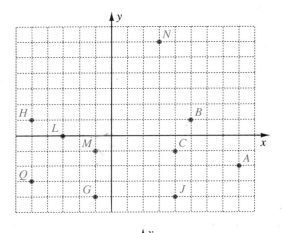

20. $\triangle ABC$ has coordinates $A(-2, 4)$, $B(6, 2)$, and $C(0, -4)$.

   a. Find the coordinates of the midpoints D, E, and F.
   b. Determine the slopes of $\overline{AB}$, $\overline{BC}$, and $\overline{AC}$.
   c. Determine the slopes of $\overline{DE}$, $\overline{DF}$, and $\overline{FE}$.
   d. What observation can you make about the slopes in **b** and **c**?

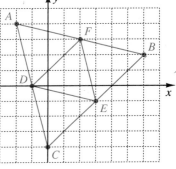

B

21. The vertices of a quadrilateral are $R(1, 4)$, $S(3, 2)$, $T(4, 6)$, and $U(2, 8)$. Graph the points and find the slope of each side. Which sides have equal slopes? What kind of quadrilateral is $RSTU$?
22. The vertices of a quadrilateral are $E(-2, 3)$, $F(4, 3)$, $G(4, -1)$ and $H(-2, -1)$. Graph the points and find the slope of each side. Which two sides have undefined slopes? What kind of quadrilateral is $EFGH$?

Estimate the slope of the indicated line to the nearest integer.

23. p 24. q 25. r 26. s 27. t

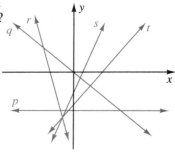

28. Points $A(-4, -2)$, $B(-1, 1)$, and $C(3, x)$ are collinear. Solve for x. (HINT: Since A, B, and C are collinear, the slope of $\overline{AB}$ is equal to the slope of $\overline{BC}$.)

29. The slope of a drainage pipe is $\frac{1}{15}$ and the horizontal distance from one end to the other is 100 ft. Find the number of feet the tile drops.

30. An airplane descends at the steady rate of 6 ft per 100 ft (horizontal distance) traveled. If its altitude is 30,000 ft before starting its decline, find its altitude after traveling a horizontal distance of 50,000 ft.

31. Find the slope of a line that crosses the x-axis at 6 and the y-axis at -2.
32. Find the slope of a line that crosses the x-axis at -6 and the y-axis at 2. How is the slope of this line related to the slope of the line in Exercise 32?
33. A line with a slope of -3 crosses the x-axis at $(8, 0)$. At what point does it cross the y-axis?

34. Find the slope of a line if its x-coordinate is always twice the y-coordinate.

35. A line contains the points $R(-5, -3)$, $S(-1, -1)$ and $T(5, x)$. Solve for x.

36. A line contains the points $X(-1, 8)$, $Y(1, 4)$ and $Z(x, -4)$. Solve for x.

37. A line with slope -1 contains the points $(5, -2)$ and $(x, -8)$. Solve for x.

38. A line with slope $\frac{3}{5}$ passes through the point $(2, 1)$. Find the coordinates of three more points on the line.

39. The vertices of $\triangle ABC$ are $A(4, 6)$, $B(-1, 2)$, and $C(2, -4)$. Find the slope of each median of the triangle.

C

40. $\triangle ABC$ has vertices $B(-6, -3)$ and $C(8, -4)$. The slope of $\overline{AB}$ is $\frac{1}{2}$. The slope of AC is -2. Find the coordinates of point A.

41. Three points A, B, and C are collinear if the slope of $\overline{AB}$ equals the slope of $\overline{BC}$. Use this fact in the following proof.

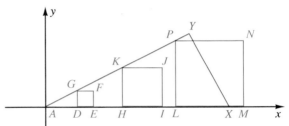

Given: $\triangle AXY$ with $A(0, 0)$, slope of $AY = \frac{1}{2}$
$DEFG$, $HIJK$, and $LMNP$ are squares with coordinates $D(4, 0)$, $H(10, 0)$, and $L(18, 0)$.

Prove: F, J, and N are collinear.

Critical Thinking

42. A line can be thought of as generated by a moving point with the rate of change in the y-coordinate divided by the rate of change in the x-coordinate as a constant. If that constant is $-\frac{1}{2}$ and the point passes through the point $(-4, 2)$, find the coordinates at which the point crosses the x-axis and the y-axis.

Mixed Review

1. $KXTR$ is a rhombus whose diagonals intersect at Q. If $m\angle KQX = 5x + 15$ and $m\angle KRT = 6x + 25$, find $m\angle RTX$.

2. If $PQ = 3x + 3$, $RS = 4x - 12$, $PS = 4x + 9$, and $QR = 6y - 5$, find the values of x and y that make $PQRS$ a parallelogram.

Computer Activity
Investigating Slopes of Lines

Use computer software to graph vertices $A(3, 3)$, $B(7, -1)$, $C(4, -4)$, and $D(0, 0)$ of rectangle $ABCD$. Compare slopes of opposite sides of the rectangle. Compare slopes of adjacent sides. What do you observe?

12-3 Slopes of Parallel and Perpendicular Lines

EXPLORE

Draw a coordinate system and a line $\overline{AB}$ as shown to the right. Use a compass and straightedge to construct the following.

a. Construct a line through the origin that is parallel to $\overline{AB}$. Find the slope of this line and compare its slope to the slope of $\overline{AB}$.

b. Construct a line through the origin that is perpendicular to $\overline{AB}$. Find the slope of this line and compare its slope to the slope of $\overline{AB}$.

The slopes of parallel lines and the slopes of perpendicular lines have special relationships, which you may have discovered in the Explore. Consider the slopes of the pair of parallel lines in each graph below.

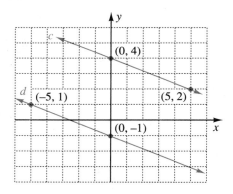

The slope of $a = \frac{3}{1}$ and the slope of $b = \frac{3}{1}$. Observe that the slope of $a =$ the slope of b.

The slope of $c = -\frac{2}{5}$ and the slope of $d = -\frac{2}{5}$. Observe that the slope of $c =$ the slope of d.

These observations lead to the following theorem.

◆ **THEOREM 12.2**

Two nonvertical lines are parallel if and only if their slopes are equal.

Theorem 12.2 is true only if neither line is parallel to the y-axis. This is because, as you learned in the previous lesson, the slope of a vertical line is undefined. If two parallel lines are vertical, then the slopes are both undefined.

Example 1

$\overline{AB}$ contains the points $(0, 0)$ and $(3, 2)$. Suppose $\overline{AB} \parallel \overline{CD}$.
Find the slope of $\overline{CD}$.

Solution

slope of $\overline{AB} = \frac{2 - 0}{3 - 0} = \frac{2}{3}$ *Definition of slope*

slope of $\overline{CD} = \frac{2}{3}$ *Theorem 12.2*

Try This

$\overline{AB}$ contains the points $(0, 0)$ and $(-2, 5)$. Suppose $\overline{AB} \parallel \overline{CD}$.
Find the slope of $\overline{CD}$.

Consider the slopes of the pair of perpendicular lines in each graph below.

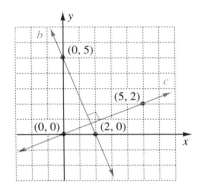

The slope of $a = 4$ and the slope of $b = -\frac{1}{4}$.   The slope of $b = -\frac{5}{2}$ and the slope of $c = \frac{2}{5}$.

Observe that $4 \cdot -\frac{1}{4} = -1$.   Observe that $-\frac{5}{2} \cdot \frac{2}{5} = -1$.

◆ THEOREM 12.3

Two nonvertical lines are perpendicular if and only if the product of their
slopes is -1.

You will be asked to complete part of the proof of Theorem 12.3 in Class
Exercise 13.

Example 2

Given $A(2, 5)$, $B(-1, -1)$, $C(-1, 4)$, and $D(9, -1)$, show that $\overline{AB} \perp \overline{CD}$.

Solution

slope of $\overline{AB} = \frac{-1 - 5}{-1 - 2} = \frac{-6}{-3} = \frac{2}{1}$ *Definition of slope*

slope of $\overline{CD} = \frac{-1 - 4}{9 - (-1)} = \frac{-5}{10} = -\frac{1}{2}$ *Definition of slope*

Since $\frac{2}{1} \cdot -\frac{1}{2} = -1$, $\overline{AB} \perp \overline{CD}$.   *Theorem 12.3*

Try This

The points $R(-2, 3)$, $S(-1, 0)$, and $T(-4, -1)$ are the vertices of a
triangle. Show that $\angle S$ is a right angle.

Class Exercises

Short Answer

Given the slopes of lines a and b, determine whether the lines are parallel, perpendicular, or neither.

1. slope of $a = \frac{1}{2}$, slope of $b = 2$
2. slope of $a = -5$, slope of $b = \frac{1}{5}$
3. slope of $a = 0$, slope of $b = \frac{0}{5}$
4. slope of a undefined, slope of $b = 0$
5. slope of $a = \frac{2}{3}$, slope of $b = -\frac{2}{3}$
6. slope of $a = 2$, slope of $b = \frac{6}{3}$
7. slope of $a = \frac{3}{4}$, slope of $b = -\frac{12}{9}$

Sample Exercises

8. Find the slope of a line parallel to the line containing the points $(2, 3)$ and $(-4, 5)$.
9. Find the slope of a line perpendicular to the line containing the points $(2, 3)$ and $(-4, 5)$.
10. Show that $(3, 9)$, $(7, 5)$, $(4, -1)$, and $(0, 3)$ are the coordinates of the vertices of a parallelogram.
11. Show that $A(4, 6)$, $B(5, 1)$, and $C(2, 4)$ are the coordinates of the vertices of a right triangle.
12. Triangle ABC has vertices with coordinates $A(-1, 6)$, $B(3, 3)$, and $C(x, 7)$. If ABC is a right triangle with $m \angle B = 90$, find the value of x.

Discussion

13. **Given:** $p \perp q$

    Prove: (slope of p)(slope of q) $= -1$

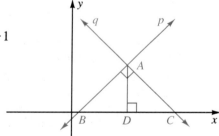

Let B and C be the points of intersection of the x-axis with p and q, respectively. Let $\overline{AD}$ be the altitude of $\triangle ABC$.

Answer the following questions to develop a convincing argument that the product of the slopes of lines p and q equals -1.

a. How can the slopes of p and q be expressed in terms of the segments $\overline{AD}$, $\overline{BD}$, and $\overline{DC}$?

b. What are the products of the slopes?

c. What relationship exists between the altitude $\overline{AD}$ and the segments $\overline{BD}$ and $\overline{CD}$ on the hypotenuse?

d. How can the expressions in **b** and **c** be used to show the product of the slopes is -1?

Exercises

A

Given coordinates for the points A, B, C, and D, determine whether $\overleftrightarrow{AB}$ and $\overleftrightarrow{CD}$ are parallel, perpendicular, or neither.

	A	B	C	D
1.	$(3, 5)$	$(7, -1)$	$(-4, 4)$	$(0, -2)$
2.	$(4, 7)$	$(8, -1)$	$(0, 1)$	$(-4, -1)$
3.	$(-2, -3)$	$(4, -1)$	$(5, -2)$	$(6, 1)$
4.	$(5, 2)$	$(10, 4)$	$(-6, 2)$	$(-4, -3)$

5. Show that $(3, 9)$, $(7, 5)$, $(3, -3)$, and $(-1, 1)$ are the coordinates of the vertices of a parallelogram.

6. Show that $(7, 9)$, $(10, -3)$, and $(2, -5)$ are the coordinates of the vertices of a right triangle. Find the coordinates of the right angle.

7. Show that $(-3, -3)$, $(-1, -2)$, $(1, -6)$, and $(-1, -7)$ are the coordinates of the vertices of a rectangle.

8. Show that $(10, 2)$, $(8, 8)$, $(-1, 5)$, and $(1, -1)$ are the coordinates of the vertices of a rectangle.

9. Find the value of y so that $(1, 2)$, $(3, 1)$, $(0, -4)$, and $(-2, y)$ are the coordinates of the vertices of a parallelogram.

10. Find the value of x so that $(1, 4)$, $(3, 5)$, $(-3, 12)$, and $(x, 13)$ are the coordinates of the vertices of a rectangle.

$\triangle ABC$ **has vertices** $A(-1, 4)$, $B(-3, -4)$, **and** $C(5, 2)$.

11. Find the slope of the altitude to $\overline{BC}$.

12. Find the slope of the altitude to $\overline{AC}$.

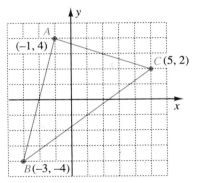

B

13. A triangle has vertices with coordinates $A(5, 1)$, $B(-1, 7)$, and $C(1, -3)$. If R is the midpoint of $\overline{AB}$, S is the midpoint of $\overline{BC}$, and T is the midpoint of $\overline{AC}$, find the slopes of $\overline{RS}$, $\overline{ST}$, and $\overline{RT}$.

14. The vertices of right triangle ABC have coordinates $A(-2, 0)$, $B(6, 4)$, and $C(x, 0)$. Find the value of x.

15. ABC is a right triangle with coordinates $A(-4, 1)$ and $C(2, -1)$. What point on the y-axis will make $m\angle B = 90$?

16. Find the value of y so that the line through $(-4, -3)$ and $(8, y)$ is parallel to the line through $(4, -4)$ and $(3, 5)$.

17. Find the value of y so that the line through $(-2, -1)$ and $(10, y)$ is perpendicular to the line through $(6, -2)$ and $(5, 7)$.

18. Find the value of a so that the line through $(7, 1)$ and $(4, 8)$ is parallel to the line through $(2, a)$ and $(a, -2)$.

19. Find the value of b so that the line through $(2, 3)$ and $(4, -5)$ is perpendicular to the line through $(4, -5)$ and (b, b).

20. Given the points $A(-3, 2)$, $B(4, -2)$ and $C(0, 6)$, find D so that $\overline{AB} \parallel \overline{CD}$ and D is on the x-axis.

21. Given the points $A(0, 4)$ and $B(-5, 1)$, and $\overline{AB} \perp \overline{AC}$, find the point at which $\overline{AC}$ crosses the x-axis.

22. $\overline{AB}$ and $\overline{CD}$ are roof lines of a house, with A at the center of the house, as shown in the figure to the right. $\overline{AM}$ and $\overline{CN}$ are vertical supports for the roof.

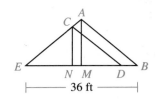

   a. If $AM = 9$, $CN = 8$, and $EB = 36$, how long should $\overline{ND}$ be if the slopes of the roof lines $\overline{AB}$ and $\overline{CD}$ are to be equal?

   b. Does EN equal ND?

   c. How long is $\overline{DB}$?

C

23. $ABCD$ is a rhombus with vertices $A(-3, 6)$, $B(5, 7)$, and $C(9, 0)$. Find the coordinates of D.

24. $ABCD$ is a parallelogram with vertices $A(3, 6)$, $B(5, 9)$, and $C(8, 2)$. Find the coordinates of D.

25. Quadrilateral $ABCD$ has vertices $A(a, b)$, $B(c, b)$, $C(c + d, e)$ and $D(a + d, e)$. Find the slope of each side. What kind of quadrilateral is $ABCD$?

Critical Thinking

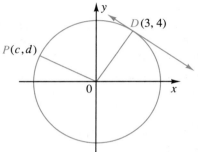

26. A circle with center at the origin contains the point $D(3, 4)$. Find each of the following.

   a. the slope of the radius $\overline{OD}$.

   b. the slope of the tangent to the circle at point D.

27. Suppose $P(c, d)$ represents any point of the circle. Write an expression in terms of c and d for the slope of the tangent to the circle at point P as P moves around the circle.

Algebra Review

Evaluate each of the following.

1. $3a + 4a + 10$ if $a = -2$

2. $q - 3 + 17$ if $q = 21$

3. $\frac{-36}{p} + 3(p + 7)$ if $p = 4$

4. $3x + 5 + 4x - 2$ if $x = -5$

5. $5 + b[b(3 + 2b) + 4]$ if $b = 2$

6. $\frac{-121}{n} + n(3 + 6) - 2n$ if $n = 11$

7. $x\sqrt{x} - x^2$ if $x = 4$

8. $4a^3 - 2a^2 + a - 1$ if $a = 2$

9. $|y| - 2y + y^2$ if $y = -3$

10. $\frac{1-y}{2} - \sqrt{y}$ if $y = 9$

Computer Activity

More on Slopes of Lines

1. Use computer software to plot the points $(1, 1)$ and $(3, 2)$. Find the slope of the line m through these points.

2. Draw a line n through $(3, 2)$ perpendicular to m. Predict the slope of line n and check your answer with the computer.

3. Draw a line through $(1, 1)$ parallel to n. Predict and check its slope as above.

12-4 Equations of Lines

EXPLORE

The relationship between Celsius and Fahrenheit degree measures can be represented by a straight line graph. Use the table of values to the right to draw a graph representing the relationship between the Celsius and Fahrenheit scales. Let Celsius be represented by the horizontal axis and Fahrenheit by the vertical axis. Estimate the temperature in degrees Celsius when the temperature is 0° Fahrenheit.

C	F
−10	14
−5	23
0	32
5	41
10	50

A relationship that can be represented by a straight line graph is called a linear relationship. The relationship between Fahrenheit and Celsius degree measures is an example of a linear relationship.

A linear relationship can be represented by an equation written in different forms. Three forms of linear equations considered in this lesson are as follows.
   slope-intercept form   *point-slope* form   *two-point* form

Recall that the y-intercept of a line is the y-coordinate of the point where the line intersects the y-axis. It is often denoted by the letter b.

◆ **THEOREM 12.4**   Slope-Intercept Form

An equation of the line that has slope m and y-intercept b is $y = mx + b$.

Example 1

Write an equation of a line that contains the point $(0, 4)$ and has slope $\frac{1}{2}$. Graph the line.

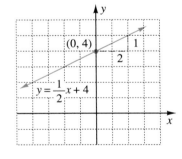

Solution

$m = \frac{1}{2}, b = 4$

$y = \frac{1}{2}x + 4$

Try This

Write an equation of a line that contains the point $(0, -3)$ and has slope -2. Graph the line.

When the equation of a line is written in the form $Ax + By = C$, where A and B are both not zero, it is said to be in standard form. If the equation of a line is written in standard form you can determine the slope and y-intercept of the line. You can do this by solving the equation for y and writing the equation in the slope-intercept form, as illustrated in the following example.

Example 2

Determine the slope and y-intercept of the line $3x + 4y = 12$. Graph the line.

Solution

$$3x + 4y = 12$$
$$4y = -3x + 12$$
$$y = -\tfrac{3}{4}x + 3$$
$$m = \tfrac{-3}{4} \qquad \textit{m represents the slope.}$$
$$b = 3 \qquad \textit{b represents the y-intercept.}$$

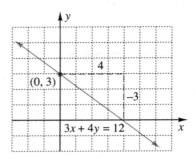

Try This

Determine the slope and y-intercept of the line $5x - 2y = 10$. Graph the line.

Given a point on a line and its slope, you can write an equation of a line in the following form.

◆ THEOREM 12.5   Point-Slope Form

An equation of the line that passes through point (x_1, y_1) and has slope m is $y - y_1 = m(x - x_1)$.

Example 3

Write an equation of a line that contains the point $(-4, 3)$ and has slope $-\tfrac{2}{3}$. Graph the line.

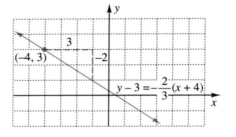

Solution

$$x_1 = -4,\ y_1 = 3,\ m = -\tfrac{2}{3}$$
$$y - 3 = -\tfrac{2}{3}(x - (-4))$$
$$y - 3 = -\tfrac{2}{3}(x + 4)$$

Try This

Write an equation of a line that contains the point $(2, -5)$ and has slope $\tfrac{4}{3}$.

Given coordinates of two points on a line, you can determine an equation of the line by finding the slope of the line and using the point-slope form.

Example 4

Find an equation of a line that contains the points $(-3, 6)$ and $(1, 2)$.

Solution

$$m = \tfrac{6 - 2}{-3 - 1} = -1 \qquad \textit{Definition of slope}$$
$$x_1 = 1,\ y_1 = 2$$
$$y - 2 = -1(x - 1) \qquad \textit{Substitute in point-slope form}$$

Try This

Find an equation of a line that contains the points $(5, -2)$ and $(0, 4)$. Graph the line.

Class Exercises

Short Answer

State the slope and y-intercept of each line.

1. $y = 2x - 4$ **2.** $y = -\frac{3}{4}x + 10$ **3.** $y = 0.2x + 5$
4. $x = -7$ **5.** $x + y = -8$ **6.** $y = 4$

7. Does the line $y = \frac{1}{2}x$ contain the origin?

8. Does the line $y = \frac{3}{4}x - 5$ contain the origin?

Sample Exercises

9. Write an equation of a line that has slope $\frac{2}{3}$ and y-intercept -2.
10. Graph the equation of the line $y = \frac{3}{4}x - 5$.
11. Find the slope and y-intercept of the line $2y - x = 5$.
12. Find an equation of a line that contains the point $(1, -3)$ and has slope 2.
13. Find an equation of the line that contains the points $(0, -4)$ and $(6, 0)$.

Discussion

14. Explain how you can find an equation of a line that is perpendicular to the line $y = -2x + 3$ through the point $(1, 1)$.
15. Triangle ABC has vertices with coordinates $A(1, 2)$, $B(-2, 3)$, and $C(4, -7)$.
Explain how you can find an equation of the line containing the median $\overline{AM}$.

Exercises

A

Write the equation of each line in the form $y = mx + b$.

1. $m = 2$, $b = 3$ **2.** $m = -4$, $b = 5$ **3.** $m = -\frac{3}{4}$, $b = -\frac{1}{2}$
4. $m = -0.2$ **5.** $m = 0$ **6.** $m = 0$
    y-intercept $= -2.5$ y-intercept $= -2$ y-intercept $= 0$

Determine the slope and y-intercept of each line and graph the equation.

7. $y = x + 4$ **8.** $y = -2x - 3$ **9.** $y = -\frac{3}{2}x + 3$
10. $x = 5$ **11.** $y = -1$ **12.** $y = \frac{3}{2}x - 4$
13. $x + 2y = 4$ **14.** $y - 4 = -2x$ **15.** $5 - 3x = 2y$

Write an equation of each line given the slope and a point on the line.

16. $m = -3$, $P(-2, 1)$ **17.** $m = \frac{2}{3}$, $P(0, 0)$ **18.** $m = -\frac{1}{2}$, $P(4, 3)$
19. $m = 0$, $P(-2, -3)$ **20.** $m = \frac{3}{2}$, $P(-3, -4)$ **21.** $m = -\frac{5}{2}$, $P(0, 4)$
22. $m = 5$, $P(2, 4)$ **23.** $m = -2$, $P(0, 0)$ **24.** $m = 0$, $P(5, 0)$

Find an equation of the line that contains the given points.

25. $(0, 0)$, $(4, 3)$ **26.** $(-2, 1)$, $(5, -3)$ **27.** $(0, 0)$, $(-3, -3)$
28. $(5, 2)$, $(-3, 2)$ **29.** $(1, 3)$, $(-4, -2)$ **30.** $(-2, 4)$, $(4, -2)$
31. $(2, 4)$, $(-2, -4)$ **32.** $(0, 3)$, $(0, 9)$ **33.** $(4, 0)$, $(-2, 0)$

B

34. Suppose for every ounce of weight added to a spring the spring stretches an additional 0.5 in. The relationship between the weight (x) and the length of the stretch (y) is given by the equation $y = 0.5x$.

y (length)
(weight)
x

   a. Find the slope of the line.
   b. Find the y-intercept.
   c. If the weight is doubled from 2 units to 4 units, how much is the spring stretched because of the additional weight?

35. Suppose the cost in dollars of a taxi is represented by the equation $C = 0.10d + 0.50$, where C is the cost of the taxi and d is the number of tenths of miles traveled.

   a. Find the slope of the line.
   b. Find the cost if the taxi travels 5 mi.

36. Suppose a gallon of gasoline costs \$1.05.

   a. Write an equation that represents the relationship between cost (y) and gallons (x).
   b. Find the slope of the graph of the line.
   c. Does the line contain the origin?

Find the slope of the line that is perpendicular to the given line.

37. $y = -2x + 3$ 38. $y = \frac{4}{3}x + 6$
39. $2x - 3y = 6$ 40. $12x + 30y = 18$

41. Find an equation of the line that contains the point $(4, 2)$ and is perpendicular to the line $y = -2x - 4$.
42. Consider a circle with center at the origin. Find an equation of the line that is tangent to the circle at the point $(-3, 4)$ on the circle.
43. The vertices of a triangle have coordinates $A(0, 0)$, $B(2, 4)$, and $C(-4, 2)$. Find an equation of the line that contains the altitude to $\overline{BC}$.
44. Find an equation of the line that contains the altitude $\overline{AD}$ of $\triangle ABC$ with vertices that have coordinates $A(-1, 5)$, $B(-7, -3)$, and $C(5, 1)$.
45. Find the point of intersection of the line $x - 3y = 1$ and the line containing the points $(1, 7)$ and $(6, -3)$.
46. If the x- and y-intercepts of a line are $(4, 0)$ and $(0, -3)$, find an equation of the line.
47. Find the area of a triangle formed by the x-axis, the y-axis, and the line $y = x - 5$.
48. Find an equation of the line that contains the median $\overline{AD}$ of $\triangle ABC$ with vertices that have coordinates $A(4, 4)$, $B(6, 2)$, and $C(-2, -4)$.
49. Find an equation of each of the lines that contain the diagonals of rectangle $ABCD$ with vertices that have coordinates $A(6, -4)$, $B(6, 2)$, $C(3, 2)$, and $D(3, -4)$.
50. Find an equation of the line that is the perpendicular bisector of the segment $\overline{AB}$ with endpoints that have coordinates $A(10, 2)$ and $B(2, -6)$.
51. If the line containing the points $E(x, 3)$ and $F(2, 0)$ is parallel to the line containing the points $D(2, 8)$ and $C(-3, -4)$, find x.

C

52. A diagonal of a square lies on the line $3x - 5y = 14$. One vertex is at $(0, 4)$. Find an equation of the line that contains the other diagonal.
53. The equations of two adjacent sides of a parallelogram are $x + 2y = 0$ and $3x + y + 3 = 0$. One vertex has coordinates $(8, -7)$. Find an equation of each of the lines that contain the other two sides of the parallelogram.
54. Find the distance between two parallel lines with equations $y = -1x + 10$ and $y = -1x + 15$.
   (HINT: Draw an accurate diagram.)
55. The coordinates of $\triangle ABC$ are $A(0, 0)$, $B(6, 0)$, and $C(4, 6)$. $\overline{AD}$ is an altitude to $\overline{BC}$. Find the coordinates of D.
56. The coordinates of the vertices of a triangle are $(0, 0)$, $(18, 0)$, and $(6, 12)$. Find the coordinates of the centroid.

Critical Thinking

57. Identify two variables that you think have some relationship, such as a person's height and weight or the number of "at bats" and the number of "hits" for a baseball player. Collect data and graph the ordered pairs.

   a. Draw a line that appears to most closely fit the data.
   b. Determine the slope and the y-intercept of the line.

estimate of best fit line

Algebra Review

Simplify.

1. $\sqrt{27} + \sqrt{3}$ 2. $\sqrt{75} - \sqrt{12}$ 3. $\sqrt{108} + 3\sqrt{3}$

Quiz

Use the points $W(-3, 6)$, $X(5, -8)$, $Y(-3, 4)$, and $Z(-1, 5)$.

1. Point W is in quadrant __?__ and point X is in quadrant __?__ .
2. State the coordinates of the midpoint of $\overline{WZ}$.
3. State the coordinates of the midpoint of $\overline{YZ}$.
4. Find the slope of $\overleftrightarrow{WY}$.
5. Find the slope of the line that is perpendicular to $\overline{XZ}$.
6. Use the form $y = mx + b$ to write an equation of the line that passes through X and Y.
7. A line with slope $-\frac{1}{2}$ passes through the points $(4, -2)$ and $(6, y)$. Find y.
8. State the slope and y-intercept of the line $-3x + 4y = 12$. Graph the line.
9. Write an equation of the line that is parallel to the line $y = -5x + 3$ and contains the point $(2, -8)$.

USING THE DISTANCE FORMULA

OBJECTIVE: *Apply the distance formula.*

12-5 The Distance Formula

The distance formula, which you used in previous chapters to find the distance between two points in the coordinate plane, is restated and proved here as a theorem.

◆ **THEOREM 12.6** Distance Formula

The distance d between points $P_1(x_1, y_1)$ and $P_2(x_2, y_2)$ is given by the formula $d = \sqrt{(x_2 - x_1)^2 + (y_2 - y_1)^2}$.

Given: points $P_1(x_1, y_1)$ and $P_2(x_2, y_2)$

Prove: $P_1 P_2 = \sqrt{(x_2 - x_1)^2 + (y_2 - y_1)^2}$

Proof Let R be the intersection of a line through P_1 parallel to the x-axis and a line through P_2 parallel to the y-axis. It follows that $\angle R$ is a right angle and that R has coordinates (x_2, y_1). $P_1 R = |x_2 - x_1|$ and $P_2 R = |y_2 - y_1|$ since the segments are parallel to the x- and y-axes, respectively. Since $\triangle P_1 R P_2$ is a right triangle, by the Pythagorean Theorem $(P_1 P_2)^2 = (P_1 R)^2 + (P_2 R)^2$. Substitution and algebra result in the following equations.

$$(P_1 P_2)^2 = (|x_2 - x_1|)^2 + (|y_2 - y_1|)^2$$
$$(P_1 P_2)^2 = (x_2 - x_1)^2 + (y_2 - y_1)^2$$
$$P_1 P_2 = \sqrt{(x_2 - x_1)^2 + (y_2 - y_1)^2}$$

Example 1
Find the distance between $A(2, 3)$ and $B(-3, -2)$.

Solution

$AB = \sqrt{(-3 - 2)^2 + (-2 - 3)^2}$ *Distance Formula*

$AB = \sqrt{25 + 25} = \sqrt{50}$

$AB = 5\sqrt{2}$

Try This
Find the distance between $C(-1, 6)$ and $D(8, -2)$.

Given the coordinates of the vertices of a triangle, you can use the distance formula to classify the triangle as scalene, isosceles, or equilateral.

Example 2

Determine whether $\triangle ABC$ is scalene, isosceles, or equilateral.

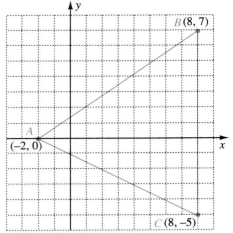

Solution

$AB = \sqrt{(8 - (-2))^2 + (7 - 0)^2} = \sqrt{149}$ *Distance*
$BC = \sqrt{(0)^2 + (7 - (-5))^2} = \sqrt{144}$ *Formula*
$AC = \sqrt{(8 - (-2))^2 + (-5 - 0)^2} = \sqrt{125}$

$\triangle ABC$ is scalene.   *Definition of scalene triangle*

Try This

Determine whether $\triangle ABC$ with vertices $A(-2, 5)$, $B(1, -1)$, and $C(4, 2)$ is scalene, isosceles, or equilateral.

Class Exercises

Short Answer

1. Find the length of $\overline{AB}$ if A has coordinates $(6, -3)$ and B has coordinates $(-1, -3)$.
2. Find the length of $\overline{CD}$ if C has coordinates $(-2, -4)$ and D has coordinates $(-2, -1)$.
3. Find the distance between the points $(0, 0)$ and $(3, 4)$.
4. Does the segment from point $(2, 2)$ to point $(3, 4)$ have the same length as the segment from point $(0, 0)$ to point $(1, 1)$?
5. Does the segment from point $(0, 0)$ to point $(3, 4)$ have the same length as the segment from point $(0, 0)$ to point $(-3, -4)$?
6. Given the coordinates of the vertices of a triangle, how many times must you apply the distance formula to find the perimeter of the triangle?

Sample Exercises

Find the distance between the given points.

7. $(6, -1), (-2, -1)$ 8. $(-1, 4), (-6, 2)$

9. Determine whether $\triangle ABC$ with vertices $A(6, 1)$, $B(-2, -3)$, and $C(0, 3)$ is scalene, isosceles, or equilateral.
10. Given the points $A(-4, 13)$, $B(-2, 7)$, and $C(2, -5)$, use the distance formula to determine if B is between A and C.
    (HINT: If B is between A and C, then $AB + BC = AC$.)

Discussion

11. Consider triangle ABC with vertices $A(-1, -6)$, $B(5, 2)$, and $C(-3, -2)$. Use the distance formula to answer the following questions.
    a. Why is the triangle a right triangle?   **b.** Which sides are the legs?
    c. Is the triangle an isosceles right triangle?   **d.** What is the area of $\triangle ABC$?

Exercises

A

Find the distance between the given points.

1. $(-4, 5), (6, 5)$ 2. $(3, 2), (3, -8)$ 3. $(4, 5), (-3, -2)$ 4. $(-2, 5), (5, -2)$
5. $(4, 0), (0, -6)$ 6. $(1, 2), (-7, 3)$ 7. $(-5, 3), (0, -4)$ 8. $(6, -2), (7, 3)$

Determine whether $\triangle ABC$ is scalene, isosceles, or equilateral.

9. $A(4, 5), B(5, -2), C(1, 1)$ 10. $A(-6, 2), B(1, 7), C(6, 3)$
11. $A(10, -5), B(-2, 1), C(7, 4)$ 12. $A(1, 1), B(-3, 5), C(\frac{2}{3} - 1, \frac{2}{3} + 3)$

Use the distance formula to determine if the triangle is a right triangle.

13. $A(1, 4), B(-2, -2), C(10, -8)$ 14. $A(5, 7), B(8, -5), C(-4, -4)$

15. Is it easier to use the definition of slope or the distance formula to determine whether a triangle is a right triangle?

Use the distance formula to determine if B is between A and C.
(HINT: If B is between A and C, then $AB + BC = AC$.)

16. $A(-3, -3), B(0, -2), C(6, 8)$ 17. $A(1, -2), B(4, 3), C(10, 12)$

18. Is it easier to use the definition of slope or the distance formula to determine if three points are collinear?

B

19. Graph and label at least four points that satisfy the condition that the distance from the point $(1, 2)$ is 5 units.
20. Given $\triangle ABC$ with vertices $A(2, 6), B(3, -5)$, and $C(-1, 7)$, find the length of the median $\overline{AD}$.
21. Given a trapezoid with vertices at points $(4, 0), (8, 0), (0, 2)$, and $(0, 4)$, find the length of the median. (HINT: Graph the trapezoid and determine which segment is the median.)
22. The distance between the points $(1, 2)$ and $(x, 8)$ is 10. Find x.
23. Given isosceles $\triangle ABC$ with $AC = BC$ and vertices with coordinates $A(-1, 4), B(-3, -2)$, and $C(x, -1)$, find x.
24. Rectangle $ABCD$ has vertices $A(0, 0), B(2, 1), C(4, -3)$, and $D(2, -4)$ and is inscribed in a circle. Find the length of the diameter of the circle.
25. Find the length of the diameter of the circle circumscribed about a right triangle with vertices $(8, 0), (5, 2)$, and $(2, -9)$.
26. Find the area of a $\triangle ABC$ with coordinates $A(3, 4), B(-3, -5)$, and $C(6, 2)$.
27. Find the area of $\triangle ABC$ with vertices $A(-3, -4), B(3, 4)$, and $C(-5, 0)$.
28. Find the area of $ABCD$ with vertices $A(-2, 3), B(3, 8), C(8, 3)$ and $D(3, 2)$.
29. Assign a coordinate system for a baseball diamond and a point A in the field as follows: $C(0, 0), D(90, 0), E(90, 90)$, $A(280, 20), B(0, 90)$. If a right fielder throws the baseball from point A to third base (point B), how far does the ball travel?
30. If a baseball player picks up the ball halfway between second base (point E) and third base (point B) and throws the ball to first base (point D), how far has the ball been thrown?

31. In a championship high school soccer match, the winning goal was kicked by Maya from a point 10 yd behind the midfield strip and 5 yd from the sideline. How far was Maya from the center of the goal when she kicked the winning goal?

32. In a championship high school basketball game, Vonetta made the winning shot from a point even with the foul line and 10 ft to the side of the foul line. How far was she from the basket?

C

33. Find the coordinates of the point equidistant from the points $(3, 11)$, $(9, 5)$, and $(7, -1)$.

34. Find the coordinates of the point that is equidistant from the points $(0, 6)$ and $(10, 0)$ and lies on the line $y = x$.

35. Given $\triangle ABC$ with vertices $A(5, 2)$, $B(1, 5)$, and $C(-1, 1)$, find the length of the altitude $\overline{AD}$.

36. Consider a three-dimensional coordinate system with an x-axis, a y-axis, and a z-axis. A cube with each edge 4 units is placed as shown in the figure to the right.

    a. Find the length of $\overline{OP}$.

    b. Find a formula for the length of the diagonal $\overline{OP}$ in a cube with one vertex at the origin and edges on the x- and y-axes. (HINT: Let P have coordinates (x_1, y_1, z_1).)

Critical Thinking

37. You can estimate the distance between points $A(x_1, y_1)$ and $B(x_2, y_2)$ by using the following formula.

$$d = \text{maximum}(|x_1 - x_2|, |y_1 - y_2|) + \tfrac{1}{3}\text{minimum}(|x_1 - x_2|, |y_1 - y_2|)$$

Use the distance formula and the formula for estimating distance between points, given above, to calculate the lengths of several segments. On the basis of these trials, what would be the greatest percent of error one could expect using the estimate formula?

Mixed Review

$\overline{AC}$ is a secant. $\overline{AD}$ is a tangent. $m\widehat{BC} = 100$, $m\angle CBD = 100$, $m\widehat{BD} = 60$

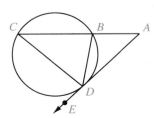

    1. Find $m\angle ABD$.

    2. Find $m\angle BCD$.

    3. Find $m\angle CAD$.

    4. Find $m\angle EDC$.

Coordinate Geometry and Statistics

The equation of a line is often used in statistics to explain the behavior of the values of one variable in terms of the values of another variable. Consider the graph below. The equation of the line is $y = -1.5x + 18$.

Occupational Safety

Hours Lost Due to Accidents

$y = -1.5x + 18$

Hours of Safety Instruction

This equation results from finding a "line of best fit" for the data shown on the graph. This line is called the **linear regression line.** The horizontal axis relates the number of hours spent in safety training prior to using a machine in the factory. The value of y represents the number of hours lost from the job due to machine-related accidents in the first year on the job.

The value of the slope of the regression line tells us that for every increase of 1 h in training, the average decrease in hours lost due to an accident related to the training area is 1.5 h, or 1 h and 30 min.

Exercises

Refer to the graph above.

1. What is the significance of the y-intercept of 18?
2. How much training, at least in theory, would result in the elimination of the accidents targeted by the training program?
3. Refer to the graph below. Write a short paragraph telling what this equation tells about the relationship between number of hours spent studying geometry and grades on a test on coordinate geometry.

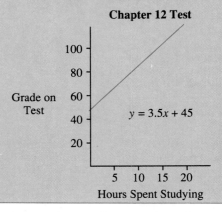

Chapter 12 Test

Grade on Test

$y = 3.5x + 45$

Hours Spent Studying

12-6 The Equation of a Circle

In Chapter 8, the definition of a circle was given as the set of all points in a plane a given distance from a fixed point called the center. A circle can be represented in various ways in the coordinate plane. One way to develop an equation of a circle is by using the distance formula, as demonstrated below.

An equation of a circle can be used to graph a circle on a computer screen.

Consider the circle to the right with center at the origin and a radius of 5 units.

Using the distance formula you obtain the following.

$$5 = \sqrt{(x - 0)^2 + (y - 0)^2} \quad \text{or} \quad x^2 + y^2 = 5^2$$

If r units is used for the radius rather than 5 units, you have the following equation of a circle with center at the origin and a radius of r units.

$$x^2 + y^2 = r^2$$

Now consider the circle to the right, which also has a radius of 5 units but has its center at $(-2, 3)$ rather than at the origin. The distance formula is used to find the distance between the point $(-2, 3)$ and the general point $P(x, y)$ in developing the following equation.

$$5 = \sqrt{(x - (-2))^2 + (y - (3))^2} \quad \text{or}$$
$$(x - (-2))^2 + (y - (3))^2 = 5^2$$

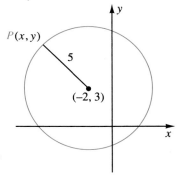

The development presented above leads to the following theorem, which gives an equation of a circle that has its center at (h, k) and radius r units.

◆ **THEOREM 12.7**

An equation of the circle with center (h, k) and radius r is
$(x - h)^2 + (y - k)^2 = r^2$.

Example 1

Write an equation of the circle with center $(3, -2)$ and radius 6.

Solution

$(x - h)^2 + (y - k)^2 = r^2$ *Theorem 12.6*
$(x - 3)^2 + (y - (-2))^2 = 6^2$ *Substitution*
$(x - 3)^2 + (y + 2)^2 = 36$

Try This

Write an equation of the circle with center $(4, -1)$ and radius 4.

Example 2

Find the center and radius of the circle. $(x - 2)^2 + (y + 6)^2 = 20$

Solution

$(x - 2)^2 + (y - (-6))^2 = (\sqrt{20})^2$ *Rewrite in*
                                         standard form.
The circle has center $(2, -6)$, radius $\sqrt{20}$ or $2\sqrt{5}$.   *Theorem 12.6*

Try This

Find the center and radius of the circle. $(x + 3)^2 + (y - 7)^2 = 50$

Class Exercises

Short Answer

Find the center and radius for each circle.

1. $x^2 + y^2 = 100$
2. $(x - 2)^2 + (y - 4)^2 = 81$
3. $(x - 1)^2 + (y + 1)^2 = 16$
4. $(x + 3)^2 + y^2 = 72$
5. $x^2 + (y + 2)^2 = 18$
6. $(x + 6)^2 + (y - (-4))^2 = 40$

Sample Exercises

Write an equation of the circle with the given center and radius.

7. $(0, 0); 6$ 8. $(-2, 3); \sqrt{12}$ 9. $(-3, 0); 3\sqrt{5}$

Sketch the graph of each circle.

10. $(x - 3)^2 + y^2 = 1$ 11. $(x + 2)^2 + (y - 1)^2 = 4$

12. For what value of r does the circle $(x - 3)^2 + (y + 4)^2 = r^2$ contain the origin?

Discussion

13. Consider a circle tangent to the x- and y-axes with radius 4 units.
    a. Explain why there is more than one such possible circle.
    b. Sketch each possible circle on the same coordinate system.
    c. Write an equation for each of the possible circles.

Exercises

A

Write an equation of each circle with the given center and radius.

1. $(0, 0)$; 5
2. $(0, 2)$; 3
3. $(-5, 0)$; 4
4. $(2, 3)$; 6
5. $(-3, -4)$; 4
6. $(-3, 5)$; 2
7. $(-1, 3)$; $2\sqrt{3}$
8. $(3, -6)$; $\sqrt{10}$
9. (a, b); c

Find the center and radius of each circle.

10. $x^2 + y^2 = 25$
11. $x^2 + y^2 = 20$
12. $x^2 + (y - 3)^2 = 12$
13. $(x + 6)^2 + y^2 = 45$
14. $(x + 4)^2 + (y - 2)^2 = 10$
15. $(x - a)^2 + (y - b)^2 = 36$

16. Sketch the graph of $(x - 2)^2 + (y + 1)^2 = 9$.
17. Sketch the graph of $(x + 1)^2 + y^2 = 4$.
18. For what value of r does the circle $(x + 5)^2 + (y - 12)^2 = r^2$ contain the origin?

B

19. Write an equation of the circle with center $(-4, 0)$ that contains the origin.
20. Write an equation of the circle with center $(3, 4)$ that contains the origin.
21. Write an equation of the circle with center $(4, -2)$ that contains the point $(0, 5)$.
22. Write an equation of the circle with center $(-2, 3)$ that contains the point $(3, 3)$.

Write an equation of each circle given the endpoints of a diameter.

23. $(-4, 0)$ and $(2, 0)$
24. $(3, 6)$ and $(3, -2)$
25. $(3, 6)$ and $(-5, 6)$

26. Write an equation of the line that is tangent to the circle $x^2 + y^2 = 25$ at the point $(-3, 4)$.
27. Write an equation of the line that contains the centers of the circles $(x + 4)^2 + (y - 2)^2 = 36$ and $(x - 5)^2 + (y + 3)^2 = 17$.
28. Write an equation of the circle with center at $(-5, -5)$ and tangent to both the x-axis and the y-axis.
29. Write an equation of a circle that has the same center as the circle $(x + 4)^2 + (y - 3)^2 = 9$ and is tangent to the y-axis.

Given the circle $x^2 + y^2 = 49$, determine if each line is a tangent to the circle, secant to the circle, or neither.

30. $x = 5$
31. $y = 9$
32. $x = -7$
33. $y = x$

Given the circle $(x + 4)^2 + (y - 3)^2 = 25$, determine if each line is tangent to the circle, secant to the circle, or neither.

34. $y = -2$
35. $y = -x$
36. $x = 1$
37. $y = 9$

38. A circle with radius of 2 units is tangent to the x-axis at the point $(6, 0)$. Is there more than one circle that satisfies these conditions? Write an equation for each possible circle.

39. Suppose the intersection of the circles shown is the origin and each circle has diameter 8 cm. Write an equation of each of the four circles.

40. Write an equation of the circle that contains the points $(-10, 0)$, $(0, 0)$, and $(0, -20)$.

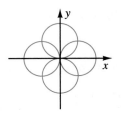

C

41. Find the area of the ring formed by the concentric circles defined by the equations $(x - 2)^2 + (y + 6)^2 = 25$ and $(x - 2)^2 + (y + 6)^2 = 36$.

42. Find an equation of the circle that has its center on the line $y = \frac{1}{2}x$ and contains the points $(0, 6)$ and $(0, -2)$.

43. Write an equation of the circle with center at $(1, 7)$ and tangent to the line $x + 3y = 12$.

44. Find the length of a tangent segment from the point $(6, 4)$ to the circle $x^2 + y^2 = 36$.

45. Suppose a sphere with center at $(0, 0, 0)$ contains the point $P(4, 4, 4)$ in a three-dimensional coordinate system. Write an equation that represents the sphere.

46. Write an equation of a sphere that has its center at $(1, 3, 2)$ and contains the point $(4, -2, 3)$.

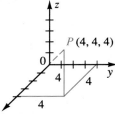

Critical Thinking

47. In the equation of the circle $x^2 + y^2 = 16$ the coefficients of x^2 and y^2 are 1. Suppose the coefficients are not 1. Sketch the following equations. Conjecture the effects if the coefficients are not 1.

   a. $x^2 + 2y^2 = 16$ **b.** $2x^2 + y^2 = 16$
   c. $x^2 + 4y^2 = 16$ **d.** $4x^2 + y^2 = 16$

   (HINT: Determine the points at which the curves cross the x- and y-axes.)

Mixed Review

1. Find the area of a rectangular field whose length is 100 yd and width is 79 yd.
2. Find the area of a circular pond with a diameter of 48 m.

Quiz

Determine whether each statement is true or false.

1. If $R(-3, 6)$ and $S(4, 2)$, then $RS = \sqrt{17}$.
2. If $A(4, -3)$ and $B(-2, -1)$, then $AB = 2\sqrt{10}$.
3. The circle with equation $(x - 4)^2 + (y + 3)^2 = 9$ has its center at $(-4, 3)$.
4. The length of the radius of the circle $(x - 2)^2 + y^2 = 16$ is 4.
5. The line $y = 5$ is tangent to the circle $x^2 + y^2 = 25$.

Write the equation of each circle with the given center and radius.

6. center $(-3, 5)$, radius $2\sqrt{7}$ 7. center $(0, -1)$, radius 3

OBJECTIVE: *Choose an appropriate placement of a figure on a coordinate system for proving theorems.*

12-7 Organizing Proofs

In geometry, statements and theorems can be proved using a variety of methods. Some theorems can be easily proved using coordinates. An important part of a coordinate proof is choosing the coordinates of the figure. Consider the following theorem.

The diagonals of a rectangle are congruent.

Note the placement of the figure below used in the coordinate proof of the theorem.

Given: $RSTV$ is a rectangle.

Prove: $TR = VS$

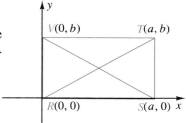

Proof Let $R(0, 0)$, $S(a, 0)$, and $V(0, b)$ be the coordinates of three vertices of the rectangle. The coordinates of T will be (a, b). From the distance formula you obtain the following.

$$VS = \sqrt{(0 - a)^2 + (b - 0)^2} = \sqrt{a^2 + b^2}$$
$$TR = \sqrt{(a - 0)^2 + (b - 0)^2} = \sqrt{a^2 + b^2}$$

Therefore, $VS = TR$ and the diagonals of a rectangle are congruent.

A second possible placement for the rectangle is shown to the right, with $R(-a, 0)$, $S(a, 0)$, $T(a, b)$, and $V(-a, b)$ as coordinates of the vertices of the rectangle. In this case from the distance formula you obtain

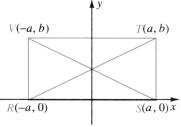

$$VS = \sqrt{(-a - a)^2 + (b - 0)^2} = \sqrt{4a^2 + b^2}$$
$$TR = \sqrt{(a - (-a))^2 + (b - 0)^2} = \sqrt{4a^2 + b^2}$$

Therefore, $VS = TR$ and, again, the diagonals of a rectangle are congruent.

In most cases a theorem can be proved by positioning the figure in any of several ways. Consider the following theorem.

The median to the base of an isosceles triangle is perpendicular to the base.

In proving this theorem, let $\triangle RTS$ be an isosceles triangle with $RT = TS$ and median $\overline{TV}$. Consider the two different positions presented for proving that median $\overline{TV}$ is perpendicular to the base of $\triangle RTS$.

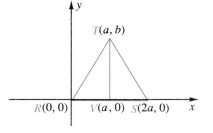

In the placement on the left $\overline{RS}$ is on the x-axis so that R has coordinates $(0, 0)$ and S has coordinates $(2a, 0)$. Since $RT = TS$, you can assign T the coordinates (a, b). Since $\overline{TV}$ is a median, V has coordinates $(a, 0)$. It follows that $\overline{TV}$ is a vertical line and hence it is perpendicular to $\overline{RS}$.

In the second possible placement, shown on the right, $\overline{TS}$ is placed on the x-axis and $\overline{TR}$ is placed on the y-axis, with the coordinates indicated. Since $\overline{TV}$ is a median, V has coordinates (a, a). To prove the theorem with this placement, you must show that the product of the slope of $\overline{TV}$ and the slope of $\overline{RS}$ is -1.

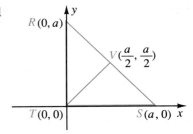

Example 1

$\triangle ABC$ is an equilateral triangle with coordinates $A(0, 0)$ and $B(2a, 0)$. Determine the coordinates of C without introducing any new letters.

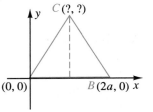

Solution

x-coordinate of $C = a$ $\frac{1}{2}$ the length of $\overline{AB}$

y-coordinate of $C = a\sqrt{3}$ Altitude of equilateral $\triangle$ is $a\sqrt{3}$.

C has coordinates $(a, a\sqrt{3})$.

Try This

Determine the coordinates of C for coordinates $B(a, 0)$ and $A(0, 0)$.

Example 2

Set up a coordinate system to prove the following statement.
The medians to the congruent sides of an isosceles triangle are congruent.

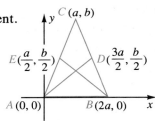

Solution

Given: isosceles $\triangle ABC$, $AC = BC$
        $\overline{BE}$ and $\overline{AD}$ are medians.

Prove: $BF = AD$

Try This

Set up a coordinate system to prove the following statement.
The medians to any two sides of an equilateral triangle are congruent.

Class Exercises

Short Answer

Supply the missing coordinates.

1. $ABCD$ is a square.

2. $ABCD$ is a rectangle.

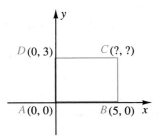

3. *ABCD* is a rhombus.

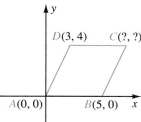

$D(3, 4)$ $C(?, ?)$

$A(0, 0)$ $B(5, 0)$ x

4. $\triangle ABC$ is isosceles.

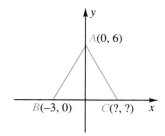

$A(0, 6)$

$B(-3, 0)$ $C(?, ?)$ x

5. *ABCD* is a parallelogram.

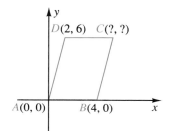

$D(2, 6)$ $C(?, ?)$

$A(0, 0)$ $B(4, 0)$ x

6. *ABCD* is an isosceles trapezoid.

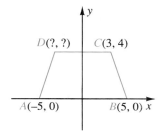

$D(?, ?)$ $C(3, 4)$

$A(-5, 0)$ $B(5, 0)$ x

Sample Exercises

Supply the missing coordinates without introducing any new letters.

7. *CDEF* is a parallelogram.

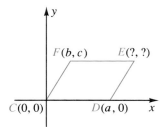

$F(b, c)$ $E(?, ?)$

$C(0, 0)$ $D(a, 0)$ x

8. $\triangle RST$ is an isosceles triangle.

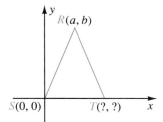

$R(a, b)$

$S(0, 0)$ $T(?, ?)$ x

Set up a coordinate system that could be used to prove each statement.

9. The diagonals of a square are congruent.

10. The opposite sides of a parallelogram are congruent.

Discussion

11. Which placement below is better for proving the following statement.
The diagonals of an isosceles trapezoid are congruent? Justify your choice.

a.

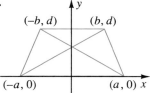

$(-b, d)$ (b, d)

$(-a, 0)$ $(a, 0)$ x

b.

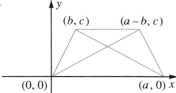

(b, c) $(a-b, c)$

$(0, 0)$ $(a, 0)$ x

Exercises

A

Supply the missing coordinates for each figure without introducing any new letters.

1. *ABCD* is a rhombus.

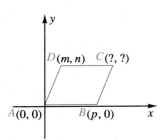

2. *RSTV* is a parallelogram.

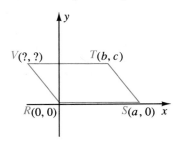

Set up a coordinate system that could be used to prove each statement.

3. The diagonals of a square bisect each other.

4. The diagonals of a parallelogram bisect each other.

5. The altitude of an isosceles triangle bisects the base.

6. The segment joining the midpoints of two sides of a triangle is one half the length of the third side.

7. The diagonals of a rhombus are perpendicular.

B

Supply the missing coordinates for each figure without introducing any new letters.

8. *ABCD* is a rhombus.

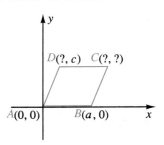

9. $\triangle ABC$ is an equilateral triangle.

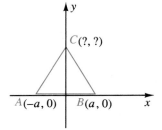

10. *KLMN* is a parallelogram.

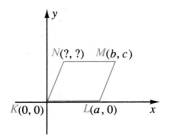

11. $\triangle DEF$ is an isosceles triangle with base $\overline{DF}$.

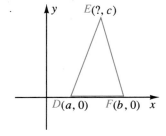

12. Consider quadrilateral *ABCD* with coordinates shown to the right. Determine the coordinates of the midpoints *E*, *F*, *G*, and *H* of sides $\overline{AB}$, $\overline{BC}$, $\overline{CD}$, and $\overline{DA}$, respectively.

13. Use the distance formula to show that $GF = HE$ and $HG = EF$.
    Is *EFGH* a parallelogram? Why or why not?

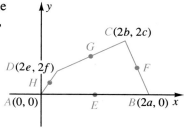

c

14. *ABCDEFGH* is a regular octagon with coordinates for *A* as shown. Determine the coordinates for points *B*, *E*, and *F*. Show that $\overline{AB} \parallel \overline{EF}$.

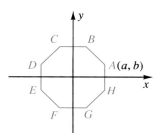

15. *ABCDEF* is a regular hexagon with coordinates for *A* as shown. Determine the coordinates for *B*, *D*, and *E* and show that $\overline{AB} \parallel \overline{DE}$.

Critical Thinking

16. Kelly, Maria, and Yoshie were trying to prove the following theorem. If *M* is the midpoint of side $\overline{AB}$ of equilateral triangle *ABC*, then the sum of the distances from *M* to sides $\overline{AC}$ and $\overline{BC}$ is equal to the length of the altitude.

    Each student used a different placement of the triangle, as shown below.

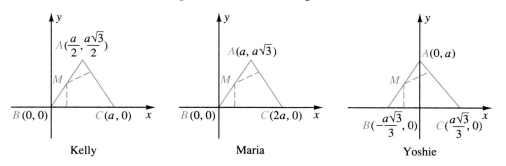

Kelly   Maria   Yoshie

    Which placement makes the proof the easiest? Explain your choice.

Algebra Review

Simplify.

1. $\dfrac{3a^2}{4a^6}$ 2. $(3x^2)^2$ 3. $\dfrac{-6a^2b^3}{2ab^2}$

Enrichment

Equations for Parabolas

In a Critical Thinking exercise in Chapter 9 you found the locus of points that are equidistant from a given line and a given point not on the line. The locus of points define a particular curve called a **parabola.** The coordinate plane and the distance formula can be used to develop equations for parabolas when the line and the point are given.

Example

Determine an equation of the parabola that is equidistant from $y = 0$ (*x*-axis) and from the point $(0, 2)$.

Solution

Let $P(x, y)$ be the general point that is equidistant from the line $y = 0$ (*x*-axis) and $(0, 2)$.

$d_1 = y - 0 = y$

$d_2 = \sqrt{(x - 0)^2 + (y - 2)^2}$

Since $d_1 = d_2$, then

$y = \sqrt{(x - 0)^2 + (y - 2)^2}$

$y^2 = (x - 0)^2 + (y - 2)^2$ *Square both sides of the equation.*

$y^2 = x^2 + y^2 - 4y + 4$ *Remove the parentheses.*

$4y = x^2 + 4$ *Addition Property of Equality*

$y = \frac{1}{4}x^2 + 1$ *Multiplication Property of Equality*

Thus $y = \frac{1}{4}x^2 + 1$ is the equation of the parabola that is equidistant from the *x*-axis and the point $(0, 2)$.

Exercises

Determine an equation for the parabola defined by each pair of lines and points.

1. $y = 0$ (*x*-axis), $(0, 1)$
2. $y = 0$ (*x*-axis), $(0, 3)$
3. $y = 2$, $(0, 3)$
4. $y = 2$, $(0, 5)$
5. $y = -2$, $(0, 2)$
6. $y = -2$, $(3, 2)$

7. Compare the equations from Exercises 1 and 2 and the equations from Exercises 3 and 4. What seems to be the effect on the equation when the point gets farther away from the line?
8. Compare the equations from Exercises 5 and 6. What seems to be the effect on the equation when the point is off the *y*-axis but the same distance from the line?
9. For the equations in Exercises 1 and 2, choose numbers for *x* and find the corresponding values for *y*. Use the same set of axes and graph the ordered pairs (x, y). Describe the change in the graph $y = ax^2 + b$ as $|a|$ changes.
10. For the equations in Exercises 1 and 3, choose numbers for *x* and find the corresponding values for *y*. Use the same set of axes. Graph the ordered pairs (x, y). Describe the change in the graph $y = ax^2 + b$ as *b* changes.

12-8 Proving Theorems

As you prove theorems using coordinate geometry, keep in mind how the placement of the figure can influence the difficulty of completing the proof.

Example 1

Use coordinates to prove the following theorem.

The diagonals of a rectangle are congruent.

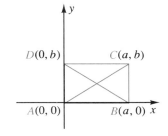

Solution

Given: $ABCD$ is a rectangle with coordinates $A(0, 0)$, $B(a, 0)$, $C(a, b)$, $D(0, b)$ and diagonals $\overline{AC}$ and $\overline{BD}$.

Prove: $AC = AD$

Proof

Statements	Reasons
1. $ABCD$ is a rectangle with coordinates $A(0, 0)$, $B(a, 0)$, $C(a, b)$, $D(0, b)$ and diagonals $\overline{AC}$ and $\overline{BD}$.	1. Given
2. $AC = \sqrt{(a - 0)^2 + (b - 0)^2}$	2. Distance Formula
3. $AC = \sqrt{a^2 + b^2}$	3. Properties of numbers
4. $BD = \sqrt{(a - 0)^2 + (0 - b)^2}$	4. Distance Formula
5. $BD = \sqrt{a^2 + b^2}$	5. Properties of numbers
6. $AC = BD$	6. Substitution Property of Equality

Example 2

Use coordinates to prove the following statement.

The median to the base of an isosceles right triangle is perpendicular to the base.

Solution

Given: Isosceles right triangle ABC has coordinates $A(0, 0)$, $B(2a, 0)$, and $C(0, 2a)$. $BM = MC$.

Prove: $\overline{AM} \perp \overline{BC}$

Proof

Statements	Reasons
1. Isosceles right triangle ABC has coordinates $A(0, 0)$, $B(2a, 0)$, $C(0, 2a)$	1. Given
2. The coordinates of M are (a, a).	2. Midpoint Formula
3. slope of $\overline{AM} = \frac{a - 0}{a - 0} = 1$	3. Definition of slope
4. slope of $BC = \frac{2a - 0}{0 - 2a} = -1$	4. Definition of slope
5. (slope of $\overline{AM}$) $\cdot$ (slope of $\overline{BC}$) $= 1 \cdot -1 = -1$	5. Properties of numbers
6. $\overline{AM} \perp \overline{BC}$	6. Two nonvertical lines are perpendicular if and only if the product of their slopes is -1.

Class Exercises

Short Answers

Refer to square *ABCD* to the right.

1. Use the distance formula to find *AC*.
2. Use the distance formula to find *BD*.
3. Compare *AC* and *BD*.
4. What conclusion can you state?
5. Find the slope of $\overline{AC}$.
6. Find the slope of $\overline{BD}$.
7. Find the product of the slopes of $\overline{AC}$ and $\overline{BD}$.
8. What conclusion can you state?

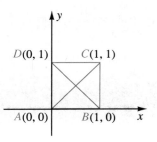

Sample Exercises

9. **Given:** parallelogram *ABCD* with coordinates as shown

   Prove: *AD = BC*, *AB = CD*

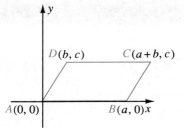

10. **Given:** isosceles $\triangle XYZ$ with *XZ = YZ* and medians $\overline{XM}$ and $\overline{YN}$

    Prove: *XM = YN*

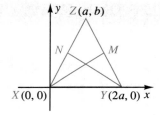

11. Use coordinate geometry to prove the following theorem.
    The opposite sides of a parallelogram are equal in length.

Discussion

12. Suppose you had to prove the following theorem.
    The diagonals of a square are perpendicular.

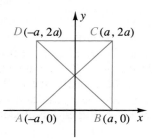

   a. For each placement above, what must you show to be able to conclude that the diagonals are perpendicular?
   b. Which placement do you think makes this task easier? Explain your choice.

Exercises

A

1. **Given:** $\triangle RST$ with coordinates as shown.
   M and N are midpoints.
   Prove: $MN = \frac{1}{2}RS$

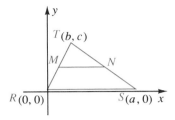

2. **Given:** $ABCD$ is a parallelogram with
   coordinates $A(0, 0)$, $B(a, 0)$, $C(c, b)$
   and $D(c - a, b)$.
   Prove: $\overline{AC}$ and $\overline{BD}$ bisect each other.

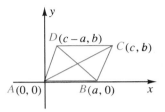

3. **Given:** $ABCD$ is an isosceles trapezoid
   with coordinates $A(0, 0)$, $B(a, 0)$,
   $C(a - b, c)$, and $D(b, c)$.
   Prove: $AC = BD$

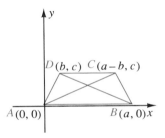

4. **Given:** quadrilateral $ABCD$ with coordinates
   $A(0, 0)$, $B(a, 0)$, $C(b, b)$, and $D(0, a)$
   Prove: $\overline{AC} \perp \overline{BD}$

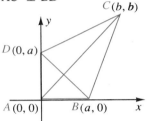

5. Use coordinates to prove the following theorem.
   The diagonals of a rhombus are perpendicular.

B

6. **Given:** Circle with center at the origin has chord $\overline{AB}$ with coordinates
   $A(0, a)$ and $B(a, 0)$. Line m is the $\perp$ bisector of $\overline{AB}$.
   Prove: m contains the center of the circle.

Prove each theorem using coordinates.

7. The median of a trapezoid is half the sum of the lengths of the bases.
8. The midpoint of the hypotenuse of a right triangle ABC is equidistant from
   the vertices. (HINT: Assign the vertices $A(0, 0)$, $B(a, 0)$, and $C(0, b)$.)
9. If the diagonals of parallelogram $ABCD$ are congruent, the parallelogram is a rectangle.
10. The medians to the congruent sides of an isosceles triangle are congruent.

C

11. The quadrilateral formed by joining the midpoints of the sides of a
    quadrilateral is a parallelogram.
12. The quadrilateral formed by joining the midpoints of the sides of an
    isosceles trapezoid is a rhombus.

13. Consider the cube shown to the right. Prove that the triangle OAB is equilateral. (HINT: Set up a three-dimensional coordinate system with O at the origin, $\overline{OD}$ on the x-axis, $\overline{OC}$ on the y-axis, and $\overline{OE}$ on the z-axis. Assign coordinates to O, A, and B.)

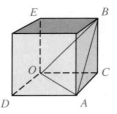

Critical Thinking

14. Consider two methods for proving the following theorem.
The diagonals of a rhombus are perpendicular.
One proof method is based on procedures developed in previous chapters (for example, using congruent triangles); the other method is based on the use of coordinates. Which proof method do you think is easier for proving the theorem given above? Explain your choice.

15. Consider the two proof methods described in Exercise 14. Indicate which method you think is easier to use for proving the following theorem.
The quadrilateral formed by joining the midpoints of the sides of a quadrilateral is a parallelogram.
Explain your choice.

Mixed Review

1. Find the surface area and volume of a cube with each edge 4 cm.
2. Find the surface area and volume of a cylinder 10 cm high with a circular base 6 cm in diameter.

Quiz

State the coordinates of point T without introducing any new letters.

1. square

2. isosceles trapezoid

3. equilateral triangle

4. rectangle

5. Use coordinate geometry to prove the following statement.
The median of a trapezoid is one half as long as the sum of its bases.

CRITICAL THINKING

Making and Supporting Decisions

Apply your critical thinking abilities to solving the following situation. It takes nine days to cross the Dryasdust Desert on foot. A messenger must deliver a secret written message to the other side of the desert, where no food and water is available, and then return. One person can carry enough food and water to last for 12 days. Food and water may be buried in plastic sacks in the desert and collected for use on the way back. There are two messengers available to carry out the task. How quickly can the two messengers get the message delivered without either messenger suffering from lack of food and water?

1. Understand the Situation
   a. What is the situation about?
   b. What conclusion, decision, or solution is required?
   c. Are there any questions which would clarify the situation?

2. Deal with the Data/Evidence/Assumptions
   a. Make a list of the most important evidence/data. Are other data needed?
   b. What evidence is opinion, not fact? Which data are not relevant?
   c. What assumptions are made? What other assumptions could be made?

3. Modify the Data/Evidence/Assumptions
   a. Try the situation with deserts requiring less days to cross.
   b. Develop a method of recording the positions of the messengers and the amount of food available.
   c. Is there any sense to having one of the other messengers return to base and then head back out to meet the other messenger returning?

4. State and Support your Conclusion/Decision/Solution
   Write a paragraph, with an accompanying diagram, describing your solution to this situation.

5. Apply the Conclusion/Decision/Solution
   What is the widest desert that can be crossed by the two messengers if they are not allowed to bury food for the return trip?

CHAPTER SUMMARY

Vocabulary

abscissa (12-1)
coordinate plane (12-1)
ordinate (12-1)
origin (12-1)
point-slope form (12-4)

quadrants (12-1)
rectangular coordinate system (12-1)
slope (12-2)
slope-intercept form (12-4)
standard form (12-4)

x-axis (12-1)
x-coordinate (12-1)
y-axis (12-1)
y-coordinate (12-1)

Key Ideas

1. Given two points with coordinates $A(x_1, y_1)$ and $B(x_2, y_2)$ the coordinates of the midpoint of $\overline{AB}$ are
$\left(\frac{x_1 + x_2}{2}, \frac{y_1 + y_2}{2}\right)$.

2. Given two points with coordinates $A(x_1, y_1)$ and $B(x_2, y_2)$ where $x_1 - x_2 \neq 0$ the slope of $\overline{AB}$ is
$\frac{y_1 - y_2}{x_1 - x_2}$.

3. Given two points with coordinates $A(x_1, y_1)$ and $B(x_2, y_2)$ the distance from A to B is
$\sqrt{(x_1 - x_2)^2 + (y_1 - y_2)^2}$.

4. The slope of a horizontal line is zero.

5. The slope of a vertical line is undefined.

6. Two nonvertical lines are parallel if their slopes are equal.

7. Two nonvertical lines are perpendicular if the product of their slopes is -1.

8. The graph of any equation that can be written in the form $ax + by = c$, with a and b not both zero, is a line. Other forms for equations of lines include:
   a. slope-intercept form $y = mx + b$ where m is the slope and b is the y-intercept.
   b. point-slope form $y - y_1 = m(x - x_1)$ where (x_1, y_1) is a point on the line and m is the slope.

9. The equation of a circle with center (h, k) and radius r is
$(x - h)^2 + (y - k)^2 = r^2$.

10. To prove a theorem using coordinate geometry, place and label the given geometric figure on coordinate axes in a position that helps to simplify work.

CHAPTER REVIEW

12-1

Graph each point on the same set of axes.

1. $A(-3, 4)$ 2. $B(2, 1)$ 3. $C(4, -2)$ 4. $D(-2\frac{1}{2}, -3)$

5. Find the coordinates of the midpoint of the segment having endpoints $X(-2, 5)$ and $Y(-6, 1)$.

6. One endpoint of $\overline{RS}$ is $R(4, -3)$ and the midpoint of $\overline{RS}$ is $M(-3, 5)$. Find the coordinates of point S.

12-2

Find the slope of the line that contains the given points.

7. $A(3, 4)$, $B(-2, 7)$ **8.** $D(4, 6)$, $E(-2, 6)$
9. $X(-4, -2)$, $Y(-6, 4)$

10. A line with slope $\frac{1}{5}$ passes through the points $(-1, 6)$ and $(4, y)$. Find y.

12-3

For the given coordinates, determine whether $\overline{LM} \parallel \overline{PQ}$, $\overline{LM} \perp \overline{PQ}$, or neither.

11. $L(3, 4)$, $M(5, -1)$, $P(-3, 7)$, $Q(-8, 5)$
12. $L(-2, 4)$, $M(5, -1)$, $P(0, 8)$, $Q(7, 3)$

13. The coordinates of the vertices of $\triangle ABC$ are $A(4, 6)$, $B(-2, 1)$, and $C(2, -2)$. Find the slope of the altitude to side $\overline{AC}$.

12-4

State the slope and y-intercept. Graph the line.

14. $3x + 2y = 10$ **15.** $y = -2$ **16.** $(y - 3) = -\frac{3}{4}(x - 8)$

Write the equation of the line for the given conditions. Use $y = mx + b$ form.

17. a line that contains the point $P(-3, 4)$ and has slope $\frac{1}{6}$
18. a line that contains the points $(4, 3)$ and $(-2, -15)$

12-5

Find the distance between each pair of points.

19. $(-4, -1)$, $(-4, 3)$ **20.** $(-2, 3)$, $(3, -2)$

21. Determine whether $\triangle ABC$ is scalene, isosceles, or equilateral if the coordinates of the vertices are $A(-3, 2)$, $B(5, 1)$, and $C(1, -6)$.

12-6

Find the center and radius of each circle.

22. $(x + 2)^2 + (y - 4)^2 = 16$ **23.** $(x - 1)^2 + y^2 = 20$

Write the equation of the circle described.

24. center at $(-3, 2)$ and radius 9
25. center at $(4, 7)$ and contains the point $(2, 11)$

12-7

26. Without introducing any new letters, find the coordinates of points A and B for the rectangle shown to the right.
27. Set up a coordinate system that could be used to prove the statement. A diagonal of a parallelogram forms two congruent triangles.

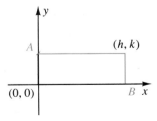

12-8

Prove the following by methods of coordinate geometry.

28. The segment joining the midpoints of two sides of a triangle is parallel to the third side of the triangle.
29. The diagonals of an isosceles trapezoid are congruent.

CHAPTER TEST

1. Give the coordinates for point P.
2. Give the coordinates for point S.
3. Give the point for $(-4, 2)$.

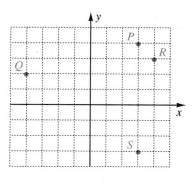

Use the points $A(-2, 6)$, $B(4, -2)$, and $C(4, -6)$.

4. Find the coordinates of the midpoint of $\overline{AB}$.
5. Find the coordinates of the midpoint of $\overline{AC}$.
6. Find the slope of $\overline{AB}$.
7. Find the slope of $\overline{AC}$.
8. Find the slope of $\overline{BC}$.
9. Find BC.
10. Find AC.

11. One endpoint of $\overline{RS}$ is $R(-5, 2)$ and the midpoint of $\overline{RS}$ is $(-1, 5)$. Find the coordinates of S.
12. Determine whether the lines $3x + 2y = 6$ and $6y = 4x + 12$ are parallel, perpendicular, or neither.
13. Determine whether the lines $2x + 5y = 8$ and $5y = -2x + 4$ are parallel, perpendicular or neither.
14. Find the slope of a line that is parallel to the line $3 + 2y = 5x$.
15. Graph $y = 2x + 5$.
16. Graph $y - 2 = \frac{3}{2}(x + 6)$.
17. Graph $x = 3$.
18. Write the equation of the line in the form $y = mx + b$ when $m = 3$ and $b = 9$.
19. Write an equation of the line given the slope $m = -\frac{1}{3}$ and point $P(-1, 3)$ on the line.
20. Write the equation of a line through the points $(6, 2)$ and $(0, -4)$.
21. Determine whether $\triangle RST$ is scalene, isosceles, or equilateral if $R(-4, 1)$, $S(5, 4)$, and $T(2, -2)$.
22. Write the equation of a circle with center $(5, 3)$ and radius 4.
23. Write the equation of a circle with center $(-2, -3)$ and radius 6.
24. State the center and radius of the circle with equation $(x - 3)^2 + (y + 5)^2 = 4$.
25. Without introducing any new letters, give the coordinates for A and B in the rhombus to the right.
26. $\triangle ABC$ is an equilateral triangle with coordinates $A(0, 0)$ and $B(5, 0)$. Determine the coordinates of C without using any new letters.
27. Set up a coordinate system to prove that opposite sides of a parallelogram are congruent.
28. Use coordinate geometry to prove the diagonals of a square are perpendicular.
29. Use coordinate geometry to prove that in an isosceles triangle, the medians to the legs are congruent.
30. Use coordinate geometry to prove that the diagonals of a rectangle are congruent.

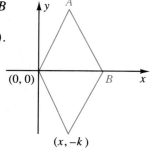

PREPARING FOR COLLEGE ENTRANCE EXAMS

Each question consists of two quantities, one in Column A and one in Column B. Compare the two quantities and choose

A if the quantity in Column A is greater;
B if the quantity in Column B is greater;
C if the two quantities are equal;
D if the relationship cannot be determined from the information given.

Column A	Column B	Column A	Column B

$5 + x = 9$
$5 + y = 9$

7. x — y

1. x — $y + x$

$x = 2$

8. $\frac{1}{x}$ — $\frac{1}{\frac{1}{x}}$

$x = 0.01$

2. x^2 — x^3

3.
$0.3 \times 10{,}000$ — 30×100

ABCD is a rectangle.

9. perimeter of *ADP* — perimeter of *APB*

10. 0 — $x^2 + 1$

The figure is a cube.

4. AC — BD

$x = 2$

5. $3x^2$ — $\frac{2x^3 + 4x^2}{x + 2}$

11. area of rectangle — area of parallelogram

12. area of shaded circle — area of outer ring

6. $m \angle ABC$ — $m \angle ADC$

Transformations

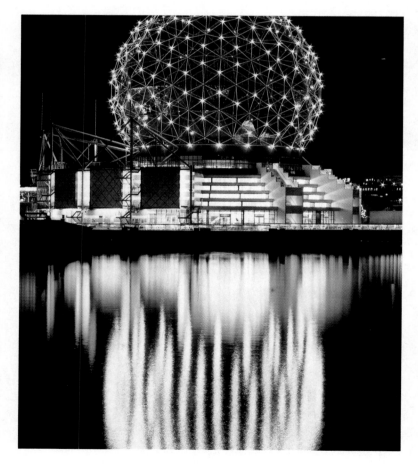

This geodesic dome and its reflection are an example of reflectional symmetry. Describe other examples of this type of symmetry.

MAPPINGS

OBJECTIVE: *Find the reflection image of a figure and lines of symmetry of a figure.*

13-1 Reflections and Line Symmetry

 EXPLORE Draw a line ℓ and a $\triangle ABC$ on one side of ℓ. Place a sheet of tracing paper over the line and triangle and trace them. Then, flip the tracing paper over and line up the tracing of ℓ with ℓ and locate the points on the other side of ℓ corresponding to A, B, and C. Label these points A', B', and C'.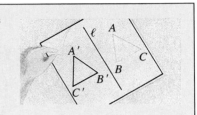

A correspondence between points of the plane is a **mapping.** A mapping which establishes a one-to-one correspondence between points in the plane is called a **transformation.** The mapping illustrated in the Explore establishes a one-to-one correspondence between points in the plane by reflecting them in a line. A transformation T maps a point P to its **image** under T, usually indicated by P'. Point P is called the **preimage** of P'.

■ DEFINITION

A **reflection in line** ℓ is a transformation that maps every point P of the plane to a point P' of the plane such that

a. if point P is on ℓ then it is mapped to itself,
b. if point P is not on ℓ then ℓ is the perpendicular bisector of $\overline{PP'}$.

In the Explore, A' is the image of A in the reflection in line ℓ. A' is called the **reflection image** of A in line ℓ.

Example 1
Find the reflection image in line m of each of the following.

a. R b. S' c. T d. V e. $\overline{RS}$ f. $\triangle RST$

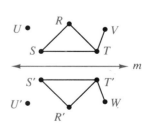

   Solution

   a. R' b. S c. T' d. W e. $\overline{R'S'}$ f. $\triangle R'S'T$

Try This
Find the reflection image in line m of each of the following.

a. U b. W c. $\overline{TV}$

The reflection image of a point in the *x*-axis or the *y*-axis can be described using the coordinates of the point. This is illustrated in the following example.

Example 2

Find the coordinates of the reflection image of point P in each of the coordinate axes.

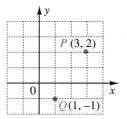

Solution

Reflection in x-axis: Image of $P(3, 2)$ is $(3, -2)$.
Reflection in y-axis: Image of $P(3, 2)$ is $(-3, 2)$.

Try This

Find the coordinates of the reflection image of point Q in each of the coordinate axes.

The reflection image of a figure is found by reflecting each point of the figure. Notice that the reflection image of the letter H in line m is again the letter H.

■ DEFINITION

A line ℓ is called the **line of reflectional symmetry** for a figure if the figure coincides with its reflection image in ℓ. The figure is said to have **reflectional symmetry** in line ℓ.

Example 3

Draw a rectangle, a parallelogram, and an isosceles triangle and identify all lines of reflectional symmetry for each figure.

Solution

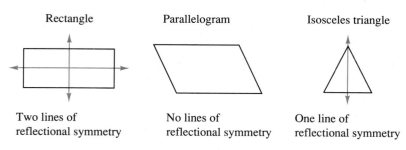

Rectangle	Parallelogram	Isosceles triangle

Two lines of reflectional symmetry

No lines of reflectional symmetry

One line of reflectional symmetry

Try This

Draw each of the following.

a. quadrilateral that has exactly one line of symmetry
b. a hexagon that has exactly two lines of symmetry

Class Exercises

Short Answer

Complete each statement.

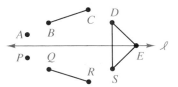

1. The reflection image in line ℓ of A is ___.
2. The reflection image in line ℓ of B is ___.
3. The reflection image in line ℓ of $\overline{BC}$ is ___.
4. The reflection image in line ℓ of $\overline{SE}$ is ___.
5. The reflection image in line ℓ of $\triangle DSE$ is ___.
6. The reflection image in line ℓ of ___ is R.
7. The reflection image in line ℓ of ___ is $\overline{DS}$.

Sample Exercises

Complete the following chart showing the coordinates of the given points reflected in the indicated axes.

Point	Image in x-axis	Image in y-axis
8. $(3, -1)$	___	$(-3, -1)$
9. $(-4, 3)$	$(-4, -3)$	
10. $(1, -2)$	___	$(-1, -2)$
11. $(-2, 3)$	$(-2, -3)$	___
12. $(5, 1)$	___	___
13. $(2, -3)$	___	___
14. $(3, -4)$	___	___
15. ___	$(-2, -2)$	___
16. $(x, -y)$	___	___
17. $(-x, y)$	___	___
18. $(-x, -y)$	___	___

19. What generalization can you state about the relationship between the coordinates of a point and those of its reflection image in the x-axis? the y-axis?

Determine whether each line appears to be a line of symmetry for each figure. Then trace the given polygon and draw its reflection image about each of the red lines.

20.

21.

22.
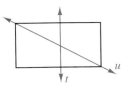

Discussion

23. The reflection image in ℓ of a pair of parallel segments is a pair of parallel segments. Give a convincing argument, using this information, to explain why the reflection image of a parallogram is a parallelogram. Do you think that the reflection image of a rectangle is always a rectangle? Explain.

Exercises

A

Complete each statement.

1. The reflection image in ℓ of A is ___ .
2. The reflection image in ℓ of G is ___ .
3. The reflection image in ℓ of $\overline{FG}$ is ___ .
4. The reflection image in ℓ of $\triangle ABC$ is ___ .

5. The reflection image in ℓ of $\overline{RS}$ is ___ .
6. The reflection image in ℓ of U is ___ .
7. The reflection image in ℓ of ___ is $\overline{VW}$.
8. The reflection image in ℓ of $RSTUVWX$ is ___ .

Find the reflection image in the *y*-axis of each of the following.

9. point A 10. point C 11. point E

Find the coordinates of the endpoints of the reflection image in the *y*-axis of each segment.

12. $\overline{CD}$ 13. $\overline{BC}$ 14. $\overline{AB}$

Trace each figure. Use tracing paper or a compass and straightedge to draw as accurately as possible the reflection image in line *p* of each figure.

15.   16.   17.

Trace each figure and draw all the lines of reflectional symmetry.

18.   19.   20.

21. Draw a hexagon with exactly one line of symmetry.
22. Draw a quadrilateral with exactly four lines of symmetry.
23. Draw a triangle with exactly three lines of symmetry.
24. Draw a figure with an infinite number of lines of symmetry.

B

Trace each figure and draw its reflection image in line *p*.

25.   26.   27.

28. The reflection image of the word HIDE in a horizontal line is again the word HIDE. Print five other words for which this is true.

29. The reflection image of the word WOW in a vertical line is again the word WOW. Print five other words for which this is true.

30. Can you decode this message? How does the decoding relate to a line reflection?

The reason this looks so strange is that it was written using a mirror.

The reflection image in the line $y = x$ of point $P(x, y)$ is point $P'(y, x)$. Use the definition of reflection in a line to find the coordinates of the reflection image in $y = x$ of each point.

31. point $A(4, 2)$
32. point $B(2, -3)$
33. point $C(1, 1)$

Find the coordinates of the reflection image in the line $y = -x$ of each point.

34. point $A(4, 2)$
35. point $C(1, 1)$

36. Points L and N are on the same side of line p and L' is the reflection image of L. If M is the intersection of line p and $\overline{L'N}$, prove that $m\angle 1 = m\angle 2$.

37. If L' is the reflection image of L in line p and M is a point on line p, prove that $LM = L'M$.

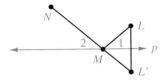

C

38. If A and B are two points and A' and B' are their reflection images in line ℓ, prove that $\overline{AB} \cong \overline{A'B'}$.

39. If the line with equation $y = x$ is reflected in the x-axis, what would the equation of its reflection be?

40. If the line with equation $y = 2x$ is reflected in the y-axis, what would the equation of its reflection image be?

41. Two cities are positioned on the same side of a straight river. A bridge is to be built. Where should the bridge B be built so that the length of the highway, $AB + BC$, is as small as possible?

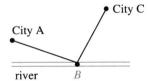

42. If cities D and E are 1 km and 2 km from the river respectively and XX' is 6 km, how far from X should the bridge B be placed so that $DB + BE$ is as small as possible?

Critical Thinking

43. Passengers in a rowboat at A decide they want to row to the north shore to pick fruit and then row to the south shore to pick corn before proceeding to island I for a picnic. Trace this figure with points A and I as shown and figure out how to locate points B and C so that the trip $AB + BC + CI$ is the least possible distance.

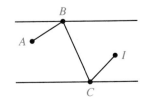

44. A small restaurant has a mirror on one wall and a partition to block off part of the restaurant for private parties. How many of the tables can the restaurant manager, standing at the cashier stand, see from direct vision or from reflection in the mirror? Explain your answer.

mirror

cashier
stand

Suppose that quadrilateral $A'B'C'D'$ is the reflection image of quadrilateral $ABCD$.

45. State the converse of the following conditional.
If $ABCD$ is a parallelogram, then $A'B'C'D'$ is a rhombus.
Is this converse true? Is the original implication true?

46. Does each statement follow logically from the other?
(a) $ABCD$ is a rhombus.   (b) $A'B'C'D'$ is a rhombus.
Explain your answer.

Mixed Review

Use the figure to the right to determine whether each statement is true or false.

1. If $\overline{AE} \cong \overline{EC}$ and $\overline{DE} \cong \overline{EB}$, then $\triangle AED \cong \triangle CEB$.

2. If $ABCD$ is a rectangle, then $\triangle ACD \cong \triangle BDC$.

3. If $\triangle AED \cong \triangle CEB$, then $ABCD$ must be a rectangle.

4. If $\overline{DB}$ and $\overline{AC}$ bisect each other, then $ABCD$ must be a rhombus.

5. If $ABCD$ is a parallelogram, then $\triangle AED$ cannot be congruent to $\triangle AEB$.

6. $ABCD$ is a rectangle if and only if $\triangle AEB \cong \triangle CED$.

Enrichment

Mirrors

When you see an object in a mirror, you are witnessing a type of line reflection. Light reflected off an object strikes the mirror and is reflected back to the eye so that the *angle of incidence* equals the *angle of reflection*. The brain then perceives the reflected image as far behind the mirror as the object is in front of the mirror. Such an image behind a mirror is called a *virtual image*.

angle of reflection

mirror

angle of
incidence

virtual image

Exercises

1. If the apple in the above drawing lies 3 ft in front of the mirror, find the distance between the apple and its virtual image.

2. Light from an object on the ground strikes a vertical mirror with an angle of incidence of 30°. If the object lies 2 m in front of the mirror and the viewer is standing directly over the object, how far is the virtual image from the viewer's eye?

13-2 Translations and Translational Symmetry

An object on a conveyor belt moves a certain distance in one direction as it moves from one robot to the next. This type of motion is a model for the transformation called a **translation.**

■ DEFINITION

A **translation** PP' is a transformation that slides all points of the plane a fixed distance in a given direction. If A is mapped to A', then $AA' = PP'$ and $AP = A'P'$.

The distance and direction for the translation PP' are given by a **directed segment** $\overrightarrow{PP'}$ showing the relationship between a point P and its **translation image** P'.

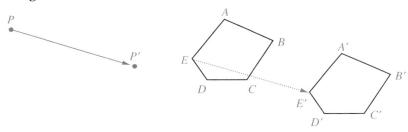

The translation image of point A is A' since the directed segment $\overrightarrow{AA'}$ has the same length and direction as $\overrightarrow{PP'}$. Similarly, the translation image of B is B' and of C is C'. We also say that the translation image of figure $ABCDE$ is $A'B'C'D'E'$.

Example 1

For the translation XY, find the translation image of each of the following.

a. A b. $\overline{UV}$ c. $\overline{CB}$

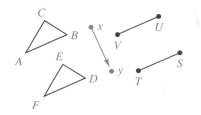

Solution

a. F b. $\overline{ST}$ c. $\overline{ED}$

Try This

Find the translation image of $\overline{AB}$ and $\triangle ABC$.

This figure illustrates how the translation image of a point can be described in terms of the original coordinates of the point. The translation XY creates a horizontal shift of 4 units and a vertical shift of 2 units. Consequently, the translation image of $A(1, 1)$ is $A'(1 + 4, 1 + 2)$ or $(5, 3)$. The image of $B(3, -1)$ under the translation XY is $B'(7, 1)$.

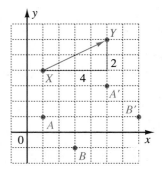

Example 2

The translation RS is defined by points $R(3, 4)$ and $S(7, 9)$. Find the translation image under RS for each point.

a. $C(3, 2)$ **b.** $D(-1, 3)$ **c.** $M(x, y)$

Solution

a. $C'(7, 7)$ **b.** $D'(3, 8)$ *The translation RS creates a horizontal shift*
c. $M'(x + 4, y + 5)$ *of 4 units and a vertical shift of 5 units.*

Try This

Find the translation image under RS for each point.

a. $(-2, 4)$ **b.** $(5, -7)$

A figure has **translational symmetry** if there is a translation that maps the figure onto itself. For example, if we assume that the figure in the box below is repeated indefinitely to the right and to the left, then the resulting pattern has translational symmetry since the translation that maps X to Y maps the entire pattern onto itself. Trace the pattern and then slide the tracing from X to Y to verify the translational symmetry.

Example 3

Imagine that the figure in the box below is repeated indefinitely to the right and to the left to form the pattern shown. This pattern has translational symmetry. If the translation image of point A is __?__ the pattern maps onto itself.

Solution

Point C

Try This

Complete this statement in two ways.
If the translation image of point B is ____ the pattern maps onto itself.

Class Exercises

Short Answer

For translation XY, find the image of each of the following.

1. point C
2. $\overline{BC}$
3. $\triangle ABC$

For the translation UV, find the image of each of the following.

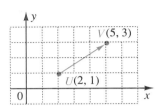

4. point $(1, 3)$
5. point $(3, -1)$
6. point (x, y)
7. the segment with endpoints $(0, 4)$ and $(1, 2)$

Sample Exercises

Consider the translation AB from $A(2, 1)$ to $B(3, 4)$. Find the translation image of each point.

8. $X(3, 1)$ 9. $Y(-2, 3)$
10. $D(5, 4)$ 11. $F(1, 6)$

12. For the translation described by the directed segment XY, find the translation image of point X.

Discussion

Use tracing paper and/or ruler to determine whether each statement is true or false. If true, give a convincing argument. If false, give a counterexample.

13. If lines p and q are perpendicular, then their translation images are also perpendicular.
14. If the translation image of line p is line q, then lines p and q are parallel.
15. If the translation image of X is Y and if the translation image of line p is line q, then XY is the distance between lines p and q.

Exercises

A

Consider translation RT. Find the image of each of the following.

1. point B 2. point C
3. point F 4. $\overline{AC}$
5. $\overline{FG}$ 6. $\angle BAC$
7. $\triangle ABC$ 8. $\angle BCA$

For translation AB from $A(1, 3)$ to $B(4, 5)$, find the image of each point.

9. $X(2, 1)$ 10. $Z(-2, 3)$
11. $Y(4, -2)$ 12. $P(x, 4)$
13. $Q(5, y)$ 14. $R(x, y)$

For translation CD from $C(3, 2)$ to $D(-1, -3)$, find the image of each point.

15. $U(1, 4)$ **16.** $V(5, 2)$ **17.** $P(3, 7)$ **18.** $A(x, y)$

19. Assume that the figure in the box below is extended indefinitely to the right and to the left. The resulting pattern has translational symmetry. Complete this statement in three different ways.
The translation that maps ___ to ___ maps the pattern onto itself.

B

Consider the translation that maps (x, y) to $(x + 2, y + 3)$.

20. What is the translation image of $(1, 4)$?
21. What is the translation image of $(-3, 5)$?
22. What point has $(2, 3)$ for its image?
23. What point has $(3, 4)$ for its image?
24. Suppose that ℓ is the line through $(-1, 3)$ and $(3, 2)$. Find the slope of ℓ. Find the slope of its translation image.
25. Suppose that m is a line with slope $\frac{3}{2}$. Find the translation image of m.
26. Suppose the translation image of the point (x, y) is the point $(x + 1, y + 2)$. If ℓ is the line through the points $(1, 2)$ and $(3, 5)$, explain why the translation image of ℓ is a line parallel to ℓ.
27. If the translation image of A is A' and of B is B', explain why points A, A', B, and B' are either collinear or are the vertices of a parallelogram.

C

28. Suppose that the translation image of $(2, 3)$ is $(4, 7)$. For this translation, write the equation of the translation image of the line $y = 2x + 3$.
29. Suppose that the translation image of $(0, 0)$ is $(2, b)$, and of the line $y = 3x - 4$ is the line itself. Find b.
30. Suppose that line ℓ is parallel to line m and perpendicular to line n. If m is translated in a direction parallel to line n, what can you say about points on ℓ and the translation images of points on m?
31. Suppose that the translation image of (x, y) is $(x + a, y + b)$ where a and b are constants. Use the distance formula to show that the distance between any two points P and Q is equal to distance between the translation images of these two points.
32. A student claimed that for the five parallelograms he tried, the translation images were again parallelograms. Does this prove that the translation images of all parallelograms are parallelograms? Explain.
33. A key-cutting machine has a guide that slides along a key that is being copied and a cutting wheel that cuts the new key. Explain how this process might be viewed as an application of translations.

Critical Thinking

34. If the translation PP' is defined by the mapping that sends (x, y) to $(x + 3, y + 4)$, what is the image of the line $y = x$ under PP'?
35. Give a convincing argument that the translation image of a line is a parallel line or the same line.
36. Suppose that $A'(x, y)$ is the image of point A under the translation PP' which maps (x, y) to $(x - 7, y + 8)$. Find the coordinates of the point A in terms of the coordinates of A'.

Mixed Review

Find the volume of each solid.

1. a right rectangular prism with length 9, width 7, and height 4
2. a right cylinder with radius 3 and height 5
3. a sphere with radius 2
4. a regular square pyramid with base edges of length 20 and slant height 26
5. a right cone with diameter 6 and height 10

CONNECTIONS ◈

Transformations and Functional Notation

Recall that a *function* is a mapping that assigns to each member of the *domain* exactly one member of the *range*. The domain is the set of all possible inputs and the range is the set of all possible outputs.

Transformations can be thought of as functions. In this chapter, we are concerned primarily with transformations whose domain and range are the plane. The notation of functions can be used to describe transformations in a compact way.

For example, consider the translation AB defined by the points $A(1, 1)$ and $B(3, 4)$. This transformation creates a horizontal shift of 2 units and a vertical shift of 3 units. Thus, the translation image of the point $(3, -1)$ is $(3 + 2, -1 + 3)$ or $(5, 2)$. If this translation is considered a function f, you can write $f(3, -1) = (5, 2)$. More generally, the transformation is described by the notation $f(x, y) = (x + 2, y + 3)$.

Exercises

Write the functional notation that describes each of the following transformations.

1. the translation CD defined by points $C(5, 8)$ and $D(9, 9)$
2. the translation RS defined by the points $R(-2, 4)$ and $S(-2, 5)$
3. the reflection in the x-axis
4. the reflection in the line $y = x$

13-3 Rotations and Rotational Symmetry

EXPLORE

How could you use tracing paper to find the image of △*ABC* when it is rotated clockwise 40° about point *O*? How does this transformation of a triangle differ from a reflection? a translation?

Rotations of objects such as gears, records, windmills, or carnival rides are common occurrences in the world around us. These motions can be studied through mappings.

▪ DEFINITION

A **rotation about a point *O* through an angle of *x*°** is a transformation that associates each point *P* of the plane with a point *P'*, called the **rotation image** of *P*. *P'* is a point in the plane such that $m\angle POP' = x$ and $OP = OP'$. Point *O* is called the **center of the rotation** and *x*° is called the **angle of rotation.**

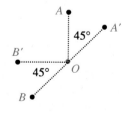

In the figure to the right, the 45° (clockwise) rotation image of *A* about point *O* is the point *A'*. Point *B'* is the 45° clockwise rotation image of *B* about point *O*. It can also be said that *A* is the 45° (counterclockwise) rotation image of *A'*. Sometimes this is simply referred to as a rotation of 45°. When no direction is specified, a positive angle measure refers to the counterclockwise direction and a negative angle measure refers to the clockwise direction.

Often, the angle of rotation is allowed to exceed the 0 to 180 degree bounds we have ordinarily placed on angle measures. An angle of 270° refers to a $\frac{3}{4}$ turn in the counterclockwise direction. An angle of −300° refers to $\frac{5}{6}$ of a turn in the clockwise direction.

Example 1

Pictured are two squares with point O the intersection of the diagonals of both squares. Find the 90° clockwise rotation image about O of each of the following.

a. point D **b.** point G **c.** $\overline{BG}$

Solution

a. point A $m \angle DOA = 90°$ and $OD = OA$
b. point H $m \angle GOH = 90°$ and $OG = OH$
c. $\overline{CH}$

Try This

Find each of the following.

a. the 90° clockwise rotation image of A
b. the 180° rotation image of E
c. the 90° counterclockwise rotation image of F

A rotation can be described in terms of coordinates with the origin as the point of rotation. For example, the 90° counterclockwise rotation image of point $A(1, 2)$ is point $A'(-2, 1)$. Notice that this rotation maps the point (x, y) to the point $(-y, x)$. This pattern always holds for the 90° counterclockwise rotation. Similar patterns exist for the 90° clockwise rotation and for the 180° rotation. A rotation of 180° is often referred to as a **half-turn**.

Example 2

Find the image of each point under a 90° counterclockwise rotation about the origin.

a. $B(3, 1)$ **b.** $C(4, -1)$ **c.** $D(-2, 3)$

Solution

a. $B'(-1, 3)$
b. $C'(1, 4)$
c. $D'(-3, -2)$

Try This

Find the image of each point under a 90° counterclockwise rotation about the origin.

a. $(2, -3)$ **b.** $(-1, -3)$

If a figure or pattern can be rotated $x°$ about a point so that the pattern appears identical to its original position, then the pattern has $x°$ **rotational symmetry.** For example, this quilt has 90°, 180°, and 270° rotational symmetry. It also has 360° rotational symmetry. However, since *any* figure can be rotated 360° onto itself, 360° rotational symmetry is usually not mentioned.

Class Exercises

Short Answer

Find the 90° clockwise rotation image about _O_ of each point.

1. _D_   **2.** _F_   **3.** _G_   **4.** _A_

Find the 90° counterclockwise rotation image about _O_ of each segment.

5. $\overline{EF}$ **6.** $\overline{CD}$

Find the 90° counterclockwise rotation image about (0, 0) of each point.

7. $A(1, 1)$ **8.** $B(-2, 1)$ **9.** $C(1, -1)$

Sample Exercises

Find the 60° rotation image about _O_ of each of the following.

10. point _C_
11. $\triangle BOC$
12. trapezoid _ADCB_
13. rhombus _AFOB_

14. Find the 90° counterclockwise rotation image of point (4, 5) about the origin.
15. Find the 90° clockwise rotation image of point (3, 2) about the origin.

Discussion

16. Explain why a 90° clockwise rotation results in the same image as a 270° counterclockwise rotation.

$OD = OB$ **Determine whether each statement is true or false. Explain your answers.**

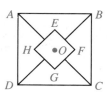

17. The 45° counterclockwise rotation image about _O_ of _D_ is _B_.
18. The 45° clockwise rotation image about _O_ of $\triangle ABC$ is $\triangle DEF$.

Exercises

Find the 90° clockwise rotation image about _O_ of each of the following.

1. point _A_   **2.** point _B_   **3.** $\overline{AB}$

Find the 90° counterclockwise rotation image about _O_ of each of the following.

4. point A' **5.** point B' **6.** $\overline{A'B'}$

ABCD and _EFGH_ are squares. Find the 90° clockwise rotation image about _O_ of each of the following.

7. point _A_   **8.** point _D_
9. point _H_   **10.** point _F_
11. $\overline{BC}$ **12.** $\overline{BE}$
13. $\overline{CG}$ **14.** $\overline{FC}$

This pattern of five squares is centered at O. Find the 90°
counterclockwise rotation image about O of each of the following.

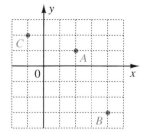

15. point A 16. square $ABIL$
17. rectangle $ABEF$ 18. rectangle $CDKL$
19. square $IJKL$ 20. $\overline{AE}$

Find the 90° counterclockwise rotation image
about $(0, 0)$ of each point.

21. $A(2, 1)$ 22. $B(4, -3)$ 23. $C(-1, 2)$

Find the 90° clockwise rotation image about
$(0, 0)$ of each point.

24. $A(2, 1)$ 25. $B(4, -3)$ 26. $C(-1, 2)$

Trace the figure and determine whether each statement is true or false.
Explain your reasoning.

27. If P' is the half-turn image of point P, then P is the half-turn
    image of P'.
28. The figure has 45° rotational symmetry.
29. The figure has 90° rotational symmetry.
30. The figure has 270° rotational symmetry.

Trace the figure and use the tracing to answer each question.

31. Does the figure have 90° rotational symmetry?
32. Does the figure have 45° rotational symmetry?
33. Does the figure have 270° rotational symmetry?
34. Does the figure have 60° rotational symmetry?
35. Does the figure have reflectional symmetry?

Trace the figure and use the tracing to answer each question.

36. Does the figure have 180° rotational symmetry?
37. Does the figure have 135° rotational symmetry?
38. Does the figure have 90° rotational symmetry?
39. Does the figure have reflectional symmetry?

B

40. If $\overline{R'S'}$ is the rotation image of $\overline{RS}$ for a rotation
    with center O, name an angle that could be
    measured to find the angle of the rotation.

The points in the figure show the results of various rotations about
point O. Use a protractor to find the measure of the rotation angle
that mapped

41. point A to point A'.
42. point B to point B'.

43. Find the 90° counterclockwise rotation image about $(0, 0)$ of $P(x, y)$.

44. Find the 90° clockwise rotation image about $(0, 0)$ of $P(x, y)$.

45. Find the 180° (half-turn) rotation image about $(0, 0)$ of each point.

    a. $A(4, 3)$ **b.** $B(-2, 3)$ **c.** $C(x, y)$

Copy △ABC and △DEF onto a piece of paper. Use tracing paper to answer each question.

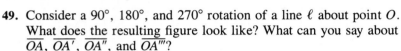

46. What rotation maps A to D?

47. What rotation maps B to E?

48. What rotation maps $\overline{EF}$ to $\overline{BC}$?

49. Consider a 90°, 180°, and 270° rotation of a line ℓ about point O. What does the resulting figure look like? What can you say about $\overline{OA}$, $\overline{OA'}$, $\overline{OA''}$, and $\overline{OA'''}$?

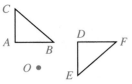

C

Assume that the rotation image of a line is a line.

50. Prove that the half-turn image of line AB is a line $A'B'$ parallel to $\overleftrightarrow{AB}$.

51. Suppose that O is the intersection of the diagonals of a parallelogram. Prove that a 180° rotation about O maps parallelogram $ABCD$ to parallelogram $CDAB$.

52. If O is a point not on line ℓ, prove that the 90° rotation image about O of line ℓ is a line perpendicular to ℓ.

53. If a rotation image of X is X' and of Y is Y', explain how you can find the center of the rotation.

Imagine that the entire plane is covered with this repeating pattern. Complete each statement and answer the question.

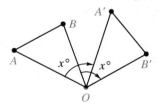

54. A 90° rotation about point ___ will map the entire pattern onto itself.

Can you complete this statement any other way?

55. A 180° rotation about point ___ will map the entire pattern onto itself.

Can you complete this statement any other way?

56. Suppose that A' and B' are the $x°$ rotation images about O of points A and B. Use the SAS Postulate to prove that $\overline{AB} \cong \overline{A'B'}$.

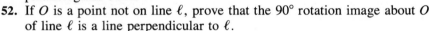

Critical Thinking

57. Consider the arcs swept out by points A and B in the rotation of the line segment OA. Explain why the lengths of the arcs are different, while the angle of rotation is the same.

58. Give a convincing argument that the lower figure to the right is not the rotation image about O of the upper figure.

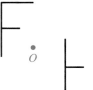

59. Give a convincing argument that a regular n-gon has $n - 1$ different rotations that map the figure onto itself.

Algebra Review

Determine whether each pair of lines are parallel, perpendicular, or neither.

1. $4x + y = 6$
$4x + y = 8$

2. $3x - y = 6$
$3x + y = 8$

3. $x + 4y = 8$
$x = -4y - 10$

4. $2x - 5y = -3$
$5x + 2y = 6$

5. $8x - 4y = 16$
$5y - 10x = 3$

6. $2x + 6y = -3$
$12y = 4x + 20$

Computer Activity

Given a point in the coordinate plane, how could you find its image under a rotation of, for example, 37°? The BASIC program below allows you to input the coordinates of any point and the degree measure of a counterclockwise rotation. It outputs the coordinates of the rotation image of the point.

Notice that the program converts degrees to radians (180° equals π radians) and that the trigonometric ratios SIN and COS are used. Although we have defined these ratios only for angles between 0° and 90°, it is possible to input any degree measure for the rotation.

```
10 PRINT "ENTER THE X-COORDINATE"
20 INPUT X
30 PRINT "ENTER THE Y-COORDINATE"
40 INPUT Y
50 PRINT "ENTER THE AMOUNT OF ROTATION IN DEGREES"
60 INPUT A
70 LET U = X * COS (3.14159 * A/180) - Y * SIN (3.14159 * A/180)
80 LET V = X * SIN (3.14159 * A/180) + Y * COS (3.14159 * A/180)
90 PRINT "THE ROTATION IMAGE IS ("; U; ", "; V; ")"
100 END
```

Exercises

1. Run the program several times with various points and a rotation of 90°. What pattern do you see?
2. Use the program to find the rotation image of (3, 5) under a 70° rotation.
3. Modify the program so that it allows the user to find the rotation image of the point under as many different rotations as desired.

13-4 Compositions of Mappings

When one transformation is performed after another, the result is called the **composition** of the two transformations. For example, consider the points A and B and the lines ℓ and m. The reflection of $\overline{AB}$ in line ℓ followed by the reflection of $\overline{A'B'}$ in line m gives the result $\overline{A''B''}$. This appears to be equivalent to a translation of $\overline{AB}$ to $\overline{A''B''}$.

Another example of a composition of transformations is when region A is rotated 90° clockwise about O followed by another 45° clockwise rotation about O. The result is equivalent to a 135° clockwise rotation about O that maps region A to region C.

The result of this composition is summarized in the following theorem.

◆ **THEOREM 13.1**

The composition of two rotations about the same center point O is a rotation about center O with an angle of rotation equal in measure to the sum of the measures of the angles of rotation of the two rotations.

Example 1

Complete each statement.

a. The composition of a 54° clockwise rotation about O and a 95° clockwise rotation about O is a ___ rotation about ___ .

b. The composition of these two rotations maps A to ___ and D to ___ .

Solution

a. 149° clockwise rotation about O b. A to I and D to L

Try This

Complete this statement.
The composition of these two clockwise rotations maps B to ___ and C to ___ .

The composition of the translation AE and the translation EI maps rectangle $ABCD$ to rectangle $IJKL$. The composition is the translation AI. This example suggests the following theorem.

THEOREM 13.2

The composition of two translations is a translation. If translation PR is followed by translation RQ, then the composition translation is the translation PQ.

Example 2

Complete each statement.

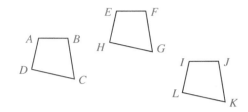

a. The composition of the translation AE followed by the translation EI is the translation ___ .
b. Under the composition of the translation AE followed by the translation EI the image of A is ___ .

Solution

a. AI b. I

Try This

The composition of the translation DL followed by the translation LH is the translation __?__ .

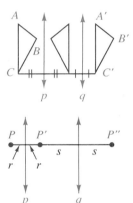

We next consider the composition of two line reflections in parallel lines. Suppose that lines p and q are parallel. The reflection of $\triangle ABC$ in line p and the reflection of its image in line q results in $\triangle A'B'C'$. Notice that this composition results in a translation that maps A to A', B to B', and C to C'. Also, $\overline{AA'} \perp p$ and AA' is twice the distance between lines p and q.

In general, suppose P is a point reflected in line p to P' where the distance PP' is $2r$. Then, suppose P' is reflected in line q to P'' where the distance $P'P''$ is $2s$. The distance PP'' is $2r + 2s$ or twice the distance, $r + s$, between p and q. The same would be true for any other point P in the plane. This argument suggests the following theorem.

THEOREM 13.3

The composition of two line reflections in parallel lines p and q is a translation in a direction perpendicular to p and q having a length equal to twice the distance between p and q.

Example 3

$p \parallel q$ Complete each statement.

a. The composition of the reflection in p followed by the reflection in q is the translation ___ .
b. The length of $\overline{DH}$ is ___ .

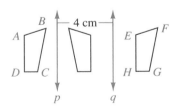

Solution

a. AE, BF, DH, or CG b. 8 cm

Try This

The composition of the reflection in p followed by the reflection in q is the translation that maps D to __?__ and $\overline{BC}$ to __?__ .

Suppose that lines p and q intersect at point O. The reflection of $\triangle ABC$ in line p and the reflection of its image in line q results in a rotation centered at O that maps A to G, B to H, and C to I. The angle of rotation is twice the angle formed by line p and line q. That is, $m\angle AOG = 2m\angle WOT$.

This example suggests the following theorem.

 THEOREM 13.4

The composition of two line reflections in lines intersecting at O is a rotation with center O and angle of rotation twice the angle from the first line to the second line.

Class Exercises

Short Answer

Determine whether each statement is true or false.

1. The composition of a 45° clockwise rotation about O followed by a 30° clockwise rotation about O is a 75° clockwise rotation about O.
2. The composition of a 35° counterclockwise rotation about O followed by a 45° clockwise rotation about O is a 75° rotation.
3. The composition of a 35° counterclockwise rotation about O followed by a 45° clockwise rotation about O is a 10° clockwise rotation.
4. The composition of a translation and a translation is again a translation.
5. The composition of a line reflection and a line reflection is always a line reflection.
6. If the distance between two points A and B on two intersecting lines p and q is 8 cm, then the composition of successive line reflections in these two lines is a translation that moves points 16 m.

Sample Exercises

Complete each statement.

7. The 45° clockwise rotation about O maps $\triangle ABC$ onto ___ and the 90° clockwise rotation about O maps $\triangle EFG$ onto ___ .
8. The composition of the 45° rotation followed by the 90° rotation maps $\triangle ABC$ onto ___ .

Discussion

9. After looking at parallelogram $WXYZ$, Raoul said that he thought the translation WX followed by the translation XY would have the same result as the translation WZ followed by the translation ZY. Do you agree? Explain why or why not.

10. Is the image of a rotation about O followed by a translation always, sometimes, or never the same as the translation followed by the rotation about O? Explain the reasoning behind your answer.

Exercises

A

Draw pictures as necessary to help complete each statement.

1. The composition of a 45° clockwise rotation about O and a 90° clockwise rotation about O is a ___ rotation about ___ .
2. The composition of a 90° clockwise rotation about O and a 45° counterclockwise rotation about O is a ___ rotation about ___ .
3. The composition of a ___ clockwise rotation about O and a 45° clockwise rotation about O is a 135° clockwise rotation about O.
4. The composition of a 135° counterclockwise rotation about O and a 45° clockwise rotation about O is a ___ rotation about O.

Complete each statement about the composition of a 45° clockwise rotation about O and a 90° clockwise rotation about O.

5. maps A to ___ and F to ___
6. maps B to ___ and D to ___
7. maps ___ to C and ___ to D
8. maps ___ to A and ___ to F

Complete each statement about the composition of the translation AE followed by the translation EI.

9. maps A to ___
10. maps D to ___
11. maps C to ___
12. maps B to ___

Consider the composition of the reflection in line p followed by the reflection in line q. Complete each statement about this translation.

13. maps A to ___   14. maps B to ___
15. maps ___ to N 16. $AL =$ ___

B

Complete each statement about the reflection in line q followed by the reflection in line s.

17. maps A to ___   18. maps L to ___
19. maps O to ___   20. maps N to ___

Complete each statement about the reflection in line p followed by the reflection in line q.

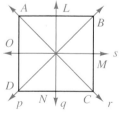

21. maps A to ___   22. maps B to ___
23. maps D to ___   24. maps L to ___
25. maps C to ___   26. maps M to ___

One translation, PQ, maps (x, y) to $(x + 3, y + 1)$ and a second translation, RS, maps (x, y) to $(x + 2, y - 1)$. Complete each statement about the composition of PQ followed by RS.

27. maps $(1, 1)$ to ___   28. maps $(-2, 3)$ to ___
29. maps $(2, -1)$ to ___   30. maps $(-3, -5)$ to ___

Complete each statement about the composition of the reflection in the line $y = 3$ followed by the reflection in the line $x = 2$.

31. maps $(1, 2)$ to ___   **32.** maps $(-1, 2)$ to ___
33. maps $(2, -3)$ to ___   **34.** maps $(-2, -3)$ to ___

Trace the figures for Exercises 35 and 36 and use tracing paper to help find the results of the compositions described.

35. Lines p and q are parallel. Draw the image of $\triangle ABC$ after a reflection in line p, followed by a 90° clockwise rotation about D, then followed by a reflection in line q.

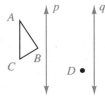

36. Lines r and s are perpendicular. Draw the image of $\triangle JKL$ after a reflection in line r, followed by a reflection in line s, followed by a counterclockwise rotation about O of 90°.

C

Lines p and q intersect at O. P'' is the image of P after reflection in line q followed by reflection in line p.

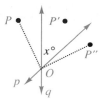

37. Prove $\overline{OP} \cong \overline{OP'}$.
38. Prove $m \angle POP'' = 2m \angle x$.

39. Given: Lines p and q are parallel.
       A' is the reflection image in p of A.
       A'' is the reflection image in q of A'.

  Prove: $\overline{AA''}$ is perpendicular to p.

40. Given: Lines p and q are parallel.
       A' is the reflection image in p of A.
       A'' is the reflection image in q of A'.
       $\overline{PQ}$ is perpendicular to p.

  Prove: $AA'' = 2PQ$

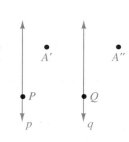

Critical Thinking

41. One square is a 180° rotation about O of the other. Do you think that one cube is a 180° rotation about O' of the other? Use a drawing, if desired, to explain your answer.

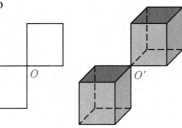

42. Plane *RST* is a plane of reflectional symmetry for the cube *ABCDEFGH*. Find eight other planes of symmetry for the cube.

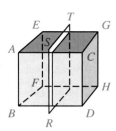

43. Consider a sphere with center *O* and radius *r*. How many planes of symmetry does the sphere have?

44. A line ℓ is an axis of symmetry of a cube if a rotation of the cube in space about the line maps the cube to itself. How many different lines of symmetry can you find for *ABCDEFGH*?

Algebra Review

Solve each inequality.

1. $3x > 9x + 6$ **2.** $4y + 3 \le 5y - 8$ **3.** $7n - 10 < 5 + 2n$
4. $-3z < -5z + 24$ **5.** $10x \ge 4x$ **6.** $8 - 5y \le 5y - 12$

Quiz

Complete each statement.

1. The reflection image in *t* of point *B* is ___ .
2. The reflection image in *t* of $\overline{HG}$ is ___ .
3. The reflection image in *t* of ___ is point *C*.

State the number of lines of reflectional symmetry for each figure.

4. equilateral triangle   **5.** square

Determine whether each statement is true or false for the translation *LM* defined by $L(-3, 5)$ and $M(2, 6)$.

6. The image of (3, 4) is (8, 5).
7. The image of (0, 0) is (2, 6).
8. The image of (x, y) is $(x + 2, y + 6)$.

9. Find the 90° clockwise rotation image about *T* of *A*.
10. Find the half-turn image about *T* of *D*.
11. Does the figure have 270° rotational symmetry?

Complete each statement about the composition of a 30° clockwise rotation about *O* followed by a 60° clockwise rotation about *O*.

12. maps $\overline{AB}$ to ___   **13.** maps *C* to ___
14. maps ___ to $\overline{HI}$ **15.** maps ___ to *G*

ISOMETRIES AND DILATIONS

OBJECTIVE: *Use properties of isometries.*

13-5 Isometries and Congruence

In Chapter 4 you studied the concept of congruence as it applies to triangles. This concept of congruence can be extended to apply to polygons and to figures which are not polygons, such as semicircles. The concept of **isometry** is the basis for generalizing the concept of congruence to figures that are not polygons. Reflections, translations, and rotations have the common property that the distance between any two points and the distance between their images are equal. Transformations with this property are called isometries.

■ DEFINITION

An **isometry** is a transformation that satisfies the following property. If P and Q are any two points and P' and Q' are the transformation images of P and Q, then $PQ = P'Q'$.

Example 1

Suppose that an isometry maps A to A', B to B', C to C', and D to D'. Find each length.

a. $A'D'$ **b.** $B'C'$

Solution

a. $A'D' = 4$ *By the definition of isometry,*
b. $B'C' = 5$ $AD = A'D'$ *and* $BC = B'C'$.

Try This

Find each length.

a. $C'D'$ **b.** $A'B'$

◆ THEOREM 13.5

A line reflection is an isometry.

Given: Line ℓ and any two points P and Q
  P' and Q' are the reflection images of P and Q.
Prove: $PQ = P'Q'$
Plan Use the definition of line reflection to show that $PXYA$ and $P'XYB$ are rectangles and that $QA = Q'B$. Use SAS congruence to show that $\triangle APQ \cong \triangle BP'Q'$ and conclude that $PQ = P'Q'$. A similar argument works when P and Q are not on the same side of ℓ.

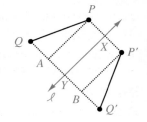

Example 2

Suppose that *GHIJKM* is the reflection image in line of *ABCDEF*. Find each length.

a. *KJ*   b. *IH*   c. *GH*

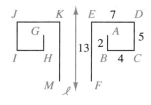

Solution

a. 7   b. 4   c. 2

Try This

Find *IJ* and *KM*.

If one isometry maps *PQ* to *P'Q'* and another isometry maps *P'Q'* to *P"Q"*, then *PQ* = *P'Q'* and *P'Q'* = *P"Q"*.

This observation is the basis of the proof of the following theorem.

◆ **THEOREM 13.6**

The composition of two isometries is an isometry.

In Lesson 13-4, you saw that a composition of reflections is either a translation or a rotation. The converse is also true. That is, every translation and every rotation can be expressed in terms of a composition of reflections. Since reflections are isometries, the following are consequences of Theorem 13.6.

▶ **COROLLARY 13.6a**

A translation is an isometry.

▶ **COROLLARY 13.6b**

A rotation is an isometry.

▦ **DEFINITION**

A figure *F* is **congruent** to figure *F'* if there is an isometry such that *F'* is the image of *F*.

Example 3

Suppose *p* is a line of symmetry for *ABCDEFGH*. Explain why quadrilaterals *ABCD* and *HGFE* are congruent.

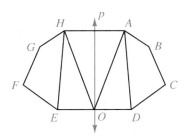

Solution

HGFE is the reflection image of *ABCD*. Since a line reflection is an isometry, these two quadrilaterals are congruent.

Try This

Explain why pentagons *ABCDO* and *HGFEO* are congruent.

The fact that congruent figures are mapped under isometries into congruent figures provides a basis for another theorem which characterizes isometries.

 THEOREM 13.7

If figure F' is the image of figure F under an isometry, then the areas of F and F' are equal.

Class Exercises

Short Answer

Determine whether each statement is true or false.

1. A line reflection is an isometry.
2. An isometry is a line reflection.
3. If a figure F' is the image of a figure F under an isometry, then F and F' are congruent.
4. A translation is an isometry.
5. An isometry is a mapping that preserves congruence.
6. If the image of a figure is congruent to the original figure, then the mapping is an isometry.

Sample Exercises

Suppose that lines p and q are both lines of symmetry for quadrilateral $ABCD$. Find each length.

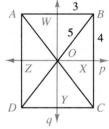

7. AO 8. CY 9. DY 10. AZ
11. Explain why you can conclude that $AX = DX$.
12. Explain why you can conclude that $WX = YX$.
13. Explain why you can conclude that $WX = YZ$.

Discussion

14. Is there a composition of two line reflections that maps the figure on the left to the figure on the right? Explain.

15. Is there a rotation that maps the figure on the left to the figure on the right? Explain.

16. Make a drawing of a $\triangle ABC$ and two parallel lines p and q. Consider the reflection of the triangle in p followed by the reflection of the image in q. Then repeat the process, first reflecting in q and then in p. Were the two final images the same? Do you think that the composition of reflections in parallel lines is commutative? Give another example to illustrate your conclusion.

Exercises

A

Suppose that $A'B'C'D'$ **is the image of parallelogram** $ABCD$
under an isometry. Find each length.

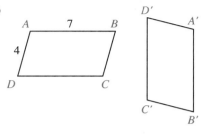

   1. $A'B'$ **2.** $A'D'$
   3. BC **4.** $B'C'$
   5. CD **6.** $C'D'$

   7. Explain how you know that $AC = A'C'$.
   8. Explain how you know that $A'B'C'D'$ is a parallelogram.

Given that lines p **and** q **are lines of symmetry of** $ABCDEF$,
complete each statement.

   9. The reflection image in line p of A is ___ .
  10. The reflection image in line q of C is ___ .
  11. $BC =$ ___   **12.** $FE =$ ___   **13.** $DE =$ ___
  14. $XD =$ ___   **15.** $FY =$ ___   **16.** $AY =$ ___

B

Given that lines p **and** q **are lines of symmetry, answer
the following.**

  17. Why is $ACDF$ a rectangle?
  18. The reflection in which line explains why $AE = FB$?
  19. The reflection in which line explains why $FB = BD$?
  20. Why are quadrilaterals $ABCX$ and $FEDX$ congruent?
  21. Why are pentagons $AFEDX$ and $FABCX$ congruent?
  22. **Given:** Lines p and q are lines of symmetry of $ABCDEF$.
       Prove: $ABDE$ is a parallelogram.

C

  23. If an isometry maps A to A', B to B', and C to C' prove that $\triangle A'B'C'$
      is congruent to $\triangle ABC$ assuming that A, B, and C are noncollinear points.
  24. Prove that if $\angle A'B'C'$ is the reflection image of a line of $\angle ABC$ then
      $m \angle ABC = m \angle A'B'C'$.

The composition of the translation described by AB followed by the reflection
in line ℓ maps the red region below onto the blue region. This composition
of isometries is called a **glide reflection** with glide line ℓ.

  25. If point P is above ℓ where is its glide reflection image?
  26. If point P is below ℓ where is its glide reflection image?
  27. If point P is on ℓ where is its glide reflection image?

Suppose that lines p and q are lines of symmetry of the figure.

28. Prove that quadrilateral *ABFJ* and quadrilateral *KJFB* are congruent.
29. Prove that the figure "S" in quadrant I and the figure "S" in quadrant III are congruent.

Critical Thinking

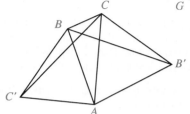

30. In $\triangle ABC$, $m\angle A = 20$. If $\triangle ABC'$ and $\triangle AB'C$ are equilateral triangles, explain how a 60° rotation of one triangle in this figure would allow you to make a comparison between BB' and CC'.

31. If R is an isometry that maps figure A to figure B, what can you say about the relationship of the borders (perimeters, circumferences, . . .) of figures A and B?

32. If $\angle ABC$ is the image of $\angle RST$ under an isometry M, give a convincing argument why $\angle ABC \cong \angle RST$.

Mixed Review

RSTU is a parallelogram.

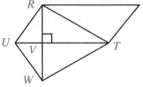

1. $RS = 12$, $RV = 6$ Find the area of $\square RSTU$.
2. $RW = 7$, $UT = 10$ Find the area of quadrilateral $URTW$.
3. $RV = 4$, $RS = 8$, $VT = 6$ Find the area of trapezoid $RSTV$.
4. If the area of $\square RSTU$ is 48 cm and $UT = 8$, find RV.
5. If $URTW$ is a kite with area 64 and $UT = 16$, find RW.
6. Find the height of trapezoid $RSTV$ if its area is 30, $RS = 7$, and $VT = 5$.

Biographical Note

Sophie Germain (1776–1831)

Sophie Germain, one of the most prominent women mathematicians of the nineteenth century, was largely self-taught. Her interests included acoustics, higher arithmetic, and the theory of elasticity.

Germain was influenced by a work of the great mathematician Gauss and wrote to him some of her own arithmetical observations. Concerned that Gauss would be prejudiced against a female mathematician, she used a man's name. Gauss was very impressed with Germain's work and eventually discovered that his correspondent was a woman. Realizing the prejudices and difficulties a woman in science must have encountered, he wrote that Germain possessed "the noblest courage, quite extraordinary talents, and a superior genius."

13-6 Dilations

A magnifying glass or a microscope can be used to enlarge your view of an object or figure. The shape of the object stays the same but the size is allowed to vary. The same effect is produced by a transformation called a **dilation.** It preserves the *shape* of a figure, but allows the *size* to change.

■ DEFINITION

A **dilation** with center O is a transformation that associates with a point P, the unique point P' on ray OP such that $\frac{OP'}{OP} = k$. We say that the **dilation image** of point P is point P'. The dilation image of O is O itself. The number k is called the **scale factor** of the dilation.

The scale factor of a dilation, like the scale factor for similarity, can be any positive real number. In the figure to the right, the scale factor is 2. The points A', B', and C' are the dilation images of points A, B, and C for the dilation with center O and scale factor 2.

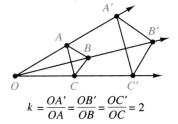

$$k = \frac{OA'}{OA} = \frac{OB'}{OB} = \frac{OC'}{OC} = 2$$

Example 1

Complete each statement for the dilation with center O and scale factor 3.

a. The image of B is ____ .

b. The image of $ABCD$ is ____ .

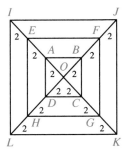

Solution

a. J since $\frac{OJ}{OB} = \frac{6}{2} = 3$

b. $IJKL$

Try This

a. If the image of F is J for the dilation with center O and scale factor k, find the value of k.

b. If the image of $EFGH$ is $ABCD$ for the dilation with center O and scale factor k, find the value of k.

Notice that if $k > 1$ the image figure is an enlargement, and if $0 < k < 1$, the image figure is a reduction. Consequently, we call the dilation an **enlargement** if $k > 1$ and a **reduction** if $0 < k < 1$. If $k = 1$, then the dilation is the **identity mapping** (the mapping that leaves all points unchanged).

Using a coordinate system, it is possible to describe a dilation with scale factor k and center at the origin as a mapping from (x, y) to (kx, ky). The following example illustrates this.

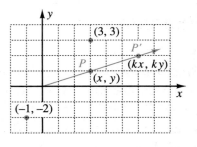

Example 2

If the scale factor of a dilation centered at the origin is 2, find the image of each point.

a. $(3, 3)$ **b.** $(-1, -2)$

Solution

a. $(6, 6)$ **b.** $(-2, -4)$ *Multiply each coordinate by 2.*

Try This

If the scale factor of a dilation centered at the origin is $\frac{1}{4}$, find the image of each point.

a. $(4, 12)$ **b.** $(-2, 3)$

Class Exercises

Short Answer

The center of each dilation is O. Complete each statement.

1. For scale factor of 2, the dilation image of H is ___ .
2. For scale factor of 3, the dilation image of G is ___ .
3. For scale factor of $\frac{1}{3}$, the dilation image of C is ___ .
4. For scale factor of $\frac{1}{2}$, the dilation image of $\triangle DEF$ is ___ .

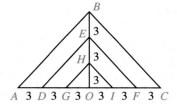

Sample Exercises

Trace $\overline{AB}$ and O as shown to the right. Draw the image of $\overline{AB}$ for each dilation.

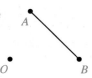

5. the dilation with center O and scale factor 2
6. the dilation with center O and scale factor $\frac{1}{2}$

Complete each statement.

7. The image of $(3, -1)$ under the dilation with center $(0, 0)$ and scale factor 2 is ___ .
8. The image of $(6, 9)$ under the dilation with center $(0, 0)$ and scale factor $\frac{1}{3}$ is ___ .
9. The image of ___ under the dilation with center $(0, 0)$ and scale factor $\frac{1}{2}$ is $(8, 4)$.

Discussion

10. For which lines ℓ is the dilation image of ℓ with center O the line ℓ itself?
11. For what value of the scale factor is the dilation image of a figure a figure of the same size and shape?
12. For what values of the scale factor is the dilation image of a figure a figure of the same shape?

Exercises

A

Trace the figure to the right. Draw the image of $\triangle ABC$ under each.

1. the dilation with center O and scale factor 2
2. the dilation with center A and scale factor 3

Trace the figure to the right. Draw the image of square $ABCD$ under each.

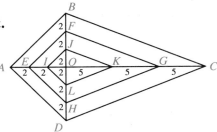

3. the dilation with center O and scale factor 2
4. the dilation with center P and scale factor 3
5. the dilation with center Q and scale factor $\frac{1}{2}$

The center of each dilation is O. Complete each statement.

6. For a scale factor of 2, the image of K is ____ .
7. For a scale factor of 2, the image of $IJKL$ is ____ .
8. For a scale factor of 3, the image of $IJKL$ is ____ .
9. For a scale factor of $\frac{1}{2}$, the image of H is ____ .
10. For a scale factor of $\frac{1}{2}$, the image of $EFGH$ is ____ .
11. For a scale factor of $\frac{1}{3}$, the image of $ABCD$ is ____ .

Consider dilations with center $(0, 0)$ in a rectangular coordinate system. Complete each statement.

12. The dilation image with scale factor 3 of $(3, 5)$ is ____ .
13. The dilation image with scale factor 2 of $(-2, 1)$ is ____ .
14. The dilation image with scale factor $\frac{1}{2}$ of $(-4, 3)$ is ____ .
15. The dilation image with scale factor $\frac{1}{5}$ of $(10, 7)$ is ____ .

B

16. If the dilation image of $(1, 2)$ is $(4, 8)$ under a dilation centered at the origin, find the scale factor. Using the same scale factor, find the coordinates of the dilation images of points $A(2, 3)$, $B(-1, 4)$, and $C(3, 5)$.
17. If $(3, 5)$ is the dilation image with scale factor 2 of point A, find the coordinates of point A.
18. Suppose that $\triangle A'B'C'$ is the dilation image of $\triangle ABC$ under the dilation with center O and scale factor k. Prove that $A'B' = kAB$.
19. Suppose that $\triangle A'B'C'$ is the dilation image of $\triangle ABC$ under the dilation with center O and scale factor k. Prove that $BC = \frac{1}{k}B'C'$.
20. If $A'B'C'D'$ is the image of square $ABCD$ under the dilation with center P and scale factor 4, and if the length of one side of $ABCD$ is 5, find the perimeter of square $A'B'C'D'$.
21. If $A'B'C'D'$ is the image of square $ABCD$ under the dilation with center P and scale factor 4, and if the area of $ABCD$ is 4, find the area of square $A'B'C'D'$.

C

22. If line ℓ' is the dilation image of line ℓ under a dilation with center O and scale factor k, prove that $\ell \parallel \ell'$ or ℓ and ℓ' are the same line.

23. Suppose that ℓ is the line through the points $(1, 5)$ and $(3, 2)$. If line ℓ' is the image of line ℓ under the dilation with center $(0, 0)$ and scale factor 2, calculate the slopes of both ℓ and ℓ'. What do you conclude?

24. Suppose that A' and B' are the images of $A(2, 3)$ and $B(4, 7)$ under the dilation with center $(0, 0)$ and scale factor k. Show that $A'B' = kAB$.

25. $\triangle A'B'C'$ is the image of $\triangle ABC$ under the dilation with center $(0, 0)$ and scale factor 2. Given $A(-1, 2)$, $B(2, 4)$, and $C(5, 2)$, how does the area of $\triangle ABC$ compare to the area of $\triangle A'B'C'$?

26. Suppose that ℓ is the line through points $A(x_1, y_1)$ and $B(x_2, y_2)$ and that ℓ' is the line through A' and B'. A' and B' are the dilation images of A and B under the dilation with center $(0, 0)$ and scale factor k. Show that ℓ and ℓ' have equal slopes.

27. $\triangle A'B'C'$ is the dilation image with center $(0, 0)$ and scale factor $\frac{1}{3}$ of $\triangle ABC$. Given $A(-3, 5)$, $B(3, 6)$, and $C(5, -2)$, find the coordinates of A', B', and C'.

Critical Thinking

28. Draw on graph paper polygon $ABCDEF$ and its dilation image $A'B'C'D'E'F'$ under the dilation with center $(0, 0)$ and scale factor 2. Estimate how many times greater the area of $A'B'C'D'E'F'$ is than the area of $ABCDEF$. Calculate the area of each to check your guess. State a generalization about the effect a dilation with scale factor k has on the area of a polygon.

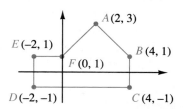

29. The figure to the right shows the result of a dilation in space which maps a smaller cube into a larger cube. If the dilation is centered at O and the scale factor is 2, what is the ratio of the surface areas of the cubes? the volumes of the cubes?

Mixed Review

Give the center and radius of each circle.

1. $x^2 + y^2 = 64$
2. $(x - 1)^2 + (y - 2)^2 = 1$
3. $(x + 4)^2 + (y - 5)^2 = 10$
4. $(x + 1)^2 + y^2 = 40$

Given each center and radius, write the equation of the circle in the form shown in Exercises 1–4.

5. center $(0, 0)$; radius 6
6. center $(1, 4)$; radius 9
7. center $(-1, 0)$; radius $\sqrt{5}$
8. center $(-2, -3)$; radius $2\sqrt{7}$

DISCRETE MATH

Fitting a Line to a Set of Data

Researchers and businesspeople who use mathematics often need to fit a line to a set of data. Such a line represents the set of data and can be used to predict trends from the data. The line *m* on the graph below fits or describes the relationships between the length of a video game and points scored.

Video Game Points per Min

Example

What score would you predict for a 12-min game?

Solution

Using line *m* as a model, a score of 1450 points seems reasonable, as the point (12,1450) appears to be on the line.

Try This

What score would you predict for an 8-min game? Lines can be fit to a set of data in several ways. One way is shown below.

1. Divide the set of points into thirds, moving from left to right. If the number is not divisible by three, put the leftover points in the middle portion.

2. Find the point in each portion that has half the points to its left and half to its right. Draw a vertical line through each. Find the point in each portion that has half the points below it and half above it. Draw a horizontal line through each.

3. Draw a line connecting the intersections of the two lines in the first and third portions. Then slide the line one third of the way to the point of intersection of the lines in the middle third.

Exercise

Find a line of fit for the data below to predict the weight of an adult male from his shoe size. What weight would you expect for a person with a size 13 shoe?

Weight by Shoe Size

13-7 Dilations and Similarity

In the figure to the right, $\triangle DEF$ is the image of $\triangle ABC$ under the dilation with center O and scale factor 2. It is also evident that the lengths of the sides of $\triangle ABC$ have been multiplied by 2 and that the two triangles are similar. These facts are the subject of the theorems in this lesson.

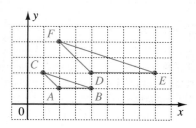

◆ **THEOREM 13.8**

If A' and B' are the images of A and B under the dilation with center O and scale factor k, then $A'B' = kAB$.

Given: points A and B and their images A' and B' under the dilation with center O and scale factor k

Prove: $A'B' = kAB$

Plan By the definition of the dilation with center O and scale factor k, you know that $k = \frac{OA'}{OA} = \frac{OB'}{OB}$. With this proportion and the SAS Similarity Theorem, you can show that $\triangle AOB \sim \triangle A'OB'$. Since corresponding sides of similar triangles are proportional, conclude that $A'B' = kAB$.

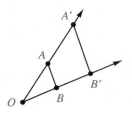

The following example shows how Theorem 13.8 may be used when one figure is the dilation image of another.

Example 1

Suppose that *GHIJKL* is the image of *ABCDEF* under the dilation with center *O* and scale factor 2. Find each length.

a. *GH*   **b.** *JK*   **c.** *FE*

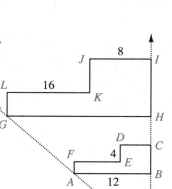

Solution

a. $GH = 2AB = 2 \cdot 12 = 24$
b. $JK = 2DE = 2 \cdot 4 = 8$
c. $KL = 2FE$ $16 = 2FE$ $FE = 8$

Try This

Complete each statement.

a. If $BC = 8$, then $HI =$ ___ .
b. If $GL = 8$, then $AF =$ ___ .
c. If ___ $= 5$, then $GL = 10$.

The next theorem describes the relationship between dilations and the concept of similarity.

◆ THEOREM 13.9

If $\triangle A'B'C'$ is the image of $\triangle ABC$ under the dilation with center O and scale factor k, then $\triangle A'B'C'$ is similar to $\triangle ABC$.

Given: $\triangle A'B'C'$ is the image of $\triangle ABC$ under the dilation with center O and scale factor k.

Prove: $\triangle A'B'C'$ is similar to $\triangle ABC$.

Plan Use Theorem 13.8 to conclude that $A'B' = kAB$, $A'C' = kAC$, and $B'C' = kBC$. Use the SSS Similarity Theorem to conclude that $\triangle A'B'C'$ is similar to $\triangle ABC$.

The concept of similarity of figures is quite general. It centers on the fact that two figures are similar if and only if you can "size" one figure and then "move" the sized figure to match the other. This idea is used in the following definition of similarity.

▓ DEFINITION

A figure F is similar to a figure F' if there is a dilation and an isometry such that the composition of the dilation and the isometry maps F onto F'.

Note that in the above definition, the dilation and the isometry may be composed in either.

In Example 2, two figures are shown to be similar by showing that one is the image of the other under a composition of a dilation and an isometry.

Example 2

Show that figures $MNKL$ and $PNSQ$, each made up of a square and semicircle, are similar.

Solution

The 180° rotation about N maps M to Z, K to X, and L to Y. The dilation with center N and scale factor 2 maps Z to P, Y to Q, and X to S. Therefore, the composition maps square $MNKL$ to $PNSQ$ and semicircle LK to semicircle SQ. You can conclude that figure $MNKL$ is similar to $PNSQ$.

Try This

Use the above definition to show that figures $ABCDEF$ and $TUVWXY$ below are similar.

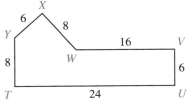

Class Exercises

Short Answer

$AB = 1$, $AC = \sqrt{5}$, $BC = 2\sqrt{2}$ $\triangle DEF$ is the image of $\triangle ABC$ under the dilation with center O and scale factor 2 and $\triangle GHI$ is the image of $\triangle DEF$ under the dilation with center O' and scale factor $\frac{3}{2}$. Find each length.

1. DE
2. EF
3. DF
4. GH
5. GI
6. HI

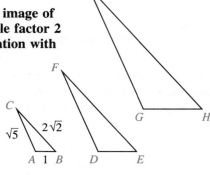

Sample Exercises

Complete each statement.

7. If $\triangle ABC$ is the dilation image of $\triangle DEF$, then the scale factor $k = $ ___ .
8. If $\triangle ABC$ is the dilation image of $\triangle GHI$, then the scale factor $k = $ ___ .
9. If $\triangle GHI$ is the dilation image of $\triangle ABC$, then the scale factor $k = $ ___ .
10. If $\triangle ABC$ is the dilation image of $\triangle DEF$, then $\triangle ABC$ is similar to ___ .

Discussion

11. If circle C_1 has radius r_1 and circle C_2 has radius r_2, how would you prove that C_1 and C_2 are similar figures in each case?

    a. if the circles have the same center
    b. if the circles have different centers

Exercises

$\triangle DEF$ is the image of $\triangle ABC$ under the dilation with center O and scale factor 2. Find each length.

1. DE 2. DF 3. BC

$EFGH$ is the image of $ABCD$ under a dilation with scale factor $\frac{5}{3}$. Find each length.

4. EF 5. FG
6. GH 7. EH

$\triangle XYZ$ is the image of $\triangle ABC$ under a dilation with scale factor 4. Complete each statement.

8. If $AB = 25$, then $XY = $ ___ .   9. If $AC = 30$, then $XZ = $ ___ .
10. If $YZ = 32$, then $BC = $ ___ .   11. If $XY = 14$, then $AB = $ ___ .
12. If $BC = $ ___ , then $YZ = 4$.   13. If ___ $= 12$, then $XZ = 48$.

14. Use a dilation to show that figures *BODF* and *AOEG* are similar if $\frac{OF}{OG} = \frac{1}{2}$ and the arcs are parts of circles tangent at *O*.

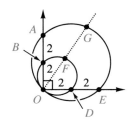

15. Explain why polygon *ABFGE* is similar to polygon *HBDJI*. Angles which appear congruent may be assumed congruent.

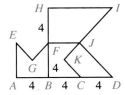

B

Suppose that $\triangle A'B'C'$ is the dilation image of $\triangle ABC$ with scale factor $\frac{1}{2}$ and $\triangle A''B''C''$ is the dilation image of $\triangle A'B'C'$ with scale factor 3. Complete each statement.

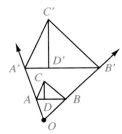

16. If $AB = 20$, then $A''B'' = \underline{\quad}$.
17. If $A''C'' = 36$, then $AC = \underline{\quad}$.
18. If $A'B' = 14$, then $AB = \underline{\quad}$.
19. If $A''B'' = 12$, then $AB = \underline{\quad}$.
20. If $B''C'' = \underline{\quad}$, then $BC = 10$.

A dilation with center O and scale factor 3 maps A to A', B to B', C to C', and D to D'.

21. Prove that if $\overline{CD}$ is an altitude of $\triangle ABC$, then $\overline{C'D'}$ is an altitude of $\triangle A'B'C'$.
22. Find the ratio of the area of $\triangle A'B'C'$ to the area of $\triangle ABC$.

C

The larger cube below is the image of the smaller cube under a three-dimensional dilation with scale factor 3.

23. Find the surface area of the larger cube.
24. Find the volume of the larger cube.
25. Find the ratio of the surface area of the larger cube to the surface area of the smaller cube? Find the ratio of the volumes.
26. Given that the dilation image of circle C is circle C' and that the scale factor of the dilation is 2, what can you conclude about the relationship between the circumference of circle C' and the circumference of circle C? Prove that your conjecture is true.

27. Explain why the letters C and U and letters I and H as shown below are similar or are not similar.

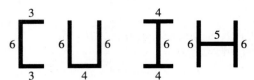

Critical Thinking

28. Suppose that figure F_1 is similar but not congruent to F_2 and F_2 is similar but not congruent to F_3. Must it be true that F_1 is similar but not congruent to F_3? Explain.

29. A point G is called a **fixed point** of a transformation if the point is its own image under the transformation. A given transformation may have a number of fixed points. For each of the following transformations, describe the fixed points in the plane under the transformation.
   a. reflection   **b.** rotation   **c.** translation
   d. dilation   **e.** composition of rotation and dilation (same center)

Algebra Review

Solve each equation.

1. $x^2 + 7x - 30 = 0$ 2. $x^2 + 8x + 16 = 0$ 3. $y^2 - 49 = 0$
4. $a^2 - 10a - 24 = 0$ 5. $2x^2 - 7x + 3 = 0$ 6. $3x^2 + 2x - 1 = 0$

Quiz

Determine whether each statement is true or false.

1. Every translation is an isometry.
2. Every dilation is an isometry.
3. Two figures are similar if there is a dilation and an isometry whose composition maps one figure onto the other.

RSTUVW is the image of ABCDEF under an isometry.

4. If $BC = 6$, find ST.
5. If $UV = 2$, what other segment must also have length 2?
6. If the area of $ABCDEF$ is 24 cm², find the area of $RSTUVW$.

△JKL is the dilation image of △GHI. The scale factor is 3.

7. If $HI = 6$, find KL.   8. If $JL = 18$, find GI.
9. True or false: $\triangle GHI \sim \triangle JKL$?

10. Find the image of $(-6, 9)$ under the dilation with center $(0, 0)$ and scale factor 3.

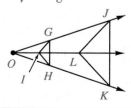

CRITICAL THINKING

Making and Supporting Decisions

Many critical thinking problems require the use of visual reasoning. Use these skills to develop a solution for the following situation.

In a certain two-person game, the players take turns placing a penny on a circular table top with a green tablecloth. The pennies may touch, but are not allowed to rest upon one another. Furthermore, they must be completely on the table—not hanging out over the edge. Once a penny is placed on the table it cannot be moved. The last player to place a penny on the table is the winner.

If each player makes an optimal move on his or her turn, will the player who went first or second be the winner?

Answer the questions in each step below to use the process of critical thinking.

1. **Understand the Situation**
   a. What is the situation about?
   b. What conclusion, decision, or solution is required?
   c. Are there any questions you could ask to clarify the problem?

2. **Deal with the Data/Evidence/Assumptions**
   a. Make a list of the most important rules and data. Is other information needed?
   b. Which data given in the situation is not relevant?
   c. What assumptions are made? What other assumptions could be made?

3. **Go Beyond the Data/Evidence/Assumptions**
   a. Try this problem with very small tables.
   b. Consider a table whose diameter is the width of a certain number of pennies.
   c. Does it make a difference if the diameter is a certain number of pennies long?

4. **State and Support your Conclusion/Decision/Solution**

   Write a paragraph, with an accompanying diagram, describing your solution to this situation.

5. **Apply the Conclusion/Decision/Solution**

   A similar situation involved a square table. What modifications, if any, would need to be made in the solution strategy to answer the same question about the game played on this table?

Exercise

Use the above process for the following situation.

Lucille found four sections of a bracelet. Each piece consisted of three links of gold. She wanted to have the four pieces joined to form one loop. A jeweler told her it would cost one dollar for each link that was opened and welded shut again. When the jeweler wrote a bill for $4, Lucille said she thought the loop could be made with less than four links being cut. Do you agree?

CHAPTER SUMMARY

Vocabulary

angle of rotation (13-3)	identity mapping (13-6)	reflection (13-1)
composition (13-4)	image (13-1)	reflectional symmetry (13-1)
dilation (13-6)	isometry (13-5)	rotation (13-3)
directed segment (13-2)	line of symmetry (13-1)	rotational symmetry (13-3)
enlargement (13-6)	mapping (13-1)	transformation (13-1)
fixed point (13-7)	preimage (13-1)	translation (13-2)
glide reflection (13-5)	reduction (13-6)	translational symmetry (13-2)
half-turn (13-3)		

Key Ideas

1. A mapping which establishes a one-to-one correspondence between points in the plane is called a transformation.
2. When one transformation is performed after another, the result is called the composition of the transformations.
3. An isometry is a transformation that preserves distance. Reflections, rotations, and translations are all isometries.
4. The composition of two isometries is an isometry.
5. A dilation with center O and scale factor k is a transformation that associates with each point P a point P' such that P' is on $\overrightarrow{OP}$ and $\frac{OP'}{OP} = k$.
6. A dilation with scale factor k and center at the origin is a mapping from (x, y) to (kx, ky).
7. A figure F is congruent to a figure F' if there is an isometry so that F' is the image of F.
8. A figure F is similar to a figure F' if there is a dilation and an isometry such that the composition of the dilation and the isometry maps F onto F'.

CHAPTER REVIEW

13-1

Complete each statement.

1. The reflection image in ℓ of A is ___ .
2. The reflection image in ℓ of B is ___ .
3. The reflection image in ℓ of $\overline{GH}$ is ___ .
4. The reflection image in ℓ of ___ is $\overline{AB}$.

5. Give the number of lines of reflectional symmetry for the letter H.

13-2

For translation RS from $R(-2, 3)$ to $S(2, 4)$, find the translation image of each point.

6. $(4, 6)$ 7. $(0, -1)$ 8. (x, y)

Complete each statement.

9. The image of point A under translation CG is ___ .
10. The image of point ___ under translation JB is point C.
11. The image of $\overline{EF}$ under translation HL is ___ .
12. The image of $ABCD$ under translation AE is ___ .

13-3

LMNOPQ is a regular hexagon. Consider rotations about R.

13. Name the 60° clockwise rotation image of L.
14. Name the half-turn image of $\overline{NO}$.
15. Does the figure have 90° rotational symmetry?
16. Does the figure have 120° rotational symmetry?

13-4

Determine whether each statement is true or false.

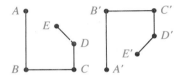

17. The composition of a 90° clockwise rotation about O followed by a 45° clockwise rotation about O is a 135° clockwise rotation about O.
18. The composition of two line reflections is always a line reflection.
19. Translation AB followed by translation BC is translation CA.

13-5

A′B′C′D′E′ is the image of ABCDE under an isometry.

20. If $AB = 6$, find the length of $\overline{A'B'}$.
21. If $D'E' = 12$, find the length of $\overline{DE}$.
22. Can you conclude that $ABCDE$ is congruent to $A'B'C'D'E'$?

13-6

Complete each statement.

23. The dilation with center $(0, 0)$ and scale factor 5 maps $(10, -5)$ to ___ .
24. The dilation with center O and scale factor 3 maps point R to ___ .
25. The dilation with center O and scale factor $\frac{1}{2}$ maps point W to ___ .

13-7

26. If LMN is the image of IJK under a dilation with scale factor 2 and $LM = 6$, find IJ.
27. Show that rectangle $AEBF$ is similar to rectangle $GCBD$.

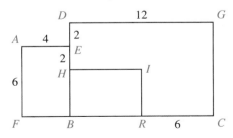

CHAPTER TEST

Determine whether each statement is true or false.

1. If $\triangle RST$ is the dilation image of $\triangle ABC$ and the scale factor is 2, then $AB = 2RS$.
2. The composition of two isometries is always an isometry.
3. Figure G is congruent to figure G' if there is an isometry that maps G to G'.
4. Two figures are similar only if there is a dilation that maps one figure onto the other.
5. Every line reflection is an isometry.

Complete each statement.

6. The reflection image in line ℓ of $\overline{MN}$ is ___ .
7. The reflection image in line ℓ of ___ is point T.
8. The letter I has ___ lines of reflectional symmetry.
9. The image of C under translation FJ is ___ .
10. The image of ___ under translation HL is M.
11. The image of $\overline{CE}$ under translation FN is ___ .

$\triangle TUV$ is an equilateral triangle. Consider rotations about O.

12. Find the $120°$ clockwise rotation image of $\overline{TO}$.
13. Find the $240°$ counterclockwise rotation image of $\overline{UV}$.
14. Does the figure have $90°$ rotational symmetry?

Complete each statement.

15. The composition of a $37°$ clockwise rotation about O and a $92°$ clockwise rotation about O is a ___ rotation about O.
16. The composition of translation QR followed by translation RS is ___ .
17. The composition of the reflection in line p followed by the reflection in line q is a translation if p and q are ___ .
18. Suppose $AE = 6$ and $EO = 2$. Find the scale factor of the dilation with center O that maps point E to point A.
19. If B is the image of F under the dilation with center O and scale factor 3 and $OF = 5$, find FB.
20. Find the image of $(8, 10)$ under the dilation with center $(0, 0)$ and scale factor $\frac{1}{2}$.
21. Show that $\triangle HOI$ is similar to $\triangle LOM$.

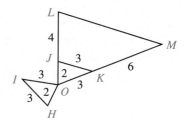

PROBLEM SOLVING

Choosing a Strategy

The problems below give you practice in choosing among the various strategies presented in the book.

Problem-Solving Strategies	
Draw a Diagram	Simplify the Problem
Make a Table	Make an Accurate Drawing
Look for a Pattern	Guess, Check, Revise
Work Backward	

Problems

Choose a strategy and solve each problem.

1. A painter had $48 to buy brushes. The two types of brushes available cost $4 and $6. In how many different ways could the painter spend all of her money buying these brushes?

2. Edie needed to think of a four-digit code for her automatic teller. She was allowed to use the numbers 0, 1, 2, 3, and 4 in any order and as often as she wished. How many different codes could Edie create?

3. A biologist has a mixture of two types of cells, type A and type B. Every two hours, each B cell produces one A cell and one B cell. Type A cells do not produce additional cells. Assume that there was one cell of each type to start. How many cells of each type would there be after one day?

4. It takes four equilateral triangles with sides of length 1 to make an equilateral triangle with sides of length 2. How many equilateral triangles with sides of length 1 does it take to make an equilateral triangle with sides of length 10?

5. A large circular park is to have six straight walking paths through it. The architect has been told to design the park so that there will be a maximum number of flower and garden areas inside the park and around the paths. What is the greatest number of flower and garden areas possible with six straight paths through the park?

6. What should be the dimensions of the bottom row of a pyramid that continues to build like the one below if there are 100 blocks to work with and as many blocks as possible are to be used?

7. A certain game has two possible scoring plays—a three-point play and an eight-point play. How many different total scores for one player are not possible in this game?

8. A math exam had 20 items. Students received two points for each correct answer and lost one point for each incorrect or missing answer. Mari had a score of 16. How many items were correctly answered on her test?

9. A computer access-code number was designated in a special way. It was a four-digit number between 1000 and 2000. Also, it was the smallest integer in this range that can be written as the sum of two positive cubes in two different ways. What was the code number?

10. A basketball series between the Aces and the Falcons is determined when one team wins three games. In how many ways can the Falcons win the series?

11. Grant always carries a lot of change in quarters, dimes, nickels, and pennies. Beth needed change for a dollar. It turned out that Grant had the most change he could possibly have had without having change for a dollar. How much money did Grant have in change?

Chapters 1–13

1. The inverse of "If an angle has measure 90, then it is a right angle" is ____ .
   a. If an angle is a right angle, then it has measure 90.
   b. If an angle does not have measure 90, then it is a right angle.
   c. If an angle does not have measure 90, then it is not a right angle.
   d. If an angle has measure 90, then it is not a right angle.

2. An angle that forms a linear pair with an interior angle of a triangle is called a(n)
   a. remote interior angle.   b. exterior angle.
   c. corresponding angle.   d. obtuse angle.

3. $\overline{AD} \cong \overline{BD} \cong \overline{BC}$, $m\angle 1 = 40$ Find $m\angle C$.

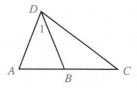

   a. 35   b. 40   c. 70   d. 110

4. In $\triangle RST$, U and V are midpoints of $\overline{RT}$ and $\overline{RS}$. If $\overline{UV} \| \overline{TS}$, which of the following statements is true?

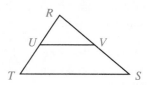

   a. $\overline{RU} \cong \overline{RV}$ b. $\overline{UV}$ is a median of $\triangle RST$.
   c. $TS = \frac{1}{2}UV$ d. $UV = \frac{1}{2}TS$

5. Which proportion is not equivalent to $\frac{a}{b} = \frac{x}{y}$?
   a. $\frac{a+b}{b} = \frac{x+y}{y}$ b. $\frac{y}{b} = \frac{x}{a}$
   c. $\frac{a}{y} = \frac{x}{b}$ d. $\frac{b}{a} = \frac{y}{x}$

6. The hypotenuse in a 45°–45°–90° triangle has length 12. Find the length of each leg.
   a. 6   b. $4\sqrt{3}$ c. $6\sqrt{2}$ d. $6\sqrt{3}$

7. Find x in the triangle below.

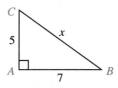

   a. $2\sqrt{3}$ b. $\sqrt{74}$ c. 8   d. $2\sqrt{37}$

8. In a circle with radius 5 in., find the length of a chord that is located 4 in. from the center.
   a. 3 in.   b. 6 in.
   c. $\sqrt{41}$ in.   d. $2\sqrt{41}$ in.

9. In space, what is the locus of points equidistant from two parallel lines?
   a. a point   b. a line
   c. a sphere   d. a plane

10. Find the area of a circle if the circumference is 10π.
    a. 20π b. 25π c. 50π d. 100π

11. Find the area of a trapezoid with height 3 and bases 10 and 12.
    a. 33   b. 66   c. 11   d. 45

12. $\square ABCD$, $AB = 8$, $AD = 6$, $m\angle A = 60$ Find the area of the parallelogram.
    a. $24\sqrt{3}$ b. 24   c. $12\sqrt{3}$ d. 48

13. Find the area of a regular hexagon if its perimeter is 48.
    a. $144\sqrt{3}$ b. 96   c. $96\sqrt{3}$ d. $192\sqrt{3}$

14. The areas of two similar polygons are in the ratio 16:25. If the radius of the smaller polygon is $4\sqrt{2}$, find the radius of the larger polygon.
    a. $5\sqrt{2}$ b. 5   c. $\frac{5\sqrt{2}}{2}$ d. 50

15. Which formula could you use to find the lateral area of a right pentagonal prism?
    a. $\frac{1}{3}Bh$ b. ph c. ℓwh d. $\frac{1}{2}p\ell$

16. A pyramid has a base with an area of 49 cm² and a height of 12 cm. Find the volume of the pyramid.

a. 294 cm³   **b.** 588 cm³
c. 84 cm³   **d.** 196 cm³

17. Find the volume of a right cylinder with base radius 4 and height 5.

a. 40π **b.** 72π
c. 80π **d.** 144π

18. Find the surface area of a sphere with diameter 12.

a. 36π **b.** 48π
c. 144π **d.** 288π

19. Find the volume of the cone below.

a. 48π **b.** 192π **c.** 24π **d.** 576π

20. Find the midpoint of $\overline{AB}$ for $A(-3, 6)$ and $B(5, -2)$.

a. $(2, 4)$ **b.** $(-1, 4)$
c. $(1, -2)$ **d.** $(1, 2)$

21. Find the slope of a line that is perpendicular to the line $2x + 3y = 6$.

a. $\frac{3}{2}$ **b.** $\frac{-3}{2}$ **c.** 2   **d.** $\frac{-2}{3}$

22. Find the slope of a line that is parallel to the line $7x - 14y = 3$.

a. $\frac{1}{2}$ **b.** 2   **c.** -2 **d.** $\frac{-1}{2}$

23. Find the equation of the line containing $(-6, 5)$ and having slope $\frac{2}{3}$.

a. $y = \frac{2}{3}x - 1$

b. $y = \frac{2}{3}x + 9$

c. $y = \frac{2}{3}x + 11$

d. $y = \frac{2}{3}x$

24. Find the equation of a circle with center $(-3, 4)$ and radius 9.

a. $(x + 3)^2 + (y - 4)^2 = 9$
b. $(x - 3)^2 + (y + 4)^2 = 9$
c. $(x + 3)^2 + (y - 4)^2 = 81$
d. $(x - 3)^2 + (y + 4)^2 = 81$

25. Which of the following figures has no lines of reflectional symmetry?

a. parallelogram   **b.** square
c. circle   **d.** isosceles triangle

26. Which transformation is not always an isometry?

a. translation   **b.** reflection
c. rotation   **d.** dilation

27. If $(-6, 15)$ is the dilation image of point X with scale factor 3 and center $(0, 0)$, find the coordinates of point X.

a. $(2, -5)$ **b.** $(-2, 5)$
c. $(6, -15)$ **d.** $(-18, 45)$

28. What is the composition of two reflections in parallel lines?

a. a translation   **b.** a reflection
c. a rotation   **d.** a dilation

29. Find the image of point P under the translation ST followed by the translation TU.

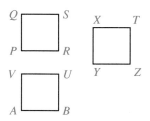

a. point A **b.** point Y
c. point V **d.** point B

30. Find the image of $(2, -4)$ under the dilation with center $(0, 0)$ and scale factor 2.

a. $(4, -2)$ **b.** $(1, -2)$
c. $(4, -8)$ **d.** $(-4, 8)$

Algebra Review

Algebraic Properties and Integer Operations

	Properties of Addition	Properties of Multiplication
Commutative Property	$a + b = b + a$	$a \cdot b = b \cdot a$
Associative Property	$(a + b) + c = a + (b + c)$	$(a \cdot b) \cdot c = a \cdot (b \cdot c)$
Identity Property	$a + 0 = a$	$a \cdot 1 = a$
Inverse Property	$a + (-a) = 0$	$a \cdot \frac{1}{a} = 1 \; (a \neq 0)$

Property of Zero for Multiplication $a \cdot 0 = 0$

Distributive Property of Multiplication over Addition $a \cdot (b + c) = a \cdot b + a \cdot c$

Exercises

Which property is illustrated by each equation?

1. $62 + 87 = 87 + 62$ **2.** $3a + 0 = 3a$ **3.** $17 \cdot 0 = 0$
4. $(3b + 1) \cdot 1 = 3b + 1$ **5.** $7 \cdot (x + b) = 7x + 7b$ **6.** $450 + (-450) = 0$
7. $(22 \cdot x) \cdot z = 22 \cdot (x \cdot z)$ **8.** $3y \cdot \frac{1}{3y} = 1$ **9.** $y \cdot z = z \cdot y$

Use the commutative and associative properties to write three equivalent expressions.

10. $(x + y) + 5$ **11.** $(a \cdot b) \cdot 5$ **12.** $4 + (c + d)$

Operations with Integers

Example 1

Simplify $-2(8 - 3 + 4)$.

Solution

$$-2(8 - 3 + 4) = -2 \cdot 8 + -2(-3) + -2(4)$$
$$= -16 + 6 - 8$$
$$= -18$$

Example 2

Simplify $x(13 + 8) - 3(x - 7)$.

Solution

$$x(13 + 8) - 3(x - 7) = 13x + 8x - 3x - (-21)$$
$$= 18x + 21$$

Exercises

Simplify.

13. $-4 + 3$ **14.** $-4 - 7$ **15.** $2 - 3 + 4 - 5 + 6$
16. $267 - 378$ **17.** $-486 - 715$ **18.** $-1764 - (-1765)$
19. $-3(7 + 2 - 3)$ **20.** $4(x + 3 + 7)$ **21.** $(3x + 4)(-3) + 5x$
22. $6 + 3(m - 4)$ **23.** $7 \cdot 5y + 3(2y - 6)$ **24.** $3(t + 7) - 7(t - 13)$
25. $(3a + 5)4 + (2a + 8)6$ **26.** $12y - 12x + 3y - 3x$ **27.** $(-7)(-3) - 8(-2)$

Algebra Review

Solving Linear Equations

Example 1

Solve $3x + 4 = 13$.

Solution

$$3x + 4 = 13$$
$$3x + 4 - 4 = 13 - 4 \qquad \text{Add } -4 \text{ to each side of the equation.}$$
$$3x = 9 \qquad \text{Combine like terms.}$$
$$\tfrac{1}{3} \cdot 3x = \tfrac{1}{3} \cdot 9 \qquad \text{Multiply each side of the equation by } \tfrac{1}{3}.$$
$$x = 3$$

Example 2

Solve $15x - 3x = 8x - 12$.

Solution

$$15x - 3x = 8x - 12$$
$$12x = 8x - 12 \qquad \text{Subtract } 3x \text{ from } 15x.$$
$$12x - 8x = 8x - 12 - 8x \qquad \text{Add } -8x \text{ to each side of the equation.}$$
$$4x = -12 \qquad \text{Combine like terms.}$$
$$\tfrac{1}{4} \cdot 4x = \tfrac{1}{4}(-12) \qquad \text{Multiply each side of the equation by } \tfrac{1}{4}.$$
$$x = -3$$

Solve.

1. $5x + 6 = 31$
2. $3x + 6 = 30$
3. $4x - 6 = 34$
4. $z - (-16) = 36$
5. $75 = p + 8$
6. $x - 3 = 2x + 10$
7. $5(3x - 2) = 35$
8. $3(2y - 3) = 27$
9. $-5a + 4(2 + 2a) = -1$
10. $\frac{x}{5} + 3 = 88$
11. $\frac{y + 6}{3} = 12$
12. $2(a + 4) = a + 10$
13. $7y - 2 = 3(3y + 3)$
14. $\frac{4b - 3}{5} = 6$
15. $-10(z + 3) = -25$
16. $5x + 9 = 8x$
17. $7(n + 8) = 3(n + 12)$
18. $3.2x - 1.7(x + 6) = 15$
19. $-25 = -\frac{4x}{5} + 3x$
20. $\frac{3}{4}x + \frac{1}{4} = 8$
21. $\frac{1}{2}(4x - 6) = 6x + 5$

Solve for the underlined variable.

22. $a\underline{y} - b = c$
23. $3(2x + \underline{a}) = b$
24. $P = 2\ell + 2\underline{w}$
25. $A = \underline{b}h$
26. $a(2\underline{b} + 2\underline{c}) = d$
27. $C = 2\pi \underline{r}$

Translate to an equation and solve.

28. Eight more than a number is 57. Find the number.
29. A number decreased by 14 is -51. Find the number.
30. Eighteen times a number is -1134. Find the number.
31. A rectangle has a length 4 times its width. Find the length and width of the rectangle if the perimeter is 36 in.
32. A linear pair of angles have measures of $(x + 50)$ and $(x + 30)$. Find the measure of each angle.

Algebra Review

Fractional Equations and Absolute Value

Example 1

Solve $\frac{4b}{12} + \frac{8}{4} = \frac{3b}{3}$.

Solution

$$\frac{4b}{12} + \frac{8}{4} = \frac{3b}{3}$$

$$\frac{4b}{4 \cdot 3} + \frac{8}{4} = \frac{3b}{3} \qquad \text{\textit{Factor the denominators to find the LCD.}}$$

$$4 \cdot 3 \left(\frac{4b}{4 \cdot 3} + \frac{8}{4}\right) = 4 \cdot 3\frac{3b}{3} \qquad \text{\textit{Multiply each side by the LCD.}}$$

$$4 \cdot 3 \frac{4b}{4 \cdot 3} + 4 \cdot 3 \cdot \frac{8}{4} = 4 \cdot 3 \cdot \frac{3b}{3} \qquad \text{\textit{Use the distributive property and multiply.}}$$

$$4b + 24 = 12b$$

$$24 = 8b$$

$$3 = b$$

Exercises

Solve.

1. $\frac{x}{2} + \frac{3}{4} = \frac{x}{8}$ **2.** $\frac{3a}{8} + \frac{2}{4} = \frac{5a}{2}$ **3.** $\frac{3a-5}{5} - \frac{3}{2} = \frac{a}{10}$

4. $\frac{5}{x} + \frac{5}{4} = \frac{5}{2}$ **5.** $\frac{3x+4}{4} + \frac{5}{2} = \frac{2x-4}{8}$ **6.** $\frac{4}{3x} - \frac{3}{2} = \frac{7}{3x}$

Example 2

$|x + 3| = 4$

Solution

$$|x + 3| = 4$$

$$x + 3 = 4 \text{ or } -(x + 3) = 4$$

$$x = 1 \text{ or } \qquad\quad x = -7$$

Example 3

$-2|x| + 6 = 0$

Solution

$$-2|x| + 6 = 0$$

$$-2|x| = -6$$

$$2|x| = 6$$

$$|x| = 3$$

$$x = 3 \text{ or } x = -3$$

Exercises

Find all values of x.

7. $|x| = 7$ **8.** $|x| = -7$ **9.** $|-x| = 7$

10. $x = |7|$ **11.** $2|x| = 7$ **12.** $x = |-7|$

13. $|x| + 1 = 7$ **14.** $|x| + |-1| = 7$ **15.** $x - |-1| = 7$

16. $-2|x| = -14$ **17.** $|2x + 1| = 14$ **18.** $|x - 1| - 1 = 7$

Algebra Review

Solving Inequalities

Example 1

Find the solution set of $-8x + 4 < -5x - 2$.

Solution

$$-8x + 4 < -5x - 2$$
$$-8x < -5x - 6 \qquad \textit{Add } -4 \textit{ to both sides.}$$
$$-3x < -6 \qquad \textit{Add } 5x \textit{ to both sides.}$$
$$-x < -2 \qquad \textit{Multiply both sides by } \tfrac{1}{3}.$$
$$x > 2 \qquad \textit{Multiply both sides by } -1, \textit{ reversing the inequality.}$$

Example 2

Find the solution set of $-12 \le 3 - 2x < 11$.

Solution

$$-12 \le 3 - 2x < 11$$
$$-15 \le -2x < 8 \qquad \textit{Add } -3 \textit{ to each component.}$$
$$-7.5 \le -x < 4 \qquad \textit{Multiply through by } \tfrac{1}{2}.$$
$$7.5 \ge x > -4 \qquad \textit{Multiply each side by } -1, \textit{ reversing the inequalities.}$$
$$-4 < x \le 7.5 \qquad \textit{Write the solution in least-to-greatest form.}$$

Exercises

Solve each inequality.

1. $-x < 9$
2. $y + 3 > 7$
3. $2y + 4 < y - 3$
4. $\frac{2a}{3} > 15$
5. $18 - 2b < b$
6. $2x + 5 > x - 2$
7. $3x + 6 > 15$
8. $2 + 3x > -6$
9. $5x + 6 > -24$
10. $-7 + 6a < 7a + 2$
11. $9d - 4 > 10d + (-12)$
12. $\frac{3y}{4} < 9$
13. $\frac{4y - 6}{3} > 3y + 2$
14. $\frac{3x}{4} - \frac{5}{8} < 0$
15. $x - 6 \ge 3x + 2$
16. $3(y + 6) < 2y + 12$
17. $\frac{8 - 3b}{5} \le -8$
18. $2(y + 5) > y + 15$
19. $5(n + 6) < 3n - 6$
20. $\frac{3x - 4}{2} \ge \frac{2x}{4}$
21. $\frac{4x}{3} + \frac{2}{5} > 0$
22. $6(w - 2) < 5(2 - w)$
23. $\frac{s}{6} + \frac{1}{7} \ge \frac{s - 30}{21}$
24. $\frac{2}{v} < 1$
25. $17 - 2p \le 17$
26. $3q + 2 \ge -5(q + 1)$
27. $\frac{3m - 1}{6} < \frac{4m - 1}{7}$
28. $\frac{t + 1}{31} < \frac{t}{30}$
29. $15 - s < 15s - 1$
30. $\frac{s + 100}{2} \ge s + \frac{100}{2}$
31. $5m + 1 > 13 - m$
32. $57 - 6b < 3 + 3b$
33. $3x - 1 \ge 4x - 3$
34. $5k - 7 > 6(k - 7)$
35. $\frac{p + 10}{7} < \frac{7p - 6}{10}$
36. $\frac{2a}{3} + 5 < \frac{2a}{5} + 3$

37. A rectangular field is 3 times as long as it is wide. If the width were increased by 10 m and the length were decreased by 25 m, the perimeter would be greater than 210 m. What is the minimum width of the original field?

38. The sum of two integers is greater than 50, but less than 60. One of the integers is one less than four times the other. Find all possible values for the integers.

Algebra Review

Solving Systems of Equations

Example 1 *Substitution Method*

Solve. $\quad 3x + 4y = 14$
$\qquad\quad x - 3y = -17$

Solution

$x - 3y = -17$
$\qquad x = 3y - 17$ $\qquad$ *Solve for x in one equation.*
$3x + 4y = 14$
$3(3y - 17) + 4y = 14$ $\qquad$ *Substitute for x in the other equation.*
$\qquad\qquad\quad y = 5$
$\quad x - 3y = -17$
$\quad x - 3(5) = -17$ $\qquad$ *Substitute for y in either equation.*
$\quad x - 15 = -17$
$\qquad\quad x = -2$

The solution is $x = -2$, $y = 5$.

Example 2 *Addition Method*

Solve. $\quad 8a - 6b = 10$
$\qquad\quad 4a - 5b = 3$

Solution

$\quad 5(8a - 6b) = 5 \cdot 10$ $\qquad$ *Multiply each equation so that, when added,*
$-6(4a - 5b) = -6 \cdot 3$ $\qquad$ *the result will be an equation in one variable.*
$\quad 40a - 30b = 50$
$\underline{-24a + 30b = -18}$ $\qquad$ *Add.*
$\qquad\quad 16a = 32$
$\qquad\qquad a = 2$
$\quad 8a - 6b = 10$
$\quad 8(2) - 6b = 10$ $\qquad$ *Substitute for a in one equation.*
$\qquad\qquad b = 1$

The solution is $a = 2$ and $b = 1$.

Exercises

Solve each system of equations using either method.

1. $a = 3b - 5$
$\quad b = -2a - 10$

2. $2x + 5y = 7$
$\quad x = \frac{-3}{2}$

3. $2a + b = 14$
$\quad 3a + b = 4$

4. $2m - 4n = 30$
$\quad 3m + 2n = -3$

5. $3p - 2q = 2$
$\quad 5p + 2q = 14$

6. $5a + 8b = 1$
$\quad 2a - 7b = -20$

7. $-2a + 5b = -3$
$\quad 2a + 3b = 11$

8. $4s - 3t = 14$
$\quad 5s = -3t + 31$

9. $2a = -9b + 24$
$\quad -9b + 4a = -6$

10. $3x - 2y = 5$
$\quad 2x = 5y - 4$

11. $5p + 4q = 29$
$\quad 3p = 13 + 2q$

12. $2(r - 2) + s = -18$
$\quad 3r + 2(s - 1) = -26$

13. $8d + 5 = 7t$
$\quad -9t + 2d = -23$

14. $2z + w = 7$
$\quad 4w - z = 37$

15. $u = \frac{2}{3}v + 7$
$\quad 2u = 3v - 6$

Algebra Review

Factoring Polynomials

Example 1

Factor $4x^4 - 20x^3 + 24x^2$ completely.

Solution

$$
\begin{aligned}
4x^4 - 20x^3 + 24x^2 &= 4x^2(x^2 - 5x + 6) \qquad \text{Factor out } 4x^2. \\
&= 4x^2(x - 3)(x - 2) \qquad \text{Factor } x^2 - 5x + 6 \text{ into} \\
&\qquad\qquad\qquad\qquad\qquad \text{two binomial factors.}
\end{aligned}
$$

Example 2

Factor $16x^2 - 64$.

Solution

$$
\begin{aligned}
16x^2 - 64 &= 16(x^2 - 4) \qquad \text{Factor out the GCF.} \\
&= 16(x + 2)(x - 2) \qquad x^2 - 4 \text{ is the difference of two squares.}
\end{aligned}
$$

Example 3

Factor completely.
$$x^4 + 6x^3 + 5x^2 - x^2y^2 - 6xy^2 - 5y^2$$

Solution

$$
\begin{aligned}
x^4 + 6x^3 + 5x^2 - x^2y^2 - 6xy^2 - 5y^2 &= x^2(x^2 + 6x + 5) - y^2(x^2 + 6x + 5) \\
&= (x^2 - y^2)(x^2 + 6x + 5) \\
&= (x + y)(x - y)(x + 1)(x + 5)
\end{aligned}
$$

Exercises

Factor completely.

1. $m^2 - 25$
2. $x^2 - 14x + 49$
3. $4y^2 - 12y + 9$
4. $x^2 + 2x - 15$
5. $4y^2 - 25$
6. $9a^2 - 81$
7. $10x^2 + 25x + 15$
8. $3y^2 - 3y - 168$
9. $8b^2 - 10b + 3$
10. $14y^2 - 49y - 28$
11. $9x^3 - 30x^2 - 75x$
12. $5c^3 - 55c^2 + 150c$
13. $cd^2 + 2c^2d + c^3$
14. $5t^2 + 5ts - 10s^2$
15. $100m^2 - 100m - 375$
16. $15z^3 + 36z^2 - 27z$
17. $9r^2 - 16p^2$
18. $81x^4 - y^4$
19. $5a^2 + 9ab - 2b^2$
20. $-150f^2 + 455fg - 294g^2$
21. $16x^3y^4 + 14x^2y^2z + 3xz^2$
22. $20u^2v^2 - 5w^4$
23. $63d^2 - 116dr^2 + 45r^4$
24. $16c(c^2 + dc) - 25d(dc + d^2)$
25. $14s^2 - 167st - 12t^2$
26. $p^4 + 2p^3q - 2pq^3 - q^4$
27. $81x^4 - 72x^2y^2 + 16y^4$
28. $500m^6n^3 - 20m^4n^4 - 39m^2n^5$
29. $(4a^2 + 12ab + 9b^2)(b + c) - 24ab(b + c)$
30. $11r^4 + 90r^3s + 16r^2s^2 + (12r - 13s)(11r^2s + 90rs^2 + 16s^3)$

Solve.

31. The product of a number increased by 1 and the number decreased by 2 is 10. Find the number.
32. The product of a number and the number increased by 2 is 35. Find the number.
33. A number squared is equal to 110 less than 21 times the number. Find the number.

Algebra Review

Simplifying Radicals

Example 1

Simplify $-3x^2y\sqrt{54x^3y^4}$. Assume x and y are positive.

Solution

$$\begin{aligned}
-3x^2y\sqrt{54x^3y^4} &= -3x^2y\sqrt{9 \cdot 6 \cdot x^2 \cdot x^1 \cdot y^4} \quad &&\textit{Find the greatest perfect square}\\
&= -3x^2y\sqrt{9x^2y^4} \cdot \sqrt{6x} \quad &&\textit{factor of } 54x^3y^4.\\
&= -3x^2y(3xy^2)\sqrt{6x}\\
&= -9x^3y^3\sqrt{6x}
\end{aligned}$$

Rationalizing the denominator means writing the fraction without a radical in the denominator.

Example 2

Rationalize the denominator of $\frac{3x\sqrt{24x^2}}{\sqrt{3}}$. Assume x is positive.

Solution

$$\begin{aligned}
\frac{3x\sqrt{24x^2}}{\sqrt{3}} &= \frac{3x\sqrt{24x^2}}{\sqrt{3}} \cdot \frac{\sqrt{3}}{\sqrt{3}} \quad &&\textit{Make the denominator a perfect square.}\\
&= \frac{3x\sqrt{72x^2}}{3}\\
&= \frac{3x\sqrt{36 \cdot 2 \cdot x^2}}{3}\\
&= 6x^2\sqrt{2}
\end{aligned}$$

Exercises

Simplify. Assume all variables are positive.

1. $\sqrt{8a^2}$

2. $\sqrt{120}$

3. $-\sqrt{144x}$

4. $\sqrt{27} + \sqrt{3}$

5. $\sqrt{75} - \sqrt{12}$

6. $\sqrt{\frac{4y^2}{9y^2}}$

7. $\sqrt{18} - \frac{\sqrt{8}}{4}$

8. $\sqrt{z^6}$

9. $\sqrt{45x^3y}$

10. $\sqrt{1600r^3}$

11. $\frac{2}{3}\sqrt{24x^2y^2}$

12. $\sqrt{\frac{81x^2}{36y^4}}$

13. $\frac{\sqrt{36x^3}}{\sqrt{2y}}$

14. $\frac{4\sqrt{8}}{\sqrt{5}}$

15. $-7x\sqrt{48x^3y^2}$

16. $6xy\sqrt{18x^3y^7z^4}$

17. $-6c^3d\sqrt{27cd^3}$

18. $\sqrt{\frac{5ab}{15a^3b^2}}$

19. $4\sqrt{3x} \cdot 6\sqrt{8x}$

20. $-7x^2\sqrt{2x^3} \cdot 5\sqrt{8x}$

21. $\frac{4}{5}x^2\sqrt{32x^3y^5}$

22. $-2x\sqrt{108x^3y^4}$

23. $6pq\sqrt{8q^5} \cdot -3p\sqrt{3p^3q^2}$

24. $\sqrt{56x^2y^3z}$

25. $\sqrt{p^2 - 4pq + 4q^2}$

26. $\sqrt{18pq^3} + \sqrt{50p^3q}$

27. $\frac{\sqrt{pq}}{\sqrt{p} + \sqrt{q}}$

28. $\sqrt{\frac{36s^3t^2}{2m}}$

29. $\frac{7}{\sqrt{3} - 5}$

30. $\sqrt{\frac{68y^2}{45a^3b^5}} \cdot \frac{a^2}{\sqrt{5b}}$

31. $\frac{\sqrt{m^2 + 6m - 7}}{\sqrt{m^2 - 4m + 3}}$

32. $\frac{\sqrt{70a} + \sqrt{56b}}{\sqrt{28a^4b^3}}$

33. $\frac{\sqrt{2xz}}{\sqrt{3xyz}} \cdot \sqrt{3z}$

34. $\frac{\sqrt{(h-k)(h+k)}}{\sqrt{h^2 + 3hk + 2k^2}}(\sqrt{h-k})^3$

35. $\frac{\sqrt{3} + \sqrt{5}}{\sqrt{3} - \sqrt{5}}$

36. $(\sqrt{12xy^3z})^5$

Algebra Review

Exponents

Example 1
Simplify $(8a^2)(6a^3)$.

Solution

$$(8a^2)(6a^3) = (8 \cdot 6)(a^2 a^3) \quad \text{To multiply, add exponents.}$$
$$= 48a^{2+3}$$
$$= 48a^5$$

Example 2
Simplify $(3x^2)(7x^{-5})$.

Solution

$$(3x^2)(7x^{-5}) = (3 \cdot 7)(x^2 x^{-5}) \quad \text{Add exponents.}$$
$$= 21x^{2+(-5)}$$
$$= 21x^{-3} \text{ or } 21\tfrac{1}{x^3}$$

Example 3
Simplify $\frac{55y^{-6}}{5y^{-8}}$.

Solution

$$\frac{55y^{-6}}{5y^{-8}} = \frac{55}{5} \frac{y^{-6}}{y^{-8}} \quad \text{To divide, subtract exponents.}$$
$$= 11y^{-6-(-8)}$$
$$= 11y^2$$

Example 4
Simplify $(6m^2 n^2 p^4)^3$.

Solution

$$(6m^2 n^3 p^4)^3 = (6m^2 n^3 p^4)(6m^2 n^3 p^4)(6m^2 n^3 p^4)$$
$$= 6^3 m^{2 \cdot 3} n^{3 \cdot 3} p^{4 \cdot 3} \quad \text{To find a power, multiply exponents.}$$
$$= 216 m^6 n^9 p^{12}$$

Exercises

Simplify.

1. $3^2 \cdot 3^4$
2. $10^5 \cdot 10^3$
3. $5^6 \cdot 5^{-4}$
4. $\frac{8^4}{8^5}$
5. $x^6 x^{-3}$
6. $3x^5 x^{-5}$
7. $\frac{3a^2}{4a^6}$
8. $(3x^2)^2$
9. $(4a^3)(7a^7)$
10. $(4y^2)^4$
11. $(-8m^6 n^2)^2$
12. $(-5p^2 q^3)(3p^3 q)$
13. $\frac{12m^3 n^{-4}}{3m^{-5} n^2}$
14. $(2a^{25})^4$
15. $\frac{-6a^2 b^3}{2ab^2}$
16. $\frac{-18m^3 p^6}{3m^3 p^6}$
17. $(-6q^3 r^2)^4$
18. $\frac{7a^3 b^6 c^4}{2a^3 b^{-1} c^4}$
19. $(3r^2)(5r^3)(2r^{-1})$
20. $(5p^2 q)^2 (2p^{-1} q)$
21. $\frac{36a^2 b^2 c}{(3a^2 b)(2ac)}$
22. $((2s^2)^3)^2$
23. $\frac{(13z)(10y^2 x)}{(2xyz)^2}$
24. $30mn \left(\frac{24mn^3}{16m^2 n} \right)$

Algebra Review

Functions

Example 1

What is the range of the function $f(x) = x^2 - 3x + 4$ given the domain, or possible x-values, $D = \{2, 3, 5, 7, 11\}$?

Solution

For $x = 2, f(2) = 2^2 - 3(2) + 4 = 2$ *The range is the set of function values for the domain.*
The values for 3, 5, 7, and 11 are also found by substitution.
The range is $\{2, 4, 14, 32, 92\}$.

Example 2

The range of $f(t) = t^2$ is $\{0, 9, 36\}$. What is its largest possible domain?

Solution

$\{-6, -3, 0, 3, 6\}$

Example 3

Given $f(x) = 3x^2$ and $g(x) = -2x^2$, find $f(2)$, $g(2)$, $f(2) + g(2)$, and $f(g(x))$.

Solution

$f(2) = 3(2)^2 = 12$ $g(2) = -2(2)^2 = -8$
$f(2) + g(2) = 12 + -8 = 4$
$f(g(x)) = f(-2x^2) = 3(-2x^2)^2 = 3 \cdot 4x^4 = 12x^4$

Exercises

State the range of each function.

1. $h(k) = 3k^2$ $D = \{-1, 0, 1, 2\}$ 2. $f(u) = u + 1$ $D = \{0, 1, 99\}$
3. $f(x) = \frac{x^3}{x^2}$ $D = \{-2, -1, 1, 2\}$ 4. $g(x) = \frac{-x^3}{x^2}$ $D = \{-2, -1, 1, 2\}$
5. $f(z) = \frac{z-5}{10} + \frac{5-z}{10}$ $D = \{\text{all real numbers}\}$ 6. $p(r) = r + 2$ $D = \{\text{all real numbers}\}$

Given $f(m)$ and $g(n)$, find $f(1)$, $g(1)$, $f(1) + g(1)$, $f(g(1))$, and $g(f(1))$.

7. $f(m) = m^2 - 1, g(n) = (n - 1)^2$ 8. $f(m) = m + 2, g(n) = 2n$
9. $f(m) = -m, g(n) = n$ 10. $f(m) = \frac{2}{m}, g(n) = \frac{1}{n}$
11. $f(m) = 3m + 9, g(n) = \frac{n}{3} - 3$ 12. $f(m) = 1, g(n) = 2n^2$

13. The length of your shadow is a function of your height. If, at a certain time, the length of your shadow is $f(h) = 0.9h + 63$, find the length of your shadow if you are 175 cm tall.
14. The length of a fun house mirror image is $f(h) = h - 2\sqrt{h}$, where h is your height. Find the height of your image if you are 169 cm tall.
15. The area of a circle as a function of its circumference c is $A(c) = \frac{c^2}{4\pi}$. What is the area of a circle with circumference 10π cm?
16. Find the perimeter of the following polygons as a function of their area.
   a. square   **b.** equilateral triangle   **c.** regular hexagon

Statistics

Frequency Distributions

The branch of mathematics that deals with the collection, organization, display, and interpretation of data is called statistics. Statistics is used to help solve problems and make decisions.

When a set of data is collected, it is often disorganized. Data can be organized using charts or tables like the frequency distribution below.

Example

Here is a set of temperatures, in degrees Fahrenheit, for the month of April.

49, 50, 49, 50, 50, 51, 49, 49, 51, 52, 51, 56, 53, 54, 50
49, 53, 53, 55, 54, 50, 57, 49, 55, 56, 58, 54, 59, 55, 54

Construct a frequency distribution.

Solution

The temperatures range from a low of 49 to a high of 59.

Temperature	Tally	Frequency
49	‖‖ |	6
50	‖‖	5
51	‖‖	3
52	|	1
53	‖‖	3
54	‖‖‖	4
55	‖‖	3
56	‖	2
57	|	1
58	|	1
59	|	1

Exercises

Construct a frequency distribution for each set of data.

1. Scores on a quiz:

    9, 10, 8, 10, 6, 9, 8, 7, 5, 10, 8, 8, 7,
    0, 2, 6, 5, 7, 6, 7, 9, 8, 7, 8, 6

2. Golf scores:

    86, 79, 68, 74, 78, 87, 83, 81, 76, 80, 88, 79,
    86, 90, 86, 75, 78, 79, 80, 87, 78, 74, 87, 80, 79

3. Heights of players on high school basketball team (centimeters):

172	168	183	201	203	178	183	196
198	196	201	198	196	178		

4. Distances jumped by members of high school track team (centimeters):

177	180	172	168	172	165	159	165	176
181	166	174	168	170	174	165	179	180

Statistics

Line Plots and Histograms

To construct a *line plot*, draw a portion of a number line and place a dot above the line for each occurrence of a value.

Example 1

Construct a line plot for this set of morning temperatures, in degrees Celsius, for the month of March in a northwestern town.

5, 7, 4, 5, 3, 2, 0, 3, 2, 4, 5, 5, 4, 5, 6, 4, 7, 7, 9, 10, 9, 11, 12, 11, 13, 11, 10, 9, 10, 11, 13

Solution

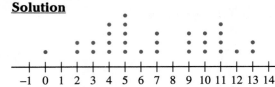

Temperature in Degrees Celsius

A bar graph called a *histogram* is useful for comparing data and can be constructed from a frequency distribution.

Example 2

Construct a histogram from this frequency distribution of heights, in centimeters, of players on a high-school basketball team.

Height	Frequency
160–169	1
170–179	2
180–189	4
190–199	5
200–210	3

Solution

Let the horizontal scale represent heights and the vertical scale represent frequency.

Height in Centimeters

Exercises

1. Construct a line plot for this set of pulse rates of 30 patients.
   76, 78, 68, 73, 80, 78, 67, 76, 75, 78, 74, 75, 81, 75, 72,
   73, 81, 67, 68, 72, 70, 78, 76, 81, 69, 71, 68, 70, 74, 76
2. Use appropriate intervals to construct a histogram for the data in Exercise 1.

Statistics

Mean, Median, and Mode

Example 1

Find the mean, median, and mode for this set of test scores from a geometry class.
75, 89, 82, 95, 63, 100, 81, 94, 92, 60, 55, 73, 82, 83, 82

Solution

There are 15 values. To find the mean (average), add the values and divide by 15.
The sum is 1206. The mean is $\frac{1206}{15} = 80.4$.
To find the median, arrange the values in order from least to greatest and choose the middle value.
55, 60, 63, 73, 75, 81, 82, 82, 82, 83, 89, 92, 94, 95, 100
The 8th number, 82, is the middle value so the median is 82.
The mode, the value which occurs most frequently, is 82.

Example 2

Inge's scores on four biology tests are 85, 90, 84, and 92. What must she score on her next exam to have an average of exactly 90?

Solution

Let x = the score on the fifth exam.
$$\frac{85 + 90 + 84 + 92 + x}{5} = 90$$
$$\frac{351 + x}{5} = 90$$
$$x = 99$$

She must score 99 to have an average of 90.

Exercises

Find the mean, median, and mode for each set of data.

1. The number of students in English classes at Washington High School:
   18, 22, 19, 25, 22, 17, 20, 21, 19, 22
2. A gymnast's scores on the parallel bars at nine gymnastics meets:
   8.7, 9.3, 9.0, 9.3, 9.3, 9.3, 9.0, 8.8, 9.0
3. Games won by the Comets in successive seasons:
   14, 12, 12, 8, 13, 5, 7, 10, 10, 12, 4, 8, 10, 11, 14, 12, 9, 9
4. The depths, in meters, of certain points of the oceans and seas of the world:
   10918, 9219, 7455, 5625, 4632, 5016, 4773, 3787, 3658, 2782, 3742, 3777, 660, 2211, 421, 6946, 183
5. Glenn's scores on five chemistry tests are 75, 85, 86, 79 and 84. What must he score on the sixth test to have an average of exactly 83?
6. The maximum score possible on algebra quizzes is 25. If Rochelle has scores of 20, 22, 21, 17, and 15 on the first five quizzes, is it possible for her to have an average of at least 21 after seven quizzes? Why or why not?

Computer Exploration 1

Angle Measures of a Triangle

Objective

Determine the sum of the measures of the angles of a triangle.

Investigation

Construct a triangle. Measure its interior angles and record the data. Find the sum of the angle measures. Repeat for other types of triangles.

	$m \angle 1$	$m \angle 2$	$m \angle 3$	Sum
Acute				
Acute				
Obtuse				
Obtuse				
Right				
Right				
Isosceles				
Isosceles				
Equilateral				
Equilateral				

Conjectures

1. Make a conjecture about the sum of the measures of the angles of a triangle.
2. Make a conjecture about the angles of an equilateral triangle.
3. Make a conjecture about the acute angles of a right triangle.

Computer Exploration 2

Exterior Angles of a Triangle

Objectives

Determine the sum of the measures of the exterior angles of a triangle.
Determine the relationship between an exterior angle and its two remote
interior angles.

Investigation

Construct a triangle and extend each side as
shown in the figure. Measure the exterior
angles and the interior angles. Record the
data. Repeat for the different triangles
shown in the charts.

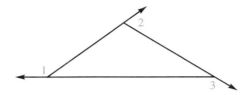

	$m\angle 1$	$m\angle 2$	$m\angle 3$	Sum
Equilateral				
Isosceles				
Right				
Obtuse				
Acute				

	$m\angle 1$	Remote $\angle$s	$m\angle 2$	Remote $\angle$s	$m\angle 3$	Remote $\angle$s
Equilateral						
Isosceles						
Right						
Obtuse						
Acute						

Conjectures

1. Using your data from the first chart, make a conjecture about the sum of
   the measures of the exterior angles of a triangle.
2. Using your data from the second chart, make a conjecture about the
   measure of an exterior angle of a triangle and the measures of its two
   remote interior angles.

Computer Exploration 3

Isosceles Triangles

Objective

Determine the type of triangle formed by the base of an isosceles triangle and the altitudes drawn from the base angles to the congruent sides.

Investigation

Construct an isosceles triangle. Draw the altitudes from the base angles. Label the intersection of the altitudes as shown. Measure segments *AF* and *BF*. Record the data. Repeat for the different triangles shown in the chart.

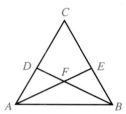

	AF	BF
Isosceles (three acute angles)		
Isosceles (one obtuse angle)		
Equilateral		
Another Isosceles		
Non-isosceles		

Conjecture

1. Make a conjecture about the type of triangle that is formed by the base of an isosceles triangle and the altitudes drawn from the base angles to the congruent sides.

Computer Exploration 4

Diagonals of a Parallelogram

Objective

Investigate the properties of the diagonals of a parallelogram.

Investigation

Draw a parallelogram and its two diagonals. Label the point of intersection of the diagonals. Measure the lengths of the four segments formed by the diagonals.

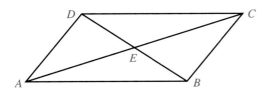

	AE	CE	BE	DE
Parallelogram 1				
Parallelogram 2				
Parallelogram 3				
Parallelogram 4				

Conjecture

1. Make a conjecture about the diagonals of a parallelogram.

Computer Exploration 5

Diagonals of a Quadrilateral

Objective

Determine the type of quadrilateral formed by diagonals that bisect each other.

Investigation

Construct a quadrilateral by drawing diagonal segments that bisect each other. Measure the angles and segments listed in the chart. Record the data. Construct other quadrilaterals as needed to make your conjectures.

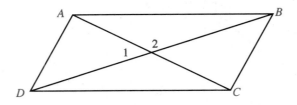

	$m\angle1$	$m\angle2$	AC	BD	Type of Quadrilateral
Quadrilateral 1					
Quadrilateral 2					
Quadrilateral 3					
Quadrilateral 4					

Conjectures

1. Make a conjecture about the type of quadrilateral that is formed by diagonals that bisect each other.
2. Make a conjecture about how the angle of the intersection of the diagonals affects the type of quadrilateral that is formed.
3. Make a conjecture about how the lengths of the diagonals affect the type of quadrilateral that is formed.

Computer Exploration 6

Diagonals of a Rhombus

Objective

Investigate the properties of the diagonals of a rhombus.

Investigation

Draw a rhombus and its two diagonals. Measure the angles formed by the diagonals. Measure the angles formed by the diagonals and the sides of the rhombus.

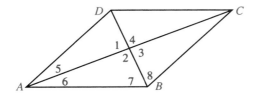

	$m\angle 1$	$m\angle 2$	$m\angle 3$	$m\angle 4$	$m\angle 5$	$m\angle 6$	$m\angle 7$	$m\angle 8$
Rhombus 1								
Rhombus 2								
Rhombus 3								
Rhombus 4								

Conjectures

1. Make a conjecture about the angles formed by the diagonals of a rhombus.

2. Make a conjecture about the pair of angles formed by a diagonal and the consecutive sides of a rhombus.

Computer Exploration 7

Median of a Trapezoid

Objective

Investigate relationships between the median and the two bases of a trapezoid.

Investigation

Draw a trapezoid and its median. Measure the length of the bases and the median. Measure the angles indicated.

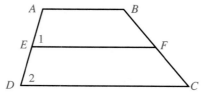

	AB	CD	EF	$m\angle 1$	$m\angle 2$
Trapezoid 1					
Trapezoid 2					
Trapezoid 3					
Trapezoid 4					

Conjectures

1. Make a conjecture about the lengths of a trapezoid's median and its two bases.

2. Make a conjecture about the position of a trapezoid's median in relation to its bases.

Computer Exploration 8

Midpoints of a Quadrilateral

Objective

Determine the type of quadrilateral formed by joining the midpoints of consecutive sides of a quadrilateral.

Investigation

Draw a quadrilateral. Label the midpoints of each side of the quadrilateral. Draw the segments joining the midpoints of consecutive sides of the quadrilateral. Measure the lengths of the sides and the angles of the newly formed quadrilateral.

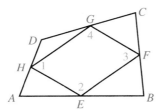

	EF	FG	GH	HE	$m \angle 1$	$m \angle 2$	$m \angle 3$	$m \angle 4$
Quadrilateral 1								
Quadrilateral 2								
Quadrilateral 3								
Quadrilateral 4								

Conjecture

1. Make a conjecture about the type of quadrilateral that is formed by joining the midpoints of consecutive sides of a quadrilateral.

Midpoints of an Isosceles Trapezoid

Objective

Determine the type of quadrilateral formed by joining the midpoints of consecutive sides of an isosceles trapezoid.

Investigation

Draw an isosceles trapezoid and label the midpoints of each side. Draw the segments joining the midpoints of consecutive sides of the isosceles trapezoid. Measure the lengths of the sides and the angles of the newly formed quadrilateral.

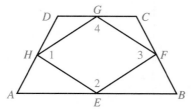

	EF	FG	GH	HE	$m\angle 1$	$m\angle 2$	$m\angle 3$	$m\angle 4$
Isosceles Trapezoid 1								
Isosceles Trapezoid 2								
Isosceles Trapezoid 3								
Isosceles Trapezoid 4								

Conjecture

1. Make a conjecture about the type of quadrilateral formed by joining the midpoints of consecutive sides of an isosceles trapezoid.

Computer Exploration 10

Triangle Midsegments

Objective

Determine special relationships between a midsegment of a triangle and the side that does not contain the endpoints of the midsegment.

Investigation

Construct a triangle and a midsegment as shown. Measure the midsegment and the side of the triangle that does not contain the midsegment's endpoints. Measure angles 1 and 2. Record the data. Repeat for the different triangles shown in the chart.

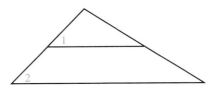

	Length of Midsegment	Length of Side	$m \angle 1$	$m \angle 2$
Equilateral				
Isosceles				
Right				
Obtuse				
Acute				

Conjectures

1. Make a conjecture about the length of the midsegment and the length of the side of a triangle not containing the endpoints of the midsegment.

2. Will the line containing the midsegment intersect the side of the triangle that does not contain the midsegment's endpoints? How do you know?

Computer Exploration 11

Triangle Side Lengths and Angle Measures

Objective
Determine the relationship between the lengths of the sides of a triangle and the measures of the angles of the triangle.

Investigation
Draw a triangle having the side lengths given in the chart for Triangle 1. Measure the angles of the triangle and the lengths of the sides of the triangle. Record your data. Repeat for the other triangles in the chart.

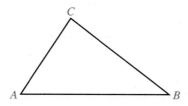

	AB	AC	BC	$m\angle C$	$m\angle B$	$m\angle A$
Triangle 1	10	12	14			
Triangle 2	21	17	25			
Triangle 3	17	20	14			
Triangle 4	18	20	19			
Triangle 5	25	15	20			
Triangle 6	20	18	16			

Conjecture
1. For each triangle, compare the measures of each side and the angle opposite that side. Make a conjecture about the relationship between the measures of the angles of a triangle and the lengths of the sides of the triangle.

Computer Exploration 12

Lines Parallel to a Side of a Triangle

Objective

Determine ratios of the lengths of segments produced by a line that is parallel to one side of a triangle and intersects the triangle's other two sides.

Investigation

Construct a triangle and label a point on a side. Draw a line through the point that is parallel to one of the other sides and intersects the third side. Measure the segments formed. Record the data. Find the ratios shown in the charts. Repeat for different types of triangles.

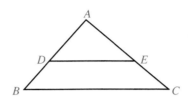

	AD	DB	AE	EC	DE	AB	AC	BC
Acute								
Obtuse								
Isosceles								
Equilateral								

	AD:DB	AE:EC	AD:AB	AE:AC	DE:BC
Acute					
Obtuse					
Isosceles					
Equilateral					

Conjectures

1. Make a conjecture about the ratios of the lengths of the segments formed by a line that is parallel to a side of a triangle and that intersects the other two sides.

2. Make a conjecture about the relationships between the ratio of the lengths of the two parallel line segments in your investigation and the ratios of the lengths of the other segments in the triangle

3. Make a conjecture about the relationship between a triangle and the triangle formed by a line that is parallel to one of its sides and that intersects the other two sides.

Computer Exploration 13

Angle Bisector Segments

Objective

Determine relationships between the segments formed by an angle bisector of a triangle and the other two sides of the triangle.

Investigation

Construct a triangle. Construct an angle bisector that intersects the opposite side. Measure segments and record your data. Compare segment ratios as shown in the chart. Repeat for the different types of triangles shown in the chart.

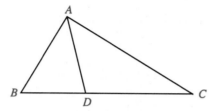

	AB	AC	BD	DC	AB:AC	BD:DC
Acute						
Obtuse						
Isosceles						
Equilateral						
Right						

Conjectures

1. Make a conjecture about the segments formed by an angle bisector of a triangle and the other two sides of the triangle.

2. Does any class of triangles have special segment ratios? If so, what data supports your conclusion?

Computer Exploration 14

Angle Bisectors of Similar Triangles

Objective

For similar triangles, determine relationships between the lengths of
corresponding angle bisectors and the lengths of corresponding sides.

Investigation

Construct a triangle. Construct an angle
bisector that intersects the opposite side.
Measure segments and record your data.
Then draw a triangle similar to the first by
giving it a different size (scale), and
construct a corresponding angle bisector.
Find the segment ratios indicated in the
second chart. Repeat for other pairs of
triangles.

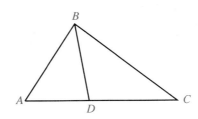

	First Triangle				Scaled Triangle			
	AB	*BC*	*AC*	*BD*	*A'B'*	*B'C'*	*A'C'*	*B'D'*
Acute								
Acute								
Obtuse								
Obtuse								

	AB:A'B'	*BC:B'C'*	*AC:A'C'*	*BD:B'D'*
Acute				
Acute				
Obtuse				
Obtuse				

Conjecture

1. Make a conjecture about the relationship between corresponding sides and
   angle bisectors of similar triangles.

Computer Exploration 15

Altitude to Hypotenuse

Objective

Determine relationships among a right triangle and the two triangles that are formed by the altitude to the hypotenuse.

Investigation

Construct a right triangle. Construct the altitude to the hypotenuse. Measure the angles indicated in the three charts. Record your data in the rows for Right Triangle 1. Repeat for other right triangles.

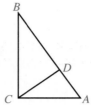

Triangle *ABC*	$m\angle BCA$	$m\angle CAB$	$m\angle ABC$
Right Triangle 1			
Right Triangle 2			
Right Triangle 3			

Triangle *BCD*	$m\angle CDB$	$m\angle BCD$	$m\angle DBC$
Right Triangle 1			
Right Triangle 2			
Right Triangle 3			

Triangle *CAD*	$m\angle ADC$	$m\angle CAD$	$m\angle DCA$
Right Triangle 1			
Right Triangle 2			
Right Triangle 3			

Conjecture

1. Make a conjecture about the relationships among a right triangle and the two triangles that are formed by the altitude to the hypotenuse.

Computer Exploration 16

Length of Altitude to Hypotenuse

Objective

Determine the relationship between the length of the altitude to the hypotenuse of a right triangle and the length of the two segments on the hypotenuse.

Investigation

Construct a right triangle. Construct the altitude to the hypotenuse. Measure the segments. Record your data. Repeat for other right triangles.

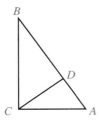

	BD	DA	CD	$BD \cdot DA$
Right Triangle 1				
Right Triangle 2				
Right Triangle 3				
Right Triangle 4				

Conjecture

1. Make a conjecture about the relationship between the length of the altitude to the hypotenuse of a right triangle and the length of the two segments on the hypotenuse.

Computer Exploration 17

Hypotenuse, Legs, and Altitude

Objective

Determine the relationship among the legs, altitude, and hypotenuse of a right triangle.

Investigation

Construct a right triangle. Construct the altitude to the hypotenuse. Measure segments and record your data. Repeat for other right triangles.

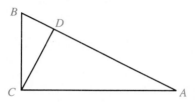

	AC	BC	AB	CD	AB · CD
Right Triangle 1					
Right Triangle 2					
Right Triangle 3					
Right Triangle 4					

Conjecture

1. Make a conjecture about the relationship between a right triangle's hypotenuse and altitude, and its two legs.

Computer Exploration 18

Hypotenuse, Hypotenuse Segments, and Legs

Objective

Given an altitude to the hypotenuse of a right triangle, determine the relationship among the hypotenuse, a leg, and a segment on the hypotenuse.

Investigation

Construct a right triangle. Construct the altitude to the hypotenuse. Measure the segments. Record your data. Find the products listed in the chart. Repeat for other right triangles.

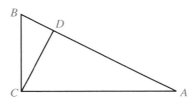

	AC	BC	AB	BD	AD	BD · AB	AD · AB
Right Triangle 1							
Right Triangle 2							
Right Triangle 3							
Right Triangle 4							

Conjecture

1. Make a conjecture about the relationship among the hypotenuse of a right triangle, the two segments formed by the altitude to the hypotenuse, and the legs.

Computer Exploration 19

Triangles and Side Lengths

Objectives

Find special relationships of side lengths in triangles, and find the type of triangle determined by certain side-length relationships.

Investigation

Construct triangles with sides of different lengths. Label the longest side *AB*. Measure the lengths of the sides. Record your data. Make the calculations required to complete the chart.

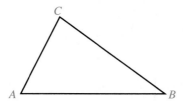

Type of Triangle	AC	BC	AB	AC²	BC²	AB²	AC² + BC²

Conjectures

1. For what type of triangle does AC^2 plus BC^2 equal AB^2?
2. For what type of triangle is $AC^2 + BC^2$ less than AB^2?
3. For what type of triangle is $AC^2 + BC^2$ greater than AB^2?

Computer Exploration 20

45°–45°–90° Triangles

Objective
Determine the relationship between the length of the hypotenuse of a
45°– 45°–90° triangle and the length of a leg.

Investigation
Construct a 45°– 45°–90° triangle. Measure the lengths of the sides. Record
your data. Calculate the ratio shown in the chart. Repeat for other
45°– 45°–90° triangles.

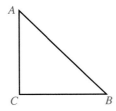

	AC	CB	AB	AB:CB
45°–45°–90° Triangle 1				
45°–45°–90° Triangle 2				
45°–45°–90° Triangle 3				
45°–45°–90° Triangle 4				

Conjecture
1. Make a conjecture about the relationship between the length of the
   hypotenuse of a 45°– 45°–90° triangle and the length of a leg. Express
   your conjecture in terms of an exact real number.

Computer Exploration 21

30°–60°–90° Triangles

Objective

Given a 30°–60°–90° triangle, determine the relationship between the lengths of the hypotenuse and the shorter leg, and the relationship between the lengths of the longer leg and the shorter leg.

Investigation

Construct a 30°–60°–90° triangle. Measure the lengths of the sides. Record your data. Calculate the ratios shown in the chart. Repeat for other 30°–60°–90° triangles.

	AC	AB	BC	AC:BC	AB:BC
30°–60°–90° Triangle 1					
30°–60°–90° Triangle 2					
30°–60°–90° Triangle 3					
30°–60°–90° Triangle 4					

Conjectures

1. Make a conjecture about the relationship between the length of the hypotenuse of a 30°–60°–90° triangle and the length of the shorter leg.

2. Make a conjecture about the relationship between the lengths of the legs of a 30°–60°–90° triangle. Express your conjecture in terms of an exact real number.

Computer Exploration 22

The Tangent Ratio

Objective

Investigate the ratio of the lengths of the two legs of similar right triangles.

Investigation

Draw a right triangle. Measure the lengths of the two legs and calculate the ratio of their lengths. Draw a triangle similar to the original one by giving it a different size (scale). Record the data. Repeat for two more similar triangles.

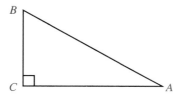

	BC	AC	$BC{:}AC$
Right Triangle			
1st Similar Triangle			
2nd Similar Triangle			
3rd Similar Triangle			

Conjecture

1. Make a conjecture about the ratio of the lengths of the legs of similar right triangles.

Computer Exploration 23

Perpendicular Bisectors of the Sides of a Triangle, I

Objective

Investigate the properties of the perpendicular bisectors of the sides of a triangle.

Investigation

Draw a triangle and the perpendicular bisector of each side. Be sure each bisector intersects one of the other sides of the triangle. Do this construction for acute, right, and obtuse triangles.

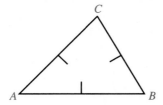

Conjectures

1. Make a conjecture about the three perpendicular bisectors of the sides of a triangle.

2. Make specific conjectures about the perpendicular bisectors of acute, right, and obtuse triangles.

Perpendicular Bisectors of the Sides of a Triangle, II

Objective

Investigate the properties of the perpendicular bisectors of the sides of a triangle.

Investigation

Draw a triangle and the perpendicular bisector of each side of the triangle. Label the intersection of the perpendicular bisectors. Draw a line segment from the intersection of the perpendicular bisectors to the vertices. Measure each segment. Repeat the construction for the other triangles in the chart.

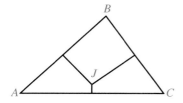

	AJ	BJ	CJ
Acute Triangle			
Obtuse Triangle			
Right Triangle			

Conjecture

1. Make a conjecture about the distance from each vertex of a triangle to the point of intersection of the perpendicular bisectors.

Angle Bisectors of a Triangle

Objective

Investigate the properties of the bisectors of the angles of a triangle.

Investigation

Draw a triangle. Draw the bisector of each of its angles. Be sure each bisector intersects a side of the triangle. Measure the perpendicular distance from the point of intersection of the angle bisectors to each of the sides of the triangle. Repeat for other triangles.

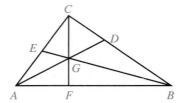

	Distance from G to:		
	$\overline{AB}$	$\overline{BC}$	$\overline{CA}$
Triangle 1			
Triangle 2			
Triangle 3			
Triangle 4			

Conjecture

1. The angle bisectors of a triangle intersect at a point. Make a conjecture about the distance from the point of intersection of the angle bisectors to each of the sides.

Computer Exploration 26

Medians of a Triangle

Objective
Investigate the properties of the medians of a triangle.

Investigation
Draw a triangle and its three medians. Label the point of intersection of the medians. Measure the length of the segments formed by the medians.

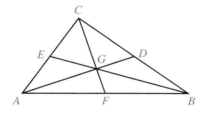

	AG	GD	BG	GE	CG	GF
Triangle 1						
Triangle 2						
Triangle 3						
Triangle 4						

Conjecture
1. The three medians of a triangle intersect at a point. This point divides each median into two segments. Make a conjecture about the relationship between the two segments of each median.

Computer Exploration 27

Similar Triangles and Perimeter

Objective
Determine the relationship between the perimeter and the corresponding sides of similar triangles.

Investigation
Construct a triangle. Measure the sides and calculate the perimeter. Record your data. Construct another triangle similar to the first one by giving it a different size (scale). Measure and record its side lengths and perimeter. Find the ratios indicated in the chart. Repeat for other pairs of triangles.

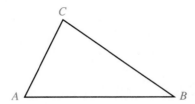

	First Triangle				Scaled Triangle			
	AB	BC	AC	Perimeter	$A'B'$	$B'C'$	$A'C'$	Perimeter
Acute								
Obtuse								
Isosceles								
Right								

	$AB{:}A'B'$	$BC{:}B'C'$	$AC{:}A'C'$	Perimeter of $\triangle ABC$: Perimeter of $\triangle A'B'C'$
Acute				
Obtuse				
Isosceles				
Right				

Conjecture
1. Make a conjecture about the ratio of two similar triangles' perimeters and the ratio of their corresponding side lengths.

Computer Exploration 28

Similar Triangles and Area

Objective
Determine the relationship between the area and the corresponding sides of similar triangles.

Investigation
Construct a triangle. Measure the sides and find the area. Record your data. Construct another triangle similar to the first one by giving it a different size (scale). Measure and record the side lengths and area. Find the ratios indicated in the chart. Repeat for other pairs of triangles.

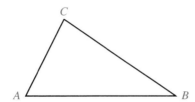

	First Triangle				Scaled Triangle			
	AB	BC	AC	Area	$A'B'$	$B'C'$	$A'C'$	Area
Acute								
Obtuse								
Isosceles								
Right								

	$AB{:}A'B'$	$BC{:}B'C'$	$AC{:}A'C'$	Area of $\triangle ABC$: Area of $\triangle A'B'C'$
Acute				
Obtuse				
Isosceles				
Right				

Conjecture
1. Make a conjecture about the ratio of two similar triangles' areas and the ratio of their corresponding side lengths.

Milestones in Mathematics

Gauss called mathematics the Queen of the sciences. Clearly then, mathematicians are her courtiers. To fully enjoy mathematics, you need a sense of its development and of the people of genius who have devoted their lives to its exploration. **Milestones in Mathematics** is a partial list of important events in mathematical history. You may want to find additional information in the library to learn more about these and other mathematicians and their contributions to the field of mathematics.

Milestones in Mathematics

c. 30,000+ BC	The knucklebones of animals were used as dice in games of chance.
c. 20,000+ BC	A wolfbone with 55 notches in two rows divided into groups of five was used for counting (discovered at Vestonice in Czechoslovakia).
c. 8,000 BC	First evidence of recorded counting.
c. 2,000 BC	The Egyptians had arrived at the value for pi of $\pi = 4(8/9)^2$.
c. 1,900 BC	Babylonian scholars used cuneiform numerals to the base 60 in the oldest-known written numeration for place value.
c. 1,700 BC	Sumerian notation was used to solve quadratic equations by the equivalent of the formula we use today.
c. 800 BC	Queen Dido founded the great city of Carthage by solving the geometric "Problem of Dido." A rigorous proof of this problem—what closed curve of specified length will enclose a maximum area—did not come until the nineteenth century.
c. 700 BC	Zero appeared in the Seleucid mathematical tables.
c. 550 BC	Pythagoras developed a logical, deductive proof of the Pythagorean theorem.
c. 300 BC	Euclid wrote the first geometry text, *Elements*.
c. 250 BC	Archimedes wrote *On Mechanical Theorems, Method* for his friend Eratosthenes.
c. 250 AD	An initial-letter shorthand for algebraic equations was developed.
c. 300 AD	Pappus of Alexandria discussed the areas of figures with the same perimeter in the *Mathematical Collection*.
c. 375 AD	Earliest known Mayan Initial Series inscriptions for expressing dates and periods of time.
c. 400 AD	Hypatia, the foremost mathematician in Alexandria, lectured on Diophantine algebra.
595	Date of an Indian deed on copper plate showing the oldest known use of the nine numerals according to the place value principle: the first written decimal numeration with the structure used today.

825 A treatise on linear and quadratic equations was published by Mohammed Al-Khwarizmi.

850 Mahavira contributed to the development of algebra in India.

1202 Leonardo of Pisa, also called Fibonacci, wrote *Liber abaci*, introducing Arabic numbers to Europe. This book contains his "rabbit problem" involving the numbers we now call Fibonacci.

1261 Yang Hui of China wrote on the properties of the binomial coefficients.

1557 The equal sign (=) came into general use during the 16th century, A.D. (The twin lines as an equal sign were used by the English physician and mathematician Robert Recorde with the explanation that "noe .2. thynges, can be moare equalle.")

1614 John Napier invented logarithms.

1639 René Descartes published his treatise on the application of algebra to geometry (analytic geometry).

1654 Blaise Pascal described the properties of the triangle we now call Pascal's triangle.

1657 Major contributions to number theory were made by Pierre de Fermat including his formulation of the "Pell" equation.

1670 G. Mouton devised a decimal-based measuring system.

1688 The calculus was published by Isaac Newton in *Principia Mathematica*.

1735 Graph theory was originated by Leonard Euler in his paper on the problem, "The Seven Bridges of Konigsberg."

1784 Maria Agnesi developed new ways to deal with problems involving infinite quantities in her book, *Analytical Institutions*.

1799 The fundamental theorem of algebra was delineated by Carl Friederich Gauss, who also developed rigorous proof as the requirement of mathematics.

1816 Sophie Germain published equations which stated the law for vibrating elastic surfaces.

1832 Evariste Galois wrote the theorem stating the conditions under which an equation can be solved.

1854 George Boole developed the postulates of "Boolean Algebra" in *Laws of Thought*.

1854 Mary Fairfax Somerville wrote books to popularize mathematics and extend the influence of the work of mathematicians.

1859 George F. B. Reimann published his work on the distribution of primes; "Reimann's Hypothesis" became one of the famous unsolved problems of mathematics.

1886 Modern combinatorial topology was created by Henri Poincare.

1888 Sonya Kovalesvskaya was awarded the Prix Bordin for her paper "On the Rotation of a Solid Body About a Fixed Point."

1897 David Hilbert published his monumental work on the theory of number fields and later clarified the foundations of geometry.

1906 Grace Chisholm Young and William Young published the first text on set theory.

1914 Srinivasa Ramanujan went to England to collaborate with G. H. Hardy on analytic number theory.

1925 Hermann Weyl published fundamental papers on group theory.

1931 Gödel showed that there must be undecidable propositions in any formal system and that one of those undecidable propositions is consistency.

1932 A completely general theory of ideal numbers was built up, on an axiomatic basis, by Emmy Noether.

1936 The minimax principle in probability and statistics was developed by Abraham Wald.

1937 Goldbach's conjecture that every even number is the sum of two primes $(12 = 5 + 7, 100 = 3 + 97)$ was established by I. M. Vinogradov for every sufficiently large even number that is the sum of, at most, four primes.

1938 Claude E. Shannon discovered the analogy between the truth values of propositions and the states of switches and relays in an electric circuit.

1942 Jacqueline Ferrand created the concept of preholomorphic functions, using these to produce a new methodology for mathematical proofs.

1951 Elizabeth Scott, Jerzy Newyman, and C. D. Shane applied statistical theories to deduce the existence of clusters of galaxies.

1953 Maria Pastori extended the usefulness of the tensor calculus in the pure mathematical investigation of generalized spaces.

1960 Advances in the application of probability and statistics were made by Florence Nightingale David.

1976 Four color problem proved using electronic computing in concert with human deduction.

1985 A new algorithm for factoring large numbers by using elliptic curves was developed by Hendrik W. Lenstra, Jr.

1985 David Hoffman discovered a fourth minimal surface, the first new minimal surface discovered since the 1700s.

???? "Fermat's Last Theorem" on the impossibility of separating any power above the second into two powers of the same degree is proved.

Symbols

$\pm$	positive or negative	$\triangle ABC$	triangle ABC
$=$	is equal to	$\square ABCD$	parallelogram $ABCD$
$\neq$	is not equal to	$\odot O$	circle O
$\approx$	is approximately equal to	$\overset{\frown}{AB}$	minor arc determined by A and B
$<$	is less than	$\overset{\frown}{ACB}$	major arc determined by A and B
$\leq$	is less than or equal to	$m\overset{\frown}{AB}$	measure of $\overset{\frown}{AB}$
$>$	is greater than	$\cong$	is congruent to
$\geq$	is greater than or equal to	$\not\cong$	is not congruent to
$\lvert x \rvert$	absolute value of x	$\parallel$	is parallel to
$\sqrt{x}$	principal square root of x	$\not\parallel$	is not parallel to
(x, y)	ordered pair	$\perp$	is perpendicular to
$\degree$	degrees	$\sim$	is similar to
$\overleftrightarrow{AB}$	line AB	$\leftrightarrow$	corresponds to
$\overline{AB}$	segment AB	$p \rightarrow q$	p implies q (if p, then q)
$\overrightarrow{AB}$	ray AB	$\sim p$	not p
$\overrightarrow{AB}$	vector AB	$\sin A$	sine of $\angle A$
$\overline{AB}$	length of AB	$\cos A$	cosine of $\angle A$
$\angle ABC$	angle ABC	$\tan A$	tangent of $\angle A$
$m\angle ABC$	measure of $\angle ABC$	π	pi, approximately 3.14

Formulas

Rectangle	**Square**	**Parallelogram**
Area: $A = \ell w$ Perimeter: $p = 2\ell + 2w$	Area: $A = s^2$ Perimeter: $p = 4s$	Area: $A = bh$

Triangle	**Trapezoid**	**Regular Polygon**
Area: $A = \frac{1}{2}bh$ $m \angle A + m \angle B + m \angle C = 180$	Area: $A = \frac{1}{2}h(b_1 + b_2)$	Area: $A = \frac{1}{2}ap$

Circle	**Right Prism**	**Regular Pyramid**
Area: $A = \pi r^2$ Circumference $= C = \pi d = 2\pi r$	Volume: $V = Bh$ Lateral Area: $LA = ph$ Surface Area: $SA = ph + 2B$	Volume: $V = \frac{1}{3}Bh$ Lateral Area: $\frac{1}{2}p\ell$ Surface Area: $SA = \frac{1}{2}p\ell + B$

Right Cylinder	**Right Cone**	**Sphere**
Volume: $V = \pi r^2 h$ Lateral Area: $LA = 2\pi rh$ Surface Area: $SA = 2\pi rh + 2\pi r^2$	Volume: $V = \frac{1}{3}\pi r^2 h$ Lateral Area: $LA = \pi r \ell$ Surface Area: $SA = \pi r \ell + \pi r^2$	Volume: $V = \frac{4}{3}\pi r^3$ Surface Area: $SA = 4\pi r^2$

Values of Trigonometric Functions

Degrees	Sin	Cos	Tan	Degrees	Sin	Cos	Tan
0°	0.0000	1.0000	0.0000				
1°	0.0175	0.9998	0.0175	46°	0.7193	0.6947	1.0355
2°	0.0349	0.9994	0.0349	47°	0.7314	0.6820	1.0724
3°	0.0523	0.9986	0.0524	48°	0.7431	0.6691	1.1106
4°	0.0698	0.9976	0.0699	49°	0.7547	0.6561	1.1504
5°	0.0872	0.9962	0.0875	50°	0.7660	0.6428	1.1918
6°	0.1045	0.9945	0.1051	51°	0.7771	0.6293	1.2349
7°	0.1219	0.9925	0.1228	52°	0.7880	0.6157	1.2799
8°	0.1392	0.9903	0.1405	53°	0.7986	0.6018	1.3270
9°	0.1564	0.9877	0.1584	54°	0.8090	0.5878	1.3764
10°	0.1736	0.9848	0.1763	55°	0.8192	0.5736	1.4281
11°	0.1908	0.9816	0.1944	56°	0.8290	0.5592	1.4826
12°	0.2079	0.9781	0.2126	57°	0.8387	0.5446	1.5399
13°	0.2250	0.9744	0.2309	58°	0.8480	0.5299	1.6003
14°	0.2419	0.9703	0.2493	59°	0.8572	0.5150	1.6643
15°	0.2588	0.9659	0.2679	60°	0.8660	0.5000	1.7321
16°	0.2756	0.9613	0.2867	61°	0.8746	0.4848	1.8040
17°	0.2924	0.9563	0.3057	62°	0.8829	0.4695	1.8807
18°	0.3090	0.9511	0.3249	63°	0.8910	0.4540	1.9626
19°	0.3256	0.9455	0.3443	64°	0.8988	0.4384	2.0503
20°	0.3420	0.9397	0.3640	65°	0.9063	0.4226	2.1445
21°	0.3584	0.9336	0.3839	66°	0.9135	0.4067	2.2460
22°	0.3746	0.9272	0.4040	67°	0.9205	0.3907	2.3559
23°	0.3907	0.9205	0.4245	68°	0.9272	0.3746	2.4751
24°	0.4067	0.9135	0.4452	69°	0.9336	0.3584	2.6051
25°	0.4226	0.9063	0.4663	70°	0.9397	0.3420	2.7475
26°	0.4384	0.8988	0.4877	71°	0.9455	0.3256	2.9042
27°	0.4540	0.8910	0.5095	72°	0.9511	0.3090	3.0777
28°	0.4695	0.8829	0.5317	73°	0.9563	0.2924	3.2709
29°	0.4848	0.8746	0.5543	74°	0.9613	0.2756	3.4874
30°	0.5000	0.8660	0.5774	75°	0.9659	0.2588	3.7321
31°	0.5150	0.8572	0.6009	76°	0.9703	0.2419	4.0108
32°	0.5299	0.8480	0.6249	77°	0.9744	0.2250	4.3315
33°	0.5446	0.8387	0.6494	78°	0.9781	0.2079	4.7046
34°	0.5592	0.8290	0.6745	79°	0.9816	0.1908	5.1446
35°	0.5736	0.8192	0.7002	80°	0.9848	0.1736	5.6713
36°	0.5878	0.8090	0.7265	81°	0.9877	0.1564	6.3138
37°	0.6018	0.7986	0.7536	82°	0.9903	0.1392	7.1154
38°	0.6157	0.7880	0.7813	83°	0.9925	0.1219	8.1443
39°	0.6293	0.7771	0.8098	84°	0.9945	0.1045	9.5144
40°	0.6428	0.7660	0.8391	85°	0.9962	0.0872	11.4301
41°	0.6561	0.7547	0.8693	86°	0.9976	0.0698	14.3007
42°	0.6691	0.7431	0.9004	87°	0.9986	0.0523	19.0811
43°	0.6820	0.7314	0.9325	88°	0.9994	0.0349	28.6363
44°	0.6947	0.7193	0.9657	89°	0.9998	0.0175	57.2900
45°	0.7071	0.7071	1.0000	90°	1.0000	0.0000	

Theorem 5.4	If both pairs of opposite sides of a quadrilateral are congruent, then the quadrilateral is a parallelogram. [5.2]
Theorem 5.5	If one pair of opposite sides of a quadrilateral are both parallel and congruent, then it is a parallelogram. [5.2]
Theorem 5.6	If both pairs of opposite angles of a quadrilateral are congruent, then the quadrilateral is a parallelogram. [5.2]
Theorem 5.7	If the consecutive angles of a quadrilateral are supplementary, then the quadrilateral is a parallelogram. [5.2]
Theorem 5.8	If the diagonals of a quadrilateral bisect each other, then the quadrilateral is a parallelogram. [5.2]
Theorem 5.9	The diagonals of a rectangle are congruent. [5.3]
Theorem 5.10	The diagonals of a rhombus are perpendicular. [5.3]
Theorem 5.11	Each diagonal of a rhombus bisects a pair of opposite angles. [5.3]
Theorem 5.12	If a parallelogram has a right angle, then it is a rectangle. [5.3]
Theorem 5.13	If a parallelogram has two adjacent sides congruent, then it is a rhombus. [5.3]
Theorem 5.14	Each pair of base angles of an isosceles trapezoid are congruent. [5.4]
Theorem 5.15	The diagonals of an isosceles trapezoid are congruent. [5.4]
Theorem 5.16	The median of a trapezoid is parallel to the bases and has a length equal to half the sum of the lengths of the bases. That is, $PQ = \frac{1}{2}(XY + WZ)$. [5.4]
Theorem 5.17	Midsegment Theorem: The segment that joins the midpoints of two sides of a triangle is parallel to the third side and has length equal to half the length of the third side. [5.5]
Theorem 5.18	The quadrilateral formed by joining the midpoints of the consecutive sides of another quadrilateral is a parallelogram. [5.5]
Theorem 5.19	If three or more parallel lines cut off congruent segments on one transversal, then they will cut off congruent segments on every transversal. [5.5]
Corollary 5.19a	A line that contains the midpoint of one side of a triangle and is parallel to another side bisects the third side. [5.5]
Theorem 5.20	Exterior Angle Inequality Theorem: The measure of an exterior angle of a triangle is greater than the measure of either remote interior angle. [5.7]
Theorem 5.21	If one side of a triangle is longer than a second side, then the measure of the angle opposite the longer side is greater than the measure of the angle opposite the shorter side. [5.7]
Theorem 5.22	If one angle of a triangle is larger than another angle, then the side opposite the larger angle is longer than the side opposite the smaller angle. [5.7]
Corollary 5.22a	The perpendicular segment from a point to a line is the shortest segment from the point to the line. [5.7]
Theorem 5.23	Triangle Inequality Theorem: The sum of the lengths of any two sides of a triangle is greater than the length of the third side. [5.7]
Theorem 5.24	SAS Inequality Theorem: If two sides of one triangle are congruent to two sides of a second triangle and the included angle of the first triangle is larger than the included angle of the second triangle, then the third side of the first triangle is longer then the third side of the second triangle. [5.8]
Theorem 5.25	SSS Inequality Theorem: If two sides of one triangle are congruent to two sides of a second triangle and the third side of the first triangle is longer than the third side of the second triangle, then the angle opposite the third side of the first triangle is larger then the angle opposite the third side of the second triangle. [5.8]

Theorem 6.1	Means-Extremes Products Theorem: In a proportion, the product of the means equals the product of the extremes. [6.1]
Theorem 6.2	Properties of Proportions: [If $\frac{a}{b} = \frac{c}{d}$, and a, b, c, and $d \neq 0$, then each of the following is true.

a. $\frac{a}{c} = \frac{b}{d}$

b. $\frac{d}{b} = \frac{c}{a}$

c. $\frac{b}{a} = \frac{d}{c}$

d. $\frac{a + b}{b} = \frac{c + d}{d}$

e. $\frac{a - b}{b} = \frac{c - d}{d}$ [6.2]

Theorem 6.3	Right Triangle Similarity: If an acute angle of one right triangle is congruent to an acute angle of another right triangle, then the triangles are similar. [6.4]
Theorem 6.4	SAS Similarity Theorem: If an angle of one triangle is congruent to an angle of another triangle and if the lengths of the sides including these angles are proportional, then the triangles are similar. [6.5]
Theorem 6.5	SSS Similarity Theorem: If corresponding sides of two triangles are proportional, then the two triangles are similar. [6.5]
Theorem 6.6	Triangle Proportional Segment Theorem: If a line parallel to one side of a triangle intersects the other two sides, then it divides the two sides proportionally. [6.6]
Theorem 6.7	If a line divides two sides of a triangle proportionally, then the line is parallel to the third side. [6.6]
Theorem 6.8	Parallels Proportional Segment Theorem: If three parallel lines intersect two transversals, then they divide the transversals proportionally. [6.6]
Theorem 6.9	Triangle Angle Bisector Theorem: If a ray bisects an angle of a triangle, then it divides the opposite side into two segments whose lengths are proportional to the lengths of the other two sides. [6.6]
Theorem 6.10	The lengths of bisectors of corresponding angles of two similar triangles are in the same ratio as the lengths of corresponding sides. [6.6]
Theorem 6.11	The lengths of altitudes from corresponding vertices of similar triangles are in the same ratio as the lengths of corresponding sides. [6.6]
Theorem 6.12	The lengths of medians from corresponding vertices of similar triangles are in the same ratio as the lengths of corresponding sides. [6.6]
Theorem 7.1	The altitude to the hypotenuse of a right triangle forms two triangles that are similar to each other and to the original triangle. [7.1]
Theorem 7.2	In a right triangle, the length of the altitude to the hypotenuse is the geometric mean between the lengths of the two segments on the hypotenuse. [7.1]
Theorem 7.3	In a right triangle with an altitude to the hypotenuse, each leg is the geometric mean between the length of the hypotenuse and the length of the segment of the hypotenuse adjacent to that leg. [7.1]
Theorem 7.4	Pythagorean Theorem: In a right triangle, the square of the length of the hypotenuse equals the sum of the squares of the lengths of the legs. [7.2]
Theorem 7.5	Converse of the Pythagorean Theorem: If a triangle has side lengths a, b, and c, and $a^2 + b^2 = c^2$, then the triangle is a right triangle with the right angle opposite the side with length c. [7.3]
Theorem 7.6	If $a < b < c$ are lengths of the sides of a triangle and **a.** $a^2 + b^2 < c^2$, then the triangle is an obtuse triangle. **b.** $a^2 + b^2 > c^2$, then the triangle is an acute triangle. [7.3]

Theorem 7.7	45°–45°–90° Triangle Theorem: The length of the hypotenuse of a 45°–45°–90° triangle is $\sqrt{2}$ times the length of the leg. [7.4]
Theorem 7.8	30°–60°–90° Theorem: In a 30°–60°–90° triangle the length of the hypotenuse is 2 times the length of the shorter leg and the length of the longer leg is $\sqrt{3}$ times the length of the shorter leg. [7.4]
Theorem 8.1	If a line is perpendicular to a radius of a circle at a point on the circle, then the line is tangent to the circle. [8.2]
Theorem 8.2	If a line is tangent to a circle, then it is perpendicular to the radius at the point of tangency. [8.2]
Theorem 8.3	The two tangent segments from an exterior point of a circle are congruent. [8.2]
Corollary 8.3a	The line through an external point and the center of a circle bisects the angle formed by the two tangents from the external point. [8.2]
Theorem 8.4	In a circle or in congruent circles congruent chords have congruent minor arcs. [8.4]
Theorem 8.5	In a circle or in congruent circles congruent minor arcs have congruent chords and congruent central angles. [8.4]
Theorem 8.6	If a diameter is perpendicular to a chord, then it bisects the chord and its minor and major arcs. [8.5]
Theorem 8.7	If a diameter bisects a chord that is not a diameter, then it is perpendicular to the chord and bisects its major and minor arcs. [8.5]
Theorem 8.8	The perpendicular bisector of a chord contains the center of the circle. [8.5]
Theorem 8.9	In the same circle or in congruent circles congruent chords are equidistant from the center. [8.5]
Theorem 8.10	In the same circle or in congruent circles, chords equidistant from the center are congruent. [8.5]
Theorem 8.11	Inscribed Angle Measure: The measure of an inscribed angle is half the measure of its intercepted arc. [8.6]
Corollary 8.11a	If two inscribed angles intercept the same arc, then the angles are congruent. [8.6]
Corollary 8.11b	If a quadrilateral is inscribed in a circle, then its opposite angles are supplementary. [8.6]
Corollary 8.11c	An angle inscribed in a semicircle is a right angle. Also, if an inscribed angle is a right angle its intercepted arc is a semicircle. [8.6]
Theorem 8.12	The measure of a tangent-chord angle is half the measure of its intercepted arc. [8.6]
Theorem 8.13	The measure of an angle formed by two chords intersecting inside a circle is one half the sum of the intercepted arcs. [8.7]
Theorem 8.14	The measure of an angle formed by two secants, two tangents, or a secant and a tangent drawn from a point on the exterior of a circle is equal to half the difference of the measures of the intercepted arcs. [8.7]
Theorem 8.15	If two chords intersect in a circle, then the product of the lengths of the segments of one chord equals the product of the lengths of the segments of the second chord. [8.8]
Theorem 8.16	If two secant segments are drawn to a circle from an exterior point, then the product of the lengths of one secant segment and its external segment equals the product of the lengths of the other secant segment and its external segment. [8.8]
Theorem 8.17	If a tangent segment and a secant segment are drawn to a circle from an exterior point, then the square of the length of the tangent segment equals the product of the lengths of the secant segment and its external secant segment. [8.8]
Theorem 9.1	The perpendicular bisectors of the sides of a triangle are concurrent in a point that is equidistant from the three vertices of the triangle. [9.5]
Theorem 9.2	The bisectors of the angles of a triangle are concurrent in a point that is equidistant from the three sides of the triangle. [9.5]

Theorem 9.3	The medians of a triangle are concurrent in a point that is two thirds of the distance from each vertex to the midpoint of the opposite side. [9.5]
Theorem 9.4	The lines that contain the altitudes of a triangle are concurrent. [9.5]
Theorem 10.1	The area of a parallelogram equals the product of the base b and the height h. $A = bh$ [10.2]
Theorem 10.2	The area of a triangle equals one half the product of the base b and the altitude h. $A = \frac{1}{2}bh$ [10.2]
Theorem 10.3	The area of a trapezoid equals one half the product of the height h and the sum of the bases b_1 and b_2. $A = \frac{1}{2}h(b_1 + b_2)$ [10.3]
Theorem 10.4	The area of any quadrilateral with perpendicular diagonals, d_1 and d_2, is half the product of the lengths of its diagonals. $A = \frac{1}{2}d_1d_2$ [10.3]
Theorem 10.5	The area of a regular polygon equals one half the product of its apothem a and its perimeter p. $A = \frac{1}{2}ap$ [10.4]
Theorem 10.6	If two polygons are similar, then the ratio of their perimeters equals the ratio of the lengths of any pair of corresponding segments. [10.5]
Theorem 10.7	If two polygons are similar, then the ratio of their areas equals the square of the ratio of the lengths of any pair of corresponding segments. [10.5]
Theorem 10.8	The ratio $\frac{C}{d}$ of the circumference C to the diameter d is the same for all circles. [10.6]
Theorem 10.9	The ratio of the length of an arc of a circle ℓ, to the circumference C equals the ratio of the degree measure of the arc, m, to 360. $\frac{\ell}{C} = \frac{m}{360}$ or $\frac{\ell}{2\pi r} = \frac{m}{360}$ [10.6]
Theorem 10.10	The area of a circle with radius r is given by the formula $A = \pi r^2$. [10.7]
Theorem 10.11	The area of a sector, with arc degree measure m, of a circle with radius r is given by the formula $A = \frac{m}{360}(\pi r^2)$. [10.7]
Theorem 11.1	The lateral area of a right prism is equal to the perimeter p of a base times the height h of the prism. $LA = ph$ The surface area is the sum of the lateral area and twice the area of a base B. $SA = ph + 2B$ [11.1]
Theorem 11.2	The lateral area of a regular pyramid is equal to one half the product of the perimeter of the base p and the slant height ℓ. $LA = \frac{1}{2}pl$ The surface area of a regular pyramid is the sum of the lateral area and the area of the base B. $SA = \frac{1}{2}p\ell + B$ [11.2]
Theorem 11.3	The volume of any prism is the product of its height and the area of its base B. $V = Bh$ [11.3]
Corollary 11.3a	The volume of a right rectangular prism is the product of its length ℓ, its width w, and its height. That is: $V = \ell wh$ [11.3]
Theorem 11.4	The volume of a pyramid is one third the product of the area of the base B and the length of the altitude h. $V = \frac{1}{3}Bh$ [11.4]
Theorem 11.5	The lateral area of a right cylinder is equal to the circumference of the base $(2\pi r)$ times the height h. $LA = 2\pi rh$
The surface area of a right cylinder is equal to the lateral area $(2\pi rh)$ plus the area of the two bases $(2\pi r^2)$ $SA = 2\pi rh + 2\pi r^2$ [11.5]
Theorem 11.6	The volume of a right cylinder is the product of π, the radius r squared, and the height h. $V = \pi r^2 h$ [11.5]
Theorem 11.7	The lateral area of a right cone is equal to the product of π, the radius r and the slant height ℓ. $LA = \pi r\ell$
The surface area of a right cone is equal to the sum of the lateral area $(\pi r\ell)$ and the area of the base (πr^2). $SA = \pi r\ell + \pi r^2$ [11.6]

Theorem 11.8	The volume of a right cone is one third the product of π, the radius r squared, and the height h. $V = \frac{1}{3}\pi r^2 h$. [11.6]
Theorem 11.9	The volume of a sphere is $\frac{4}{3}$ the product of π and the radius r cubed. $V = \frac{4}{3}\pi r^3$ The surface area of a sphere is four times the product of π and the radius r squared. $S = 4\pi r^2$ [11.7]
Theorem 11.10	If the lengths of two corresponding parts of two similar solids are in a ratio of $a : b$, then **a.** the ratio of any corresponding lengths is $a : b$, **b.** the ratio of corresponding surface areas is $a^2 : b^2$, **c.** the ratio of corresponding volumes is $a^3 : b^3$. [11.8]
Theorem 12.1	If the coordinates of the endpoints of the segment $P_1 P_2$ are $P_1(x_1, y_1)$ and $P_2(x_2, y_2)$, then the coordinates of the midpoint of $\overline{P_1 P_2}$ are $(\frac{x_1 + x_2}{2}, \frac{y_1 + y_2}{2})$. [12.1]
Theorem 12.2	Two nonvertical lines are parallel if and only if their slopes are equal. [12.3]
Theorem 12.3	Two nonvertical lines are perpendicular if and only if the product of their slopes is -1. [12.3]
Theorem 12.4	An equation of the line that has slope m and y-intercept b is $y = mx + b$. [12.4]
Theorem 12.5	Point-Slope Form: An equation of the line that passes through point (x_1, y_1) and has slope m is $y - y_1 = m(x - x_1)$.
Theorem 12.6	Distance Formula: The distance d between points $P_1(x_1, y_1)$ and $P_2(x_2, y_2)$ is given by the formula $d = \sqrt{(x_2 - x_1)^2 + (y_2 - y_1)^2}$. [12.5]
Theorem 12.7	An equation of a circle with center (h, k) and radius r is $(x - h)^2 + (y - k)^2 = r^2$. [12.6]
Theorem 13.1	The composition of two rotations about the same center point O is a rotation about center O with an angle of rotation equal in measure to the sum of the measures of the angles of rotation of the two rotations. [13.4]
Theorem 13.2	The composition of two translations is a translation. If translation PR is followed by translation RQ, then the composition translation is the translation PQ. [13.4]
Theorem 13.3	The composition of two line reflections in parallel lines p and q is a translation in a direction perpendicular to p and q having a length equal to twice the distance between p and q. [13.4]
Theorem 13.4	The composition of two line reflections intersecting at O is a rotation with center O and angle of rotation twice the angle from the first line to the second line. [13.4]
Theorem 13.5	A line reflection is an isometry. [13.5]
Theorem 13.6	The composition of two isometries is an isometry. [13.5]
Corollary 13.6a	A translation is an isometry. [13.5]
Corollary 13.6b	A rotation is an isometry. [13.5]
Theorem 13.7	If figure F' is the image of figure F under an isometry, then the areas of F and F' are equal. [13.5]
Theorem 13.8	If A' and B' are the images of A and B under the dilation with center O and scale factor k, then $A'B' = kAB$. [13.7]
Theorem 13.9	If $\triangle A'B'C'$ is the image of $\triangle ABC$ for the dilation with center O and scale factor k, then $\triangle A'B'C'$ is similar to $\triangle ABC$. [13.7]

Glossary

Abscissa (p. 533) The first number in an ordered pair, the *x*-coordinate

Acute (p. 14) An angle that measures betweeen 0 and 90 degrees

Acute triangle (p. 26) A triangle having all acute angles

Adjacent angles (p. 64) Two angles that have the same vertex and a common side, but that have no common interior points

Alternate exterior angles (p. 106) Two nonadjacent exterior angles on opposite sides of the transversal

Alternate interior angles (p. 106) Two nonadjacent interior angles on opposite sides of the transversal

Altitude (p. 189) A segment from a vertex of a triangle to the line containing the opposite side perpendicular to that side (p. 441) Of a parallelogram, a segment perpendicular to a pair of opposite sides and having endpoints on those sides (p. 485) Of a prism, a segment perpendicular to both bases with endpoints in the planes of the bases

Angle (p. 13) A figure consisting of two noncollinear rays with a common endpoint

Angle of depression (p.331) The angle made by the line of sight with the horizontal when an observer sights downward

Angle of elevation (p. 331) The angle made by the line of sight with the horizontal when an observer sights upward

Angle of rotation (p. 588) The angle through which a transformation is rotated about a point

Apothem (p. 455) In a regular polygon, the distance from the center to a side

Arc (p. 355) Two points and a continuous part of a circle between the points

Area of a region (p. 437) The number of square units contained in the region

Auxiliary line (p. 123) A line added to a figure, often used to help prove a proof

Base (p. 177) In an isosceles triangle, the third side, in addition to the congruent pair (p. 443) Any side of a parallelogram (p. 484) In a prism, one of a pair of identical, parallel faces (p. 491) In a pyramid, the face that does not contain the vertex

Base angles (p. 177) The angles opposite the congruent pair of sides in an isosceles triangle or (p. 220) the pairs of angles formed by a base and the legs in a trapezoid

Base of a parallelogram (p. 441) Any side of a parallelogram may be called a base

Bases of a trapezoid (p. 220) In a trapezoid, the parallel sides

Biconditional (p. 33) When a conditional and its converse are both true and are combined into one statement using the phrase "if and only if"

Bisector (p. 20) Any point, line, part of a line, or plane that divides the segment into two congruent segments

Boundary (p. 437) The points that make up the sides of a figure

Center (p. 341) A given point in the interior of a circle that is equidistant from all points on the circle

Center of a regular polygon (p. 455) The center of its inscribed circle

Central angle (p. 355) For a circle, an angle whose vertex is the center of the circle

Centroid (p. 411) The point of intersection of the medians of a triangle

Chord (p. 341) A segment that joins two points on a circle

Circle (p. 341) The set of all points in a plane that are a given distance from a given point in the plane called the center

Circumcenter (p. 410) The point that is equidistant from the vertices of a triangle

Circumference (p. 467) In a circle, the length of the boundary

Circumscribed polygon (p. 341) A polygon with each of its sides tangent to a circle

Collinear (p. 4) Points all in one line

Common tangent (p. 351) A line that is tangent to two coplanar circles

Complementary angles (p. 63) Two angles whose measures have a sum of 90

Composition (p. 594) Two transformations performed one after another

Concentric circles (p. 341) Two circles in the same plane with the same center

Conclusion (p. 32) In an if-then statement, the part following "then" that tells the result of the statement

Concurrent lines (p. 410) Three or more coplanar lines that have a point in common

Conditional (p. 32) An if-then statement consisting of a hypothesis (*if*) and a conclusion (*then*)

Cone (p. 511) A solid figure with a vertex and a circular base

Congruent (p. 20) Describes angles or segments that have the same measure or length

Congruent arcs (p. 355) Arcs with equal measure that lie in the same circle or in congruent circles

Congruent circles (p. 341) Circles that have congruent radii

Congruent triangles (p. 149) Triangles having a correspondence between the vertices such that each pair of corresponding sides and each pair of corresponding angles are congruent

Construction (p. 391) A geometric figure produced by using only a compass and straightedge

Contradiction (p. 230) A statement involving conflicting elements

Contrapositive (p. 34) Formed by interchanging the hypothesis and the conclusion of a conditional statement and negating both

Converse (p. 33) Formed by interchanging the hypothesis and the conclusion of a conditional statement

Convex polygon (p. 135) A polygon whose exterior angles measure 360 and whose diagonals all lie in the interior of the polygon

Coordinate(s) (p. 9) An ordered pair of numbers (x, y) that can be used to describe the location of a point on a plane

Coordinate plane (p. 533) The plane containing a rectangular coordinate system

Coplanar (p. 4) Points or lines all in one plane

Corollary (p. 178) A theorem that follows directly from another theorem

Correspondence (p. 149) The matching up of similar parts of two triangles, including the measure of angles and length of sides

Corresponding angles (p. 106) Two nonadjacent angles on the same side of the transversal such that one is an exterior angle and the other is an interior angle

Cosine ratio (p. 325) For a given acute angle in a right triangle, the ratio of the length of the adjacent leg to the length of the hypotenuse

Counterexample (p. 33) A single example that shows a general conditional statement to be false

Cylinder (p. 506) A solid figure having congruent circular bases in a pair of parallel planes

Deductive reasoning (p. 45) A process in which conclusions are drawn logically from given information

Degree (p. 13) A unit of measure for angles

Diagonal of a polygon (p. 135) A segment joining two nonconsecutive vertices

Diagram (p. 58) A figure that shows the given information, a key element in a two-column proof

Diameter (p. 341) A chord through the center of a circle

Dilation (p. 605) A transformation that preserves the shape of a figure, but allows the size to change

Directed segment (p. 583) A segment showing the distance and direction for a translation by showing the relationship between a point P and its translation image P'

Distance (p. 8) The absolute value of the difference of the coordinates for any two points on a number line

Edges (p. 485) The sides of the faces of polyhedrons

Enlargement (p. 605) A dilation with a scale factor greater than one

Equiangular (p. 26) Having all angles congruent

Equidistant (p. 189) The condition of a point P lying between two points A and B such that $PA = PB$

Equilateral (p. 27) Having all sides congruent

Exterior of an angle (p. 14) Those points on a plane separated by an angle which lie outside the angle

Exterior angle of a triangle (p. 129) Forms a linear pair with the adjacent interior angle of the triangle

Extremes (p. 255) In the proportion $\frac{a}{b} = \frac{c}{d}$, the first and fourth terms, or a and d

Faces (p. 485) Polygonal regions that make up a polyhedron

45°–45°–90° triangle (p. 312) A triangle whose angles measure 45°, 45°, and 90°

Geometric mean (p. 295) When a, b, and x are positive numbers and $\frac{a}{x} = \frac{x}{b}$, x is the geometric mean between a and b

Given (p. 58) A statement of facts given to be true, a key element in a two-column proof

Half-turn (p. 589) A rotation of 180°

Height (p. 443) The length of an altitude

Hypotenuse (p. 26) In a right triangle, the side opposite the right angle

Hypothesis (p. 32) In an if-then statement, the part following "if" that states the conditions necessary for the result to be true

Identity mapping (p. 605) A dilation with a scale factor of one

Incenter (p. 411) The point of concurrency of the angle bisectors of a triangle and the center of the inscribed circle of the triangle

Included (p. 153) Either an angle or a side of a triangle, lying between either two sides or two angles, respectively

Indirect proof (p. 230) A proof in which, after first assuming the negation of what is to be proved, a contradiction is reached through logical reasoning

Inscribed angle (p. 366) An angle with vertex on a circle and sides that contain chords of the circle

Inscribed polygon (p. 341) A polygon with all of its vertices on a circle

Interior of an angle (p. 14) Those points on a plane separated by an angle which lie inside the angle

Intersection (p.4) With two figures, the set of points both figures have in common

Inverse (p. 34) Formed when both the hypothesis and the conclusion in a conditional statement are negated

Isometry (p. 600) A concept used as the basis for generalizing the concept of congruence to figures that are not polygons; reflections, translations, or rotations having the common property that the distance between any two points and the distance between their images are equal

Isosceles triangle (p. 177) A triangle with a pair of congruent sides

Isosceles trapezoid (p. 220) A trapezoid with congruent nonparallel sides

Kite (p. 450) A quadrilateral with two distinct pairs of congruent adjacent sides

Lateral area (p. 486) The sum of the areas of the lateral faces of a prism

Lateral edge (p. 485) The common edge shared by adjacent lateral faces of a prism

Lateral face (p. 485) Of a prism, a parallelogram-shaped region formed by joining the vertices of the bases of the prism (p. 491) Of a pyramid, one of the faces containing the vertex of a pyramid

Legs (p. 26) In a right triangle, the sides not opposite the hypotenuse or (p. 177) the congruent sides of an isosceles triangle. Also (p. 220) the nonparallel sides of a trapezoid

Length of an arc (page 466) In a circle, the fractional part of the circumference subtended by the arc

Linear pair (p. 64) A pair of adjacent angles with two noncommon sides on the same line. Two angles that form a linear pair are supplementary

Line of symmetry (p. 578) A line in which a figure coincides with its reflection image

Locus (pl. loci) (p. 415) A set of points and only those points that satisfy one or more conditions

Major arc (p. 355) The arc in the exterior of the central angle of a circle

Mapping (p. 577) A correspondence between points of a plane

Means (p. 255) In the proportion $\frac{a}{b} = \frac{c}{d}$, the second and third terms, or b and c

Median (p. 189) A segment from a vertex of a triangle to the midpoint of the opposite side or (p. 221) the segment joining the midpoint of the legs of a trapezoid

Midpoint (p. 20) The midpoint of a segment is the point that divides the segment into two congruent segments

Midsegment (p. 224) The segment that joins the midpoints of two sides of a triangle

Minor arc (p. 355) The endpoints and all the points on both the circle and the interior of the central angle of the circle

Negation of a statement (p. 230) A statement having opposite meaning

Noncollinear (p. 4) Points that are not in one line

Noncoplanar (p. 4) Points or lines that are not in the same plane

Oblique cone (p. 511) A cone in which the axis is not perpendicular to the base

Oblique cylinder (p. 506) A cylinder in which the axis is not perpendicular to the bases

Oblique prism (p. 485) A prism with lateral edges not perpendicular to the bases

Obtuse (p. 14) An angle that measures between 90° and 180°

Obtuse triangle (p. 26) A triangle having one obtuse angle

Opposite angle (p. 153) In triangle ABC, angle B is opposite $\overline{AC}$, angle C is opposite $\overline{AB}$

Ordinate (p. 533) The second number in an ordered pair, the y-coordinate

Origin (p. 533) In a coordinate system, the intersection of the x-axis and the y-axis

Orthocenter (p. 412) The point of intersection of the lines containing the altitudes of a triangle

Parallel lines (p. 105) Coplanar lines that do not intersect

Parallelogram (p. 201) A quadrilateral with two pairs of parallel sides

Parallel planes (p. 105) Planes that do not intersect

Perimeter of a polygon (p. 437) The sum of the lengths of its sides

Perpendicular (p. 69) At a right angle to a given line or plane

Perpendicular bisector (p. 70) A line, segment, ray, or plane that is perpendicular to a segment and bisects it

Perpendicular lines (p. 69) Two lines that intersect at right angles

Point of tangency (p. 341) The point at which a line in the plane of a circle intersects that circle

Point-slope form (p. 547) One form of linear equation; for a line having slope m and passing through point (x_1, y_1), $y - y_1 = m(x - x_1)$

Polyhedron (p. 485) A three-dimensional solid made up of polygonal regions called faces

Postulate (p. 4) A statement that is accepted as true without proof

Prism (p. 485) A polyhedron with a pair of identical faces, called bases, that lie in parallel planes

Proof (p. 46) A valid argument which shows that a mathematical statement, called a theorem, is true

Proportion (p. 255) An equation stating that two ratios are equal

Protractor (p. 13) A tool marked in degree units that can be used to find the measure of an angle

Prove (p. 58) A statement of the conclusion to be established, a key element in a two-column proof

Pyramid (p. 491) A polyhedron in which all faces but one have a vertex in common

Pythagorean Triple (p. 308) Any three whole numbers a, b, and c for which $a^2 + b^2 = c^2$

Quadrants (p. 533) In a coordinate plane, the four regions formed by the intersecting axes

Radius of a circle (p. 341) In a circle, a segment with one endpoint the center and the other endpoint on the circle; the length of this segment

Radius of a regular polygon (p. 455) The distance from the center to a vertex

Ratio (p. 255) For any two numbers, x and y, the quotient obtained by dividing x and y

Ray (p. 13) A ray, $\overrightarrow{AB}$, is the part of $\overline{AB}$ that contains the point A and all the points on the same side of A as B

Reasons (p. 58) Numbered reasons in the right column of a proof, such as definitions, postulates (including properties of algebra), and previously proven theorems

Rectangle (p. 213) A quadrilateral with four right angles

Rectangular coordinate system (p. 533) A horizontal number line and a vertical number line intersecting at a point called the origin

Reduction (p. 605) A dilation with a scale factor less than one but greater than zero

Reflection (p. 577) A transformation that maps every point P of the plane to a point P' such that if point P is on ℓ then it is mapped to itself, or if point P is not on ℓ then ℓ is the perpendicular bisector of PP'

Reflectional symmetry (p. 578) Symmetry in which a figure coincides with its reflection image in ℓ

Region of a figure (p. 437) The figure and its interior

Regular polygon (p. 136) A polygon that is both equilateral and equiangular

Regular pyramid (p. 491) A pyramid with a regular polygon as the base and all lateral edges congruent

Remote interior angles (p. 129) The two angles of the triangle that are not adjacent to the exterior angle

Rhombus (p. 213) A quadrilateral with four congruent sides

Right angle (p. 14) An angle that measures 90°

Right cone (p. 511) A cone in which the axis is perpendicular to the base

Right cylinder (p. 506) A cylinder in which the axis is perpendicular to the bases

Right prism (p. 485) A prism in which the lateral edges are perpendicular to the bases

Right triangle (p. 26) A triangle having one right angle

Rotation (p. 588) A transformation about a point O through an angle of $x°$ that associates each point P of the plane with a point P'

Rotational symmetry (p. 589) Symmetry such that a figure or pattern can be rotated $x°$ about a point so that the pattern appears identical to its original position

Same-side interior angles (p. 106) Two interior angles on the same side of the transversal

Scalene (p. 27) Having no sides congruent

Secant (p. 341) A line that contains a chord of a circle

Sector of a circle (page 473) A region formed by two radii and an arc of a circle

Segment (p. 9) A set of points consisting of two points, called endpoints, and all the points between these points

Segment of a circle (p. 474) A region formed by an arc and its chord

Semicircle (p. 355) One of two arcs formed when the endpoints of the arcs are the endpoints of the diameter of a circle

Side (p. 13) The two rays with a common vertex that form an angle

Similar polygons (p. 264) Two polygons that have the same shape

Sine ratio (p. 325) For a given acute angle in a right triangle, the ratio of the length of the opposite leg to the length of the hypotenuse

Skew lines (p. 105) Lines that are not coplanar and do not intersect

Slant height (p. 491) The height of any one of the lateral faces of a regular pyramid or the distance from the vertex to the base along the surface of a right cone

Slope (p. 538) The degree of steepness of a line, determined by the change in the vertical distance divided by the change in the horizontal distance

Slope-intercept form (p. 547) One form of linear equation; for slope m and y-intercept b, $y = mx + b$

Space (p. 3) The set of all points

Sphere (p. 342) The set of all points in space a given distance from a point called the center of the sphere

Square (p. 213) A quadrilateral with four right angles and four congruent sides

Standard form (p. 547) An equation of a line written in the form $Ax + By = C$, where A and B are both not zero

Statements (p. 58) Numbered statements in the left column of a proof that must be shown to be true in order to prove the conclusion

Supplementary angles (p. 63) Two angles whose measures have a sum of 180

Surface area (p. 485) The area of the surfaces enclosing a polyhedron

Tangent (p. 341) A line in the plane of a circle that intersects the circle in exactly one point, the point of tangency

Tangent-chord angle (p. 368) An angle that has its vertex on a circle with one side tangent to the circle at the vertex and the other side containing a chord

Tangent ratio (p. 319) For a given acute angle in a right triangle, the ratio of the length of the opposite leg to the length of the adjacent leg

Theorem (p. 46) A mathematical statement that must be proven before being accepted

30°–60°–90° triangle (p. 313) A triangle whose three angles measure 30°, 60°, and 90°

Transformation (p. 577) A mapping that establishes a one-to-one correspondence between points in the plane

Translation (p. 583) A transformation that slides all points of the plane a fixed distance in a given direction

Translational symmetry (p. 584) Symmetry in which a translation maps a figure onto itself

Transversal (p. 106) A line that intersects two coplanar lines in two different points

Trapezoid (p. 220) A quadrilateral with exactly one pair of parallel sides

Triangle (p. 26) A figure formed by three segments joining three noncollinear points

Trigonometric ratio (p. 319) A ratio of the lengths of two sides of a right triangle

Trigonometry (p. 319) The study of the relationships between the sides and the angles of triangles

Two-column proof (p. 57) A style of proof in which statements that lead to the desired conclusion are listed in the left column and a reason for each statement is listed in the right column

Vertex (pl. vertices) (p. 13) The common endpoint at which two noncollinear rays meet, forming an angle

Vertex angle (p. 177) The angle opposite the base in an isosceles triangle

Vertical angles (p. 64) Two nonadjacent angles formed by a pair of intersecting lines

Volume (p. 496) The number of cubic units contained in a solid

x-axis (p. 533) The horizontal number line in the coordinate system

x-coordinate (p. 533) The first number in an ordered pair

y-axis (p. 533) The vertical number line in the coordinate system

y-coordinate (p. 533) The second number in an ordered pair

Selected Answers

CHAPTER 1

Lesson 1-1 Try This
Point E

Exercise Set 1-1
1. $\overleftrightarrow{AB}$ 3. $\overleftrightarrow{AB}$, $\overleftrightarrow{AC}$ 5. E

7.   9.

11.   13.

15. true   17. false   19. $\overleftrightarrow{TU}$ 21. Post. 2   23. Post. 4
25. Post. 2   27. false

29. true   31. true   33. Post. 2   35. Post. 4
37. **a.**   **b.** not possible   **c.**

d.   **e.**   **f.**   **39.** 10

Algebra Review
1. 3   3. 7.5   5. 0   7. 5   9. 7   11. 2

Lesson 1-2 Try This
1. 3   2. 16, $PQ + QR = 14 + 16 = 30 = PR$
3. $E(1, -4)$, $F(3, -2)$ $(2, 3)$ is between E and F.

Exercise Set 1-2
1. 9   3. 12   5. 9   7. 36   9. 36   11. 3   13. 21   15. 8
17. 31   19. $14\frac{1}{4}$ 21. 6, 12   23. 8, 38   25. 6, 8
27. 15 in.   29. 17   31. 15   33. A 35. 3   37. 4, 24
39. 5, 30   41. ± 4 43. 5, 9, 7, 8
45. They are reflections of each other.

Algebra Review
1. 7   3. 13

Lesson 1-3 Try This
1. 85°, acute   2. 91   3. 72, 32

Exercise Set 1-3
1. 10   3. 85   5. 80   7. $\angle 5$, $\angle JKL$, $\angle LKJ$, $\angle K$
9. right, 90   11. obtuse, 140   13. acute, 55   15. 19
17. 24, 48   19. 48, 26
21. false

23. true
25. false

27. 70   29. 20   31. 160   33. 56   35. 50   37. 36

39.   41.

43.

45. Sometimes; true when C is in the interior of $\angle ABD$.
47. never, different vertices
49. always   51. 120, 130

Mixed Review
1. D 3. collinear   5. 13

Lesson 1-4 Try This
1. 16   2. 64

Exercise Set 1-4
1. $\overline{DE} \cong \overline{EF}$, $\overline{EH} \cong \overline{HJ}$, $\overline{GH} \cong \overline{HI}$ 3. $\overline{GS} \cong \overline{SH}$ 5. $\overline{AB}$
and $\overline{CD}$, $\overline{BC}$ and $\overline{DE}$; $\overline{AB} \cong \overline{CD}$, $\overline{BC} \cong \overline{DE}$ 7. -2 9. 30,
30, 60   11. 9, 9, 18   13. 45   15. 45   17. 90   19. 54,
27, 27   21. 144, 72, 72   23. 10 ft   25. true, def. of $\cong$
seg.   27. true, Post. 11   29. no   31. no   33. no
35. true   37. false   39. true   41. 32   43. 45   45. 15
47. $D(2.5, 4.5)$, $E(5, 4.5)$; $AB = 5$, $DE = \frac{1}{2}AB$; yes
49. $\frac{a+b}{2}$ 51. The pitcher's mound is on the $\angle$ bis. of the $\angle$
formed by third base, home plate (vertex), and first base. It
is near the midpt. of the seg. joining first base and third
base.

Algebra Review
1. 5   3. $\sqrt{29}$ 5. $\sqrt{37}$

Lesson 1-5 Try This
1. $\triangle PRS$, $\triangle STQ$ 2. $\triangle TUV$, $\overline{UV} \cong \overline{TV} \cong \overline{TU}$ 3. $\sqrt{13}$;
$\triangle ABC$ is isos. since $\overline{AB} \cong \overline{AC}$.

Exercise Set 1-5
1. $\triangle AEC$, $\triangle CED$, $\triangle BED$, $\triangle AEB$ 3. $\overline{BE}$, $\overline{ED}$, $\overline{DB}$
5. $\triangle AEB$ 7. $\triangle BED$ 9. $\triangle AEB$ 11. equilateral
13. isos.   15. acute   17. obtuse   19. isos.
21. equilateral   23. obtuse   25. 4, $2\sqrt{5}$, $2\sqrt{5}$; isos.
27. sometimes   29. always   31. sometimes   33. 30
35. 56, 34   37. 72   39. 5, 6, 5; isos.   41. Constructions
may vary.   43.

Mixed Review
1. 75   3. 30

Lesson 1-6 Try This

1. If all ∠s of △KLM have measure <90, then △KLM is acute. **2.** If 2 lines intersect, then they form rt. ∠s. $\overrightarrow{AB}$ and $\overrightarrow{CD}$ intersect, but do not form rt. ∠s. **3.** If M is between A and B, then M is the midpt. of $\overline{AB}$. (not true) **4.** I: If △EFG is not an obtuse △, then it does not contain an obtuse ∠. C: If △EFG does not contain an obtuse ∠, then it is not an obtuse △.

Exercise Set 1-6

1. H: You are funny. C: You will make people laugh. **3.** H: A pt. is in the int. of an ∠. C: It cannot be in the ext. of the ∠. **5.** H: ∠A ≅ ∠B, C: $m\angle A = m\angle B$ **7.** H: △JKL has 3 acute ∠s. C: △JKL is acute. **9.** If a man lives in Houston, then he lives in Texas. **11.** If 4 pts. are all in one plane, then the pts. are coplanar. **13.** If R is between S and U, and T is between R and U, then T is between S and U. **15.** If a line bisects a seg., then it contains the midpt. of the seg. (T) **17.** If pts. lie on the same line, then they are collinear. (T) **19.** If you go to law school, then you will become a judge. (F) **21.** If a △ is equilateral, then it is also an isos. △. (T) **23.** If 2 ∠s are ≅, then they have the same measure. **25.** If 2 ∠s are ≅, then the 2 ∠s each measure 30. **27.** If 2 lines are intersecting lines, then the 2 lines have a common pt. **29.** If △ABC is isos., then △ABC is equilateral. **31.** (25) I: If 2 ∠s do not each measure 30, then they are not ≅. C: If 2 ∠s are not ≅, then they do not each measure 30. (26) I: If you are not 21 years old or older, then you cannot legally vote. C: If you cannot legally vote, then you are not 21 years old or older. **33.** If 2 ∠s are ≅, then they have the same measure. If 2 ∠s have the same measure, then they are ≅. **35.** If $\overrightarrow{BD}$ is the bis. of ∠ABC, then D is in the interior of the ∠ and ∠ABD ≅ ∠DBC. If D is in the interior of ∠ABC and ∠ABD ≅ ∠DBC, then $\overrightarrow{BD}$ is the bis. of ∠ABC. **37.** H: Jim may vote. C: He is at least 18 years old. **39.** H: A number ends in 5. C: It is odd. **41.** H: ∠s have the same measure. C: The ∠s are ≅. **43.** If $\overrightarrow{GJ}$ bisects ∠HGI, then ∠HGJ ≅ ∠JGI. Converse is true. **45.** If 2 sides of a △ are ≅, then it is isos. Converse is true. **47.** A △ is acute if and only if all of its ∠s are acute. A △ is obtuse if and only if one of its ∠s is obtuse. A △ is a rt. △ if and only if one of its ∠s is a rt. ∠. A △ is equiangular if and only if all of its ∠s are ≅. **49.** Inverse: If a △ is not equilat., then it is not isos. Contrapositive of inverse: If a △ is not not isos. then the △ is not not equilat. (same as converse)

51.

Conditional				Contrapositive		
p	q	$p \rightarrow q$		$\sim q$	$\sim p$	$\sim q \rightarrow \sim p$
T	T	T		F	F	T
T	F	F		F	T	T
F	T	T		T	F	F
F	F	T		T	T	T

A conditional and its contrapositive are equivalent. The converse and inverse are equivalent to each other, but not to the original conditional.

Mixed Review

1. right **3.** equiangular

Lesson 1-7 Try This

1. No; if an ∠ is obtuse, then it is >90°. **2.** $\overline{SW} \cong \overline{WT}$; if a line bisects a seg., then it divides the seg. into 2 ≅ seg.

Exercise Set 1-7

1. $\overline{LM} \cong \overline{MN} \cong \overline{NL}$ **3.** △GEF is a rt. △. **5.** If an ∠ is a rt. ∠, then the ∠ measures 90. **7.** If a △ has at least 2 ≅ sides, then it is isos. **9.** If a ray in the interior of an ∠ divides it into 2 ≅ ∠s, then it bisects the ∠. **11.** If a pt. divides a line seg. into 2 ≅ seg., then it is the midpt. of the seg. **13.** The conditional has the wrong hypothesis. **15.** Conditional: If a ray is an ∠ bis., then it divides the ∠ into 2 ≅ ∠s. **17.** Conditional: If a △ is scalene, then it has no ≅ sides. Conclusion: △ABC has no ≅ sides. **19.** Conditional: If 2 ∠s have = measure, then they are ≅. Conclusion: ∠PQR ≅ ∠STW **21.** Conditional: If N is in the interior of ∠KLM, then $m\angle KLN + m\angle NLM = m\angle KLM$. Conclusion: $m\angle KLM = 90$. **23.** (1) If a line bisects a seg., then it divides it into 2 ≅ seg. (2) If a line bisects a seg., then it contains the seg.'s midpt. **25.** (1) If N is between S and T, then $SN + NT = ST$. (2) If a pt. is between 2 other pts., then the 3 pts. are collinear. **27.** △KML is isos. (Def. of isos. △) **29.** ∠S ≅ ∠T (Def. of ≅ ∠s) **31.** $\overline{GT} \cong \overline{TH}$ **33.** Jerome earned an A. **35.** $\overrightarrow{AB}$ is not the bis. of ∠CAD. **37.** If a line is a bis. of a seg., then it contains the midpt. of the seg.

Algebra Review

1. commutative **3.** associative

Lesson 1-8 Try This

1. Add. Prop. **2.** Since $3(x - 2) = 9$, $3x - 6 = 9$ (Dist. Prop.). Also, $3x = 15$ (Add. Prop.), and so $x = 5$ (Div. Prop.). **3.** $m\angle E = m\angle E$ (Reflex. Prop.) so ∠E ≅ ∠E (def. ≅). **4.** Suppose ∠A ≅ ∠C and ∠B ≅ ∠C. From symmetry of congruence (Th. 1.1), ∠C ≅ ∠B. But then ∠A ≅ ∠C and ∠C ≅ ∠B, so trans. of congruence (Th. 1.1) allows the conclusion that ∠A ≅ ∠B.

Exercise Set 1-8

1. $RS = PQ$ **3.** $JK = PQ$ **5.** $m\angle T = m\angle T$ **7.** $AB + EF = CD + GH$ **9.** $PQ \cdot TU = RS \cdot VW$ **11.** $ST = 90 + 60$ **13.** Seg. congruence is symmetric. **15.** ∠ congruence is symmetric. **17.** Seg. congruence is trans. **19.** If $15p + 4 = 64$, then $15p = 60$ (Sub. Prop.). and $p = 4$ (Div. Prop.). **21.** If $3(n + 1) = 99$, then $n + 1 = 33$ (Div. Prop.) and $n = 32$ (Sub. Prop.). **23.** $AB + CD = GH$ **25.** $m\angle RST$ **27.** $m\angle 1 = m\angle 2$ **29.** $m\angle JKL = 37$ **31.** $\overline{AB} \cong \overline{EF}$, $\overline{AC} \cong \overline{BD}$, $\overline{AC} \cong \overline{CE}$, $\overline{AD} \cong \overline{CF}$, $\overline{BD} \cong \overline{CE}$, $\overline{BD} \cong \overline{DF}$, $\overline{AE} \cong \overline{BF}$, $\overline{BC} \cong \overline{DE}$ **33.** Since GH is a real number, $GH = GH$ by the reflex. prop. of real numbers. Thus, $\overline{GH} \cong \overline{GH}$ by the def. ≅ seg. **35. a.** no **b.** yes **c.** yes **d.** no

1. B, C, D 3. B 5. 55   7. $\angle EBA \cong \angle ABC$, $\overline{AB} \cong \overline{CD}$

Chapter Review

1. true   2. true   3. false   4. 17   5. 17   6. C 7. 57
8. $\angle ACF \cong \angle FCB$ 9. 8   10. $\triangle KLM$ 11. $\triangle KMN$
12. 10   13. H: A number is positive. C: It is > 0.   14. If Mr. Wong lives in Ohio, then he lives in the U.S.   15. If the sides of a $\triangle$ are $\cong$, then it is equilat.   16. $EF = GH$
17. If the measure of an $\angle$ is 90, then it is a rt. $\angle$.
18. $AB = CD$ 19. symmetric

CHAPTER 2

Exercise Set 2-1

1. 1. c, 2. c, 3. a, 4. b   3. 1.g, 2.e   5. 1. g, 2. b
7. 1. g, 2. g, 3. c, 4. d   9. 1. Given 2. Given 3. Def. equiang. $\triangle$ 4. Th. 1.3   11. 1. Q is between P and R. (Given) 2. Seg. Add. Post. 4. Sub. Prop. 5. $PQ = PR - QR$
13. 1. Given 2. $\angle$ Add. Post. 3. $\angle$ Add. Post. 4. $m\angle LKP = m\angle 1 + m\angle 2 + m\angle 3$.   15. Conclusion: $GI = IJ$ 1. G, H, I, J are collinear. (Given) 2. $GH + HI = GI$ (Seg. Add. Post.) 3. $GH + HI = IJ$ (Given) 4. $GI = IJ$ (Subst.)

Mixed Review

1. $\overline{DE} \cong \overline{EF}$ 3. 50

Lesson 2-2 Try This

1. $m\angle EFH = 144$, $m\angle HFG = 36$ 2. $m\angle 3 = 50$, $m\angle 4 = 130$

Exercise Set 2-2

1. $\angle GCA, \angle ACD$ 3. $\angle GCB, \angle ECD$ 5. $\angle ACE, \angle GCB$
7. 30   9. 150   11. 70   13. $m\angle AXG = 60$, $m\angle GXF = 30$ 15. 45 and 45   17. 1. Given 2. Given 3. Th. 2.2 4. Th. 1.3   19. 30, 60   21. 25
23. always   25. never (sum of measures >90)

27. Comp: 22.5, supp: 112.5   29. comp: $60 + 2x$, supp: $150 + 2x$ 31. $m\angle DEB = 57$, $m\angle FED = 33$
33. $m\angle DEF = 28$, $m\angle DEB = 62$ 35. 50 and 130
37. 54, 36   39. 72   41. 1. $\angle 1$ is supp. to $\angle 2$. $\angle 4$ is supp. to $\angle 3$. (Given) 2. $m\angle 1 + m\angle 2 = 180$, $m\angle 4 + m\angle 3 = 180$ (Def. supp. $\angle$s) 3. $\angle 2 \cong \angle 3$ (Given) 4. $m\angle 2 = m\angle 3$ (Def. $\cong$ $\angle$s) 5. $m\angle 1 + m\angle 2 = m\angle 4 + m\angle 3$ (Subst.) 6. $m\angle 1 = m\angle 4$ (Sub. Prop.) 7. $\angle 1 \cong \angle 4$ (Def. $\cong$ $\angle$s)   43. Let the measures of the $\angle$s be x. Then $x + x = 180$, so $x = 90$ and the $\angle$s are rt. $\angle$s.
45. Let the measure of $\angle$ be x. $x + 2(90 - x) = x + 180 - 2x = 180 - x =$ measure of the supp.

Algebra Review

1. 25   3. 0

Lesson 2-3 Try This

1. 72   2. $\overline{PS} \cong \overline{SQ}$, $\overline{PR} \perp \overline{RQ}$, S is the midpt. of $\overline{PQ}$.

Exercise Set 2-3

1. b   3. d   5. $m\angle 1 = m\angle 2 = m\angle 3 = m\angle 4 = 90$
7. $\angle TXS, \angle SXR$ 9. 63   11. 60   13. 36   15. 1. Given 2. Given 3. Def. $\perp$ 4. Def. $\perp$ bis.   17. 1. Given 2. Def. comp. $\angle$s 3. $\angle$ Add. Post. 4. $m\angle QPR = 90$ 5. Def. rt. $\angle$ 6. $\overline{PQ} \perp \overline{PR}$ (Def. $\perp$)
19.   21.

23. $\frac{YC}{AC} = \frac{1}{4}$, $\frac{YC}{XC} = \frac{1}{2}$, $\frac{AX}{YC} = 2$ **25.** sometimes   **27.** never
29. $180 - x$ **31.** 90, 90   **33.** 1. $\angle 1$ is comp. to $\angle 2$
(Given) 2. $m\angle 1 + m\angle 2 = 90$ (Def. comp.) 3. $m\angle 1 +$
$m\angle 2 = m\angle JKL$ ($\angle$ Add. Post.) 4. $m\angle JKL = 90$ (Subst.)
5. $\angle JKL$ is a rt. $\angle$. (Def. rt. $\angle$) 6. $\overline{JK} \perp \overline{KL}$ (Def. $\perp$)
35. false

37. Put compass tip on P and make an arc that forms a seg.
on l. Construct the $\perp$ bis. to this seg.

Mixed Review

1. H: A $\triangle$ is isos. C: It has 2 $\cong$ sides.   **3.** If a $\triangle$ has
2 $\cong$ sides, then it is isos.   **5.** $m\angle B = m\angle D$

Lesson 2-4 Try This

1. A is in the interior of $\angle BEF$ **2.**

Exercise Set 2-4

1. no   **3.** no   **5.** yes   **7.** yes   **9.** no   **11.** yes
13. no   **15.** yes
17.   **19.**

21.   **23.**

25.

27.

29.

1. Given 2. Def. $\perp$
3. $m\angle 1 = 90$, $m\angle 2 = 90$
4. $m\angle 1 = m\angle 2$

31.

33.

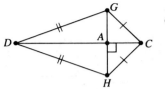

$\angle GAC$ is a rt. $\angle$,
$CG < HD$, etc.

35. The sum of these distances is the same no matter what
pt. is chosen. (The sum is $=$ to the alt. of the $\triangle$.) To test
this, pick any pt., measure the distances, find the sum, and
then try this with other pt.

Algebra Review

1. $(x + 2)(x + 1)$ **3.** $(m - 3)(m - 2)$
5. $(n - 7)(n + 3)$ **7.** $(2y + 1)(y - 2)$
9. $(3x - 1)(2x + 3)$

Exercise Set 2-5

1. If 2 intersecting lines form $\cong$ adj. $\angle$s, then they are $\perp$.
3.

5. If 2 $\angle$s are $\cong$ and supp., then they are rt. $\angle$s.

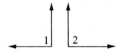

Given: $\angle 1 \cong \angle 2$, $\angle 1$ and $\angle 2$ are supp.
Prove: $\angle 1$ and $\angle 2$ are rt. $\angle$s.
7. If 2 $\angle$s are vert. $\angle$s, then they are $\cong$.

Given: $\angle 1$ and $\angle 2$ are vert. $\angle$s.
Prove: $\angle 1 \cong \angle 2$ **9.** $\angle ABD \cong \angle DBC$ **11.** $m\angle JKL =$
90   **13.** $\overline{SX} \perp \overline{WY}$ **15.** 1. $\angle 1 \cong \angle 2$, $\angle 3 \cong \angle 4$ (Given)
2. $\angle 2 \cong \angle 3$ (Th. 2.2) 3. $\angle 1 \cong \angle 3$ (Th. 1.1) 4. $\angle 1 \cong \angle 4$
(Th. 1.1)   **17.** 1. $\overline{RT} \perp \overline{PQ}$, $\overline{WY} \perp \overline{PQ}$ (Given) 2. $\angle 1$ and
$\angle 3$ are rt. $\angle$s. (Def. rt. $\angle$) 3. $\angle 1 \cong \angle 3$ (Th. 2.4)
19.

L

S M T

1. $\overline{LM} \perp \overline{ST}$ (Given) 2. $\angle LMS$ is a rt. $\angle$. (Def. $\perp$) 3.
$m\angle LMS = 90$ (Def. rt. $\angle$)

21.

1. $m\angle KLM = 90$ (Given) 2. $\angle KLM$ is a rt. $\angle$. (Def. rt. $\angle$)
3. $\overline{KL} \perp \overline{LM}$ (Def. $\perp$)

23.

1. $\overline{AB} \perp \overline{BC}$, $\overline{DC} \perp \overline{BC}$ (Given) 2. $\angle ABC$ is a rt. $\angle$.
$\angle DCB$ is a rt. $\angle$. (Def. $\perp$) 3. $\angle ABC \cong \angle DCB$ (Th. 2.4)
25. 1. O is the midpt. of $\overline{BC}$. $\triangle AOB$ is isos. with $\overline{OA} \cong \overline{OB}$.
(Given) 2. $CO \cong OB$ (Def. midpt.) 3. $\overline{OA} \cong \overline{CO}$ (Th. 1.2)
4. $\triangle AOC$ is isos. (Def. isos. $\triangle$) **27.** 1. B is between A and
C. E is between D and F. (Given) 2. $AB + BC = AC$,
$DE + EF = DF$ (Seg. Add. Post.) 3. $AC = DF$, $BC = EF$
(Given) 4. $AB + EF = DF$ (Subst.) 5. $AB + EF =$
$DE + EF$ (Subst.) 6. $AB = DE$ (Sub. Prop.)

Mixed Review

1. equilateral **3.** $\triangle BCG$ **5.** $\sqrt{10}$

Lesson 2-6 Try This

1. $GI = HJ$, Common Seg. Th. **2.** $\overleftrightarrow{AC}$ is the $\perp$ bis. of $\overline{DB}$.

Exercise Set 2-6

1. $\overline{MP} \cong \overline{NQ}$ **3.** $\overline{IE} \cong \overline{KA}$ **5.** 8 **7.** 18 **9.** $\overline{QR} \cong \overline{RS}$
11. $\overline{QR} \cong \overline{RS}$ **13.** $\overline{FH} \perp \overline{EG}$ **15.** false **17.** false
19. 1. $\angle 1$ and $\angle 2$ are comp. (Given) 2. $m\angle 1 + m\angle 2 =$
90 (Def. comp. $\angle$s) 3. $m\angle 1 + m\angle 2 = m\angle UTW$ ($\angle$ Add.
Post.) 4. $m\angle UTW = 90$ (Subst.) 5. $\angle UTW$ is a rt. $\angle$. (Def.
rt. $\angle$) 6. $\triangle UTW$ is a rt. $\triangle$. (Def. rt. $\triangle$) **21.** 1. $\overline{AB} \cong \overline{BD}$,
$\overline{BC} \cong \overline{DE}$ (Given) 2. $\overline{BD} \cong \overline{CE}$ (Common Seg. Th.)
3. $\overline{AB} \cong \overline{CE}$ (Th. 1.1) **23.** $\overline{RS} \cong \overline{MN}$ and $\overline{TU} \cong \overline{MN}$.
25. Yes; $AB = CD$ by the Common Seg. Th. **27.** 1. $\overline{GI} \cong$
$\overline{HJ}$, $\overline{IK} \cong \overline{JL}$ (Given) 2. $\overline{GH} \cong \overline{IJ}$, $\overline{IJ} \cong \overline{KL}$ (Common Seg.
Th.) 3. $\overline{GH} \cong \overline{KL}$ (Th. 1.1) **29.** 1. $\overline{AC} \cong \overline{BD}$ (Given)
2. $AC = BD$ (Def. $\cong$ seg.) 3. $BC = BC$ (Reflex. prop.)
4. $AC - BC = BD - BC$ (Sub. Prop.) 5. $AB = CD$ (Seg.
Add. Post.) 6. $\overline{AB} \cong \overline{CD}$ (Def. $\cong$ seg.)
31. always **33.** never **35.** 1. $\angle 1$ and $\angle 3$ are comp.
(Given) 2. $m\angle 1 + m\angle 3 = 90$ (Def. comp. $\angle$s)
3. $m\angle 2 + m\angle 3 = m\angle ADC$ ($\angle$ Add. Post.) 4. $m\angle 1 +$
$m\angle ADC = 180$ (Th. 2.1) 5. $m\angle 1 + m\angle 2 + m\angle 3 = 180$
(Subst.) 6. $m\angle 2 + 90 = 180$ (Subst.) 7. $m\angle 2 = 90$ (Sub.
Prop.) 8. $\angle 2$ is a rt. $\angle$. (Def. rt. $\angle$) 9. $\overline{AD} \perp \overline{DB}$ (Def. $\perp$)
37. Incorrect Reasoning: There is no common seg. in the fig.
Proof: 1. $\overline{AB} \cong \overline{DE}$, $\overline{AC} \cong \overline{DF}$ (Given) 2. $AB = DE$, $AC =$
DF (Def. $\cong$ seg.) 3. $AB + BC = AC$, $DE + EF = DF$
(Seg. Add. Post.) 4. $DE + BC = DF$ (Subst.) 5. $EF =$
$DF - DE$, $BC = DF - DE$ (Sub. Prop.) 6. $EF = BC$
(Subst.) 7. $\overline{EF} \cong \overline{BC}$ (Def. $\cong$ seg.)

Algebra Review

1. $x > 7$ **3.** $x < 0$ **5.** $x > -3$

Lesson 2-7 Try This

1. $\angle XTW \cong \angle UTV$ **2.** $\angle MRT \cong \angle QRT$ **3.** $\angle 3 \cong \angle 5$

Exercise Set 2-7

1. $\angle PTQ \cong \angle RTS$ **3.** $\angle CBE \cong \angle DBF$ **5.** $\angle ABF \cong$
$\angle EBG$ (Common $\angle$ Th.) **7.** $\angle 2 \cong \angle EBC$ ($\cong$ Supp. Th.)
9. $\angle 3 \cong \angle 4$ (Th. 2.11) **11.** $\angle EBG \cong \angle BFG$ (Th. 2.1)
13. $m\angle 4 = 55$ ($\cong$ Supp. Th., Vert. $\angle$ Th.) **15.** 76
17. false **19.** true **21.** 1. $\angle LMQ \cong \angle PMN$ (Given)
2. $\angle LMP \cong \angle QMN$ (Common $\angle$ Th.) **23.** 1. $\angle 2 \cong \angle 3$,
$\overline{HP} \perp \overline{PQ}$, $\overline{JQ} \perp \overline{PQ}$ (Given) 2. $\angle HPQ$, $\angle JQP$ are rt. $\angle$s.
(Def. $\perp$ lines) 3. $m\angle HPQ = m\angle JQP = 90$ (Def. rt. $\angle$)
4. $m\angle 1 + m\angle 2 = 90$, $m\angle 3 + m\angle 4 = 90$ ($\angle$ Add. Post.)
5. $\angle 1$ is comp. to $\angle 2$. $\angle 4$ is comp. to $\angle 3$. (Def. comp. $\angle$s)
6. $\angle 1 \cong \angle 4$ ($\cong$ Comp. Th.) **25.** 1. $\overrightarrow{QT}$ bisects $\angle SQU$.
(Given) 2. $\overline{TQ} \perp \overline{PR}$ (Given) 3. $\angle 6 \cong \angle 7$ (Def. $\angle$ bis.)
4. $\angle PQT$ and $\angle RQT$ are rt. $\angle$s. (Def. $\perp$) 5. $m\angle PQT =$
$m\angle RQT = 90$ (Def. rt. $\angle$) 6. $m\angle 5 + m\angle 6 = 90$,
$m\angle 7 + m\angle 8 = 90$ ($\angle$ Add. Post.) 7. $\angle 5$ is comp. to $\angle 6$.
$\angle 8$ is comp. to $\angle 7$. (Def. comp. $\angle$s) 8. $\angle 5 \cong \angle 8$ ($\cong$
Comp. Th.) **27.** 1. $\angle 1 \cong \angle 2$, $\angle 3 \cong \angle 4$ (Given)
2. $\angle 2 \cong \angle 4$ (Vert. $\angle$ Th.) 3. $\angle 1 \cong \angle 4$ (Th. 1.1)
4. $\angle 1 \cong \angle 3$ (Th. 1.3) **29.** 1. $\angle BFE \cong \angle ECA$,
$\angle CFD \cong \angle ECA$ (Given) 2. $\angle BFE \cong \angle CFD$ (Th. 1.3)
3. $\angle BFD \cong \angle CFE$ (Common $\angle$ Th.) **31.** 1. $\overline{RS} \perp \overline{XY}$
(Given) 2. $\angle RSX$ and $\angle RSY$ are rt. $\angle$s. (Def. $\perp$ lines)
3. $\angle RSX \cong \angle RSY$ (Th. 2.4) **33.** 1. $\angle A$ and $\angle C$ are
supp., $\angle B$ and $\angle C$ are supp. (Given) 2. $m\angle B + m\angle C =$
180, $m\angle B + m\angle C = 180$ (Def. supp. $\angle$s) 3. $m\angle A +$
$m\angle C = m\angle B + m\angle C$ (Subst.) 4. $m\angle A = m\angle B$ (Sub.
Prop.) 5. $\angle A \cong \angle B$ (Def. $\cong \angle$s) **35.** The formula holds
for all acute $\angle$s.

Mixed Review

1. $\angle KGL$ **3.** $\angle JGK$ **5.** 48 **7.** $m\angle NGM$

Chapter Review

1. 1. b 2. b 3. a 4. c **2.** 40 **3.** $\angle AFB$, $\angle EFD$ **4.** 20
5. 90 **6.** $\overline{FD}$ **7.** yes **8.** no **9.** yes **10.** If a $\triangle$ is an
equilat. $\triangle$, then it is an isos. $\triangle$.
Given: $\triangle IJK$ is equilat. Prove: $\triangle IJK$ is isos.

11. 1. $\angle 1 \cong \angle 2$ (Vert. $\angle$ Th.) 2. $\angle 2 \cong \angle 3$ (Given)
3. $\angle 1 \cong \angle 3$ (Th. 1.1) 4. $\angle 3 \cong \angle 4$ (Vert. $\angle$ Th.)
5. $\angle 1 \cong \angle 4$ (Th. 1.1) **12.** $\overline{PR} \cong \overline{QS}$ **13.** 5
14. $\angle PTQ \cong \angle RTS$ **15.** 1. $\angle 3$ is supp. to $\angle 1$. (Given)
2. $m\angle 1 + m\angle 2 = 180$ (Given) 3. $\angle 2$ is supp. to $\angle 1$.
(Def. supp. $\angle$s) 4. $\angle 2 \cong \angle 3$ ($\cong$ Supp. Th.)

CHAPTER 3

Lesson 3-1 Try This

1. Answers may vary.   2. $\angle ADB$ and $\angle DBC$, $\angle DAC$ and $\angle ACB$

Exercise Set 3-1

1. plane $EDJK$ 3. plane $FEKL$ 5. Answers may vary: plane $ABCDEF \parallel$ plane $GHIJKL$, plane $ABHG \parallel$ plane $EDJK$, plane $BCIH \parallel$ plane $FEKL$, plane $CDJI \parallel$ plane $AFLG$ 7. $\overline{AG}$, $\overline{FL}$ 9. $\overline{GH}$, $\overline{JK}$ 11. $\angle 3$ and $\angle 7$, $\angle 2$ and $\angle 6$ 13. $\angle 2$ and $\angle 3$, $\angle 7$ and $\angle 6$ 15. $\angle 8$ and $\angle 6$ 17. corr.   19. alt. ext.   21. alt. int.   23. alt. ext.   25. $\angle 1$ and $\angle 6$, $\angle 5$ and $\angle 4$ 27. $\angle DCA$ 29. always   31. sometimes   33. sometimes   35. always   37. never   39. $\parallel$ lines   41. $\parallel$ lines   43. $\parallel$ lines   45. $\parallel$ and intersecting lines   47. $\overline{DF}$ 49. none   51. Answers may vary: $\overline{BE}$, $\overline{CE}$, $\overline{BF}$, $\overline{CF}$ 53. 12   55. $\parallel$ lines CD and EF cut by trans. $\overline{AK}$ 57. $A(-4, -1)$, $B(-2, 0)$, $D(2, 2)$, $E(4, 3)$; $F(6, 4)$, $G(8, 5)$, $H(-1, -2)$, $I(1, -1)$, $K(5, 1)$, $L(7, 2)$ 59. $\parallel$ lines in a coord. plane have = ratios of $\frac{y}{x}$.   61. 18 (3 groups of 6 $\parallel$ lines)   63–65. Answers may vary.   67. not always true

Mixed Review

1. $\angle PUQ$ and $\angle TUS$ 3. $\angle PUQ$ and $\angle QUR$ 5. $\angle TUR$

Lesson 3-2 Try This

1. 60   2. 42.5

Exercise Set 3-2

1. 115   3. 115   5. 65   7. 110   9. 28   11. 70   13. 70   15. 42   17. $\angle ACD$ 19. None have names.   21. 7   23. 6   25. $x = 53$, $y = 62$ 27. $x = 30$, $y = 90$ 29. $m\angle CEF = 75$, $m\angle CGH = 75$ 31. 1. $a \parallel b$ (Given) 2. $\angle 2 \cong \angle 3$ (If $\parallel$ lines are cut by a trans., alt. int. $\angle$s are $\cong$.) 3. $m\angle 1 + m\angle 3 = 180$ (Def. linear pair) 4. $m\angle 1 + m\angle 2 = 180$ (Subst.) 5. $\angle 1$ and $\angle 2$ are supp. (Def. supp. $\angle$s)   33. 28   35. 56   37. 1. $p \parallel q$ (Given) 2. $\angle 1 \cong \angle 6$ (If $\parallel$ lines are cut by a trans., alt. int. $\angle$s are $\cong$.) 3. $s \parallel t$ (Given) 4. $\angle 6 \cong \angle 7$ (If $\parallel$ lines are cut by a trans., alt. int. $\angle$s are $\cong$.) 5. $\angle 1 \cong \angle 7$ (Trans. Prop.)   39. 1. $\overline{AD} \parallel \overline{BE}$ (Given) 2. $\angle DAB$ and $\angle EBA$ are supp. (If $\parallel$ lines are cut by a trans., same-side int. $\angle$s are $\cong$.) 3. $m\angle DAB + m\angle EBA = 180$ (Def. supp.) 4. $\overline{CA}$ bisects $\angle DAB$. (Given) 5. $m\angle 1 = \frac{1}{2}m\angle DAB$ (Def. $\angle$ bis.) 6. $2m\angle 1 = m\angle DAB$ (Mult. Prop.) 7. $m\angle 2 + m\angle EBC = m\angle EBA$ ($\angle$ Add. Post.) 8. $2m\angle 1 + m\angle 2 + m\angle EBC = 180$ (Subst.) 9. $\angle 1$ and $\angle 2$ are comp. (Given) 10. $m\angle 1 + m\angle 2 = 90$ (Def. comp.) 11. $m\angle 1 + m\angle EBC = 90$ (Add. Prop.) 12. $m\angle EBC = m\angle 2$ (Subst.) 13. $\overline{BC}$ bisects $\angle ABE$ (Def. $\angle$ bis.)   41. 1. $\overline{AM} \parallel \overline{BD}$ (Given) 2. $\angle AMB \cong \angle CBD$ (If $\parallel$ lines are cut by a trans., corr. $\angle$s are $\cong$.) 3. $\overline{BD}$ bisects $\angle ABC$. (Given) 4. $\angle CBD \cong \angle ABD$ (Def. $\angle$ bis.) 5. $\angle ABD \cong \angle AMB$ (Trans. Prop.)   43. (Refer to figure for Class Exercises 1–6.) Given: $a \parallel b$ Prove: $\angle 1 \cong \angle 5$ 1. $a \parallel b$ (Given) 2. $\angle 2$ and $\angle 3$ are supp. (If $\parallel$ lines are cut by a trans., same-side int. $\angle$s are supp.) 3. $\angle 1$ and $\angle 3$ are supp. (Def. linear pair) 4. $\angle 1 \cong \angle 5$ (2 $\angle$s supp. to the same $\angle$ are $\cong$.)

Algebra Review

1. $x = 1$, $y = 9$ 3. $x = 5\frac{2}{3}$, $y = \frac{2}{3}$

Lesson 3-3 Try This

1. $m\angle 4 + m\angle 5 = 180$ 2. 11

Exercise Set 3-3

1. $a \parallel c$ (If 2 lines are cut by a trans. and corr. $\angle$s are $\cong$, the lines are $\parallel$.)   3. $c \parallel b$ (If 2 lines are cut by a trans. and same-side int. $\angle$s are supp., the lines are $\parallel$.)   5. $b \parallel c$ (If 2 lines are cut by a trans. and corr. $\angle$s are $\cong$, the lines are $\parallel$.)   7. yes (If 2 lines are cut by a trans. and same-side int. $\angle$s are supp., the lines are $\parallel$.)   9. $\angle 3$ and $\angle 7$, $\angle 1$ and $\angle 8$ 11. yes   13. no   15. 15   17. 12   19. 8   21. $x = 118$, $y = 0$ 23. $x = 15$, $y = -12$ 25. $\angle 1$ and $\angle 3$ are supp. (Given) 2. $\angle 1$ and $\angle 2$ are supp. (Def. linear pair) 3. $\angle 3 \cong \angle 2$ (Subst.) 4. $p \parallel q$ (If 2 lines are cut by a trans. and alt. int. $\angle$s are $\cong$, the lines are $\parallel$.)   27. 65   29. 1. $m \perp p$, $n \perp p$ (Given) 2. $\angle 1$ and $\angle 2$ are rt. $\angle$s. (Def. $\perp$) 3. $\angle 1 \cong \angle 2$ (Rt. $\angle$s are $\cong$.) 4. $m \parallel n$ (If 2 lines are cut by a trans. and corr. $\angle$s are $\cong$, the lines are $\parallel$.)   31. 1. $\angle BCD \cong \angle CDE$; $m\angle B + m\angle D = 180$ (Given) 2. $m\angle B + m\angle C = 180$ (Subst.) 3. $\overline{AB} \parallel \overline{CD}$ (If 2 lines are cut by a trans. and same-side int. $\angle$s are supp., the lines are $\parallel$.)   33. a. reflex: no, symmetric: yes, trans: no   b. reflex: no, symmetric: yes, trans: no

Mixed Review

1. acute   3. obtuse

Lesson 3-4 Try This

1. 40   2. acute

Exercise Set 3-4

1.   3. not possible   5.   7.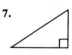

9. 70   11. 55   13. 50   15. 50   17. 104   19. 20, 60, 100; obtuse   21. 80, 80, 20   23. Given: $\triangle ABC$ is equiang. Prove: $m\angle A = m\angle B = m\angle C = 60$ 1. $\triangle ABC$ is equiang. (Given) 2. $m\angle A = m\angle B = m\angle C$ (Def. equiang.) 3. $m\angle A + m\angle B + m\angle C = 180$ (Sum of measures of $\angle$s of a $\triangle$ is 180.) 4. $3(m\angle A) = 180$ (Subst.) 5. $m\angle A = 60$ (Mult. Prop.) 6. $m\angle A = m\angle B = m\angle C = 60$ (Subst.)   25. 18, 18, 144   27. 31, 31, 118   29. 130   31. 40   33. 54   35. Extend $\overline{BA}$ to form a $\triangle CBF$. 1. $\overline{AB} \parallel \overline{DE}$ (Given) 2. $\angle D \cong \angle BFC$ (If $\parallel$ lines are cut by a trans., corr. $\angle$s are $\cong$.) 3. $m\angle B + m\angle C + m\angle BFC = 180$ (Sum of measures of $\angle$s of a $\triangle$ is 180.) 4. $m\angle B + m\angle C + m\angle D = 180$ (Subst.)   37. $\angle$s labeled 1 are $\cong$ (corr. $\angle$s); $\angle$s labeled 2 are $\cong$ (alt. int. $\angle$s); $m\angle 1 + m\angle 2 + m\angle 3 = 180$ 39. 80

Mixed Review

1. 45, 135

Lesson 3-5 Try This

1. 45 2. 100 3. ∠WYZ ≅ ∠WYX (All rt. ∠s are ≅.),
∠XWY ≅ ∠ZWY (An ∠ bis. forms 2 ≅ ∠s.), ∠WXY ≅
∠WZY (If 2 ∠s of 1 △ are ≅ to 2 ∠s of another △, then
the third ∠s are ≅.)

Exercise Set 3-5

1. 35 3. 105 5. 40 7. 170 9. 60 11. 78
13. 3. Rt. ∠s are ≅. 4. Reflex. Prop. 5. If 2 ∠s of one △
are ≅ to 2 ∠s of another △, the third ∠s are ≅.
15. 1. $\overline{AB} \perp \overline{BD}$, $\overline{CD} \perp \overline{BD}$ (Given) 2. ∠ABE is a rt. ∠.
∠CDE is a rt. ∠. (Def. ⊥) 3. ∠ABE ≅ ∠CDE (Rt. ∠s
are ≅.) 4. ∠1 ≅ ∠2 (Given) 5. ∠A ≅ ∠C (If 2 ∠s of
one △ are ≅ to 2 ∠s of another △, the third ∠s are ≅.)
17. 20 19. 52 21. 27 23. 65 and 25 25. m∠FAD =
120, m∠DEF = 105, m∠ADE = 60, m∠AFE = 75
27. 1. $\overline{CE}$ bisects ∠BCD. (Given) 2. ∠DCE ≅ ∠ECB
(Def. ∠ bis.) 3. m∠DCE = m∠ECB (Def. ≅ ∠s)
4. m∠DCE + m∠ECB = m∠DCB (∠Add. Post.)
5. 2m∠DCE = m∠DCB (Subst.) 6. m∠DCB = m∠A +
m∠B (Ext. ∠ Th.) 7. 2(m∠DCE) = m∠A + m∠B
(Subst.) 8. ∠A ≅ ∠B (Given) 9. m∠A = m∠B
(Def. ≅ ∠s) 10. 2(m∠DCE) = 2(m∠A) (Subst.)
11. m∠DCE = m∠A (Mult. Prop.) 12. ∠DCE ≅ ∠A
(Def. ≅ ∠s) 13. $\overline{CE} \parallel \overline{AB}$ (If 2 lines are cut by a trans.and
corr. ∠s are ≅, the lines are ∥.)
29. 1. Label E on line $\overline{AB}$ so that A is between E and B.
Draw auxiliary $\overline{AC}$. (2 pt. determine a line.) 2. m∠EAC =
m∠B + m∠BCA (Ext. ∠ Th.) 3. m∠EAC = m∠1 +
m∠DAC (∠ Add. Post.) 4. m∠1 + m∠DAC = m∠B +
m∠BCA (Subst.) 5. m∠2 = m∠DAC + m∠DCA (Ext. ∠
Th.) 6. m∠1 + m∠DAC + m∠2 = m∠B + m∠BCA +
m∠2 (Add. Prop.) 7. m∠1 + m∠DAC + m∠2 =
m∠B + m∠BCA + m∠DAC + m∠DCA (Subst.)
8. m∠1 + m∠2 = m∠B + m∠BCA + m∠DCA (Add.
Prop.) 9. m∠BCA + m∠DCA = m∠C (∠ Add. Post.)
10. m∠1 + m∠2 = m∠B + m∠C (Subst.) 31. 1. Draw
auxiliary $\overline{DB}$, label E so that B is between E and D. (2 pt.
determine a line.) 2. m∠ABE = m∠2 + m∠ADB (Ext. ∠
Th.) 3. m∠EBC = m∠BDC + m∠4 (Ext. ∠ Th.)
4. m∠1 = m∠ABE + m∠EBC (∠ Add. Post.) 5. m∠3 =
m∠ADB + m∠BDC (∠ Add. Post.) 6. m∠ABE +
m∠EBC = m∠2 + m∠3 + m∠4 (Subst.) 7. m∠1 =
m∠2 + m∠3 + m∠4 (Subst.)

Algebra Review

1. 9 and 17

Lesson 3-6 Try This

1. 11 2. 9 3. 60

Exercise Set 3-6

1. 1080 3. 2160 5. (p − 2)180 7. 13 9. 12
11. $128\frac{4}{7}$ 13. $147\frac{3}{11}$ 15. $158\frac{14}{17}$ 17. $51\frac{3}{7}$ 19. 20
21. m∠1 = m∠2 = 135 23. 24

25.

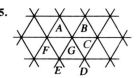

m∠AGB + m∠BGD = 180 so m∠AGB + m∠BGC +
m∠CGD = 180 and similarly m∠AGF + m∠FGE +
m∠EGD = 180. Thus, the sum of the measures of the
6 ∠s is 360. 27. m∠1 = 90, m∠2 = 135, m∠3 =
135, 90 + 135 + 135 = 360 29. 108 + 108 + 144 = 360
31. 6 33. 18 35. 90 37. 360 39. sum of ∠s =
(n − 4)180 41. 35; $d = \frac{n(n-3)}{2}$

Mixed Review

1. $\overline{ST} \cong \overline{VT}$ 3. ∠ABC ≅ ∠CBD

Chapter Review

1. ∠2 and ∠7, ∠3 and ∠6 2. ∠2 and ∠3, ∠6 and ∠7
3. ∠1 and ∠8, ∠5 and ∠4 4. ∠1 and ∠3, ∠2 and ∠4,
∠5 and ∠7, ∠6 and ∠8 5. Alt. int. ∠s are ≅.
6. Same-side int. ∠s are supp. 7. Corr. ∠s are ≅.
8. Alt. ext. ∠s are ≅. 9. 157 10. $\overline{ST} \parallel \overline{RU}$ (If alt. int. ∠s
are ≅, the lines are ∥.) 11. $\overline{SR} \parallel \overline{TU}$ (If same-side int. ∠s
are sup., the lines are ∥.) 12. $\overline{SR} \parallel \overline{TU}$ (If corr. ∠s are ≅,
the lines are ∥.) 13. $\overline{ST} \parallel \overline{RU}$ (If, in a plane, 2 lines are ⊥
to the same line, the lines are ∥.) 14. x = 2 15. x = 2
16. x = 160 17. 1. $\overline{AB} \parallel \overline{CD}$, ∠1 ≅ ∠2 (Given)
2. ∠1 ≅ ∠ABC (Th. 3.2) 3. ∠2 ≅ ∠ABC (Subst.)
4. $\overline{AD} \parallel \overline{BC}$ (Post. 14) 18. 92 19. 50 20. 10
21. ∠UST 22. 55 23. 85 24. ∠SUT, ∠2, ∠T
25. 1440 26. 25 27. 120 28. 45

CHAPTER 4

Lesson 4-1 Try This

1. $\overline{VU}$, $\angle W$ **2.** 73, 14

Exercise Set 4-1

1. $\overline{DE}$ **3.** $\angle E$ **5.** $\angle C$ **7.** $\triangle CBA$ **9.** 17 **11.** 95
13. $\angle A \cong \angle F$, $\angle B \cong \angle E$, $\angle C \cong \angle D$, $\overline{AB} \cong \overline{FE}$,
$\overline{AC} \cong \overline{FD}$, $\overline{BC} \cong \overline{ED}$ **15.** $\angle K \cong \angle L$, $\angle J \cong \angle M$,
$\angle H \cong \angle N$, $\overline{KJ} \cong \overline{LM}$, $\overline{JH} \cong \overline{MN}$, $\overline{KH} \cong \overline{LN}$ **17.** 17
19. 68 **21.** 27 **23.** $\angle T$ **25.** $\overline{AT}$ **27.** $\overline{MA}$ **29.** 50
31. 130 **33.** 20 **35.** 25 **37.** 70 **39.** 3 **41.** yes
43. no **45.** $\overline{AB}$, $\overline{AC}$, and $\overline{AD}$ or $\overline{BE}$, $\overline{CE}$, and $\overline{DE}$ **47.** $\angle L$
49. $\overline{JK}$ **51. a.** 4 **b.** 2 The $\triangle$s are $\cong$ if either $\triangle ABC \cong$
$\triangle XYZ$ or $\triangle ABC \cong \triangle YXZ$.

Mixed Review

1. 16 **3.** 97 **5.** obtuse

Lesson 4-2 Try This

1. ASA **2.** SAS **3.** SSS

Exercise Set 4-2

1. $\triangle ABC \cong \triangle DFE$, SAS **3.** $\triangle ABC \cong \triangle FDE$, SSS
5. No conclusion can be made. **7.** $\overline{AC} \cong \overline{EF}$ **9.** $\overline{WX} \cong$
$\overline{YZ}$ **11.** $\angle 2$ **13.** $\angle BCD$, $\overline{CD}$, or $\angle 1$, $\overline{BD}$ **15.** SAS
17. $\triangle DCE$ **19.** $\overline{BE} \cong \overline{CE}$ by Corr. parts of $\cong \triangle$s
are $\cong$. **21.** Place through the midpt. of $\overline{AD}$ and $\overline{BC}$.
$\overline{AF} \cong \overline{FD}$, $\overline{BF} \cong \overline{FC}$, $\angle AFB \cong \angle CFD$ (Vert. $\angle$s are $\cong$.);
$\triangle AFB \cong \triangle DFC$ by SAS. $\overline{AB} \cong \overline{DC}$ by Corr. parts of
$\triangle$s are $\cong$. **23.** $9x - 48 = 6x - 15$, $3x = 33$, $x = 11$,
$AB = 16$, $DE = 16$, $AC = 10$, $DF = 10$, $\overline{AB} \cong \overline{DE}$, $\overline{AC} \cong$
$\overline{DF}$. By SAS, $\triangle ABC \cong \triangle DEF$. **25.** 79 **27.** $(-4, 4)$ or
$(-4, -2)$ **29.** $(2, 3)$ or $(6, 3)$ **31.** $\triangle FAB \cong \triangle FED$,
$\triangle FAC \cong \triangle FEC$, $\triangle FAD \cong \triangle FEB$, $\triangle FBC \cong \triangle FDC$
33. ASA, $m\angle A = 61 = m\angle D$, $AC = 14 + BC = BD$,
$m\angle ECA = 29 = m\angle FBD$ **35.** $AD = DC = DB$,
$m\angle ADC = m\angle ADB = m\angle CDB = 90$. By SAS,
$\triangle ADC \cong \triangle BDC$, $\triangle ADC \cong \triangle ADB$, and $\triangle BDC \cong$
$\triangle ADB$. **37.** Answers may vary.

Mixed Review

1. 45 **3.** 45 **5.** 60 **7.** $\triangle GFH \cong \triangle JKL$, SAS
9. $\triangle XYW \cong \triangle DEC$, SSS

Exercise Set 4-3

1. 1. Given 2. Given 3. Given 4. ASA **3.** 1. Given 2. Def.
$\angle$ bisector 3. Reflex. Prop. 4. Given 5. $\triangle RTQ \cong \triangle RTS$
5. 1. $\overline{DE} \cong \overline{DF}$ (Given) 2. $\overline{DH}$ bisects $\overline{EF}$. (Given)
3. $\overline{EH} \cong \overline{FH}$ (Def. seg. bis.) 4. $\overline{DH} \cong \overline{DH}$ (Reflex. Prop.)
5. $\triangle DHE \cong \triangle DHF$ (SSS) **7.** 1. $\overline{AB} \cong \overline{CD}$ (Given)
2. $\angle 1 \cong \angle 4$ (Given) 3. $\overline{AC} \cong \overline{CA}$ (Reflex. Prop.)
4. $\triangle ABC \cong \triangle CDA$ (SSS) **9.** 1. $\overline{HI} \cong \overline{KI}$ (Given)
2. $\angle 1 \cong \angle 2$ (Given) 3. $\overline{JI} \cong \overline{IL}$ (Given) 4. $\triangle HIJ \cong \triangle KIL$
(SAS) **11.** $\triangle ABC \cong \triangle ADC$ by SSS **13.** $\triangle ABC \cong$
$\triangle ADC$ by SAS **15.** $\triangle EFI \cong \triangle GFH$ by SAS
17. 1. $\overline{BD} \perp$ plane M (Given) 2. $\overline{BD} \perp \overline{AB}$, $\overline{BD} \perp \overline{CB}$
(If a line is $\perp$ to a plane at B, it is $\perp$ to all lines in the plane
that contain B.) 3. $\angle ABD$, $\angle CDB$ are rt. $\angle$s ($\perp$ seg. form
rt. $\angle$s.) 4. $\angle ABD \cong \angle CBD$ (All rt. $\angle$s are $\cong$.) 5. $\overline{AB}$

$\overline{BC}$ (Given) 6. $\overline{BD} \cong \overline{BD}$ (Reflex. Prop.) 7. $\triangle ABD \cong$
$\triangle CBD$ (SAS) **19.** 1. $\overline{AI}$ bisects $\angle BAC$ (Given) 2. $\angle BAI \cong$
$\angle CAI$ (Def. $\angle$ bisector) 3. $\overline{AB} \cong \overline{AC}$ (Given) 4. $\overline{AI} \cong \overline{AI}$
(Reflex. Prop.) 5. $\triangle ABI \cong \triangle ACI$ (SAS) **21.** The SSS
Post. implies that a $\triangle$ of fixed side length has a unique
shape, hence it is less likely to collapse. **23.** $BD = CD$, so
$9x - 2 = 4x + 3$, $5x = 5$, $x = 1$. $AB = 12$, $AC = 12$, so
$\overline{AB} \cong \overline{AC}$. $\overline{AD} \cong \overline{AD}$ (Reflex. Prop.) so $\triangle ABD \cong \triangle ACD$
by SSS. **25.** By the Vert. $\angle$ Th., $m\angle AOD = m\angle BOC$. So
$2x + 9 = 3x + 5$, $x = 4$. $AO = 14$, $OB = 14$, $OC = 15$,
$DO = 15$, so $\overline{AB}$ and $\overline{CD}$ bisect each other. **27.** sometimes
true **29.** always true; If $\overline{AB} \cong \overline{AC}$ and $\overline{BD} \cong \overline{DC}$ then by
Reflex. Prop., $\overline{AD} \cong \overline{AD}$ and SSS, $\triangle ADB \cong \triangle ADC$, so
$\angle BAD \cong \angle CAD$.

Mixed Review

1. skew or $\parallel$ **3.** interior **5.** lies in the same plane also

Exercise Set 4-4

1. AB **3.** $m\angle C$ **5.** 1. Given 2. Given 3. An $\angle$ bis. forms
$2 \cong \angle$s. 4. $\overline{BD} \cong \overline{BD}$ 5. SAS 6. Corr. parts of $\cong \triangle$s are
$\cong$. **7.** 1. $\overline{AC}$ bisects $\overline{BD}$, $\overline{BD}$ bisects $\overline{AC}$ (Given) 2. $\overline{BO} \cong$
$\overline{DO}$, $\overline{CO} \cong \overline{AO}$ (A seg. bis. forms $2 \cong$ seg.) 3. $\angle 1 \cong \angle 2$
(Vert. $\angle$.) 4. $\triangle BOC \cong \triangle DOA$ (SAS) 5. $\overline{CB} \cong \overline{AD}$ (Corr.
parts of $\cong \triangle$s are $\cong$.) **9.** 1. D bisects $\overline{CE}$. (Given)
2. $\overline{CD} \cong \overline{ED}$ (A seg. bis. forms $2 \cong$ seg.) 3. $\angle 1 \cong \angle 2$,
$\angle C \cong \angle E$ (Given) 4. $\triangle BCD \cong \triangle FED$ (ASA) 5. $\overline{BD} \cong$
$\overline{FD}$ (Corr. parts of $\cong \triangle$s are $\cong$.) **11.** 1. O is the midpt. of
$\overline{AB}$ and $\overline{CD}$. (Given) 2. $\overline{AO} \cong \overline{BO}$, $\overline{DO} \cong \overline{CO}$ (A seg. midpt.
forms $2 \cong$ seg.) 3. $\angle AOD \cong \angle BOC$ (Vert. $\angle$ Th.)
4. $\triangle AOD \cong \triangle BOC$ (SAS) 5. $\angle A \cong \angle B$ (Corr. parts
of $\cong \triangle$s are $\cong$.) 6. $\overline{AD} \parallel \overline{BC}$ (If 2 lines are cut by a trans.
and a pair of alt. int. $\angle$s are $\cong$, the lines are $\parallel$.)
13. Since $AP = DP$, $BP = CP$, and $\angle APB \cong \angle CPD$
(Vert. $\angle$ Th.), $\triangle APB \cong \triangle DPC$ by SAS. Therefore $AB =$
CD, as corr. parts of $\cong \triangle$s are $\cong$. **15.** 1. $AB \cong DC$,
$\angle A \cong \angle D$ (Given) 2. $\overline{AD} \cong \overline{AD}$ (Reflex. Prop.)
3. $\triangle ABD \cong \triangle DCA$ (SAS) 4. $\overline{BD} \cong \overline{AC}$ (Corr. parts
of $\cong \triangle$s are $\cong$.) 5. $\overline{BC} \cong \overline{BC}$ (Reflex. Prop.) 6. $\triangle ABC \cong$
$\triangle DCB$ (SSS) 7. $\angle B \cong \angle C$ (Corr. parts of $\cong \triangle$s are $\cong$.)
17. 26 **19.** Given: $m\angle BGC = m\angle DGC = 65$, $\overline{BG} \cong \overline{DG}$
Prove: $\overline{BF} \cong \overline{DF}$ 1. $m\angle BGC = m\angle DGC$ (Given)
2. $\angle BGC \cong \angle DGC$ ($\angle$s of $=$ measure are $\cong$.)
3. $\angle BGF \cong \angle DGF$ ($\cong$ Supp. Th.) 4. $\overline{BG} \cong \overline{DG}$ (Given)
5. $\overline{GF} \cong \overline{GF}$ (Reflex. Prop.) 6. $\triangle BGF \cong \triangle DGF$ (SAS)
7. $\overline{BF} \cong \overline{DF}$ (Corr. parts of $\cong \triangle$s are $\cong$.) **21.** Given: $\angle A$
and $\angle B$ are rt. $\angle$s. $m\angle CAB = m\angle DBA = 32$ Prove:
$\angle D \cong \angle C$ 1. $\angle A$ and $\angle B$ are rt. $\angle$s. (Given) 2. $\angle A \cong$
$\angle B$ (All rt. $\angle$s are $\cong$.) 3. $\angle CAB \cong \angle DBA$ (Given)
4. $\angle D \cong \angle C$ (If 2 $\angle$s of a $\triangle$ are $\cong$ to 2 $\angle$s of another $\triangle$,
then the third $\angle$s are $\cong$.) **23.** $AC = \sqrt{13}$, $DF = \sqrt{13}$
25. $\triangle ABC \cong \triangle DEF$ by SSS. So $\angle A \cong \angle D$, as corr.
parts of $\cong \triangle$s are $\cong$. **27.** 1. $AB \cong CF$, $\angle 1 \cong \angle 2$,
$\overline{AF} \perp \overline{AB}$, $\overline{BG} \perp \overline{CF}$ (Given) 2. $\angle IAB$ and $\angle IGF$ are rt.
$\angle$s. ($\perp$ lines meet to form rt. $\angle$s.) 3. $\angle IAB \cong \angle IGF$ (All
rt. $\angle$s are $\cong$.) 4. $\triangle ABI \cong \triangle GFI$ (ASA) 5. $\overline{AI} \cong \overline{GI}$ (Corr.
parts of $\cong \triangle$s are $\cong$.) 6. $\overline{IH} \cong \overline{IH}$ (Reflex. Prop.)
7. $\triangle AHI \cong \triangle GHI$ (SSS) **29.** Draw auxiliary line AC. 1.
$\overline{AD} \cong \overline{AB}$, $\overline{CD} \cong \overline{CB}$ (Given) 2. $\overline{AC} \cong \overline{AC}$ (Reflex. Prop.)

3. $\triangle ACD \cong \triangle ACB$ (SSS) **4.** $\angle D \cong \angle B$ (Corr. parts of $\cong \triangle s$ are $\cong$.) **31.** Each face is identical, so the distance from a vertex to an opp. midpt. will be the same for each face ($AB = AC = DC = DE$), and the distance between 2 adj. midpt. will be the same for each face ($BC = CE$). The 2 $\triangle s$ are then $\cong$ by SSS.

Algebra Review

1. 46, 52, 82 **3.** 98, 27, 55

Lesson 4-5 Try This

1. You can prove $\triangle BAE \cong \triangle BCD$ by SAS. Then $\angle 3 \cong \angle 4$ by corr. parts of $\cong \triangle s$. **3.** 1. Given 2. $\triangle ABE \cong \triangle CBD$, SAS 3. Corr. parts of $\cong \triangle s$ are $\cong$., 4. $\angle 2 \cong \angle 5$, Supp. of $\cong \angle s$ are $\cong$.

Exercise Set 4-5

1. $\triangle ABC$, $\triangle DCB$ **3.** $\triangle ADC$, $\triangle BCD$ or $\triangle ACB$, $\triangle BDA$ **5.** $\triangle ACB$, $\triangle BDA$ or $\triangle ADC$, $\triangle BCD$ **7.** $\overline{BC}$ **9.** $\angle CAF$ **11.** 1. $\angle ADC \cong \angle ACD$ (Given) 2. $\angle 1 \cong \angle 2$ (Given) 3. $\overline{CD} \cong \overline{CD}$ (Reflex. Prop.) 4. $\triangle BCD \cong \triangle EDC$ (ASA) 5. $\overline{BC} \cong \overline{ED}$ (Corr. parts of $\cong \triangle s$ are $\cong$.) **13.** 1. $\angle 1 \cong \angle 2$ (Given) 2. $\overline{PQ} \cong \overline{RQ}$ (Given) 3. $\angle Q \cong \angle Q$ (Reflex. Prop.) 4. $\triangle PQV \cong \triangle RQT$ (ASA) 5. $\overline{QT} \cong \overline{QV}$ (Corr. parts of $\cong \triangle s$ are $\cong$.) **15.** $AB = CD = 19$ **17.** 11 **19.** 1. $\overline{ST} \cong \overline{VW}$, $\angle S \cong \angle V$, $\angle STR \cong \angle VWU$ (Given) 2. $\triangle RST \cong \triangle UVW$ (ASA) 3. $\angle R \cong \angle U$ (Corr. parts of $\cong \triangle s$ are $\cong$.) 4. $\overline{RS} \parallel \overline{UV}$ (If 2 lines are cut by a trans. and alt. int. $\angle s$ are $\cong$, the lines are $\parallel$.) **21.** 1. $\angle 1 \cong \angle 2$ (Given) 2. $\angle EDB \cong \angle CDA$ (Common $\angle$ Th.) 3. $\overline{BD} \cong \overline{AD}$ (Given) 4. $\overline{ED} \cong \overline{CD}$ (Given) 5. $\triangle EDB \cong \triangle CDA$ (SAS) 6. $\angle 5 \cong \angle 6$ (Corr. parts of $\cong \triangle s$ are $\cong$.) **23.** 1. $\overline{AE} \cong \overline{DF}$, $\angle E \cong \angle F$, $\overline{EC} \cong \overline{FB}$ (Given) 2. $\triangle AEC \cong \triangle DFB$ (SAS) 3. $\overline{AC} \cong \overline{DB}$ (Corr. parts of $\cong \triangle s$ are $\cong$.) 4. $\overline{AB} \cong \overline{CD}$ (Common Seg. Th.) **25.** 1. $\angle ADC \cong \angle ACD$ (Given) 2. $\overline{CD} \cong \overline{CD}$ (Reflex. Prop.) 3. $\triangle ADC \cong \triangle ACD$ (ASA) 4. $\overline{AC} \cong \overline{AD}$ (Corr. parts. of $\cong \triangle s$ are $\cong$.) 5. $\overline{BC} \cong \overline{ED}$ (Given) 6. $\overline{AB} \cong \overline{AE}$ (Seg. Add. Post.) **27.** A—36 B—24 C—8

Algebra Review

1. 4 **3.** 108 or 84

Lesson 4-6 Try This

$BA = BD = 14$ by Th. 4.2. $BD = DC = 14$, so $\angle DBC \cong \angle DCB$ by Th. 4.1.

Exercise Set 4-6

1. $\overline{BD} \cong \overline{CD}$ (Th. 4.2) **3.** $\angle 1 \cong \angle 2$ (Th. 4.1) **5.** $\angle ABC \cong \angle ACB$ (Th. 4.1) **7.** 14 **9.** 14 **11.** 59 **13.** 3 **15.** 9 **17.** 9 **19.** 1. Given 2. Base $\angle s$ of an isos. $\triangle$ are $\cong$. 3. Given 4. ASA 5. Corr. parts of $\cong \triangle s$ are $\cong$. 7. Sides opp. $\cong \angle s$ are $\cong$. 8. Def. isos. $\triangle$. **21.** $4x = 6x - 15$, $2x = 15$, $4x = 30$, $AB = BC = 30$ **23.** By Th. 4.1, $m\angle X = m\angle Z$, so $4x + 60 = 14x + 30$. $30 = 10x$, $x = 3$, $m\angle X = m\angle Z = 72$, $m\angle Y = 2x + 30 = 36$. **25.** 1. $\triangle ADC$ is isos. with vertex A (Given) 2. $\overline{AC} \cong \overline{AD}$ (Def. isos. $\triangle$) 3. $\angle ACD \cong \angle ADC$ (Isos. $\triangle$ Th.) 4. $\overline{BC} \cong \overline{ED}$ (Given) 5. $\overline{BD} \cong \overline{EC}$ (Common Seg. Th.) 6. $\triangle AEC \cong \triangle ABD$ (SAS) 7. $\overline{AE} \cong \overline{AB}$ (Corr. parts of $\cong \triangle s$ are $\cong$.) 8. $\triangle ABE$ is isos. (Def. isos. $\triangle$)

27. 1. $\overline{AB} \cong \overline{AC}$ (Given) 2. $\angle ABC \cong \angle ACB$ (Isos. $\triangle$ Th.) 3. $\overline{BE}$ bisects $\angle ABC$, $\overline{CD}$ bisects $\angle ACB$. (Given) 4. $m\angle ABE = \frac{1}{2}m\angle ABC$, $m\angle ACD = \frac{1}{2}m\angle ACB$ ($\angle$ Bis. Th.) 5. $\angle ABE \cong \angle ACD$ (Trans. Prop.) 6. $\angle A \cong \angle A$ (Reflex. Prop.) 7. $\triangle ABE \cong \triangle ACD$ (ASA) 8. $\overline{AD} \cong \overline{AE}$ (Corr. parts of $\cong \triangle s$ are $\cong$.) **29.** $m\angle ABC = m\angle BAC + m\angle BCA$, by the Ext. $\angle$ Th. If $m\angle DBC = 2m\angle DAC$, then $m\angle DAC = m\angle BCA$, so by Th. 4.2 $AB = BC$. **31.** Given: $\triangle ABC$ is isos. with base $\overline{BC}$. D is midpt. of $\overline{BC}$. Prove: $\overline{AD}$ bisects $\angle BAC$ 1. $\triangle ABC$ is isos. with base $\overline{BC}$. (Given) 2. D is midpt. of BC. (Given) 3. $\overline{BD} \cong \overline{CD}$ (A midpt. forms 2 $\cong$ seg.) 4. $\overline{AB} \cong \overline{AC}$ (Def. of isos. $\triangle$) 5. $\overline{AD} \cong \overline{AD}$ (Reflex. Prop.) 6. $\triangle ABD \cong \triangle ACD$ (SSS) 7. $\angle BAD \cong \angle CAD$ (Corr. parts of $\cong \triangle s$ are $\cong$.) 8. $\overline{AD}$ bisects $\angle BAC$. (Def. $\angle$ bisector) **33.** $\angle ABE$ and $\angle CDE$ are $\cong$. $\angle ABE$ and $\angle CDE$ are rt. $\angle s$. $\overline{BE} \cong \overline{DE}$, so by Th. 4.1 $\angle EBD \cong \angle EDB$. $m\angle ABE + m\angle EBD = m\angle CDE + m\angle EDB$, so, by the $\angle$ Add. Post. $\angle ABD \cong \angle CDB$. **35.** 1. $\overline{AB} \cong \overline{FE}$, $\angle A \cong \angle F$ (Given) 2. $\overline{AD} \cong \overline{FC}$ (Given) 3. $\overline{AC} \cong \overline{FD}$ (Common Seg. Th.) 4. $\triangle ABC \cong \triangle FED$ (SAS) 5. $\angle ACB \cong \angle FDE$ (Corr. parts of $\cong \triangle s$ are $\cong$.) 6. $\overline{GD} \cong \overline{GC}$ (If 2 $\angle s$ of a $\triangle$ are $\cong$, then the sides opp. them are $\cong$.) 7. $\triangle CDG$ is isos. (Def. isos. $\triangle$) **37.** 1. $\angle B \cong \angle C$ (Given) 2. $\overline{BC} \cong \overline{CB}$ (Reflex. Prop.) 3. $\triangle ABC \cong \triangle ACB$ (ASA: $\angle B \cong \angle C$, $\overline{BC} \cong \overline{CB}$, $\angle C \cong \angle B$) 4. $\overline{AB} \cong \overline{AC}$ (Corr. parts of $\cong \triangle s$ are $\cong$.) **39.** No; it assumes that A, B, C, D are collinear and that $\angle 3$ and $\angle 4$ are ext. $\angle s$ of $\triangle EBC$. **41.** Answers may vary; e.g., if $m\angle DCB = m\angle DBC$ and $m\angle DAC = m\angle DCA$.

Mixed Review

1. 52, 60, 68; acute **3.** 5

Exercise Set 4-7

1. $\angle CAB \cong \angle DAB$ or $\angle ABC \cong \angle ABD$ **3.** $\angle CAB \cong \angle DAB$ or $\angle ABC \cong \angle ABD$ **5.** $\angle CAB \cong \angle DAB$ and $\angle ABC \cong \angle ABD$, or $\angle CAB \cong \angle DAB$ and $\overline{AC} \cong \overline{AD}$, or $\angle ABC \cong \angle ABD$ and $\overline{CB} \cong \overline{DB}$ **7.** $\angle BCA \cong \angle EDF$ or $\angle A \cong \angle F$ **9.** $\overline{AB} \cong \overline{EF}$ or $\overline{BC} \cong \overline{ED}$ **11.** 1. $\angle B$ and $\angle D$ are rt. $\angle s$. (Given) 2. $\triangle ABC$ and $\triangle CDA$ are rt. $\triangle s$. (Def. rt. $\triangle$) 3. $\overline{AB} \cong \overline{CD}$ (Given) 4. $\overline{AC} \cong \overline{AC}$ (Reflex. Prop.) 5. $\triangle ABC \cong \triangle CDA$ (HL Th.) **13.** 1. $\angle A$ and $\angle B$ are rt. $\angle s$. (Given) 2. $\triangle AOD$ and $\triangle BOC$ are rt. $\triangle s$. (Def. rt. $\triangle$) 3. $\overline{OD} \cong \overline{OC}$ (Given) 4. O is midpt. of $\overline{AB}$. (Given) 5. $\overline{AO} \cong \overline{OB}$ (A midpt. forms 2 $\cong$ seg.) 6. $\triangle AOD \cong \triangle BOC$ (HL Th.) **15.** 1. $\angle A$ and $\angle B$ are rt. $\angle s$. (Given) 2. $\angle A \cong \angle B$ (All rt. $\angle s$ are $\cong$.) 3. O is midpt. of $\overline{AB}$. (Given) 4. $\overline{AO} \cong \overline{OB}$ (A midpt. forms 2 $\cong$ seg.) 5. $\angle AOD \cong \angle BOC$ (Given) 6. $\triangle AOD \cong \triangle BOC$ (ASA) **17.** $\overline{DE} \perp \overline{AC}$, $\overline{BF} \perp \overline{AC}$ (Given) 2. $\angle DEC$ and $\angle BFA$ are rt. $\angle s$. ($\perp$ seg. form rt. $\angle s$.) 3. $\triangle DEC$ and $\triangle BFA$ are rt. $\triangle s$. (Def. rt. $\triangle$) 4. $\overline{DE} \cong \overline{BF}$ (Given) 5. $\overline{CD} \cong \overline{AB}$ (Given) 6. $\triangle DEC \cong \triangle BFA$ (HL Theorem) 7. $\angle 1 \cong \angle 2$ (Corr. parts of $\cong \triangle s$ are $\cong$.) **19.** 1. $\overline{DE} \perp \overline{AC}$, $\overline{BF} \perp \overline{AC}$ (Given) 2. $\angle DEC$ and $\angle BFA$ are rt. $\angle s$. ($\perp$ seg. form rt. $\angle s$.) 3. $\triangle DEC$ and $\triangle BFA$ are rt. $\triangle s$. (Def. rt. $\triangle$) 4. $\overline{DE} \cong \overline{BF}$ (Given) 5. $\overline{CD} \cong \overline{AB}$ (Given) 6. $\triangle DEC \cong \triangle BFA$ (HL Theorem) 7. $\overline{AF} \cong \overline{CE}$ (Corr. parts of $\triangle s$ are $\cong$.) 8. $\overline{AE} \cong \overline{CF}$ (Common Seg. Th.) **21.** 1. $\overline{CD} \perp \overline{AB}$, $\overline{BE} \perp \overline{AC}$ (Given) 2. $\angle CDB$ and $\angle BEC$ are rt. $\angle s$. ($\perp$ seg. form rt.

∠s.) 3. △CDB and △BEC are rt. △s. (Def. rt. △) 4. $\overline{BE} \cong$ $\overline{CD}$ (Given) 5. $\overline{BC} \cong \overline{BC}$ (Reflex. Prop.) 6. △BEC $\cong$ △CDB (HL Th.) 7. ∠ECB $\cong$ ∠DBC (Corr. parts of $\cong$ △s are $\cong$.) 8. $\overline{AB} \cong \overline{AC}$ (Converse of Isos. △ Th.) 9. △ABC is isos. (Def. isos. △) 23. 26. **25.** △APD, △BPD, △CPD are all rt. △s since $\overline{DP}$ is $\perp$ to the roof and $\overline{AP}, \overline{BP}, \overline{CP}$ are all in the plane of the roof. It is given that $\overline{AD} \cong \overline{BD} \cong \overline{CD}$ and by the Reflex. Prop. $\overline{DP} \cong \overline{DP}$, so △APD $\cong$ △BPD $\cong$ △CPD by the HL Th. Then $\overline{AP} \cong \overline{BP} \cong \overline{CP}$ since they are corr. parts of $\cong$ △s, so $AP = BP = CP$.
27. Given: rt. △ABC and rt. △DEF, $\overline{AC} \cong \overline{DF}$, ∠A $\cong$ ∠D, ∠B and ∠E are rt. ∠s. Prove: △ABC $\cong$ △DEF 1. ∠B and ∠E are rt. ∠s. (Given) 2. ∠B $\cong$ ∠E (Rt. ∠s are $\cong$.) 3. ∠A $\cong$ ∠D (Given) 4. $\overline{AC} \cong \overline{DF}$ (Given) 5. △ABC $\cong$ △DEF (AAS)
29. Given: isos. △ABC with D the midpt. of base $\overline{BC}$, $\overline{DE} \perp \overline{BA}, \overline{DF} \perp \overline{AC}$ Prove: $\overline{DE} \cong \overline{DF}$ 1. $\overline{DE} \perp \overline{BA}$, $\overline{DF} \perp \overline{AC}$ (Given) 2. ∠DEB and ∠DFC are rt. ∠s. ($\perp$ lines form rt. ∠s.) 3. △DEB and △DFC are rt. △s. (Def. rt. △) 4. D is midpt. of $\overline{BC}$. (Given) 5. $\overline{BD} \cong \overline{DC}$ (A midpt. forms 2 $\cong$ seg.) 6. △ABC is isos. (Given) 7. ∠B $\cong$ ∠C (Isos. △ Th.) 8. △DBE $\cong$ △DCF (HA Theorem) 9. $\overline{DE} \cong \overline{DF}$ (Corr. parts of $\cong$ △s are $\cong$.) **31.** If 2 sides and the not included ∠ of a △ are $\cong$ respectively to 2 sides and the not included ∠ of another △, the △s are $\cong$.

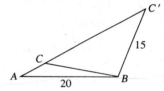

SSA should not be a post. because the measure of the included ∠ may vary.

Algebra Review
1. $y^3 - 2y^2 + 3y$ **3.** $y - 5$ **5.** $y - 4$

Lesson 4-8 Try This
1. a. median **b.** alt. **2.** E is on the $\perp$ bis. of $\overline{BD}$.

Exercise Set 4-8
1. an alt. **3.** an alt., a median, a $\perp$ bis. **5.** $\overline{AD}$ is a median for △ACE and a $\perp$ bis. of $\overline{EC}$, △AEC is isos, ∠1 $\cong$ ∠2, $\overline{BG} \cong \overline{GF}$. **7.** $\overline{AD}$ is an ∠ bis. of ∠BAF, $\overline{AC} \cong \overline{AE}$, $\overline{BG} \cong \overline{FG}$, △AEC is isos. **9.** △ABG **11.** Th. 4.6 **13.** 9 **15.** Th. 4.7 **17.** an ∠ bis. **19.** 8 **21.** By Th. 4.9, P lies on the ∠ bis. As 2 pt. determine only 1 line (Post. 2), $\overline{BP}$ is the ∠ bis. of ∠B. **23.** yes **25.** $AC = \sqrt{3^2 + 4^2} = \sqrt{25} = 5$ $AB = \sqrt{0^2 + 5^2} = \sqrt{25} = 5$, so $AB = AC$ and △ABC is isos. with base $\overline{BC}$. In an isos. △, the median to the base is the alt. to the base (by Th. 4.6). As $\overline{AD}$ is the median to the base, it is also an alt. **27.** By Ex. 25, $\overline{AD}$ is an alt. to the base of the isos. △ABC. By Th. 4.6, $\overline{AD}$ bisects ∠CAB. By Th. 4.10, D is equidistant from $\overline{AC}$ and $\overline{AB}$. **29.** The transmitter station must be built on the ∠ bis. of the ∠ formed by q and p, but not within the city. **31.** Given: q is the $\perp$ bis. of $\overline{AB}$ and P is on q. Prove:

$\overline{PA} \cong \overline{PB}$ 1. q is the $\perp$ bis. of $\overline{AB}$ (Given) 2. C is the midpt. of $\overline{AB}$, ∠PCA and ∠PCB are rt. ∠s. (Def. $\perp$ bis.) 3. ∠PCA $\cong$ ∠PCB (All rt. ∠s are $\cong$.) 4. $\overline{AC} \cong \overline{BC}$ (A midpt. forms 2 $\cong$ seg.) 5. $\overline{PC} \cong \overline{PC}$ (Reflex. Prop.) 6. △PCA $\cong$ △PCB (SAS) 7. $\overline{PA} \cong \overline{PB}$ (Corr. parts of $\cong$ △s are $\cong$.)
33. Given: P is on the ∠ bis. $\overline{BP}$. Prove: $\overline{PA} \cong \overline{PC}$ 1. ∠PAB and ∠PCB are rt. ∠s. ($\perp$ seg. form rt. ∠s.) 2. △PAB and △PCB are rt. △s. (Def. rt. △) 3. $\overline{BP}$ is ∠ bis. for ∠ABC. (Given) 4. ∠PBA $\cong$ ∠PBC (∠ bis. forms 2 $\cong$ ∠s.) 5. $\overline{PB} \cong \overline{PB}$ (Reflex. Prop.) 6. △PAB $\cong$ △PCB (HA Th.) 7. $\overline{PA} \cong \overline{PC}$ (Corr. parts of $\cong$ △s are $\cong$.) **35.** Given: isos. △ABC, base $\overline{BC}$, $\overline{AD}$ is an alt. Prove: $\overline{AD}$ is a median and $\perp$ bis. of △ABC. 1. $\overline{AD}$ is an alt. to the base of isos. △ABC. (Given) 2. $\overline{AD}$ bisects $\overline{BC}$. (Th. 4.6) 3. $\overline{AD} \perp \overline{BC}$ (Alt. is $\perp$ to base.) 4. D is the midpt. of $\overline{BC}$ (Def. bis.) 5. $\overline{AD}$ is a median of △ABC. (Def. median) 6. $\overline{AD}$ is $\perp$ bis. of $\overline{BC}$. (Def. $\perp$ bisector) **37.** False. For a counterexample, take any isos. △ with the ∠ opp. the base $> 90°$. By Th. 4.6, the alt. from the base bisects the vertex ∠.

Algebra Review
1. $(7y^2 - 9)(7y^2 + 9)$ **3.** $(3y - 8)(3y + 8)$ **5.** $-1(x + 9)(x - 8)$

Chapter Review
1. ∠S **2.** $\overline{RS}$ **3.** ∠BAC **4.** 10 **5.** 6 **6.** △STR **7.** △SRU $\cong$ △STU, SAS **8.** △EAB $\cong$ △EDC, ASA **9.** No conclusion can be made. **10.** △DAB $\cong$ △DCB, SSS **11.** △DAB $\cong$ △DCB, SAS **12.** 1. E is the midpt. of $\overline{DC}$. (Given) 2. $\overline{ED} \cong \overline{EC}$ (Def. midpt.) 3. ∠1 $\cong$ ∠2 (Given) 4. $\overline{BE} \cong \overline{BE}$ (Reflex. Prop.) 5. △DEB $\cong$ △CEB (SAS) **13.** 1. G bisects $\overline{DF}$. (Given) 2. $\overline{GD} \cong \overline{GF}$ (Def. bis.) 3. ∠1 $\cong$ ∠2 (Given) 4. $\overline{EG} \cong \overline{EG}$ (Reflex. Prop.) 5. △EDG $\cong$ △EFG (SAS) **14.** 1. ∠1 is a rt. ∠. (Given) 2. $m\angle1 = 90$ (Def. rt. ∠) 3. $m\angle1 + m\angle2 = 180$ (Def. linear pair) 4. $m\angle2 = 90$ (Sub. Prop.) 5. $m\angle1 = m\angle2$ (Trans. Prop.) 6. ∠1 $\cong$ ∠2 (Def. $\cong$ ∠s) 7. $\overline{EG} \cong \overline{EG}$ (Reflex. Prop.) 8. ∠3 $\cong$ ∠4 (Given) 9. △EDG $\cong$ △EFG (ASA) 10. $\overline{DE} \cong \overline{EF}$ (Corr. parts of $\cong$ △s are $\cong$.) **15.** $\overline{WT}$ **16.** ∠TAS **17.** 1. $\overline{QA} \cong \overline{TA}$ (Given) 2. ∠QAS $\cong$ ∠TAW (Given) 3. $\overline{AW} \cong \overline{AS}$ (Given) 4. △QAS $\cong$ △TAW (SAS) 5. ∠1 $\cong$ ∠2 (Corr. parts of $\cong$ △s are $\cong$.) **18.** $\overline{JE} \cong \overline{JG}$ **19.** ∠2 $\cong$ ∠8 **20.** ∠1 $\cong$ ∠2 (Corr. parts of $\cong$ △s are $\cong$.) **21.** $\overline{FC} \cong \overline{EB}$, ∠F $\cong$ ∠E, or ∠FCA $\cong$ ∠EBD **22.** ∠FCA $\cong$ ∠EBD **23.** $\overline{FC} \cong \overline{EB}$ **24.** 1. ∠1 $\cong$ ∠2 (Given) 2. $\overline{AB} \cong \overline{BC}$ (Given) 3. ∠BAC $\cong$ ∠BCA (Isos. △ Th.) 4. $\overline{AC} \cong \overline{AC}$ (Reflex. Prop.) 5. △AEC $\cong$ △CDA (AAS) **25.** true **26.** false **27.** false **28.** true

CHAPTER 5

Lesson 5-1 Try This

1. $AD = BC = 54$ **2.** $m\angle T = m\angle R = 38$, $m\angle S = m\angle U = 142$

Exercise Set 5-1

1. Opp. $\angle$s of a $\square$ are $\cong$. **3.** Opp. sides of a $\square$ are $\cong$.
5. 20 **7.** 11 **9.** 105 **11.** 16 **13.** 15 **15.** 132 **17.** 125
19. 3 **21.** 79 **23.** 120 **25.** 85 **27.** $AB = CD = 58$, $BC = AD = 36$ **29.** 1. $ABCD$ is $\square$, $AECF$ is $\square$. (Given)
2. $\angle D \cong \angle B$ (Opp. $\angle$s of $\square$ are $\cong$.) 3. $\overline{CD} \cong \overline{AB}$, $\overline{AD} \cong \overline{CB}$, $\overline{AF} \cong \overline{CE}$ (Opp. sides of $\square$ are $\cong$.) 4. $AD = CB$, $AF = CE$ (Def. $\cong$ seg.) 5. $AD = AF + FD$, $CD = CE + EB$ (Seg. Add. Post.) 6. $AF + FD = CE + EB$ (Subst.) 7. $FD = ED$ (Add. Prop.) 8. $\overline{FD} \cong \overline{EB}$ (Def. $\cong$ seg.) 9. $\triangle CDF \cong \triangle ABE$ (SAS) **31.** 1. $ABCD$ is $\square$. (Given) 2. $\overline{AB} \cong \overline{CD}$ (Opp. sides of $\square$ are $\cong$.)
3. $CD = AB$ (Def. $\cong$) 4. A, F, E, C are collinear. (Given)
5. $\angle DCA \cong \angle BAC$ ($\parallel$ lines cut by trans., alt. int. $\angle$s are $\cong$.) 6. $\overline{AF} \cong \overline{CE}$ (Given) 7. $\triangle DEC \cong \triangle BFA$ (SAS)
8. $\angle AFB \cong \angle CED$ (Corr. parts of $\cong$ $\triangle$s are $\cong$.)
9. $\overline{DE} \parallel \overline{BF}$ (Lines cut by a trans. and alt. int. $\angle$s are $\cong$, lines are $\parallel$.) **33.** 120 **35.** 120 **37.** 120 **39.** 1. $\square ABCD$, $\overline{DE} \cong \overline{FB}$ (Given) 2. $\overline{DA} \cong \overline{CB}$ (Opp. sides of $\square$ are $\cong$.)
3. $DA = CB$ (Def. $\cong$) 4. $DE + EA = FB + CF$ (Seg. Add. Post.) 5. $DE + EA = DE + CF$ (Subst.) 6. $EA = CF$ (Add. Prop.) 7. $\overline{EA} \cong \overline{CF}$ (Def. $\cong$) 8. $\angle EXA \cong \angle FXC$ (Vert. $\angle$s)
9. $\overline{AD} \parallel \overline{BC}$ (Def. $\square$). 10. $\angle EAX \cong \angle FCX$ ($\parallel$ lines cut by a trans., alt. int. $\angle$s are $\cong$.) 11. $\triangle XAE \cong \triangle XCF$ (AAS)
12. $\overline{EX} \cong \overline{XF}$ (corr. parts of $\cong$ $\triangle$s) 13. X bisects $\overline{EF}$. (Def. seg. bis.) **41.** 1. $\triangle ABC$; $\overline{PF} \parallel \overline{AB}$, $\overline{PE} \parallel \overline{AC}$ (Given) 2. $AFPE$ is a $\square$. (Def. $\square$) 3. $\overline{EP} \cong \overline{AF}$, $\overline{EA} \cong \overline{PF}$ (Opp. sides of $\square$ are $\cong$.) 4. $\angle ACB \cong \angle EPB$, $\angle ABC \cong \angle FPC$ (Lines cut by trans., alt. int. $\angle$s are $\cong$.) 5. $\overline{AB} \cong \overline{AC}$ (Given)
6. $\angle ABC \cong \angle ACB$ (If $\angle$s of a $\triangle$ are $\cong$, sides opp. are $\cong$.)
7. $\angle ABC \cong \angle EPB \cong \angle FPC \cong \angle ACB$ (Trans. Prop.)
8. $\overline{EB} \cong \overline{EP}$, $\overline{FP} \cong \overline{FC}$ (If $\angle$s of a $\triangle$ are $\cong$, sides opp. are $\cong$.) 9. $AB = AE + EB$, $AC = AF + FC$ (Seg. Add. Post.)
10. $AB + AC = AE + EB + AF + FC$ (Add. Post.)
11. $AB + AC = AE + EP + AF + FP$ (Subst.)
43. 2 planes are equidistant at all pt. In order for a ceiling to be $\parallel$ to floor, studs in wall joining them must be same length.

Mixed Review

1. $\triangle BDA \cong \triangle BDC$ (SAS) **3.** $\triangle BDA \cong \triangle BDC$ (HL)
5. $p \parallel q$ (If alt. int. $\angle$s are $\cong$, the lines are $\parallel$.) **7.** $p \parallel q$ (If corr. $\angle$s are $\cong$, the lines are $\parallel$.) **9.** $p \parallel q$ (If alt. ext. $\angle$s are $\cong$, the lines are $\parallel$.)

Lesson 5-2 Try This

$x = 16$, $y = 16$

Exercise Set 5-2

1. If both pairs of opp. sides of quad. are $\cong$, it is a $\square$.
3. no **5.** If diag. of quad. bisect each other, it is a $\square$.
7. If both pairs of opp. sides of a quad. are $\cong$, it is a $\square$.
9. $x = 70$, $y = 10$ **11.** $x = 36$, $y = 23$ **13.** $x = 6$, $y = 12$ **15.** yes **17.** no **19.** no **21.** 1. $\triangle ABC \cong \triangle CDA$ (Given) 2. $\overline{AB} \cong \overline{DC}$, $\overline{AD} \cong \overline{BC}$ (Corr. parts of $\cong$ $\triangle$s) 3. $ABCD$ is a $\square$. (If both pairs of opp. sides of quad. are $\cong$, it is a $\square$.) **23.** 4 poles are bolted together

at pt. A, B, and C so that $\overline{AB} \cong \overline{CD}$ and $\overline{AD} \cong \overline{BC}$. If opp. sides are $\cong$, as the swing moves, $ABCD$ is always a $\square$, and $\overline{CD} \parallel$ to $\overline{AB}$. **25.** $X_1 X_2$ and $Y_1 Y_2$ are $\cong$ and $\parallel$. $X_1 X_2 Y_2 Y_1$ is a $\square$. $X_1 Y_1 \parallel X_2 Y_2$. **27.** $x = 81\frac{2}{3}$, $y = 8$ **29.** $x = 5$, $y = 1$
31. 1. $\overline{AD} \parallel \overline{BC}$, $\overline{EF} \parallel \overline{BC}$, $\overline{AD} \parallel \overline{FE}$ (Def. $\square$) 2. $\overline{AD} \cong \overline{BC}$, $\overline{FE} \cong \overline{BC}$, $\overline{AD} \cong \overline{FE}$ (If 2 lines are $\parallel$ to a third line, they are $\parallel$ to each other.) 3. $ADEF$ is a $\square$. (If 1 pair of opp. sides of quad. are both $\parallel$ and $\cong$, it is a $\square$.) **33.** 1. $\angle A \cong \angle C$, $\angle B \cong \angle D$ (Given) 2. $m\angle A + m\angle B + m\angle C + m\angle D = 360$ (Sum of $\angle$s of quad. $= 360$.) 3. $m\angle A = m\angle C$, $m\angle B = m\angle D$ (Def. $\cong$) 4. $m\angle A + m\angle B + m\angle A + m\angle B = 360$ (Substitution) 5. $2(m\angle A + m\angle B) = 360$ (Distr. Prop.) 6. $m\angle A + m\angle B = 180$ (Division)
7. $\angle A$ and $\angle B$ are supp. (Def. supp. $\angle$s) 8. $\overline{AD} \parallel \overline{BC}$ (If 2 lines are cut by a trans. and same-side int. $\angle$s are supp. the lines are $\parallel$.) 9. $\overline{AB} \parallel \overline{DC}$ (As in 1–8.) 10. $ABCD$ is a $\square$. (Def. $\square$) **35.** 1. $ABCD$ is $\square$. (Given) 2. $\overline{CD} \cong \overline{AB}$, $\overline{AD} \cong \overline{BC}$ (If quad. is $\square$, opp. sides are $\cong$.) 3. $\overline{AB} \parallel \overline{CD}$, $\overline{AD} \parallel \overline{BC}$ (Def. $\square$) 4. $\angle ACD \cong \angle CAB$, $\angle ACB \cong \angle CAD$ ($\parallel$ lines cut by trans., alt. int. $\angle$s are $\cong$.) 5. $\triangle BCF \cong \triangle DAE$ (SAS) 6. $\overline{DE} \cong \overline{FB}$ (Corr. parts of $\cong$ $\triangle$s) 7. $\triangle DCF \cong \triangle BAE$ (SAS) 8. $\overline{BE} \cong \overline{DF}$ (Corr. parts of $\cong$ $\triangle$s) 9. $BFDE$ is a $\square$. (If opp. sides of quad. are $\cong$, it is a $\square$.) **37.** 1. $\overline{AB} \cong \overline{BC} \cong \overline{CD} \cong \overline{DE} \cong \overline{EF} \cong \overline{FA}$ (Def. reg. poly.) 2. $\angle BAF \cong \angle CDE$ (Def. reg. poly.) 3. $\triangle FAB \cong \triangle CDE$ (SAS) 4. $\overline{BF} \cong \overline{CE}$ (Corr. parts of $\cong$ $\triangle$s) 5. $BCEF$ is $\square$. (If quad. has opp. sides $\cong$, it is $\square$.) **39.** 1. $\overline{AB} \parallel \overline{CD}$, $\overline{AD} \parallel \overline{BC}$ (Given) 2. $\angle ADB \cong \angle DBC$, $\angle ABD \cong \angle CDB$ ($\parallel$ lines cut by trans., alt. int. $\angle$s are $\cong$.) 3. $\overline{DB} \cong \overline{DB}$ (Reflex. Prop.)
4. $\triangle DAB \cong \triangle BCD$ (ASA) 5. $\overline{AD} \cong \overline{BC}$, $\overline{AB} \cong \overline{DC}$ (Corr. parts of $\cong$ $\triangle$s are $\cong$.) 6. $ABCD$ is $\square$. (Def. $\square$)

Lesson 5-3 Try This

1. 22 **2.** -15

Exercise Set 5-3

1. $\cong$ diag., diag. bisect each other, diag. bisect opp. $\angle$s
3. rhombus **5.** 6 **7.** 70 **9.** 43 **11.** 45 **13.** true
15. false **17.** false **19.** All sides are $\cong$, all $\angle$s are rt. $\angle$s. **21.** 1. $ABCD$ is $\square$, $m\angle 3 + m\angle 4 = 90$ (Given)
2. $m\angle DAB + m\angle 3 + m\angle 4 = 180$ ($\angle$ Sum Th.)
3. $m\angle DAB + 90 = 180$ (Subst.) 4. $m\angle DAB = 90$ (Add. Prop.) 5. $ABCD$ is rect. (If $\square$ has rt. $\angle$, it is rect.)
23.   **25.**

27. $AB = DC = AD = 34$ **29.** $AC = \sqrt{41}$ and $BD = \sqrt{41}$, therefore $\overline{AC} \cong \overline{BD}$ (Def. $\cong$ seg.) **31.** $(-2, -2)$
33. $(-1, -5)$ **35.** 1. $\overline{WX} \cong \overline{ZY}$, $\overline{WZ} \cong \overline{XY}$ (Given)
2. $WXYZ$ is $\square$. (Def. $\square$) 3. $\overline{WY} \cong \overline{ZX}$ (Given) 4. $WXYZ$ is rect. (If diag. of $\square$ are $\cong$, $\square$ is rect.) **37.** 1. $WXYZ$ is rhombus. (Given) 2. $\overline{ZX}$ bisects $\overline{XY}$. (Diag. of $\square$ bisect each other.) 3. $\overline{WV} \cong \overline{VY}$ (Def. seg. bis.) 4. $WV = VY$ (Def. $\cong$ seg.) 5. $WV = WR + RS$, $VY = VT + TY$ (Seg. Add. Post.) 6. R is midpt. of $\overline{WV}$. T is midpt. of $\overline{VY}$. (Given) 7. $\overline{WR} \cong \overline{RV}$, $\overline{VT} \cong \overline{TY}$ (Def. seg. bis.) 8. $WR = RV$, $VT = TY$ (Def. $\cong$ seg.) 9. $WV = 2RV$, $VY = 2VT$ (Subst.)

10. $2RV = 2VT$ (Subst.) 11. $RV = VT$ (Mult. Prop.)
12. $\overline{RV} \cong \overline{VT}$ (Def. $\cong$ seg.) 13. $\overline{WY} \perp \overline{ZX}$ (Diag. of rhom. are $\perp$.) 14. $\angle SVR \cong \angle SVT$ (Def. $\perp$ lines) 15. $\overline{SV} \cong \overline{SV}$ (Reflex. Prop.) 16. $\triangle SVR \cong \triangle SVT$ (SAS) 17. $\overline{SR} \cong \overline{ST}$ (Corr. parts of $\cong$ $\triangle$s) 18. $\triangle RST$ is isos. (Def. isos. $\triangle$)
39. 1. $ABCD$ is square. (Given) 2. $\angle ADE$, $\angle CBA$, $\angle C$ and $\angle A$ are rt. $\angle$s. (Def. square) 3. $m\angle ADE = 90$ (Def. rt. $\angle$) 4. $\overline{DB}$ bisects $\angle ADE$. (Diag. of rhom. bisect opp. $\angle$s.)
5. $m\angle EDF = \frac{1}{2} m\angle ADE$ (Def. $\angle$ bis.) 6. $m\angle EDF = \frac{1}{2}(90) = 45$ (Subst.) 7. $\overline{EF} \perp \overline{BD}$ (Given) 8. $\angle DFE$ is a rt. $\angle$. (Def. $\perp$ lines) 9. $m\angle DFE = 90$ (Def. rt. $\angle$)
10. $m\angle DFE + m\angle FED + m\angle EDF = 180$ ($\angle$ Sum Th.)
11. $90 + m\angle FED + 45 = 180$ (Subst.) 12. $m\angle FED = 45$ (Add. Prop.) 13. $\angle FED \cong \angle EDF$ (Def. .$=\angle$s) 14. $\overline{DF} \cong \overline{FE}$ (If $\angle$s of a $\triangle$ are $\cong$, sides opp. are $\cong$.) 15. Draw $\overline{EB}$. (2 pt. determine a line.) 16. $\overline{EB} \cong \overline{EB}$ (Reflex. Prop.)
17. $\overline{FB} \cong \overline{BC}$ (Given) 18. $\triangle EFB \cong \triangle ECB$ (HL Th.)
19. $\overline{FE} \cong \overline{EC}$ (Corr. parts of $\cong$ $\triangle$s) 20. $DF = FE = EC$ (Trans. Prop.) **41.** A cube is made up of $\cong$ squares and a square has all sides $\cong$, so $\overline{AE} \cong \overline{CG}$, $\overline{FE} \cong \overline{FG}$, and $\overline{AB} \cong \overline{BC}$. A square is a rect., so all $\angle$s are rt.$\angle$s. Therefore, $\angle EFG \cong \angle ABC$ and $\overline{AC} \cong \overline{EG}$ by corr. parts of $\cong$ $\triangle$s. Thus, $ACGE$ is a rect.
43. 1. $ABCD$ is rhom. (Given) 2. $\overline{AB} \cong \overline{BC} \cong \overline{CD} \cong \overline{AD}$ (Def. rhom.) 3. $\overline{AC}$ and $\overline{BD}$ bisect each other. (Diag. of a rhom. bisect each other.) 4. E is midpt. of $\overline{AC}$ and $\overline{BD}$. (Def. seg. bis.) 5. $\overline{AE} \cong \overline{EC}$, $\overline{BE} \cong \overline{ED}$ (Def. midpt.) 6. $\triangle BEA \cong \triangle BEC \cong \triangle DEC \cong \triangle DEA$ (SSS) 7. $\angle EAB \cong \angle EAD$, $\angle ABE \cong \angle EBC$, $\angle BCE \cong ECD$, $\angle EDC \cong \angle EDA$ (Corr. parts of $\cong$ $\triangle$s) 8. $\overline{AC}$ bisects $\angle BAD$ and $\angle BCD$, $\overline{BD}$ bisects $\angle ABC$ and $\angle CDA$. (Def. $\angle$ bis.) **45.** 1. $ABCD$ is $\square$. (Given) 2. $\overline{AB} \cong \overline{DC}$, $\overline{AD} \cong \overline{BC}$ (If quad. is $\square$ opp. sides are $\cong$.) 3. $\overline{AB} \cong \overline{BC}$ (Given) 4. $\overline{AB} \cong \overline{BC} \cong \overline{DC} \cong \overline{AD}$ (Trans. Prop.) 5. $ABCD$ is a rhom. (Def. rhom.) **47.** yes: a, b, c, e, f; no: d **49.** yes: a, c, e; no: b, d, f

Algebra Review
1. $x = \pm\sqrt{15}$ 3. $y = \pm\frac{2}{3}$

Lesson 5-4 Try This
1. $m\angle F = m\angle G = 60$, $m\angle E = m\angle H = 120$ 2. 27

Exercise Set 5-4
1. 33.5 3. 17.15 5. 5 7.-9. always 11. never
13. 16, 64 15. 6 cm 17. 1. $\overline{AB} \parallel \overline{CD}$, $\overline{AP}$ bisects $\angle A$. (Given) 2. $\angle DAP \cong \angle PAB$ (Def. $\angle$ bis.) 3. $\angle PAB \cong \angle DPA$ (If 2 $\parallel$ lines are cut by a trans., alt. int. $\angle$s are $\cong$.) 4. $\angle DAP \cong \angle DPA$ (Trans. Prop.) 5. $\overline{DA} \cong \overline{DP}$ (Th. 4.2) 6. $\triangle APD$ is isos. (Def. isos. $\triangle$)
19. 1. $\triangle ABC$ is isos. with base $\overline{BC}$. (Given) 2. $\angle B \cong \angle C$ (Base $\angle$s of isos. $\triangle$ are $\cong$.) 3. $\angle AED \cong \angle B$ (Given) 4. $\overline{BC} \parallel \overline{ED}$ (Lines cut by a trans. and corr. $\angle$s are $\cong$, lines are $\parallel$.) 5. $\angle C \cong \angle ADE$ (Lines cut by a trans., corr. $\angle$s are $\cong$.) 6. $\angle AED \cong \angle ADE$ (Trans. Prop.) 7. $\overline{AE} \cong \overline{AD}$ (If $\angle$s of an isos. $\triangle$ are $\cong$, sides opp. are $\cong$.) 8. $AE = AD$, $AB = AC$ (Def. $\cong$ seg.) 9. $AB = AE + EB$, $AC = AD + DC$ (Seg. Add. Post.) 10. $AE + EB = AD + DC$ (Subst.) 11. $EB = DC$ (Add. Prop.) 12. $\overline{EB} \cong \overline{DC}$ (Def. $\cong$ seg.) 13. $BEDC$ is an isos. trap. with $\overline{BE} \cong \overline{CD}$.

(Def. isos. trap.) **21.** not isos. **23. a.** 1. Trap. $ABCD$ (Given) 2. $\overline{AD} \parallel \overline{BC}$ (Def. of trap.) 3. Draw $\overline{FE}$ through $N \parallel$ to $\overline{AB}$. (Through a pt. not on a line, there exists 1 and only 1 line $\parallel$ to the given line.) 4. $AFEB$ is a $\square$. (Def of $\square$) 5. $\angle FDN \cong \angle ECN$ (Alt. int. $\angle$s are $\cong$.) 6. N is midpt. of $\overline{DC}$. (Given) 7. $\overline{DN} \cong \overline{CN}$ (A midpt. forms 2 $\cong$ seg.) 8. $\angle DNF \cong \angle ECNE$ (Vert. $\angle$s.) 9. $\triangle DNF \cong \triangle CNE$ (ASA Post.) 10. $\overline{DF} \cong \overline{CE}$, $\overline{FN} \cong \overline{EN}$ (CPCTC) 11. N is midpt. of $\overline{FE}$. (Def. of midpt.) 12. $\overline{AF} \cong \overline{BE}$, $\overline{AB} \cong \overline{FE}$ (Opp. sides of a $\square$ are $\cong$.) 13. M is midpt. of $\overline{AB}$. (Given) 14. $AM = \frac{1}{2}AB$, $FN = \frac{1}{2}FE$; $MB = \frac{1}{2}AB$; $NE = \frac{1}{2}FE$ (Midpt. Th.) 15. $AB = FE$ (Def. of $\cong$ seg.) 16. $\frac{1}{2}AB = \frac{1}{2}FE$ (Mult. Prop.) 17. $AM = FN$, $MB = NE$ (Subst.) 18. $\overline{AM} \cong \overline{FN}$, $\overline{MB} \cong \overline{NE}$ (Def. of $\cong$.) 19. $AMNF$ and $MBEN$ are $\square$. (If one pair of opp. sides of a quad. are both $\parallel$ and $\cong$, then it is a $\square$.) 20. $\overline{MN} \parallel \overline{AD}$, $\overline{MN} \parallel \overline{BC}$ (Def. of $\square$) **b.** (Repeat steps 1–19.) 20. $\overline{AF} \cong \overline{MN}$, $\overline{BE} \cong \overline{MN}$ (Opp. sides of a $\square$ are $\cong$.) 21. $MN = AF$, $MN = BE$, $DF = EC$ (Def. of $\cong$ seg.) 22. $2MN = AF + BE$ (Add. Prop.) 23. $MN = \frac{1}{2}(AF + BE)$ (Div. Prop.) 24. $MN = \frac{1}{2}(AD + DF + BE)$ (Seg. Add. Post.) 25. $MN = \frac{1}{2}(AD + EC + BE)$ (Subst.) 26. $MN = \frac{1}{2}(AD + BC)$ (Seg. Add. Post.) **25.** 1. Draw $\overline{DE} \parallel \overline{AB}$. (2 pt. determine a line.) 2. $ABCD$ is trap. (Given) 3. $\overline{AD} \parallel \overline{BE}$ (Def. trap.) 4. $ABED$ is $\square$. (Def. $\square$) 5. $m\angle B + m\angle DEC = 180$ (Consec.$\angle$s of a $\square$ are supp.) 6. $m\angle BED + m\angle DEC = 180$ (Linear Post.) 7. $\angle B \cong \angle DEC$ (Def. $\cong$ $\angle$s) 8. $\angle B \cong \angle C$ (Given) 9. $\angle DEC \cong \angle C$ (Trans. Prop.) 10. $\overline{DE} \cong \overline{DC}$ (If $\angle$s of $\triangle$ are $\cong$, sides opp. are $\cong$.) 12. $\overline{DC} \cong \overline{AB}$ (Trans. Prop.) 13. $ABCD$ is isos. trap. (Def. isos. trap.) **27.** 3; P must be equidistant from A, B, and C.

Mixed Review
1. 720 2. 120 3. 60

Lesson 5-5 Try This
1. 24, 12 2. 15

Exercise Set 5-5
1. 20 3. 16 5. 32 7. 16 9. 16 11. no 13. 40
15. 13 17. $a = 3.5$ 19. Th. 5.20; if 3 or more $\parallel$ lines cut off $\cong$ seg. on 1 trans., they will cut off $\cong$ seg. on every trans. 21. $X = (0, 3)$, $Y = (-4, 5)$, $XY = \sqrt{20} = 2\sqrt{5}$, $BC = \sqrt{80} = 4\sqrt{5}$, $2\sqrt{5} = \frac{1}{2}(4\sqrt{5})$ 23. Locate midpt. of XZ and YZ, then find the distance between those 2 midpt. Apply the Midseg. Th. to find XY, which is twice the distance between the midpt. of XZ and YZ. 25. $MN = 5$, $AB = 10$ 27. $EC = 11\frac{1}{5}$ 29. 1. $\overline{AB} \cong \overline{AC}$ (Given) 2. E is midpt. of $\overline{AB}$. D is midpt. of $\overline{CB}$. (Given) 3. $\overline{AC} \parallel \overline{DE}$ (Midseg. Th.) 4. $2DE = AC$ (Midseg. Th.) 5. $2EB = AB$ (Def. midpt.) 6. $2DE = 2EB$ (Trans. Prop.) 7. $DE = EB$ (Mult. Prop.) 8. $\overline{DE} \cong \overline{EB}$ (Def. $\cong$ seg.) 9. $\triangle BDE$ is isos. (Def. isos. $\triangle$) 31. 1. D is midpt. of $\overline{AB}$. E is midpt of $\overline{AC}$. (Given) 2. Draw $\overline{DF}$ so $DE = EF$. (Ruler Post.) 3. $AE = CE$ (Def. midpt.) 4. $ADCF$ is $\square$. (Th. 5.8) 5. $\overline{AD} \parallel \overline{FC}$ (Th. 5.1) 6. $AD = FC$ (Def. $\cong$) 7. $AD = DB$ (Def. midpt.) 8. $FC = DB$ (Subst.) 9. $\overline{BD} \parallel \overline{CF}$ (Def. $\square$) 10. $DBCF$ is $\square$. (Th. 5.8) 11. $\overline{DE} \parallel \overline{BC}$ (Def. $\square$) 12. $DE + EF = DF$ (Seg. Add. Post.) 13. $2DE = DF$ (Subst.) 14. $\overline{DF} \cong \overline{BC}$ (Th. 5.1) 15. $DF = BC$ (Def. $\cong$) 16. $2DE = BC$ (Trans. Prop.)

17. $DE = \frac{1}{2}BC$ (Div.) **33.** 6 **35.** 1. $\overrightarrow{AD} \parallel \overrightarrow{BE} \parallel \overrightarrow{CF}$
(Given) 2. Draw $\overline{DX} \parallel \overline{AB}$ with X on $\overline{BE}$ and $\overline{EY} \parallel \overline{AC}$ with Y
on $\overline{CF}$. (Post. 15) 3. $ABXD$, $BCYE$ are $\square$s. (Def. $\square$)
4. $\overline{AB} \cong \overline{DX}$, $\overline{BC} \cong \overline{EY}$ (Th. 5.1) 5. $\overline{AB} \cong \overline{BC}$ (Given)
6. $\overline{DX} \cong \overline{EY}$ (Subst.) 7. $\angle DEX \cong \angle EFY$ (Post. 13)
8. $\angle DAB \cong \angle EBC$ (Post. 13) 9. $\angle DAB \cong \angle EBC$,
$\angle EBC \cong \angle EYC$ (Th. 5.2) 10. $\angle DXB \cong \angle EYC$ (Subst.)
11. $\angle DXE \cong \angle EYF$ ($\cong$ Supp. Th.) 12. $\triangle DXE \cong \triangle EYF$
(AAS $\cong$) 13. $\overline{DE} \cong \overline{EF}$ (CPCTC) **37.** yes

Lesson 5-6 Try This

1. $\overline{AB}$ does not intersect $\overline{CD}$. **2.** b and c

Exercise Set 5-6

1. $\angle A$ is not supp. to $\angle B$. **3.** $\angle A$ and $\angle B$ are vert. $\angle$s.
5. $\triangle ABC$ is an equilat. $\triangle$. **7.** yes **9.** yes **11.** yes **13.** It
follows that $AC \cong AB$ by corr. parts of $\cong \triangle$s. This contradicts the fact that $AC \neq AB$. The assumption $\overline{AD} \perp \overline{BC}$ must
be false. Therefore, $\overline{AD} \not\perp \overline{BC}$. **15.** Assume $\angle 3 \cong \angle 5$.
Then $a \parallel b$ since corr. $\angle$s are $\cong$. This contradicts the fact
that $a \not\parallel b$. The assumption must be false. Therefore,
$\angle 3 \not\cong \angle 5$. **17.** Assume $\overline{BC} \cong \overline{CD}$. Since it is given that
$\overline{AB} \cong \overline{AD}$ and $\overline{AC} \cong \overline{AC}$, by Reflex. Prop. conclude
$\triangle ABC \cong \triangle ADC$. Then $\angle 1 \cong \angle 2$ because corr. parts
of $\cong \triangle$s. This contradicts fact $\angle 1 \not\cong \angle 2$. The assumption
$\overline{BC} \cong \overline{CD}$ is false. Therefore, $\overline{BC} \not\cong \overline{CD}$. **19.** Assume
$\overline{AC} \perp \overline{BD}$. Then $\angle ACB \cong \angle ACD$. Since $\overline{AC}$ is a median,
$\overline{BC} \cong \overline{CD}$ because a median of a $\triangle$ divides base into
$2 \cong$ seg. $\overline{AC} \cong \overline{AC}$ by Reflex. Prop. Conclude $\triangle ACB \cong$
$\triangle ACD$ by SAS. Then $\overline{AB} \cong \overline{AD}$ by corr. parts of $\cong \triangle$s.
This contradicts fact $\triangle ABD$ is scalene. The assumption
$\overline{AC} \perp \overline{BC}$ must be false. Therefore, $\overline{AC} \not\perp \overline{BD}$. **21.** Assume
$\overline{MN} \cong \overline{QP}$. Since $\overline{MN} \perp \overline{NP}$ and $\overline{QP} \perp \overline{NP}$, $\angle MNP$ and
$\angle QPN$ are rt. $\angle$s. $\angle MNP \cong \angle QPN$ because all rt. $\angle$s are
$\cong$. $\overline{NP} \cong \overline{NP}$ by the Reflex. Prop. Then $\triangle MNP \cong \triangle QPN$
by SAS. $\angle M \cong \angle Q$ since corr. parts of $\cong \triangle$s are $\cong$. This
contradicts fact $\angle M \cong \angle Q$. The assumption $\overline{MN} \cong \overline{QP}$
must be false. Therefore, $\overline{MN} \not\cong \overline{QP}$. **23.** Assume $\angle BAC \cong$
$\angle DAC$. Since $\overline{AC} \perp M$, $\overline{AC} \perp \overline{BC}$ and $\overline{AC} \perp \overline{CD}$ because a
line $\perp$ to a plane is $\perp$ to every line in the plane. Then
$\angle ACB$ and $\angle ACD$ are rt. $\angle$s and $\cong$ since all rt. $\angle$s are $\cong$.
$\overline{AC} \cong \overline{AC}$ by Reflex. Prop. $\triangle ACB \cong \triangle ACD$ by ASA. Then
$\angle B \cong \angle D$ by corr. parts of $\cong \triangle$s. This contradicts
fact $\angle B \not\cong \angle D$. The assumption $\angle BAC \cong \angle DAC$
must be false. Therefore, $\angle BAC \not\cong \angle DAC$.
25. Given: $\overline{BC} \perp \overline{AD}$, $\overline{AB}$ and $\overline{AD}$ are sides of $\angle BAD$.
Prove: $\overline{BC} \not\perp \overline{AB}$. Proof: Assume $\overline{BC} \perp \overline{AB}$. Since
$\overline{BC} \perp \overline{AD}$, $\overline{AB} \parallel \overline{AD}$ by Th. 3.8. This contradicts the given
information, so the assumption must be false. Therefore,
$\overline{BC} \not\perp \overline{AB}$. **27.** Given: $\triangle ABC$ in plane M, D not in plane
M Prove: $\overline{BD}$ is skew to $\overline{AC}$. Proof: Assume $\overline{BD}$ is not skew
to $\overline{AC}$. Then $\overline{BD}$ and $\overline{AC}$ are coplanar. Therefore, D would be
in same plane as ABC. This contradicts fact that D is not in
plane M. Therefore, $\overline{BD}$ is skew to $\overline{AC}$.

Mixed Review

1. 125 **3.** 80

5. sometimes true

yes / no

---

7. sometimes true

9. always true

yes 45° 45°

Lesson 5-7 Try This

1. $\angle C$ **2.** $\overline{CD}$ **3.** a and c

Exercise Set 5-7

1. $\overline{AB}$, $\overline{BC}$, $\overline{AC}$ **3.** $\overline{MQ}$, $\overline{QP}$, $\overline{NP}$, $\overline{MN}$ **5.** $\overline{BC}$, $\overline{AC}$, $\overline{AB}$
7. $\overline{BC}$, $\overline{AC}$, $\overline{AB}$ **9.** $\angle C$, $\angle B$, $\angle A$ **11.** $\overline{AC}$, $\overline{BA}$, $\overline{BC}$, $\overline{BD}$,
$\overline{DC}$, $\overline{DE}$, $\overline{CE}$ **13.** yes **15.** no **17.** no **19.** 6
21. $m\angle 6 > m\angle 1$ **23.** $m\angle 2 > m\angle 4$ **25.** a possible, no;
b possible, no; c possible, yes; d not possible; e not possible
27. $< x$ and $> 10 - x$ **29.** 1. $m\angle 1 > m\angle EDC$ (Ext. $\angle$
Inequal. Th.) 2. $m\angle EDC > m\angle 2$ (Ext. $\angle$ Inequal. Th.)
3. $m\angle 1 > m\angle 2$ (Trans. Prop.) **31.** 1. Draw $\overline{AC}$.
(2 pt. determine a line.) 2. $AB + BC > AC$ ($\triangle$ Inequal. Th.)
3. $AB + BC + CD > AC + CD$ (Add. Prop.) 4. $AC +$
$CD > AD$ ($\triangle$ Inequal. Th.) 5. $AB + BC + CD > AD$
(Trans. Prop.) **33.** 1. Suppose $\overline{PQ}$ is not shortest seg. from
P to ℓ. (Indirect proof assumption) 2. Choose N on ℓ such
that $PN < PQ$. ($\overline{PQ}$ is not shortest seg. to ℓ.) 3. $\overline{PQ} \perp \ell$
(Given) 4. $\angle PQN$ is a rt. $\angle$. (Def. $\perp$) 5. $m\angle PQN = 90$
(Def. rt. $\angle$) 6. $m\angle P + m\angle PNQ + m\angle PQN = 180$
($\angle$ Sum Th.) 7. $m\angle P + m\angle PNQ = 90$ (Add. Prop.)
8. $m\angle PNQ < 90$ (Def. $<$) 10. $PQ < PN$ (If 1 $\angle$ of $\triangle$ is
larger than a second $\angle$, the side opp. larger $\angle$ is $>$ than side
opp. smaller $\angle$.) 11. $\overline{PQ}$ is shortest segment from P to ℓ.
(Indirect logic) **35.** $138 + 46\sqrt{3}$ km; the intersection of
$\overline{AC}$ and $\overline{BD}$. **37.** $\angle A$ **39.** $\angle B$ **41.** Assume 1 side, $\overline{BC}$, is
longer than, or at least as long as, the other 2 sides, $\overline{AC}$ and
$\overline{AB}$. Then statements 1 and 2 are true. Draw $\overline{AD} \perp \overline{BC}$, using fact that from a pt. not on a line a $\perp$ be drawn to the
line. Since $\angle ADB$ and $\angle ADC$ are rt. $\angle$s, $AB > BD$ and
$AC > DC$. Thus $AB + AC > BD + DC$. Conclude $AB +$
$AC > BC$. **43.** 1. $\triangle ABC$; $\overline{AD}$, $\overline{BE}$, and $\overline{CF}$ are alt. (Given)
2. $\overline{AD} \perp \overline{CD}$, $\overline{CF} \perp \overline{AF}$, $\overline{BE} \perp \overline{AC}$ (Def. alt.) 3. $AB > AD$,
$BC > BE$, $AC > CF$ ($\perp$ seg. from pt. to line is shortest seg-
ment from pt. to line.) 4. $AB + BC + AC > AD + BE +$
CF (Add Prop.) **45.** 3, 4, 5; 2, 5, 5; 4, 4, 4

Algebra Review

1. $-7, 7$ **3.** $-7, 7$ **5.** $-\frac{7}{2}, \frac{7}{2}$ **7.** $-6, 6$ **9.** 8 **11.** $-7\frac{1}{2}$,
$6\frac{1}{2}$

Exercise Set 5-8

1. $AC > AB$ **3.** $m\angle 2 > m\angle 1$ **5.** never **7.** always
9. never **11.** 1. $\overline{AB} \cong \overline{CD}$ (Given) 2. $\overline{BC} \cong \overline{BC}$ (Reflex.
Prop.) 3. $m\angle ABC > m\angle BCD$ (Given) 4. $AC > BD$ (SAS
Inequal. Th.) **13.** 1. $\overline{AC}$ is a median. (Given) 2. $\overline{BC} \cong \overline{CD}$
(Def. median) 3. $m\angle 1 > m\angle 2$ (Given) 4. $\overline{AC} \cong \overline{AC}$
(Reflex. Prop.) 5. $AB > AD$ (SAS Inequal. Th.)

$\angle > m\angle D$ **17.** $m\angle A < m\angle D$
$AE = BF$, D is midpt. of $\overline{AB}$. (Given)
$\angle B$ (If 1 side of $\triangle$ is longer than second side,
of $\angle$ opp. longer side is $>$ measure of $\angle$ opp.
.e.) 3. $BD = AD$ (Def. midpt.) 4. $DF < DE$ (SAS
Th.)   **21.** 1. $RU > RT$, $\overline{VU} \cong \overline{ST}$ (Given)
$\angle RTU > m\angle RUT$ (If 1 side of $\triangle$ is longer than second
s..e, the measure of $\angle$ opp. longer side is $> \angle$ opp. shorter
side.) 3. $\overline{TU} \cong \overline{TU}$ (Reflex. Prop.) 4. $SU > TV$ (SAS Inequal. Th.)   **23.** 1. $m\angle MNQ > m\angle MNP$, $\overline{NP} \cong \overline{NQ}$
(Given) 2. $MN = MN$ (Reflex. Prop.) 3. $MQ > MP$
(If 1 $\angle$ of $\triangle$ is $>$ than second $\angle$, side opp. $> \angle$ is longer
than side opp. $< \angle$.) 4. $m\angle MPQ > m\angle MQP$ (If 1 side of
$\triangle$ is longer than second side, the measure of $\angle$ opp. longer
side is $> \angle$ opp. shorter side.   **25.** 1. $m\angle 1 = m\angle 2$
(Given) 2. $\overline{BE} \cong \overline{EC}$ (If $\angle$s of $\triangle$ are $\cong$, sides opp. are $\cong$.)
3. $\overline{AE} \cong \overline{AE}$ (Reflex. Prop.) 4. $m\angle 3 + m\angle AEB =$
$m\angle 4 + m\angle AEC = 180$ (Def. linear pair) 5. $m\angle 3 +$
$m\angle AEB = m\angle 4 + m\angle AEC$ (Trans. Prop.) 6. $m\angle 3 >$
$m\angle 4$ (Given) 7. $m\angle AEB < m\angle AEC$ (Algebra)
8. $AC > AB$ (SAS Inequal. Th.)
27. 1. $\overline{AC} \perp$ plane N, $AD > AB$ (Given) 2. Let E be on
$\overline{CD}$ so that $BC = CE$. (Construction) 3. $\overline{AC} \cong \overline{AC}$
(Reflex. Prop.) 4. $\angle ACB$ and $\angle ACE$ are rt. $\angle$s (Def. $\perp$)
5. $\angle ACB \cong \angle ACE$ (All rt. $\angle$s are $\cong$.) 6. $\triangle ACB \cong \triangle ACE$
(SAS) 7. $\overline{AB} \cong \overline{AE}$, $AB = AE$ (CPCTC, Def. $\cong$)
8. $AD > AE$ (Subst.) 9. $AC^2 = AD^2 - CD^2 = AE^2 - CE^2$
(Pythagorean Th.) 10. $AD^2 - AE^2 = CD^2 - CE^2$
(Add. Prop.) 11. $AD^2 - AE^2 > 0$ ($AD > AE$)
12. $CD^2 - CE^2 > 0$ (Subst.) 13. $CD > CE$ (Algebra)
14. $CD > BC$ (Subst.)   **29.** Since $\triangle ABC$ is
equilat., $\overline{AB} \cong \overline{BC} \cong \overline{CA}$. $\angle PAB$ and $\angle PAC$ are rt. $\angle$s
since $\overline{PA} \perp \overline{AB}$ and $\overline{PA} \perp \overline{AC}$. In rt. $\triangle$, other 2 angles are
acute, so $PB > PA$, $PB > AB$, $PC > BC$, and $PC > CA$,
because side of $\triangle$ opp. $> \angle$ is longer than side opp. $< \angle$.
Therefore, since $\angle PAB \cong \angle PAB$, the longest side is $\overline{PB}$ or
$\overline{PC}$.

Algebra Review
1. 6   **3.** ± 8

Chapter Review
1. 32   **2.** 55, 125   **3.** RA   **4.** 8   **5.** 65   **6.** Yes, if both
pairs of opp. $\angle$s are $\cong$, then the quad is $\square$.   **7.** Yes, if
diag. bisect each other, then quad. is $\square$.   **8.** Yes, 2 $\triangle$s are
$\cong$ by SAS, so opp. sides are $\cong$ and quad. is $\square$.   **9.** Yes, if
both pairs of opp. sides are $\parallel$, then quad. is $\square$.   **10.** always
11. sometimes   **12.** always   **13.** sometimes   **14.** bases
15. 35   **16.** 10   **17.** 17   **18.** false   **19.** true   **20.** true
21. false   **22.** $\angle ABC$ is not an obtuse $\angle$.   **23.** contradiction
24. $\overline{ST}$, $\overline{RT}$, $\overline{RS}$ **25.** $\angle Y$ **26.** 4, 10   **27.** $EF = FG$
28. $DE < DG$ **29.** $DE > FG$

CHAPTER 6

Lesson 6-1 Try This
1. a. $\frac{3}{5}$ **b.** $\frac{10}{9}$ **2.** $\frac{15}{7}$ **3. a.** yes   **b.** no   **c.** yes   **4. a.** 5
b. 3

Exercise Set 6-1
1. $\frac{5}{7}$ **3.** $\frac{16}{9}$ **5.** $\frac{y}{21}$ **7.** $\frac{3}{5}$ **9.** $\frac{5}{6}$ **11.** yes   **13.** yes   **15.** 12
17. $\frac{75}{8}$ **19.** $\frac{3}{2} = \frac{6}{4}$, $\frac{4}{2} = \frac{6}{3}$ **21.** $\frac{3}{4} = \frac{9}{12}$, $\frac{9}{3} = \frac{12}{4}$ **23.** $\frac{2}{3}$
25. 60, 120   **27.** $\frac{4}{9}$ **29.** $\frac{5}{2}$ **31.** $\frac{AD}{DB} = \frac{\sqrt{5}}{2\sqrt{5}} = \frac{AE}{EC} = \frac{\sqrt{2}}{2\sqrt{2}} = \frac{1}{2}$
33. Answers may vary. $\frac{AD}{AB} = \frac{DE}{BC} = \frac{\sqrt{5}}{3\sqrt{5}} = \frac{1}{3}$, $\frac{AB}{AC} = \frac{AD}{AE} =$
$\frac{\sqrt{5}}{\sqrt{2}} = \frac{\sqrt{10}}{2}$ **35.** $\frac{1+x}{1} = \frac{1}{x}$, $x^2 + x = 1$, $x^2 + x - 1 = 0$,
$x = 1 - x^2$ $x = (1 - x)(1 + x)$, $\frac{x}{1-x} = \frac{1+x}{1}$, $\frac{1+x}{1} =$
$\frac{x}{1-x} = \frac{DF}{AD} = \frac{FH}{HC}$ **37.** You cannot draw a diag. from vert. to
itself or to its 2 adj. vert. So no. of diag. $= n - 3$. $\frac{n-3}{360} =$
$\frac{2}{7}$, $7n - 21 = 720$, $7n = 741$, $n = \frac{741}{7}$, not a whole no. The
proposition is contradictory since the poly. must have a
whole no. for no. of sides.

Mixed Review
1. 56   **3.** 68   **5.** 56

Lesson 6-2 Try This
1. $\frac{3}{18} = \frac{7}{42}$, $\frac{42}{7} = \frac{18}{3}$, $\frac{7}{3} = \frac{42}{18}$, $\frac{10}{7} = \frac{60}{42}$, $-\frac{4}{7} = -\frac{24}{42}$ **2. a.** $\frac{13}{5}$
b. $\frac{y+8}{8}$ **3.** 1. $\frac{AB}{AD} = \frac{AC}{AE}$ (Given) 2. $\frac{AB - AD}{AD} = \frac{AC - AE}{AE}$ (Prop.
of Propor.) 3. $\frac{BD}{AD} = \frac{CE}{AE}$ (Seg. Add. Post.)

Exercise Set 6-2
1. $\frac{7}{14} = \frac{8}{16}$, $\frac{16}{8} = \frac{14}{7}$, $\frac{8}{7} = \frac{16}{14}$, $\frac{15}{8} = \frac{30}{16}$, $-\frac{1}{8} = -\frac{2}{16}$ **3.** $\frac{5}{125} =$
$\frac{3}{75}$, $\frac{75}{3} = \frac{125}{5}$, $\frac{3}{5} = \frac{75}{125}$, $\frac{200}{3} = \frac{50}{75}$ **5.** $\frac{u}{v} = \frac{8}{9}$, $\frac{9}{8} = \frac{v}{u}$, $\frac{8}{u} =$
$\frac{9}{v}$ $\frac{u+8}{8} = \frac{v+9}{9}$, $\frac{u-8}{8} = \frac{v-9}{9}$ **7.** $\frac{4}{y}$ **9.** $\frac{x+y}{y}$ **11.** $\frac{4}{3}$
13. 1. $\frac{LQ}{QM} = \frac{LR}{RN}$ (Given) 2. $\frac{LQ}{LR} = \frac{QM}{RN}$ (Prop. of Propor.)
15. 1. $\frac{LQ}{QM} = \frac{LR}{RN}$ (Given) 2. $\frac{QM}{LQ} = \frac{RN}{LR}$ (Prop. of Propor.)
3. $\frac{QM + LQ}{LQ} = \frac{RN + LR}{LR}$ (Prop. of Propor.) 4. $\frac{LM}{LQ} = \frac{LN}{LR}$ (Seg.
Add. Post.)   **17** 1. $\frac{LQ}{QM} = \frac{LR}{RN}$ (Given) 2. $\frac{QM}{LQ} = \frac{RN}{LR}$ (Prop. of
Propor.) 3. $\frac{LQ + QM}{LQ} = \frac{RN + LR}{LR}$ (Prop. of Propor.)   **19.** $\frac{b}{a}$
21. $\frac{u}{v}$ **23.** $\frac{u + 2v}{v}$ **25.** 5   **27.** $\frac{8}{5}$ **29.** 4, -1 **31.** 3, -3
33. 30, 21, 45   **35.** 14, 18, 39   **37.** 9, 12, 16   **39.** 28, 15,
27   **41.** 10, 16, 15   **43.** 1. $\frac{a}{b} = \frac{c}{d}$ (Given) 2. $ad = bc$
(Means/Extr.) 3. $\frac{a}{c} = \frac{b}{d}$ (Conv. of Means/Extr.)   **45.** 1. $\frac{a}{b} = \frac{c}{d}$
(Given) 2. $bc = ad$ (Means/Extr.) 3. $\frac{b}{a} = \frac{d}{c}$ (Conv. of
Means/Extr.)   **47.** 1. $\frac{a}{b} = \frac{c}{d}$ (Given) 2. $ad = bc$
(Means/Extr.) 3. $ad - bd = bc - bd$ (Sub. Prop.)
4. $(a - b)d = b(c - d)$ (Dist. Prop.) 5. $\frac{a-b}{b} = \frac{c-d}{d}$ (Conv.
of Means/Extr.)   **49.** $7\frac{1}{2}$ in. by $12\frac{1}{2}$ in.   **51.** 78 ft   **53.** 3,
6, 4, 8   **55.** 12, 6, 6, 3   **57.** $\frac{a}{b} = \frac{a+c+e+g...}{b+d+f+h...}$
59. Sometimes true; only if terms are added within ratio
itself and not across $=$ sign do new ratios form a propor.

Mixed Review
1. 34   **3.** 68   **5.** 118   **7.** 64   **9.** 46   **11.** 26
13. 1. $\triangle PQR$ is isos. (Given) 2. $\overline{PQ} \cong \overline{PR}$ (Def. isos. $\triangle$)
3. $\overline{PT}$ is an alt. (Given) 4. $\overline{PT}$ bisects $\angle QPR$. (In isos. $\triangle$ the
alt. to the base bisects the vertex $\angle$.) 5. $\angle QPS \cong \angle RPS$
(An $\angle$ bis. forms 2 $\cong \angle$s.) 6. $\overline{PS} \cong \overline{PS}$ (Reflex. Prop.)
7. $\triangle PQS \cong \triangle PRS$ (SAS)

Lesson 6-3 Try This

8

Exercise Set 6-3

1. $\angle E$ **3.** $\angle U$ **5.** $\frac{6}{5}$ **7.** $\frac{5}{6}$ **9.** 30   **11.** $\angle C$ **13.** $\frac{84}{5}$
15. $\frac{70}{3}$ **17.** $\frac{5}{3}$ **19.** $\frac{3}{5}$ **21.** 32   **23.** $\angle P$ **25.** 15   **27.** 8
29. (3, 2) or (3, 4)   **31.** $C'(-2, 1\frac{1}{2})$, $D'(-2, 3\frac{1}{2})$; $C'(-4, 1\frac{1}{2})$, $D'(-4, 3\frac{1}{2})$ **33.** 18   **35.** 24   **37.** 52   **39.** $\frac{56}{9}$
41. 1. $\overline{AB} \parallel \overline{DE}$ (Given) 2. $\angle CDE \cong \angle A$, $\angle CED \cong \angle B$ (When $\parallel$ lines are cut by a trans., corr. $\angle$s are $\cong$.) 3. $\angle C \cong \angle C$ (Reflex. Prop.) 4. $CD + DA = CA = 9$, $CE + EB = CB = 12$ (Seg. Add.) 5. $\frac{6}{9} = \frac{8}{12} = \frac{12}{18}$ (Prop. of Propor.) 6. $\frac{CD}{CA} = \frac{CE}{CB} = \frac{DE}{AB}$ (Subst.) 7. $\triangle ABC \sim \triangle DEC$ (Def. $\sim$ $\triangle$s.)   **43.** $x\sqrt{2}$ **45.** $x\sqrt{2}$ **47.** 1. $\triangle ACD$ and $\triangle ABC$ are rt. $\triangle$s. $y = x\sqrt{2}$ (Given) 2. $\angle ADC \cong \angle ACB$ (All rt. $\angle$s are $\cong$.) 3. $\angle A \cong \angle A$ (Reflex. Prop.) 4. $\angle ACD \cong \angle ABC$ (If 2 $\angle$s of one $\triangle$ are $\cong$ to 2 $\angle$s of another $\triangle$, the third $\angle$s are $\cong$.) 5. $m\angle ACD = m\angle ABC = 45$ (Acute $\angle$s of rt. $\triangle$ are comp.) 6. $CD = x$, $CB = y = x\sqrt{2}$ (If 2 $\angle$s of $\triangle$ are $\cong$, sides opp. are $\cong$.) 7. $m\angle DCB = 45$ (Acute $\angle$s of rt. $\triangle$ are comp.) 8. $DB = x$ (If 2 $\angle$s of $\triangle$ are $\cong$, sides opp. are $\cong$.) 9. $AB = AD + DB = x + x = 2x$ (Seg. Add. Post.) 10. $\frac{AC}{AB} = \frac{CD}{CB} = \frac{AD}{AC} = \frac{1}{\sqrt{2}}$ (Subst.) 11. $\triangle ACD \sim \triangle ABC$ (Def. $\sim$ $\triangle$s)
49. always true   **51.** sometimes true   **53. a.** 3, 5, 7, 9, 11 **b.** 4, 7, 10, 13, 16 **c.** 2, 7, 12, 17, 22

Algebra Review

1. $x + (x + 12) + (x + 24) = 180$; 48, 60, 72
3. $3x + 4x + 6x = 39$; 9, 12, 18
5. $2x + 4x + 7x + 11x = 360$; 30, 60, 105, 165

Lesson 6-4 Try This

1. 18, 15   **2.** $\frac{75}{8}$

Exercise Set 6-4

1. $\triangle AED$ **3.** 8   **5.** 10   **7.** $\frac{20}{3}$, 9   **9.** $\triangle ABE \sim \triangle ACD$, 4, 5   **11.** $\triangle ZXY \sim \triangle WXZ \sim \triangle WZY$, $\frac{64}{15}$, $\frac{136}{15}$ **13.** 1. $\angle ABC$ and $\angle BDC$ are rt. $\angle$s. (Given) 2. $\angle ABC \cong \angle BDC$ (All rt. are $\cong$.) 3. $\angle C \cong \angle C$ (Reflex. Prop.) 4. $\triangle ABC \sim \triangle BDC$ (Th. 6.3)   **15.** 1. $\angle ADB$, $\angle DEC$, and $\angle ABC$ are rt. $\angle$s. (Given) 2. $\triangle ABC$, $\triangle DEC$, $\triangle ADB$ are rt. $\triangle$s. (Def. rt. $\triangle$s) 3. $\angle A \cong \angle A$, $\angle C \cong \angle C$ (Reflex. Prop.) 4. $\triangle ABC \sim \triangle ADB$, $\triangle ABC \sim \triangle DEC$ (Th. 6.3) 5. $\triangle ADB \sim \triangle DEC$ (Trans. Prop.)   **17.** $134\frac{5}{14}$ ft   **19.** 75 m   **21.** 1. $\overline{AB} \parallel \overline{ED}$ (Given) 2. $\angle 3 \cong \angle 4$ ($\parallel$ lines cut by trans., alter. int. $\angle$s are $\cong$.) 3. $\angle 1 \cong \angle 2$ (Vert. $\angle$s are $\cong$.) 4. $\triangle ABC \sim \triangle EDC$ (AA) 5. $\frac{AB}{ED} = \frac{BC}{DC}$ (Def. $\sim$ $\triangle$s)   **23.** $\triangle DFE \sim \triangle CFB$, $\frac{16}{3}$, $\frac{63}{4}$ **25.** When diag. $\overline{OT}$ passes through M, then $\triangle OMN$ and $\triangle OTU$ are $\sim$ as they are both rt. $\triangle$s and share $\angle MON$.
27. similar   **29.** Given: $\overline{AB} \parallel \overline{A'B'}$ Prove: $\triangle LAB \sim \triangle LB'A'$ 1. $\overline{AB} \parallel \overline{A'B'}$ (Given) 2. $\angle B' \cong \angle A$, $\angle B \cong \angle A'$ ($\parallel$ lines cut by trans., alter. int. $\angle$s are $\cong$.) 3. $\triangle LAB \sim \triangle LB'A'$ (Post. 19)   **31.** $\frac{x}{20} = \frac{AB}{A'B'}$, $A'B' = \frac{20\,AB}{x}$
33. halved   **35.** 1. $\angle A$, $\angle C$ are rt. $\angle$s. (Given) 2. $\angle A \cong \angle C$ (All rt. $\angle$s are $\cong$.) 3. $\triangle AEB$ is isos. (Given) 4. $\angle EAB \cong \angle EBA$ (Isos. $\triangle$ Th.) 5. $\triangle DAB \sim \triangle FCA$. (Post. 19) 6. $\frac{AD}{CF} = \frac{BD}{AF}$ (Lengths of sides of $\sim$ $\triangle$s are in propor.) 7. $AD \cdot AF = CF \cdot BD$ (Prop. of Propor.)   **37.** 1. $\overline{AB} \cong \overline{AC}$ (Given) 2. $\angle ABC \cong \angle C$ (Isos. $\triangle$ Th.) 3. $\angle A \cong \angle CBD$

(Given) 4. $\triangle ABC \sim \triangle BDC$ (Post. 19) 5. $\frac{AC}{BD} = \frac{BC}{CD}$ (Def. $\sim$ $\triangle$s) 6. $AB = AC$ (Def. $\cong$ seg.) 7. $\frac{AB}{BD} = \frac{BC}{CD}$ (Subst.)   **39.** 12   **41.** 108°: $\angle ABC$, $\angle BCD$, $\angle CDE$, $\angle DEA$, $\angle EAB$, $\angle EJA$, $\angle AFB$, $\angle BGC$, $\angle CHD$, $\angle DIE$, $\angle DJB$, $\angle EFC$, $\angle AGD$, $\angle BHE$, $\angle CIA$; 36°: $\angle EAJ$, $\angle JAF$, $\angle FAB$, $\angle ABF$, $\angle FBG$, $\angle GBC$, $\angle BCG$, $\angle GCH$, $\angle HCD$, $\angle CDH$, $\angle HDI$, $\angle IDE$, $\angle DEI$, $\angle IEJ$, $\angle JEA$; 72°: $\angle AJB$, $\angle AFE$, $\angle BFC$, $\angle BGA$, $\angle CGD$, $\angle CHB$, $\angle DHE$, $\angle DIC$, $\angle EIA$, $\angle EJD$, $\angle EAC$, $\angle DAB$, $\angle ABD$, $\angle EBC$, $\angle BCE$, $\angle ACD$, $\angle CDA$, $\angle BDE$, $\angle DEB$, $\angle CEA$ **43.** $\frac{EJ}{EF} = \frac{EF}{EB}$, $\frac{x}{1} = \frac{1}{1+x}$, $x + x^2 = 1$, $x^2 + x - 1 = 0$. By the quad. eq. $x = \frac{-1 \pm \sqrt{5}}{2}$. So that $x > 0$, $x = \frac{-1 + \sqrt{5}}{2}$.

Mixed Review

1. If 2 $\triangle$s are equilat., then they are $\sim$.   **3.** If 2 $\triangle$s are not $\sim$, then they are not equilat.   **5.** Any 2 $\sim$ $\triangle$s with scale factor $\neq 1$ are $\neq$.

Lesson 6-5 Try This

1. $\frac{AB}{XY} = \frac{AC}{XZ}$ **2.** $\frac{2}{1}$ **3.** $x = 6 = AD = AE$, $BC = AC = 9$

Exercise Set 6-5

1. $\frac{126}{11}$ or $\frac{198}{7}$, SAS   **3.** $\frac{21}{5}$, SAS   **5.** $\frac{95}{4}$ or $\frac{76}{5}$, SAS   **7.** $\frac{25}{4}$, SAS   **9.** $\frac{14}{3}$, SAS or SSS   **11.** $\frac{UA}{RB} = \frac{UZ}{RN}$ **13.** $\frac{XY}{UV} = \frac{YZ}{VW} = \frac{XZ}{UW}$ **15.** no   **17.** 1. $\frac{AO}{CO} = \frac{BO}{DO}$ (Given) 2. $\angle 1 \cong \angle 2$ (Vert. $\angle$s are $\cong$.) 3. $\triangle AOB \sim \triangle COD$ (SAS) 4. $\angle B \cong \angle D$ (Def. $\sim$ $\triangle$s)   **19.** $\frac{12}{5}$ **21.** 2.1 m   **23.** $\frac{DC}{AC} = \frac{FC}{EC} = \frac{DF}{AE}$ **25.** Increase by ≈ 0.74 ft.   **27.** $\triangle ABF \sim \triangle ACE$ **29.** none   **31.** none   **33.** $WY = 3XZ$ since $\triangle WOY \sim \triangle XOZ$ by SAS and $\frac{WY}{XZ} = \frac{OW}{OX} = 3$.   **35.** $\frac{DE}{CB} = \frac{DF}{AC} = \frac{EF}{AB} = \frac{2}{1}$ so $\triangle DFE \sim \triangle FED$ and then $\angle DFE \cong \angle CAB$.   **37.** 1. $\angle A \cong \angle CBD$ (Given) 2. $\angle C \cong \angle C$ (Reflex. Prop.) 3. $\triangle ACB \sim \triangle BCD$ (AA) 4. $\frac{AC}{BC} = \frac{BC}{DC}$ (Lengths of corr. sides of $\sim$ $\triangle$s are propor.) 5. $AC \cdot DC = BC \cdot BC$ (Prop. of Propor.)   **39.** $\frac{AB}{AC} = \frac{DE}{DF}$ (since $AB = DE$ and $AC = DF$) and $\angle B \cong \angle E$ but $\triangle$s are not $\sim$.   **41. a.** $AC_3 \cdot AC_4 = (AB_3)^2$, $AC_4 \cdot AC_5 = (AB_4)^2$ **b.** $AB_3 \cdot AB_4 = (AC_4)^2$, $AB_4 \cdot AB_5 = (AC_5)^2$

Algebra Review

1. 3, -3 **3.** 2, -2 **5.** -2, 2   **7.** 4, -4

Lesson 6-6 Try This

1. $\frac{10}{3}$ **2.** 3, $\frac{15}{4}$ **3.** $\frac{65}{17}$, $\frac{156}{17}$

Exercise Set 6-6

1. 9, $\triangle$ Propor. Seg.   **3.** 12, $\parallel$s Propor. Seg.   **5.** $\frac{81}{7}$, $\parallel$s Propor. Seg.   **7.** $\frac{3}{5}$ **9.** $\frac{40}{3}$ **11.** $\frac{21}{5}$ **13.** 8   **15.** $\frac{11}{4}$ **17.** Method works by $\triangle$ Propor. Seg. Th.   **19.** 6, 2, $\frac{21}{2}$, $\frac{7}{2}$ **21.** 10
23. Plan: Extend lines CA and DB so they intersect at pt. E. $\triangle EAB \sim \triangle ECD$ by AA. ($\angle E \cong \angle E$ by Reflex. Prop., $\angle EAB \cong \angle ECD$ because corr. $\angle$s are $\cong$ when $\parallel$ lines are cut by a trans.) Draw $\overrightarrow{EX}$. Where it intersects $\overline{CD}$ is point Y. We know that $\frac{EA}{EC} = \frac{EB}{ED}$. Also $\frac{EA}{EC} = \frac{AX}{CY}$ and $\frac{EB}{ED} = \frac{XB}{YD}$. By subst., $\frac{AX}{CY} = \frac{XB}{YD}$. By a Prop. of Propor. (switching the means) $\frac{AX}{XB} = \frac{CY}{YD}$.   **25.** 1. Draw aux. seg. $\overline{BE} \parallel$ to $\overline{CD}$. Extend $\overline{AC}$ to E. (Through a pt. not on a given line, a line $\parallel$ to the given line may be drawn.) 2. $\angle 1 \cong \angle 2$ (Given) 3. $\angle 1 \cong \angle 4$ ($\parallel$ lines cut by trans., corr. $\angle$s are $\cong$.) 4. $\angle 2 \cong \angle 4$ (Th. 1.3) 5. $\angle 2 \cong \angle 3$ ($\parallel$ lines cut by trans., alter. int. $\angle$s are $\cong$.)

6. $\angle 3 \cong \angle 4$ (Th. 1.3) 7. $\overline{CE} \cong \overline{CB}$ (Sides opp. $\cong \angle$s are $\cong$.) 8. $\frac{AD}{DB} = \frac{AC}{CE}$ ($\triangle$Propor. Seg. Th.) 9. $\frac{AD}{DB} = \frac{AC}{CB}$ (Subst.)
27.

Given: $\triangle BAC \sim \triangle EDF$, $\overline{BG}$ and $\overline{EH}$ are alt.
Prove: $\frac{BG}{EH} = \frac{AB}{DE}$
Proof: $\angle A \cong \angle D$ (Def. $\sim \triangle$s), $\angle AGB \cong \angle DHE$ (All rt. $\angle$s are $\cong$.), $\triangle AGB \sim \triangle DHE$ (AA), so $\frac{BG}{EH} = \frac{AB}{DE}$
29. $\frac{12}{5}$, $\frac{18}{5}$ 31. a. never b. $\overline{AX} \parallel \overline{BB'}$ (Th. 3.1), so $\frac{AB}{BC} = \frac{XB'}{B'C}$ (Th. 6.6). Also, $\overline{B'Y} \parallel \overline{CZ}$ so by Th. 6.6, $\frac{XB'}{B'C} = \frac{XY}{YZ}$. Put the 2 eq. together to get $\frac{AB}{BC} = \frac{XY}{YZ}$.

Mixed Review

1. 82.5 mi 3. 10 mi 5. scalene 7. acute, isosceles

Chapter Review

1. $\frac{t}{5}$ 2. $\frac{11}{3}$ 3. $4y:5$ 4. $\frac{5x}{2y}$ 5. $\frac{35}{3}$ 6. 6 7. 30°, 150°
8. 15, 27 9. 5y 10. $\frac{w}{4}$ 11. $\frac{x}{3}$ 12. $\frac{4-w}{w}$ 13. 17
14. 13 15. 19 16. 4 17. -6, 2 18. -2, 3 19. 3 mi
20. 60 yd x 40 yd 21. 52 22. 23 23. 15 24. 8 25. $\frac{2}{3}$
26. $\triangle SWX$, AA 27. 1. $\overline{RS} \parallel \overline{UT}$ (Given) 2. $\angle RSU \cong \angle TUS$ ($\parallel$ lines cut by trans., alt. int. $\angle$s are $\cong$.)
3. $\angle WXS \cong \angle VXU$ (Vert. $\angle$s are $\cong$.) 4. $\triangle WXZ \sim \triangle VXU$ (AA) 28. ≈ 25.5 ft 29. $6\frac{3}{4}$ or 6 ft 9 in. 30. yes, SAS
31. $\triangle$s not $\sim$ 32. yes, SSS 33. $\frac{RT}{GI} = \frac{ST}{HI}$ 34. $\frac{WX}{DE} = \frac{XY}{EF} = \frac{WY}{DF}$ 35. 1. $\square DFGI$ (Given) 2. $\overline{DF} \parallel \overline{IG}$ (Def. $\square$)
3. $\angle FDG \cong \angle IGD$ ($\parallel$ lines cut by trans., alt. int. $\angle$s are $\cong$.) 4. $\angle DJE \cong \angle GJH$ (Vert. $\angle$s are $\cong$.) 5. $\triangle DJE \sim \triangle GJH$ (AA) 6. $\frac{DE}{GH} = \frac{EJ}{HJ}$ (Sides of $\sim \triangle$s are propor.)
7. $DE \cdot HJ = EJ \cdot GH$ (Means/Extr.) 36. $\frac{20}{7}$ 37. 6

CHAPTER 7

Lesson 7-1 Try This

1. $\frac{2\sqrt{5}}{5}$ 2. 6 3. 20 4. 10

Exercise Set 7-1

1. $2\sqrt{2}$ 3. $\frac{\sqrt{2}}{2}$ 5. $\frac{2\sqrt{5}}{15}$ 7. 12 9. $\sqrt[4]{15}$ 11. 10, $x = \sqrt{30}$ 13. 3, $z = \sqrt{39}$ 15. y, $y = \sqrt{130}$
17. $4\sqrt{3}$ 19. 12 21. $GH = 6\sqrt{3}$, $HK = 6$ 23. xy
25. xc 27. 27 29. $\frac{32}{3}$ 31. $\frac{8}{5}$ 33. $4\sqrt{3}$ 35. 2 or 8
37. $\frac{64}{5}$ 39. $8\sqrt{2}$ 41. $8\sqrt{3}$ km 43. $16\sqrt{3}$ cm 45. By Th. 7.1, $\triangle ACB$, $\triangle ADC$, and $\triangle CDB$ are $\sim$. Because $\overline{DB}$ in $\triangle DCB$ corr. to $\overline{CB}$ in $\triangle ACB$ and $\overline{CB}$ in $\triangle DCB$ corr. to $\overline{AB}$ in $\triangle ACB$, $\frac{DB}{CB} = \frac{CB}{AB}$, or $\frac{y}{a} = \frac{a}{c}$. Because $\overline{AD}$ in $\triangle ACD$ corr. to $\overline{AC}$ in $\triangle ACB$ and $\overline{AC}$ in $\triangle ACD$ corr. to $\overline{AB}$ in $\triangle ACB$, $\frac{AD}{AC} = \frac{AC}{AB}$ or $\frac{b}{x} = \frac{c}{b}$. 47. Given AB is the geo. mean between BC and AC or $\frac{BC}{AB} = \frac{AB}{AC}$, prove $\frac{AB}{AC} = \frac{AC}{AD}$. If $CD = AB$, then all propor. can be written in terms of AB and BC. Given $\frac{BC}{AB} = \frac{AB}{AB + BC}$ prove $\frac{AB}{AB + BC} = \frac{AB + BC}{2AB + BC} \cdot \frac{BC}{AB} = \frac{AB}{AB + BC}$ is equiv. to $(BC)^2 + AB \cdot BC = AB^2$. Now add $(AB)^2 + AB \cdot BC$ to both sides of the eq. to get $(BC)^2 + 2AB \cdot BC + (AB)^2 = 2(AB)^2 + AB \cdot BC$ or $(AC + BC)^2 = AB(2AB + BC)$. $(AC + BC)^2 = AB(2AB + BC)$ is equiv. to the propor. $\frac{AB}{AB + BC} = \frac{AB + BC}{2AB + BC}$.
49. Let $AD = x$ and $DC = d - x$. By Th. 7.2, $\frac{x}{c} = \frac{c}{d-x}$ or $x(d - x) = c^2$. By Th. 7.3, $\frac{x}{a} = \frac{a}{d}$ and $\frac{d-x}{b} = \frac{b}{d}$. Multiply the propor.: $\frac{x}{a} \cdot \frac{d-x}{b} = \frac{a}{d} \cdot \frac{b}{d}$ or $d^2 \cdot x(d - x) = a^2 b^2$, so $d^2 c^2 = a^2 b^2$, or $cd = ab$. Product of length of alt. to hyp. and length of hyp. $=$ product of lengths of the two legs.

Algebra Review

1. 2 3. $4a$ 5. $\frac{3}{4}$ 7. $5a$ 9. $\frac{\sqrt{3a}}{3}$ 11. $\frac{2c\sqrt{5}}{5}$

Lesson 7-2 Try This

17

Exercise Set 7-2

1. 5 3. 8 5. $2\sqrt{6}$ 7. 10 9. $2\sqrt{2}$ 11. $\sqrt{5}$
13. $6\sqrt{2}$ 15. ≈ 25 in. 17. 10 19. $2\sqrt{2}$ 21. $4\sqrt{2}$
23. Answers may vary. $d = \sqrt{2}s$ 25. 20 27. $\sqrt{23}$
29. $\frac{3\sqrt{5}}{5}$ 31. $8\sqrt{3}$ 33. $a = 10$, $b = 2\sqrt{29}$ 35. $x = 1$, $y = 2\sqrt{2}$, $h = 3$ 37. $10 + 2\sqrt{39}$ 39. $4\sqrt{2}$ ft ≈ 5 ft 8 in. 41. yes 43. 24 45. $2\sqrt{6}$ 47. $6 + 2\sqrt{5} + 2\sqrt{10} + 2\sqrt{2}$ 49. Construct a rt. $\triangle$ with hyp. $=$ the length of seg. shown in text. 51. $AB = \sqrt{2}$, $AC = \sqrt{3}$, $AD = 2$, $AE = \sqrt{5}$ Construct seg. with lengths $\sqrt{6}$ and $\sqrt{7}$. 53. Draw a vert. line through point F, as shown.

By the Pythag. Th., $PC^2 + x^2 = c^2$, $DQ^2 + y^2 = d^2$, $AP^2 + x^2 = a^2$, and $QB^2 + y^2 = b^2$. Then, $a^2 + b^2 = AP^2 + x^2 + QB^2 + y^2 = DQ^2 + x^2 + PC^2 + y^2 = (PC^2 + x^2) + (DQ^2 + y^2) = c^2 + d^2$. NOTE: $PC = QB$ and $AP = DQ$ 55. $d = \sqrt{3}s$

Mixed Review

1. alt. int.   **3.** 110   **5.** $180 - m\angle BEF$ **7.** 120

Lesson 7-3 Try This

1. no   **2.** No; it is an acute $\triangle$.

Exercise Set 7-3

1. obtuse   **3.** acute   **5.** rt.   **7.** acute   **9.** acute   **11.** rt.
13. obtuse   **15.** yes, yes; $9^2 + 40^2 = 41^2$ and $18^2 + 80^2 = 81^2$ **17.** obtuse   **19.** $x = 47$; 14, 48, 50   **21.** $90\sqrt{2}$
23. $ED^2 + DC^2 = EC^2$, so $25 + 576 = 601$. $EC = AC = \sqrt{601}$. If $\triangle ABC$ is rt. then $BC^2 + AB^2 = AC^2$. $144 + 529 = 673$, which is > 601. $\triangle ABC$ is acute.   **25.** Using the Dist. Form., $AC = \sqrt{13}$, $BC = 5$, and $AB = 6$. By Th. 7.6, $AC^2 + BC^2 = AB^2$ if $\triangle ABC$ is rt. $13 + 25 > 36$, so $\triangle ABC$ is acute.   **27.** $a^2 + b^2 = (2n + 1)^2 + (2n^2 + 2n)^2 = 4n^4 + 8n^3 + 8n^2 + 4n + 1$. $c^2 = (2n^2 + 2n + 1)^2 = 4n^4 + 8n^3 + 8n^2 + 4n + 1$ so $a^2 + b^2 = c^2$, and a, b, and c is a Pythag. Triple.   **29.** $\triangle A'B'C'$ will be acute by Th. 7.6, if $(a + k)^2 + (b + k)^2 > (c + k)^2$. $a^2 + 2ak + k^2 + b^2 + 2bk + k^2 = c^2 + 2k^2 + 2k(a + b)$. By $\triangle$ Ineq. Th., $a + b \geq c$, so $c^2 + 2k^2 + 2k(a + b) > c^2 + 2ck + k^2$. $(a + k)^2 + (b + k)^2 = c^2 + 2k^2 + 2k(a + b) > c^2 + 2kc + k^2 = (c + k)^2$.

Algebra Review

1. 3   **3.** 5   **5.** -2 **7.** 2   **9.** $\frac{1}{3}$

Lesson 7-4 Try This

1. $12\sqrt{2}$ cm ≈ 17 cm   **2.** length = $5\sqrt{3}$, diag. length = 10

Exercise Set 7-4

1. 6, $6\sqrt{2}$ **3.** 2.5, $\frac{5\sqrt{2}}{2}$ **5.** 7, 7   **7.** $4\sqrt{3}$, 8   **9.** 3, $3\sqrt{3}$ **11.** 5, 10   **13.** 12   **15.** $12 + 12\sqrt{3}$ **17.** $5\sqrt{2}$ cm   **19.** 6   **21.** 6   **23.** 60   **25.** 90   **27.** 45   **29.** 6   **31.** $6\sqrt{3}$ **33.** 12   **35.** $3\sqrt{3}$ m   **37.** $26 + 8\sqrt{2} + 6\sqrt{3}$ **39.** $x = 3\sqrt{2}$, $y = \frac{3\sqrt{2}}{2}$, $z = \frac{3\sqrt{6}}{2}$ **41.** Construct $\triangle ACD$ such that $\triangle ACD \cong \triangle ACB$ and the rt. $\angle$s are adj.

$\triangle ABD$ is equiang., since $30° + 30° = 60°$. By Cor. 4.2a, $\triangle ABD$ is equilat. Therefore, $2a = c$. By Pythag. Th., $a^2 + b^2 = c^2$. Subst. $2a$ for c: $c = 2a$, $a^2 + b^2 = 4a^2$ or $b^2 = 3a^2$ and $b = \sqrt{3}a$.   **43.** 15   **45.** $AG = 8$, $AF = 4\sqrt{3}$ **47.** Alt. $\overline{BD}$ divides $\triangle ABC$ into 2 smaller $30°$–$60°$–$90°\triangle$s, $\triangle ABD$ and $\triangle BCD$. By Th. 7.6, $h = \sqrt{3}x$ and $y = \sqrt{3}h$. Subst. for h, $y = \sqrt{3} \cdot \sqrt{3}x = 3x$, so y is 3 × as long as x.

Mixed Review

1. always   **3.** never   **5.** always   **7.** never

Lesson 7-5 Try This

1. $\tan A = \frac{5}{12}$, $\tan B = \frac{12}{5}$ **2.** ≈ 8.15 **3.** ≈ 21

Exercise Set 7-5

1. $\tan A = \frac{12}{5}$, $\tan B = \frac{5}{12}$ **3.** $\tan A = \frac{8}{15}$, $\tan B = \frac{15}{8}$ **5.** 0.343   **7.** 62   **9.** 0.7002   **11.** 57.2900   **13.** 50°
15. 80°   **17.** 45   **19.** 8.40   **21.** 50°   **23.** 25   **25.** ≈ 24
27. ≈ 6.95 **29.** ≈ 35.75 **31.** ≈ 11.41 cm   **33.** 53, 37
35. ≈ 10 **37.** 21.45   **39.** ≈ 77, ≈ 13 **41.** ≈ 326 m
43. Given a as the length of side opp. $\angle A$ and b as the length of side adj. to $\angle A$, then as $m\angle A$ increases, a remains the same and b decreases. So the ratio $\frac{a}{b}$, or $\tan A$, increases. yes, $\tan 89.43 \approx 100$

Mixed Review

1. ASA   **3.** SAS

Lesson 7-6 Try This

1. ≈ 13.42 **2.** ≈ 64 **3.** ≈ 33.29

Exercise Set 7-6

1. $\sin \angle A = \cos \angle B = \frac{12}{13}$, $\cos \angle A = \sin \angle B = \frac{5}{13}$ **3.** $\sin \angle A = \cos \angle B = \frac{18}{17}$, $\cos \angle A = \sin \angle B = \frac{15}{17}$ **5.** 0.6561
7. 40   **9.** 85   **11.** $x \approx 23.93$, $y \approx 10.16$ **13.** a. $x = 35 \cdot \cos 37°$, $y = 35 \cdot \cos 53°$ b. $x = 26 \cdot \cos 23°$, $y = 26 \cdot \cos 67°$ c. $x = 75 \cos 74°$, $y = 75 \cos 16°$ **15.** $m\angle A \approx 62$, $m\angle B \approx 28$ **17.** 24.61   **19.** 57.96   **21.** $\sin 45° = \frac{\sqrt{2}}{2}$, $\sin 60° = \frac{\sqrt{3}}{2}$, $\cos 30° = \frac{\sqrt{3}}{2}$, $\cos 45° = \frac{\sqrt{2}}{2}$, $\cos 60° = \frac{1}{2}$, $\tan 30° = \frac{\sqrt{3}}{3}$, $\tan 45° = 1$, $\tan 60° = \sqrt{3}$ **23.** ≈ 14.83 cm
25. $\frac{\sqrt{39}}{8}$ **27.** sometimes   **29.** never   **31.** 8, 60   **33.** ≈ 4.88, ≈ 11.13 **35.** 250.47 m   **37.** $\sin A = 0.6$, $\cos A = 0.8$, $\sin B = 0.8$, $\cos B = 0.6$ **39.** 60 km east   **41.** a. 1   b. 1
c. $(\sin x)^2 + (\cos x)^2 = 1$ d. $\frac{\sin x}{\cos x} = \tan x$ e. By Pythag.
Th., $a^2 + b^2 = c^2$. Divide by c^2: $\left(\frac{a}{c}\right)^2 + \left(\frac{b}{c}\right)^2 = 1$. $\frac{a}{c} = \sin A$, $\frac{b}{c} = \cos A$, so $(\sin A)^2 + (\cos A)^2 = 1$. $\tan A = \frac{a}{b} = \frac{\frac{a}{c}}{\frac{b}{c}} = \frac{\sin A}{\cos A}$.

Algebra Review

1. -5, 5   **3.** -4, 10   **5.** -1, 11   **7.** $-17\frac{1}{2}$, 16

Lesson 7-7 Try This

1. ≈ 7.9 m   **2.** ≈ 5.23 km

Exercise Set 7-7

1. ≈ 275.19 ft   **3.** ≈ 4.20 km   **5.** ≈ 158.60 ft   **7.** ≈ 5.71 km   **9.** ≈ 25.16 km   **11.** ≈ 2.08 min   **13.** ≈ 1145.43 m

Mixed Review

1. $\angle S$ **3.** $\overline{RT}$ **5.** 8   **7.** 3:2

Chapter Review

1. 9   **2.** $2\sqrt{6}$ **3.** 15   **4.** 18   **5.** $2\sqrt{13}$ **6.** 15
7. $2\sqrt{14}$ **8.** 8 in.   **9.** obtuse   **10.** rt.   **11.** acute
12. $7\sqrt{2}$ **13.** $x = 5$, $y = 10$ **14.** $x = 4$, $y = 4\sqrt{3}$, $z = 4\sqrt{3}$ **15.** ≈ 0.4245 **16.** ≈ 2.4751 **17.** $\approx 37°$
18. ≈ 2.9713 **19.** ≈ 55 **20.** $\sin 32° = \frac{4}{x}$, ≈ 7.5483
21. $\cos 72° = \frac{x}{14}$, ≈ 4.3262 **22.** $\sin x = \frac{7}{12}$, $\approx 19°$
23. ≈ 240 ft

CHAPTER 8

Exercise Set 8-1

1. $\overline{PA}$, $\overline{PB}$, $\overline{PE}$, $\overline{PF}$; 8   **3.** 2   **5.** $\overline{EF}$ **7.** $\overline{PE} \cong \overline{PF}$ (radii of $\odot P$), $\overline{QE} \cong \overline{QF}$ (radii of $\odot Q$), $\overline{PQ} \cong \overline{PQ}$ (Reflex. Prop.), $\triangle PEQ \cong \triangle PFQ$ (SSS)
9. $\triangle ABC$ **11.** $\overrightarrow{AC}$, $\overrightarrow{BC}$, $\overleftrightarrow{AB}$; the larger circle   **13.** 2
15. none
17.   **19.**   **21.**

23. never true   **25.** always true   **27.** 0.035 cm
29. 0.297 in.   **31.** never   **33.** always   **35.** 2

Mixed Review

1. 105   **3.** 25   **5.** 50   **7.** 3.6 cm

Lesson 8-2   Try This

1. 13   **2.** $\sqrt{176}$ **3.** 86

Exercise Set 8-2

1. 24   **3.** 64   **5.** 142   **7.** 9   **9.** 2   **11.** 3   **13.** 24
15. 1. $\angle 1 \cong \angle 2 \cong \angle 3$ (Given) 2. $m\angle 1 = m\angle 2 = m\angle 3$ (Def. $\cong \angle$s) 3. $m\angle 1 + m\angle 2 + m\angle 3 = 360$ (No. of degrees in $\odot$) 4. $m\angle 1 = m\angle 2 = m\angle 3 = 120$ (Div. Prop.) 5. $m\angle ADH = m\angle CDH = m\angle CFH = m\angle BFH = m\angle BEH = m\angle AEH = 90$ (Line tan. to $\odot$ is $\perp$ to radius at point of tan.) 6. $m\angle A = m\angle B = m\angle C = 60$ (Sum of measures in quad. is 360.) 7. $\triangle ABC$ is equiang. and therefore equilat.   **17.** Edges of board are line seg. If a line is $\perp$ a radius of $\odot$ at pt. on $\odot$, then line is tan. to $\odot$. 2 edges of board are tan. to $\odot$.   **19.** 1. $\overline{PA}$ and $\overline{PB}$ are tan. to $\odot O$. (Given) 2. $\overline{PA} \cong \overline{PB}$ (Tan. seg.from ext. point of $\odot$ are $\cong$.) 3. $\overline{PO} \cong \overline{PO}$ (Reflex. Prop.) 4. $\overline{OA} \cong \overline{OB}$ (Radii of $\odot$ are $\cong$.) 5. $\triangle PAO \cong \triangle PBO$ (SSS) 6. $\angle OPA \cong \angle OPB$ (Corr. parts of $\cong \triangle$s) 7. $\overline{OP}$ bis. $\angle PBA$. (Def. $\angle$ bis.)
21.

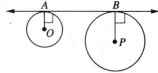

23. 1. $\overline{PA}$ and $\overline{PB}$ are tan. from ext. pt. P. (Given) 2. $\overline{PA} \cong \overline{PB}$ (Tan. seg. from ext. pt. of $\odot$ are $\cong$.) 3. $\triangle PAB$ is isos. (Def. isos. $\triangle$) 4. $\angle 3 \cong \angle 4$ (Base $\angle$s of isos. $\triangle$ are $\cong$.)
25. 19   **27.** 30   **29.** 1. $\overline{AB} \parallel \overline{DE}$ (Given) 2. $m\angle ABC + m\angle EDB = 180$ ($\parallel$ lines cut by a trans., same-side int. $\angle$s are supp.) 3. $m\angle ABC = 2m\angle OBC$, $m\angle EDB = 2m\angle BDO$ (Line through ext. pt. and center of $\odot$ bis. $\angle$ formed by tan. from ext. pt.) 4. $2m\angle OBC + 2m\angle BDO = 180$ (Subst.) 5. $2(m\angle OBC + m\angle BDO) = 180$ (Dist. Prop.) 6. $m\angle OBC + m\angle BDO = 90$ (Div. Prop.) 7. $m\angle OBC + m\angle BDO + m\angle BOD = 180$ (Sum of measures of $\angle$s of $\triangle$ is 180.) 8. $m\angle BOD = 90$ (Sub. Prop.) 9. $\angle BOD$ is a rt. $\angle$. (Def. rt. $\angle$) 10. $\overline{BO} \perp \overline{DO}$ ($\perp$ lines form rt. $\angle$s.)
31. 1. quad. $WXYZ$ circumscribed about a $\odot$ (Given) 2. $\overline{XM} \cong \overline{XN}$, $\overline{YN} \cong \overline{YO}$, $\overline{ZO} \cong \overline{ZP}$, $\overline{WP} \cong \overline{WM}$ (Tan. seg.

from ext. pt. of circle are $\cong$.) 3. $XM = XN = x$, $YN = YO = y$, $ZO = ZP = z$, $WP = WM = w$ (Def. $\cong$ seg.) 4. $WX = w + x$, $XY = x + y$, $YZ = y + z$, $WZ = w + z$ (Seg. Add. Post.) 5. $XY + WZ = (x + y) + (w + z)$, $WX + YZ = (w + x) + (y + z)$ (Add Prop.) 6. $XY + WZ = WX + YZ$ (Trans. Prop.)   **33.** $P_1 P_2 \ldots P_n$ is reg. poly. of n sides. $\triangle A_1 O P_1 \cong \triangle A_2 O P_1 \cong A_2 O P_2 \cong \ldots$ by ASA so $\overline{A_1 P_1} \cong \overline{P_1 A_2} \cong \overline{A_2 P_2}$ by corr. parts of $\cong \triangle$s. Therefore, $\overline{P_1 P_2} \cong \overline{P_2 P_3} \cong \ldots$, so the poly. is reg.

Mixed Review

1. $\frac{u}{v} = \frac{7 + y}{7}$ or $\frac{x + 5}{5}$ **3.** $\frac{x}{y} = \frac{5}{7}$ **5.** $\frac{21}{5}$

Lesson 8-3   Try This

1. 50   **2.** $10\sqrt{2}$

Exercise Set 8-3

1. 24   **3.** 13   **5.** $ED = 10$; no, they are not.   **7.** 40   **9.** 12
11. $6\sqrt{3}$ **13.** 9   **15.** $\frac{85}{8}$ or 10.625   **17.** 1. $m\angle CAP = m\angle DBP = 90$ (Line tan. to $\odot$, is $\perp$ to radius at pt. of tan.) 2. $\angle CAP \cong \angle DBP$ (Def. $\cong \angle$s) 3. $\angle CPA \cong \angle DPB$ (Vert. $\angle$s are $\cong$.) 4. $\triangle CAP \sim \triangle DPB$ (AA) 5. $\angle PCA \cong \angle PDB$ (Corr. $\angle$s of $\sim \triangle$s are $\cong$.)   **19.** $8\sqrt{3}$ **21.** 1. $\overline{AB}$ and $\overline{CD}$ are common ext. tan. that intersect at P. (Given) 2. $\overline{PA} \cong \overline{PC}$, $\overline{PB} \cong \overline{PD}$ (Tan. seg. from ext. pt. of $\odot$ are $\cong$.) 3. $PA - PB = PC - PD$ (Sub. Prop.) 4. $AB = CD$ (Seg. Add. Post.) 5. $\overline{AB} \cong \overline{CD}$ (Def. $\cong$ seg.)   **23.** 1. $\odot C$, $\odot D$ with common int. tan. $\overline{AB}$ (Given) 2. $m\angle CAB = m\angle DBA = 90$ (Line tan. to $\odot$ is $\perp$ to radius at pt. of tan.) 3. $\angle CAB \cong \angle DBA$ (Def. $\cong \angle$s) 4. $\overline{AC} \parallel \overline{DB}$ (If lines cut by a trans. and pair of alt. int. $\angle$s are $\cong$, lines are $\parallel$.) 5. $\angle ACD \cong \angle BDC$ (Lines are $\parallel$, alt. int. $\angle$s are $\cong$.) 6. $\overline{AC} \cong \overline{BD}$ (Radii of $\cong \odot$s are $\cong$.) 7. $\triangle CAP \cong \triangle DBP$ (ASA) 8. $\overline{CP} \cong \overline{DP}$, $\overline{AP} \cong \overline{BP}$ (Corr. parts of $\cong \triangle$s) 9. $\overline{AB}$ and $\overline{CD}$ bisect each other. (Def. seg. bis.)   **25.** side length $= 40$, about 14.6 cm shorter
27.

29. 4, 8 total

Algebra Review

1. $5x - 10$ **3.** $-6y + 24$ **5.** $12x - 18y - 48z$
7. $-16x - 48y + 56$

Lesson 8-4   Try This

1. a. 90   **b.** 205   **2. a.** 162   **b.** $m\widehat{ED} = m\widehat{DC} = 42$

Exercise Set 8-4

1. 80   **3.** 258   **5.** 80   **7.** $\widehat{AEC}$ and $\widehat{BAE}$ or $\widehat{AB}$ and $\widehat{CE}$
9. 140   **11.** 90   **13.** 220   **15.** 52   **17.** 34   **19.** 83
21. 1. $\widehat{AB} \cong \widehat{CD}$ (Given) 2. $\overline{BC} \cong \overline{BC}$ (Reflex. Prop.)
3. $m\widehat{AB} + m\widehat{BC} = m\widehat{BC} + m\widehat{CD}$ (Add. Prop.) 4. $m\widehat{AC} = m\widehat{BD}$ (Arc Add. Post.) 5. $\widehat{AC} \cong \widehat{BD}$ (Def. $\cong$ arcs)   **23.** 1. $\odot O$ with tan. $\overleftrightarrow{CA}$ and $\overleftrightarrow{CB}$ (Given) 2. $\overline{OA} \perp \overleftrightarrow{CA}$, $\overline{OB} \perp \overleftrightarrow{CB}$

(Line is tan. to $\odot$, then it is $\perp$ to radius at pt. of tan.)
3. $m\angle OAC = m\angle OBC = 90$ (Def. of $\perp$) 4. $m\angle OAC + m\angle ACB + m\angle OBC + m\angle AOB = 360$ (Sum of measures of $\angle$s of quad. $= 360$.) 5. $m\angle ACB = x$ (Given) 6. $90 + x + 90 + m\angle AOB = 360$ (Subst.) 7. $x + m\angle AOB = 180$ (Sub. Prop.) 8. $m\angle AOB = 180 - x$ (Sub. Prop.) 9. $m\overarc{AB} = 180 - x$ (Def. arc measure) **25.** $(0, 2)$ **27.** $(\sqrt{2}, \sqrt{2})$ **29.** 1. Circumscribed $\triangle XYZ$, $m\angle X = x$, $m\angle Y = y$ (Given) 2. $m\angle AOB = 180 - x$, $m\angle BOC = 180 - y$ (See Ex. 24.) 3. $m\angle AOC = 360 - (180 - x) - (180 - y)$ (Arc Add. Post.) 4. $m\angle AOC = x + y$ (Add. Prop.) 5. $m\overarc{AC} = x + y$ (Def. arc measure) **31.** 10 chords, $\frac{n(n-1)}{2}$, 20 arcs, $n(n-1)$

Mixed Review

1. 20 **3.** 105 **5.** 20

Lesson 8-5 Try This

1. 246 **2.** $z = 8$, $\overline{AB}$ and $\overline{BE}$ are equidist. from O and $\cong$ by Th. 8.10.

Exercise Set 8-5

1. 7 **3.** 148 **5.** 90 **7.** 138 **9.** 6 **11.** 3 **13.** 28 **15.** 13 **17.** 90 **19.** 70 **21.** $2\sqrt{2}$ **23.** 31 **25.** 1. $\overline{AD} \perp \overline{BC}$, $\overline{AD}$ is a dia. (Given) 2. $\overline{AD}$ bisects $\overarc{BAC}$. (If dia. is $\perp$ to a chord, it bisects chord's major arc.) 3. $\overarc{BA} \cong \overarc{AC}$ (Def. bis.) 4. $\overline{BA} \cong \overline{AC}$ ($\cong$ arcs have $\cong$ chords.) 5. $\triangle ABC$ is isos. (Def. isos. $\triangle$) **27.** 24 in. **29.** 1. $\odot P$, dia. $\overline{CD}$ bisects $\overline{AB}$. (Given) 2. $\overline{AE} \cong \overline{BE}$ (Def. bis.) 3. $\overline{PA} \cong \overline{PB}$ (Radii $\cong$ in same $\odot$.) 4. $\overline{PE} \cong \overline{PE}$ (Reflex. Prop.) 5. $\triangle APE \cong \triangle BPE$ (SSS) 6. $\angle AEP \cong \angle BEP$ (Corr. parts of $\cong \triangle$s) 7. $m\angle AEP + m\angle BEP = 180$ (Linear Pair Post.) 8. $m\angle AEP = m\angle BEP = 90$ (Div. Prop.) 9. $\overline{CD} \perp \overline{AB}$ (Def. $\perp$ lines) 10. $m\angle APD = m\angle BPD$ (Corr. parts of $\cong \triangle$s) 11. $\overarc{AD} \cong \overarc{DB}$ (Def. arc measure) 12. $\angle APC \cong \angle BPC$ ($\angle$s supp. to $\cong$ $\angle$s are $\cong$.) 13. $\overarc{AC} \cong \overarc{BC}$ (Def. arc measure) **31.** 1. $\overline{AB} \cong \overline{CD}$ (Given) 2. Draw $\overline{OT} \perp \overline{AB}$, $\overline{OS} \perp \overline{CD}$ (Through a given pt. not on line there is exactly 1 line in plane $\perp$ given line.) 3. $\angle ATO$, $\angle CSO$ are rt. $\angle$s. ($\perp$ lines form rt.$\angle$s.) 4. $\triangle ATO$ and $\triangle CSO$ are rt. $\triangle$s. (Def. rt. $\triangle$) 5. $\overline{OA} \cong \overline{OB} \cong \overline{OC} \cong \overline{OD}$ (Radii of same $\odot$ are $\cong$.) 6. $\overline{OT}$ and $\overline{OS}$ are on dia. (Def. dia.) 7. $\overline{AT} \cong \overline{BT}$, $\overline{CS} \cong \overline{DS}$ (If a dia. is $\perp$ chord, it bisects chord.) 8. $AT = \frac{1}{2}AB$, $CS = \frac{1}{2}CD$ (Def. seg. bis.) 9. $\overline{AT} \cong \overline{CS}$ (Subst.) 10. $\triangle CSO \cong \triangle ATO$ (HL Th.) 11. $\overline{OS} \cong \overline{OT}$ (Corr. parts of $\cong \triangle$s) 12. $OS = OT$ (Def. $\cong$ seg.) **33.** Locate A, B, and C on inner arc. Find $\perp$ bis. of $\overline{AB}$ and $\overline{BC}$. Their intersection is center O of circle. $\overline{OA}$ is radius. **35.** 1. $AB = CD$, $\overline{OX} \perp \overline{AB}$, $\overline{OY} \perp \overline{CD}$ (Given) 2. $OX = $ dist. $\overline{AB}$ to O, $OY = $ dist. $\overline{CD}$ to O (Def. dist. from line to pt.) 3. $OX = OY$ (In same $\odot$, $\cong$ chords are equidist. from center.) 4. $\overline{OX} \cong \overline{OY}$ (Def. $\cong$ seg.) 5. $\angle 1 \cong \angle 2$ (Base $\angle$s of isos. $\triangle$ are $\cong$.) 6. $m\angle 1 = m\angle 2$ (Def. $\cong$ $\angle$s) **37.** $C(-4, 3)$, $D(4, 3)$ **39.** $x^2 + 3^2 = 25$, $x = \pm 4$; $C(-4, 3)$, $D(4, 3)$ **41.** always

Algebra Review

1. 8 **3.** 6 **5.** $-\frac{1}{2}$ **7.** -7

Lesson 8-6 Try This

1. 92, 46 **2.** 59, 112

Exercise Set 8-6

1. 31 **3.** 59 **5.** 110 **7.** 70 **9.** 48 **11.** 27 **13.** 40 **15.** 20 **17.** $m\angle A = 135$, $m\angle B = 90$, $m\angle C = 45$, $m\angle D = 90$ **19.** 44 **21.** 1. inscribed trap. $ABCD$ with $\overline{AB} \parallel \overline{DC}$ (Given) 2. $\overarc{AD} \cong \overarc{BC}$ (See Class Ex. 16.) 3. $\angle ACD \cong \angle BDC$ (Def. arc measure) 4. $\overline{AB} \cong \overline{AB}$ (Reflex. Prop.) 5. $\overarc{DA} + \overarc{AB} = \overarc{CB} + \overarc{BA}$ (Add. Prop.) 6. $\overarc{DB} \cong \overarc{CA}$ (Seg. Add. Post.) 7. $\angle BCD \cong \angle ADC$ (Def. arc measure) 8. $\triangle ACD \cong \triangle BDC$ (ASA) 9. $\overline{BC} \cong \overline{AD}$ (Corr. parts of $\cong \triangle$s) 10. $ABCD$ is isos. (Def. isos. trap.) **23.** 1. $\overline{AB}$, $\overline{CB}$ are dia. $\odot X$ and $\odot Y$ are tan. at B. (Given) 2. $m\angle AEB = m\angle CDB = 90$ (An $\angle$ inscribed in a semicircle is a rt. $\angle$.) 3. $\angle AEB \cong \angle CDB$ (All rt. $\angle$s are $\cong$.) 4. $\angle ABE \cong \angle DBC$ (Vert. $\angle$s are $\cong$.) 5. $\triangle AEB \sim \triangle CDB$ (AA) 6. $\angle 1 \cong \angle 2$ (Corr. $\angle$s of $\sim \triangle$s) **25.** 1. inscribed $\angle BAC$ (Given) 2. $\overline{OA} \cong \overline{OB}$ (Radii in same $\odot$ $\cong$.) 3. $\angle BAC \cong \angle ABO$ (Isos. $\triangle$ Th.) 4. $m\angle BAC \cong m\angle ABO$ (Def. $\cong$ $\angle$s) 5. $m\overarc{BC} = m\angle BOC$ (Def. arc measure) 6. $m\angle BOC = m\angle BAC + m\angle ABO$ (Ext. $\angle$ Th.) 7. $m\overarc{BC} = m\angle BAC + m\angle ABO$ (Subst.) 8. $m\overarc{BC} = 2m\angle BAC$ (Subst.) 9. $m\angle BAC = \frac{1}{2}m\overarc{BC}$ (Div. Prop.) **27.** 1. inscribed $\angle BAC$ (Given) 2. $m\angle BAD = \frac{1}{2}m\overarc{BD}$, $m\angle CAD = \frac{1}{2}m\overarc{CD}$ (Case 1) 3. $m\angle BAC = m\angle BAD - m\angle 2$ (Sub. Prop.) 4. $m\angle BAC = \frac{1}{2}m\overarc{BD} - \frac{1}{2}m\overarc{CD}$ (Subst.) 5. $m\angle BAC = \frac{1}{2}(m\overarc{BD} - m\overarc{CD})$ (Dist. Prop.) 6. $m\angle BAC = \frac{1}{2}m\overarc{BC}$ (Arc Add. Post.) **29.** 1. inscribed quad. $ABCD$ (Given) 2. $m\angle A = \frac{1}{2}m\overarc{BCD}$, $m\angle C = \frac{1}{2}m\overarc{BAD}$ (Th. 8.11) 3. $m\angle A + m\angle C = \frac{1}{2}m\overarc{BCD} + \frac{1}{2}m\overarc{BAD}$ (Add. Prop.) 4. $m\angle A + m\angle C = \frac{1}{2}(m\overarc{BCD} + m\overarc{BAD})$ (Dist. Prop.) 5. $m\angle A + m\angle C = \frac{1}{2}(360) = 180$ (Arc Add. Post.) 6. $\angle A$, $\angle C$ are supp. (Def. supp. $\angle$s) 7. $m\angle B = \frac{1}{2}m\overarc{ADC}$, $m\angle D = \frac{1}{2}m\overarc{ABC}$ (Inscribed $\angle$ measure) 8. $m\angle B + m\angle D = \frac{1}{2}m\overarc{ADC} + \frac{1}{2}m\overarc{ABC}$ (Add. Prop.) 9. $m\angle B + m\angle D = \frac{1}{2}(m\overarc{ADC} + m\angle ABC)$ (Dist. Prop.) 10. $m\angle B + m\angle D = \frac{1}{2}(360) = 180$ (Arc Add. Post.) 11. $\angle B$ and $\angle D$ are supp. (Def. supp. $\angle$s) **31.** 6 **33.** 1. $\odot O \cong \odot P$, chord $\overline{AB} \cong$ chord $\overline{DE}$, adj. $\angle A \cong$ adj. $\angle D$ (Given) 2. $\overarc{AB} \cong \overarc{DE}$ (In $\cong \odot$s, $\cong$ chords have $\cong$ minor arcs.) 3. $m\overarc{AB} = m\overarc{DE}$ (Def. $\cong$ arcs) 4. $m\angle C = \frac{1}{2}m\overarc{AB}$, $m\angle F = \frac{1}{2}m\overarc{DE}$ (Measure of inscribed $\angle \frac{1}{2}$ measure of intercepted arc.) 5. $m\angle C = m\angle F$ (Subst.) 6. $\angle C \cong \angle F$ (Def. $\cong$ $\angle$s) 7. $\triangle ABC \cong \triangle DEF$ (AAS) **35.** $6\frac{2}{3}$ **37.** Always; the diag. bisect each other so quad. is a $\square$. Opp. $\angle$s are inscribed in semicircles and are rt.$\angle$s.

Algebra Review

1. $a^2 b^2$ **3.** $x^2 - y^2$ **5.** $24x^2 y^3$ **7.** $(x^2 + 16)(x - 2)$

Lesson 8-7 Try This

1. 92 **2.** 52 **3.** 100

Exercise Set 8-7

1. 83 **3.** 24 **5.** 62 **7.** 35 **9.** 38 **11.** 60 **13.** 51 **15.** $\frac{1}{2}(x - y)$ **17.** 90 **19.** 135 **21.** 160 **23.** 52 **25.** 90 **27.** 1. secants $\overline{PA}$ and $\overline{PD}$ (Given) 2. Draw aux. line $\overline{BD}$. (2 pt. determine a line.) 3. $m\angle ABD = m\angle BDP +$

$m\angle P$ (Measure of ext. $\angle$ of $\triangle$ = sum of measures of 2 remote int. $\angle$s.) 4. $\frac{1}{2}m\widehat{AD} = \frac{1}{2}m\widehat{BC} + m\angle P$ (Measure of inscribed $\angle$ is $\frac{1}{2}$ measure of its intercepted arc.) 5. $m\angle P = \frac{1}{2}m\widehat{AD} - \frac{1}{2}m\widehat{BC}$ (Sub. Prop.) 6. $m\angle P = \frac{1}{2}(m\widehat{AD} - m\widehat{BC})$ (Dist. Prop.) **29.** 70 **31.** No. For $\overline{AD} \parallel \overline{PB}$, $\angle 1$ must be supp. to $\angle 2$. But $m\angle 1 + m\angle 2 = 187\frac{1}{2}$. **33.** 80 **35.** 48 **37.** 40 **39.** 50 **41.** 2

Mixed Review

1. $x = 58$, $y = 16$ **3.** $x = 43$, $y = 18$ **5.** $\approx 36°$

Lesson 8-8 Try This

1. $\frac{120}{7}$ **2.** $\frac{167}{7}$ **3.** $\frac{32}{3}$

Exercise Set 8-8

1. 3 **3.** 13 **5.** 4 **7.** $\frac{84}{11}$ **9.** $7\frac{4}{9}$ **11.** $\frac{7 + \sqrt{661}}{2}$ **13.** $AQ = 12$, $CQ = 3$ **15.** $u = 10$, $v = 12$ **17.** scalene **19.** $AB = 7$, $CD = 8$ **21.** ≈ 34.8 mi **23.** 40 **25.** $AP \cdot PB = PE^2$, $PD \cdot PC = PE^2$ (Th. 8.17), $AP \cdot PB = PD \cdot PC$ (Trans. Prop.), $DP \cdot PC = 15 \cdot 6 = 90$ **27.** $\frac{CG}{DG} = \frac{5}{7}$, $\frac{EG}{FG} = \frac{5}{7}$ **29.** 1. $\odot$s intersect at A and B. Chords $\overline{AF}$ and $\overline{BE}$ intersect at G. chords $\overline{HI}$ and $\overline{EF}$ (Given) 2. Draw aux. line $\overline{BA}$. (2 pt. determine a line.) 3. $m\angle BEF = m\angle BAF$, $m\angle BCI = m\angle BAF$ ($\angle$s intercepting same arc have same measure.) 4. $m\angle BEF = m\angle BCI$ (Trans. Prop.) 5. $\angle BEF \cong \angle BCI$ (Def. $\cong$ $\angle$s) 6. $\overline{CD} \parallel \overline{EF}$ (Lines cut by trans. and corr. $\angle$s are $\cong$, lines are $\parallel$.) **31. a.** Always true by Th. 8.16. **b.** Sometimes true; true if $PC = PC'$. **c.** Always true; $PC \cdot PD = PC' \cdot PD'$, $\frac{PC}{PC'} = \frac{PD'}{PD}$ $\angle P \cong \angle P$, $\triangle PCC' \sim \triangle PD'D$ by SAS, $\triangle PCC' \sim \triangle PB'B$, $\triangle PD'D \sim \triangle PB'B$, $\triangle PB'B \sim \triangle PAA'$, $\triangle PD'D \sim \triangle PAA'$, $\frac{PD}{PA'} = \frac{PD'}{PA}$, $PD \cdot PA = PA' \cdot PD'$.

Algebra Review

1. $x^2 + 2x + 1$ **3.** $a^2 + 10a + 25$ **5.** $m^2 + m - 6$ **7.** $3s^2 + 5s - 12$

Chapter Review

1. true **2.** false **3.** false **4.** false **5.** 90 **6.** 10 **7.** 6 **8.** 2 **9.** 3 **10.**

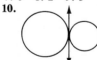

11. 43 **12.** 127 **13.** 140 **14.** 48 **15.** $7\sqrt{2}$ **16.** $\sqrt{17}$ **17.** true **18.** false **19.** false **20.** 83 **21.** 164 **22.** 16 **23.** 97 **24.** 4 **25.** 4

CHAPTER 9

Lesson 9-1 Try This

Exercise Set 9-1

1. **3.**

5. **7.**

9. 4.5 cm / 6 cm / 7.5 cm

4.5 cm / 6 cm / 7.5 cm   right

11.

13. SAS Post.; because it is easier to construct $\cong$ seg. than $\cong$ $\angle$s.

15. **17.**

19.

AC | AC | BC | BC

21. **23.**

25.

27.

29.

25. Have your work checked.   **27.**

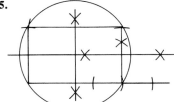

Mixed Review

1. 3   **3.** 2

Exercise Set 9-3

1. Const. 8   **3.** Const. 8 at A and also at B **5.** Const. 9 twice   **7.** Const. 10   **9.**

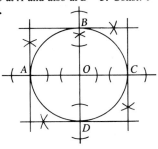

Algebra Review

1. $y < -6$ **3.** $y > \frac{9}{2}$ **5.** $x \geq \frac{4}{5}$

Lesson 9-2 Try This

Use Const. 5 to draw $90°$ $\angle$. Use Const. 4 to draw $45°$ $\angle$. Use Const. 4 to draw $22\frac{1}{2}°$ $\angle$.

Exercise Set 9-2

1. Const. 6   **3.** Const. 6   **5.** Const. 5   **7.** Const. 7
9. Const. 7
11.   **13.**

11.   **13.**

15.

15.

17. Draw a line $\overline{EF} = n$ using Const. 1. Use Const. 5 to construct $\perp$ lines at E and F and cut off line seg. $\overline{EH}$ and $\overline{FG}$ each $= n$ using Const. 1. Connect F and G to make sq. $EFGH$.   **19.**

17.   **19.**

21. Answers may vary. Draw a line seg. ≈ 8 cm long. Bisect it to get 2 seg. each ≈ 4 cm. Bisect one of these to get a seg. ≈ 2 cm. Draw a line and cut off a seg. ≈ 2 cm (AB) using Const. 1. Construct a $\perp$ at A ($\overline{AD}$) using Const. 5 and cut off a seg. on $\overline{AD} \cong \overline{AB} \approx 2$ cm. Draw arcs ≈ 2 cm from B and D to intersect at C making sq. $ABCD$.

21. 1. Construct $\perp$ at P. 2. Find the length from vertex to P. 3. Mark off same length from vertex on other ray. 4. Label pt. *R*. 5. Construct ⊥ at *R*. 6. Mark center of ⊙ at inter-section of both ⊥s. 7. Draw ⊙.

23.

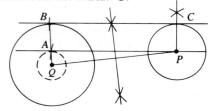

Mixed Review

1. $\frac{2}{x} = \frac{x}{3}$; $x = \sqrt{6}$ **2.** $\frac{5}{y} = \frac{y}{3}$; $y = \sqrt{15}$ **3.** $\frac{5}{z} = \frac{z}{2}$;
$z = \sqrt{10}$ **4.** $\frac{2}{z} = \frac{z}{5}$; $z = \sqrt{10}$ **5.** $\frac{2}{x} = \frac{x}{3}$; $x = \sqrt{6}$
6. $\frac{3}{y} = \frac{y}{5}$; $y = \sqrt{15}$

Exercise Set 9-4

1.

10 cm

3. Const. 12

5. Invert proportion and use Const. 12. **7.** Const. 13
9.

$\frac{\sqrt{2}}{2}$

$\frac{1}{2}$

11. Const. 13 with seg. of length 1 and 8
13. Use Const. 11 to divide the seg. into 3 parts and put 2 of these together to make the longer seg.
15.

17.

19. Const. 13 with seg. of length 2*a* and *b*
21.

23. $x = \frac{10}{3}$

Mixed Review

1. $\frac{x}{y} = \frac{3}{3}$, $\frac{x}{y} = \frac{6}{z}$

Lesson 9-5 Try This

2. 45

Exercise Set 9-5

1. Use Const. 3 to find the midpt. of each side, connect each midpt. to the opp. vertex. **3.** Use Const. 6 to draw the 3 al-titudes. **5.** Use Const. 3 to draw the ⊥ bis. of each side. Their intersection is the center of the circumscribed ⊙.
7. rt. △ on, obtuse △ outside **9.** acute △ inside, rt. △ in-side, obtuse △ inside **11.** 6 **13.** 24 **15.** 8 **17.** $\frac{1}{2}x$
19. Given: isos. △*ABC*, $\overline{AB} \cong \overline{AC}$, median $\overline{AD}$ Prove: $\overline{AD}$ bisects ∠*BAC*. 1. $\overline{AB} \cong \overline{AC}$ (Given) 2. ∠*B* ≅ ∠*C* (Isos. △ Th.) 3. $\overline{AD}$ is median. (Given) 4. $\overline{BD} \cong \overline{CD}$ (Def. median) 5. △*ADB* ≅ *ADC* (SAS) 6. ∠*BAD* ≅ ∠*CAD* (Corr. parts of ≅△s) 7. $\overline{AD}$ bisects ∠*BAC*. (Def. ⊥ bis.) **21.** $\frac{5\sqrt{3}}{6}$
23. 1. *r*, *s*, *t* ⊥ bis. of sides of △*ABC* (Given) 2. $\overline{WA} \cong \overline{WB}$, $\overline{XB} \cong \overline{XC}$, $\overline{YA} \cong \overline{YC}$ (Def. bis.) 3. ∠*OWA*, ∠*OWB*, ∠*OXB*, ∠*OXC*, ∠*OYC*, ∠*OYA* are rt. ∠s and are ≅. (⊥ lines form ≅ rt. ∠s.) 4. $\overline{OW} \cong \overline{OW}$, $\overline{OX} \cong \overline{OX}$, $\overline{OY} \cong \overline{OY}$ (Reflex. Prop.) 5. △*OWA* ≅ △*OWB*, △*OXB* ≅ △*OXC*, △*OYC* ≅ △*OYA* (SAS) 6. $\overline{OA} \cong \overline{OB}$, $\overline{OB} \cong \overline{OC}$, $\overline{OA} \cong \overline{OC}$ (Corr. parts of ≅ △s) 7. $\overline{OA} \cong \overline{OB} \cong \overline{OC}$ (Trans. Prop.)
25. 1. $\overline{DX}$, $\overline{EY}$, and $\overline{FZ}$ are medians. (Given) 2. $\overline{EZ} \cong \overline{ZD}$, $\overline{DY} \cong \overline{YF}$, $\overline{EX} \cong \overline{XE}$ (Def. median) 3. $\frac{EZ}{EZ} = 1$, $\frac{DY}{DY} = 1$, $\frac{FX}{FX} = 1$ (Algebra) 4. $\frac{EZ}{ZD} = 1$, $\frac{DY}{YF} = 1$, $\frac{FX}{XE} = 1$ (Subst.) 5. $\frac{EZ}{ZD} \cdot \frac{DY}{FY} \cdot \frac{FX}{XE} = 1 \cdot 1 \cdot 1 = 1$ (Mult. Prop.) 6. $\overline{DX}$, $\overline{EY}$, and $\overline{FZ}$ are concurrent. (Ceva's Th.) **27.** 1. $\overline{DX}$, $\overline{EY}$, and $\overline{FZ}$ are alt. (Given) 2. $\overline{FZ} \perp \overline{DE}$, $\overline{DX} \perp \overline{EF}$, $\overline{EY} \perp \overline{DF}$ (Def. alt.) 3. ∠*EYF*, ∠*EYD*, ∠*FZD*, ∠*FZE*, ∠*DXE*, and ∠*DXF* are rt. ∠s. (Def. ⊥ lines) 4. △*EYF*, △*DXF*, △*DXE*, △*FZE*, △*FZD*, and △*EYD* are rt. △s. (Def. rt. △) 5. △*EYF* ~ △*DXF*, △*DXE* ~ △*FZE*, △*FZD* ~ △*EYD* (Rt. △~) 6. $\frac{YF}{XF} = \frac{EF}{DF}$, $\frac{XE}{ZE} = \frac{DE}{FE} = \frac{ZD}{YD} = \frac{FD}{ED}$ (Def. ~△s) 7. $\frac{YF}{XF} \cdot \frac{XE}{ZE} \cdot \frac{ZD}{YD} = \frac{EF}{DF} \cdot \frac{DE}{FE} \cdot \frac{FD}{ED}$ (Mult. Prop.) 8. $\frac{YF}{XF} \cdot \frac{XE}{ZE} \cdot \frac{ZD}{YD} = 1$ (Algebra) 9. $\overline{DX}$, $\overline{EY}$, and $\overline{FZ}$ are concurrent. (Ceva's Th.)

Algebra Review

1. $2a\sqrt{2}$ **3.** $-12\sqrt{x}$ **5.** $3\sqrt{3}$ **7.** z^3

Lesson 9-6 Try This

1. plane equidist. between *A* and *B* **2.** sphere with radius 3 in. **3.** cylinder with radius 1 cm

Exercise Set 9-6

1. 50-yd line **3.** ⊙ with dia. given hyp. and endpt. of dia. deleted **5.** concentric ⊙ with radius $\frac{1}{2}$ that of given ⊙
7. 2. lines on either side of track ∥, and 4 mi from, railroad track **9.** bis. of ∠*ABC* **11.** ⊙ with radius $\frac{1}{2}$ the length of diag. with center at intersection of diag. **13.** plane equidist. from and ∥ given planes **15.** plane ⊥ line at given pt.
17. line through *O* and *P* **19.** line seg. ∥ $\overline{BC}$ connecting midpt. of $\overline{AB}$ and $\overline{AC}$ **21.** semicircle **23.** $x = -1.5$
25. $y = x + 3$ **27.** arc from tan. to tan., which includes center of ⊙ when chord is a dia. **29.** major arcs of ⊙

Mixed Review
1. obtuse   3. obtuse   5. obtuse

Lesson 9-7   Try This
2. 2 pt. equidist. between 2 ⊙s and 2 tang.   3. a line ⊥ plane containing 2 ∥ lines and equidist. between 2 pt. and the 2 lines

Exercise Set 9-7
1. The ∠bis. of ∠APB, ∠APD, ∠DPC, and ∠CPB
3.   5.

7.   9.

11.   13.

15.

17. 4, 5, 6, 7, or 8 pts.

19. isos.   21. $x > r$
23. 2 ⊙s 2 cm from plane containing P, where 2 planes ∥ plane containing P intersect sphere
25. 4   27. $y = 1, x = 0$
29.

Algebra Review
1. $y < -6$ 3. $n < -18$

Lesson 9-8   Try This
1. Copy $\overline{BC}$. Construct ⊥ at C. Using radius $\overline{AB}$ and center B, make an arc. Pt. of intersection with ⊥ is A. Draw $\overline{AB}$.
2.

Exercise Set 9-8
1.

3. Construct 2 lines ∥ to, and 2 cm from, the sides of the ∠ in the interior of the ∠. Construct a ⊥$\overline{BC}$ from their pt. of intersection B to one of the sides of the ∠. Draw a circle with center B and radius $\overline{BC}$.
5.   7.

9.   11.

13.   15.

17.   19.

21.

Collapsible compass   Rusty compass

23. c **25.** b

Mixed Review
1. 144° **3.** T **5.** T

Chapter Review
1. Const. 1 **2.** Const. 4 **3.** Const. 2
4.

5. Const. 6 **6.** Const. 5 **7.** Const. 7

8.

9.

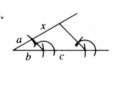

10. Const. 9 **11.** Const. 8 **12.** Const. 10

13.

14.

15.

16. c **17.** b **18.** a **19.** 9 **20.** ⊙ with center T and radius 2 cm **21.** line $\parallel \overline{AB}$ and $\overline{CD}$ such that it is ⊥ bis. of $\overline{AD}$ and $\overline{BC}$ **22.** 4 pt.: pt. of intersection of lines $\parallel$, and 3 cm to, line ℓ and of ⊙R with radius 4 cm **23.** 2 pt.: pt. of intersection of two ⊙s, X and Y, with centers 5 m apart and radii of 3 m

24.

25.

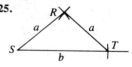

CHAPTER 10

Lesson 10-1 Try This
1. 44 **2.** 177 **3.** Let N be the intersection of $\overline{KJ}$ and $\overline{GH}$. Find area $GNKL = 8.68$ cm² and area $NHIJ = 42.78$ cm². Add both for area $GHIJKL$.

Exercise Set 10-1
1. $A = 117, p = 44$ **3.** $A = 30, p = 16\sqrt{2}$ **5.** $\ell = 18$, $A = 180$ **7.** $w = y - 5, p = 4y - 10$ **9.** 330
11. 96 **13.** 382 **15.** Post. 21 **17.** Post. 23 **19.** 240
21. $144\sqrt{3}$ **23.** always **25.** sometimes **27.** 56 m²
29. 224 **31.** 134.2 yd **33.** 32–4 × 8 ft plywood sheets
35. $BN = \frac{2}{3}BC$ **37.** The pen should be 16 ft by 16 ft sq.
39. 7 cm by 3 cm, 25 cm² **41.** Let $IF = y, EF = x$.
$FG = W - Y, FH = L - x$, with L = length of large rect., W = width. $EFLD$ and $IFHB$ are ~ to $ABCD$, so $\frac{x}{W-Y} = \frac{L}{W}$, and $\frac{Y}{L-x} = \frac{W}{L}$. Then $\frac{x}{W-Y}\cdot\frac{Y}{L-x} = \frac{L}{W}\cdot\frac{W}{L} = 1$, or $XY = (W-Y)(L-X)$, so region X has same area as region Y.

Mixed Review
1. 10 **3.** $\sqrt{69}$ **5.** 8 **7.** 10 **9.** $6\sqrt{6}$

Lesson 10-2 Try This
1. 75 **2.** 36

Exercise Set 10-2
1. 151.2 m² **3.** 6 cm **5.** $y^2 + 5y + 6$ **7.** 7 cm
9. $4x$ **11.** 72 **13.** 153.6 **15.** 16 **17.** 21,168 m²
19. $39\sqrt{3}$ **21.** $120\sqrt{2}$ **23.** $\frac{7}{4}$ **25.** Alt. to $\overline{AB}$ is $\frac{1}{2}$ alt. to $\overline{EF}$. **27.** Area is quadrupled. **29.** area of shaded region: $\frac{75}{2}$, area of unshaded region: $\frac{25}{2}$, ratio of shaded area of area of $\triangle RST$: $\frac{3}{4}$
31.

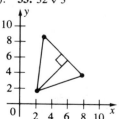

As in Ex. 30, the following pairs of △s have = areas:
(i) $\triangle ABX$ and $\triangle ACX$, (ii) $\triangle ABY$ and $\triangle CBY$, (iii) $\triangle ACZ$ and $\triangle BCZ$, (iv) $\triangle OYA$ and $\triangle OYC$, (v) $\triangle OXB$ and $\triangle OXC$, (vi) $\triangle OZA$ and $\triangle OZB$. By (i) and (v), area ($\triangle AOB$) = area ($\triangle ABX$) − area ($\triangle OXB$) = area ($\triangle ACX$) − area ($\triangle OXC$) = area ($\triangle AOC$). Similarly, area ($\triangle AOB$) = area ($\triangle BOC$). Since area ($\triangle ABC$) = area ($\triangle AOB$) + area ($\triangle AOC$) + area ($\triangle BOC$), conclude area ($\triangle AOB$) = area ($\triangle AOC$) = area ($\triangle BOC$) = $\frac{1}{3}$ area ($\triangle ABC$). By (iv), (v), and (vi), conclude each of the small △s has area = $\frac{1}{6}$ area ($\triangle ABC$). **33.** $32\sqrt{3}$
35. 20

37. $\frac{k^2}{\sqrt{2}}$; about 15 ft **39.** Let $b = AB = CD$ be base length of the $\square$, and let h_1, h_2 be the heights of the shaded $\triangle$s. area of shaded region $= \frac{1}{2}h_1b + \frac{1}{2}h_2b = \frac{1}{2}(h_1 + h_2)b = \frac{1}{2}$ (height of $\square$)$b = \frac{1}{2}$ (area of $\square$) **41. a.** $BE = \sqrt{2}$, $BH = \sqrt{3}$
b. $\frac{\sqrt{3}}{2}$ **c.** $\sqrt{2}$ **d.** $\frac{\sqrt{2}}{4}$ **43.** Area of $\triangle LMN$ is sum of areas of $\triangle LFM$, $\triangle MFN$, and $\triangle NFL$. $\triangle LMN$ is equilat., so $LM = MN = LN$. Thus area $\triangle LMN = \frac{1}{2}a \cdot LM + \frac{1}{2}b \cdot MN + \frac{1}{2}c \cdot LN = \frac{a + b + c}{2} \cdot LM$. This means that no matter where pt. F is inside $\triangle LMN$, $a + b + c = \frac{2}{LM} \cdot$ area $\triangle LMN$.

Mixed Review
1. $5\sqrt{2}$ **3.** 8 **5.** $16\sqrt{2}$

Lesson 10-3 Try This
96.05

Exercise Set 10-3
1. 300 **3.** 59.85 **5.** 40 **7.** median 12, area 84 **9.** 38.4
11. 216 **13.** need AB **15.** 108 **17.** 7200 m² **19. a.** $637.50 **b.** $2437.50 **21.** $60\sqrt{2}$ **23.** 20
25. $2\sqrt{34} \approx 11.7$ cm **27.** 24 **29.** 8 **31.** $95\sqrt{3} + 119$
33. $\triangle GHK$ and $\triangle KIJ$ have = bases and alt., and so have = areas. Area $GHIK$ = area $\triangle GHK$ + area $\triangle HIK$, area $HIJK$ = area $\triangle HIK$ + area $\triangle KIJ$. So, since area $\triangle KIJ$ = area $\triangle GHK$, the areas of the 2 quad. are =.
35. $\frac{RS}{PQ + RS} = \frac{1}{1 + \frac{PQ}{RS}}$ **37.** $4\sqrt{5}$ **39.** 18,744 m²
41. Let P be midpt. of base $\overline{AB}$, let Q be midpt. of base $\overline{DC}$. Heights of $APQD$ and $PBCQ$ are same. Area of $APQD = \frac{1}{2}(AP + DQ)h$ and area of $PBCQ = \frac{1}{2}(PB + QC)h$. Areas are = since $AP = PB$ and $DQ = QC$. **43.** Area $NLMP$ is 5 times area $\triangle LMO$. If $LM = x$, then area $NLMP = \frac{x + 4x}{2}h = \frac{5x}{2}h$ and area $\triangle LMO = \frac{x}{2}h$. **45. a.** Draw a circle and an inscribed quad. Use a ruler to measure its sides. **b.** Sides of quad. are 8, 6, $3\sqrt{10}$, and $\sqrt{10}$ so, area = 39. To check, note that diag. from $(-3, -4)$ to $(3, 4)$ is a dia. of $\odot$, hence by Cor. 8.11c, diag. divides quad. into 2 rt. $\triangle$s, with areas $\frac{1}{2}8 \cdot 6 = 24$, and $\frac{1}{2}(3\sqrt{10})(\sqrt{10}) = 15$. area of quad = 39 **c.** Formula for area depends only on lengths of sides of quad. Side lengths of quad. can be preserved while changing its area. (Consider a sq. with side s and a rhom. with side s.) If formula were valid for all quad., it would assign same area to all quad. with $\cong$ sides, which is wrong. The restriction that quad. has its vertices on a $\odot$ removes all ambiguity. **d.** If quad. is a rect., with a sq. as special case, then $c = a$ and $d = b$, and $s = a + b$. Formula then gives $A = \sqrt{baba} = \sqrt{b^2a^2} = ba$, which is area of rect. If $b = a$, $A = a^2$, area of square with side length a.

Mixed Review
1. 90 **3.** 5 **5.** AD **7.** 150 **9.** 5

Lesson 10-4 Try This
$3\sqrt{3}$ cm, $54\sqrt{3}$ cm²

Exercise Set 10-4
1. $12\sqrt{3}$ **3.** 313.5 **5.** 696 **7.** 60, 30 **9.** 36, 54
11. 10, $30\sqrt{3}$, 5, $75\sqrt{3}$ **13.** $8\sqrt{2}$, 64, 8, 256 **15.** 10, $10\sqrt{2}$, $40\sqrt{2}$, 200 **17.** 18, 18, 108, $486\sqrt{3}$ **19.** true

21. true **23.** true **25.** $54\sqrt{3}$ **27.** $3\sqrt{2}$ cm, $2\sqrt{6}$ cm **29.** $27\sqrt{3}$ **31.** 3, $2\sqrt{3}$ **33.** side ≈ 16, apothem ≈ 11 **35.** $(144\sqrt{2} + 72)$ ft² **37.** $20.78
39. area of $\triangle = \frac{1}{2}\left(\frac{\sqrt{3}}{2}s\right)s = \frac{\sqrt{3}s^2}{4}$, area of hexagon = $\frac{1}{2}\left(\frac{\sqrt{3}}{2} \cdot \frac{s}{2}\right)3s = \frac{3\sqrt{3}s^2}{8}$, ratio of areas $= \frac{\frac{\sqrt{3}}{4}s^2}{\frac{3\sqrt{3}s^2}{8}} = \frac{2}{3}$
41. $1 + \sqrt{2}$ **43.** Area is multiplied by 4. **45.** No; there is no pattern to justify such a chain of reasoning. On a 4×4 grid, an octagon has the most sides possible; on a 5×5, a nonagon.

Algebra Review
1. $2h$ **3.** at least 98

Lesson 10-5 Try This
1:2

Exercise Set 10-5
1. By Th. 10.6, the ratio of perimeters $= \frac{12}{8} = \frac{3}{2}$. By computation, the ratio $= \frac{12 \times 6}{8 \times 6} = \frac{72}{48} = \frac{3}{2}$. **3.** 1:2, 1:4 **5.** a:b, a^2:b^2 **7.** 1:4, 1:16 **9.** 3:4, 3:4 **11.** $\sqrt{p}$:$\sqrt{q}$, $\sqrt{p}$:$\sqrt{q}$ **13.** 1:4 **15.** 169:400 **17.** All ratios are 5:6. **19.** $225 **21. a.** 4:1 **b.** 4:5 **23.** $\frac{80}{9}$, $\frac{100}{9}$ **25.** $112,500 **27.** $585 **29.** 7776 m² **31.** 1:16 **33.** 2:1 **35.** $\sqrt{2}$:1, 2:1 **37.** $12\sqrt{2}$ in. **39.** Lines should intersect the altitude at $4\sqrt{6}$ and $4\sqrt{3}$ units from B.

Mixed Review
1. alt. int. or $\cong$ **3.** 180 **5.** 51 **7.** true

Lesson 10-6 Try This
1. 31.4 cm **2.** 120

Exercise Set 10-6
1. 8, 8π **3.** 4, 8π **5.** 176 cm **7.** 10 cm **9.** 90 **11.** 18 **13.** 63π cm **15.** $36 + 3\pi$ cm **17.** $4\sqrt{3}\pi$ cm **19.** 4 gal **21.** $32 + 4\pi$ ft **23.** $\frac{12\pi}{5}$ **25.** $\frac{8\pi}{9}$, $\frac{16\pi}{9}$ **27. a.** $\ell = \frac{mC}{360}$ **b.** $m = 360\frac{\ell}{C}$ **29.** $\frac{\pi(\text{radius})}{2}$ **31.** $6\pi + 24$ in.

Algebra Review
1. $10x(x + 3)(x - 3)$ **3.** $8(t^2 + 1)(t + 1)(t - 1)$
5. $5(x - 3)(x + 1)$ **7.** $2(3 + x)(3 - x)$
9. $(2x - 3)(x + 4)$

Lesson 10-7 Try This
1. 8 **2.** $\frac{175\pi}{2}$ **3.** $\frac{45\pi}{2}$ **4.** $16\pi - 32$

Exercise Set 10-7
1. 16π **3.** 49π **5.** 5π **7.** $\frac{361\pi}{16}$ **9.** 8π
11. 11 **13.** $2\sqrt{2}$ **15.** $0.4(\sqrt{10})$ **17.** 16π **19.** $\frac{100}{\pi}$
21. 4π cm² **23.** 8π cm² **25.** 13.08 cm² **27.** 21.37 cm²
29. $12\pi - 9\sqrt{3}$ **31.** 36, $\frac{360}{n}$ **33.** 4:3 **35.** 90 **37.** $\frac{9}{2}\pi - 9$ **39.** $\frac{36}{25}$ times as much **41.** $\frac{13\pi}{16}$ sq in. **43.** $\frac{1}{3}$ **45.** Shaded area = area of 2 semicircles on legs $-$ area of semicircle containing $\triangle ABC$ + area of $\triangle ABC = \frac{1}{2}\pi\left(\frac{AB}{2}\right)^2 + \frac{1}{2}\pi\left(\frac{BC}{2}\right)^2 - \frac{1}{2}\pi\left(\frac{AC}{2}\right)^2 + \frac{1}{2}(AB)(BC) = \frac{1}{8}\pi(AC)^2 - \frac{1}{8}\pi(AC)^2 + \frac{1}{2}(AB)(BC) = \frac{1}{2}(AB)(BC)$ = area $\triangle ABC$ where the Pythag. Th. has been used. **47.** $\frac{(\sqrt{3} - \frac{\pi}{2})r^2}{\sqrt{3}r^2} = 1 - \frac{\sqrt{3}\pi}{6}$

49. $63 - 36\sqrt{3} \approx 0.646$ **51.** As long as $\sim$ fig. are used, with 1 straight seg. of appropriate length, it will work for any fig.

Mixed Review

1. false **3.** false **5.** false

Chapter Review

1. 32 **2.** 48 **3.** 20.4 **4.** $p = 30 + 10\sqrt{3}$, $a = 50\sqrt{3}$ **5.** 33.6 **6.** $\frac{21}{2}$ **7.** 120 **8.** $9\sqrt{3}$ **9.** 4 cm **10.** 20 **11.** 6.2 cm **12.** $96\sqrt{3}$ **13.** 100 m² **14.** $150\sqrt{3}$ **15.** true **16.** false **17.** true **18.** 147 **19.** 12π **20.** $6\sqrt{2}\pi$ **21.** $\frac{35\pi}{9}$ **22.** 8π **23.** $16\sqrt{3}$

CHAPTER 11

Lesson 11-1 Try This

1. $LA = 540$, $SA = 600$ **2.** $LA = 360$, $SA = 360 + 75\sqrt{3}$

Exercise Set 11-1

1. 112 **3.** 216 **5.** $LA = 96\frac{1}{3}$, $SA = 126\frac{1}{3}$ **7.** $LA = 108$, $SA = 188$ **9.** $LA = 136x^2$, $SA = 276x^2$ **11.** $LA = 60 + 30\sqrt{2}$, $SA = 85 + 30\sqrt{2}$ **13.** never **15.** sometimes **17.** sometimes **19.** 1136 **21.** 814 cm² **23.** $LA = 100$ cm², $SA = 150$ cm² **25.** 5.2 cm **27.** 4 cm **29.** $2\sqrt{3}$ cm **31.** Since $\overline{AD} \parallel \overline{GF}$ and $\overline{DG} \parallel \overline{AF}$, ADGF is a $\square$. By Th. 5.3, $\overline{DF}$ bisects $\overline{AG}$. Midpt. of $\overline{AG}$ is O, so O is also midpt. of $\overline{DF}$. **33.** $24\sqrt{2}$ ft **35.** 27 cm² **37.** Faces must be identical.

39. a. 42 sq units

b.   **c.**

Mixed Review

1. 9.58 **3.** 18° **5.** 9.14

Lesson 11-2 Try This

1. $LA = 60$, $SA = 96$ **2.** $LA = 80\sqrt{3}$ cm², $SA = 130\sqrt{3}$ cm²

Exercise Set 11-2

1. $LA = 80$, $SA = 105$ **3.** $LA = 72$, $SA = 72 + \frac{27\sqrt{3}}{2}$ **5.** $l = 25$, $LA = 700$, $SA = 896$ **7.** $LA = 260x^2$, $SA = 360x^2$ **9.** $60 + \frac{25\sqrt{3}}{4}$ sq in. **11.** 9 cm **13.** 11 cm **15.** $64\sqrt{3}$ cm² **17.** $108\sqrt{3}$ **19.** 16 cm² **21.** $\sqrt{3}x^2$ **23.** $LA = \frac{3s^2}{2}$, $SA = (\frac{3}{2} + \frac{\sqrt{3}}{2})s^2$

Algebra Review

1. $y = 4x - 3$ **3.** $y = 8$ **5.** $y = -\frac{3}{10}x - \frac{1}{5}$

Lesson 11-3 Try This

1. 18 ft³ **2.** $28\sqrt{3}$ cm³

Exercise Set 11-3

1. 280 cm³ **3.** 343 cm³ **5.** 90 **7.** $36\sqrt{3}$ cm³ **9.** 15 cu ft **11.** Volume is mult. by 8. **13.** 270.2 cu yd **15.** 102 cm³ **17.** 3450 m³ **19.** 4 in., 4 in., $4\sqrt{2}$ in. **21.** $\sqrt[3]{18}$ cm **23.** $7779.85 **25.** $\frac{\sqrt{3}}{4}s^3$ cu units

Mixed Review

1. 176 **3.** 24

Lesson 11-4 Try This

1. 216.75 cm³ **2.** $\frac{50\sqrt{3}}{3}$ cm³

Exercise Set 11-4

1. 8 **3.** 384 **5.** $4583\frac{1}{3}$ **7.** $3456\sqrt{3}$ **9.** 108 cm³
11. 140 cm³ **13.** 12 **15.** 1280 cm³ **17.** $\frac{400\sqrt{3}}{9}$ cm
19. Vol. of taller pyramid is twice vol. of shorter pyramid.
21. 112 cm³ **23.** Heights of pyramids are in the ratio
$\frac{9}{10}$. **25.** $\frac{9}{2}$ cm³ **27.** $\frac{256\sqrt{2}}{3}$ cm³ **29.** Vol. of double pyramids
is $\frac{2}{3}$ vol. of hexagonal prism.

Algebra Review

1. $x = 1, y = 3$ **3.** $p = 1, q = -1$

Lesson 11-5 Try This

1. $LA = 64\pi$ cm², $SA = 96\pi$ cm² **2.** 5 cm

Exercise Set 11-5

1. $LA = 48\pi$, $SA = 80\pi$, $V = 96\pi$ **3.** $LA = 18\pi$ cm²,
$SA = 26\pi$ cm², $V = 18\pi$ cm³ **5.** $LA = 140\pi$, $SA = 340\pi$,
$V = 700\pi$ **7.** $r = 4$, $LA = 32\pi$, $SA = 64\pi$
9. 62.963π cu yd **11.** 130π cm² **13.** 324π cu ft
15. $SA = 920\pi$ sq in., $V = 3600\pi$ cu in. **17.** about 50
min **19.** $(1000 - 160\pi)$ cu in. **21.** No; if r is doubled, V
is quadrupled. **23.** $\frac{4}{7}$ **25.** $SA = (232 + 6\pi)$ cm²,
$V = (160 - 4\pi)$ cm³ **27.** If r and h are each doubled, then
SA is quadrupled. Vol. is multiplied by 8.

Algebra Review

1. $m = 7$

3. $m = -\frac{5}{6}$

5. $m = 2$

7. $m = -\frac{5}{4}$

Lesson 11-6 Try This

1. 15 cm **2.** Vol. is doubled.

Exercise Set 11-6

1. $LA = 60\pi$, $SA = 96\pi$, $V = 96\pi$ **3.** $l = 10$,
$LA = 80\pi$, $SA = 144\pi$, $V = 128\pi$ **5.** $h = 5\sqrt{3}$, $l = 10$,
$SA = 75\pi$, $V = \frac{125\sqrt{3}}{3}\pi$ **7.** $\pi(\sqrt{2} + 1)36$ **9.** vol. of
cone $= 3\pi h$ cu in., vol. of cylinder $= 4\pi h$ cu in., vol of
cylindrical cup is $>$. **11.** 65π cm² **13.** Vol. is doubled.
15. 40π cm³ **17.** 448π cm³ **19.** $\frac{100\pi}{27}$ min
21. $V = \frac{970}{3}\sqrt{2}\pi$, $SA = (110\sqrt{2} + 146)\pi$

23. $\frac{\pi 6572}{3}$ cu units **25.** If a cone has $\frac{1}{3}$ vol. of a cylinder,
then it has same base diameter and height as the cylinder.
Converse is false. A counter example is a cylinder with base
diameter $2r$ and height h and a cone with base diameter r and
height $4h$. vol. of cylinder $= \pi r^2 h$, vol. of
cone $= \frac{1}{3}\pi(\frac{r}{2})^2 4h = \frac{1}{3}\pi r^2 h$

Mixed Review

1. 10 cm **3.** 9

Lesson 11-7 Try This

1. $SA = 100\pi$ cm², $V = \frac{500\pi}{3}$ cm³ **2.** 324π cm²

Exercise Set 11-7

1. $SA = 196\pi$, $V = \frac{1372\pi}{3}$ **3.** $SA = 16\pi$, $V = \frac{32\pi}{3}$
5. $SA = 256\pi$, $V = \frac{2048\pi}{3}$ **7.** $r = 6$, $SA = 144\pi$
9. $\frac{9\pi}{2}$ cm³ **11.** 2 cm **13.** $\frac{352\sqrt{11}}{3}\pi$ cm³ **15.** 12π
17. $\frac{256\pi}{3}$ cm³ **19.** $1600\pi + \frac{4000}{3}\pi$ **21.** $\frac{5}{6}$ **23.** none of
these **25.** SA of sphere is equal to $4\pi r^2$. Lateral surface
area of cylinder is equal to $2\pi r h = 2\pi r \cdot 2r = 4\pi r^2$. Both
SA of sphere and lateral area of cylinder are $4\pi r^2$. **27.** $\frac{3}{2}$
29. It will remain as 1 solid. Holes do not join to form a cut.

Algebra Review

1. $3 < x < 7$

3. $x < -\frac{10}{3}$ or $x > 5$

5. $1 < x < 3$

7. $0 < x \le 6$

Lesson 11-8 Try This

1. 160π **2.** 297 cm²

Exercise Set 11-8

1. 8 to 5 **3.** 512 to 125 **5.** 125 cm³ **7.** 9 to 4
9. 225 cm² **11.** 64 to 1 **13.** 64 to 1 if walls are imagined
as having small width or 16 to 1 if width does not change
(i.e., walls treated as 2-dimensional) **15.** 3h **17.** Larger
tank has $(1.5)^3$ or 3.375 times vol. of smaller tank. Larger
tank has lower price per unit capacity, making it the better
buy. **19.** Particles 0.5 cm in dia. are more effective. Larger
particle has 4 times SA of one of smaller particles, but there
are 8 times as many of smaller particles per unit vol. Smaller
size has twice total SA of larger size. **21.** Weight increases
proportionally to vol. (or cube of factor). Strength increases
as sq. of factor.

Mixed Review

1. 6 3. 125 5. 90 7. 15 9. $4\sqrt{3}$

Chapter Review

1. 12 vert., 18 edges, 8 faces 2. $LA = 36$ cm², $SA = 72$ cm² 3. $LA = 180$, $SA = 180 + 108\sqrt{3}$ 4. $LA = 45$, $SA = 45 + \frac{25\sqrt{3}}{4}$ 5. 6 cm 6. 210 7. 270 8. 96 sq in.
9. $160\sqrt{3}$ cu in. 10. 384 11. 9 cm 12. 400π
13. $LA = 58.8\pi$, $SA = 156.8\pi$, $V = 205.8\pi$ 14. 75π
15. $LA = 255\pi$, $SA = 480\pi$, $V = 600\pi$ 16. 21π
17. $SA = 196\pi$ 18. $V = \frac{32\pi}{3}$ 19. 36π 20. 3:4
21. 9:16 22. 3:4 23. 27:64 24. 135

Lesson 12-1 Try This

1. a. (0, 2) b. (−2, 0) 2. (1, 2) 3. (−1, −1)

Exercise Set 12-1

1. (2, 1) 3. E 5. I 7. II 9. II 11. $(\frac{5}{2}, \frac{1}{2})$
13. $(\frac{1}{2}, -2)$ 15. (2, 6) 17. (2, 1) 19. $(\frac{1}{2}, -\frac{1}{2})$
21. $(\frac{a}{2}, \frac{b}{2})$
23.

25. (−2, 8) 27. (4, −3) 29. (90, 45)
31. parallelogram

33. $(2, -\frac{5}{2})$, which is the midpoint of $\overline{MP}$ 35. $(-1, -\frac{3}{2})$
37. $(\frac{x_1 + 2x_2}{3}, \frac{y_1 + 2y_2}{3})$, $(\frac{2x_1 + x_2}{3}, \frac{2y_1 + y_2}{3})$

Algebra Review

1. $9x^4y^2z^8$ 3. n^{30} 5. $\frac{3}{31}$

Lesson 12-2 Try This

$-\frac{1}{7}, -\frac{16}{7}, 2$

Exercise Set 12-2

1. −1; neg. 3. $-\frac{1}{4}$; neg. 5. 0; zero 7. $-\frac{5}{4}$; neg.
9. undef. 11. $-\frac{1}{2}$ 13. $\frac{3}{10}$ 15. $\frac{7}{2}$ 17. 1 19. 1
21. slope of $\overline{RS} = -1$, of $\overline{ST} = 4$, of $\overline{UT} = -1$, and of $\overline{RU} = 4$; $RSTU$ is a parallelogram. 23. 0

25. −3 27. 1 29. $6\frac{2}{3}$ ft 31. $\frac{1}{3}$ 33. (0, 24)
35. $x = 2$ 37. $x = 11$ 39. Median from A has slope 2, from B slope $-\frac{1}{4}$, from C slope −16. 41. 1. Coord. of D, H, and L are (4, 0), (10, 0), (18, 0). (Given) 2. Let coord. of G, K, and P be (4, y_1), (10, y_2), (18, y_3). (Every pt. on a given line ∥ y-axis has same x-coord.) 3. $\overline{AY}$ has a slope of $\frac{1}{2}$. (Given) 4. G, K, and P are on $\overline{AY}$ and have coord. G (4, 2), K (10, 5), P (18, 9). (Slope formula with A (0, 0) and coord. in 2) 5. $DEFG$, $HIJK$, and $LMNP$ are squares. (Given)

6. $\overline{GF} \parallel \overline{DE}$, $\overline{JK} \parallel \overline{HI}$, $\overline{NP} \parallel \overline{LM}$ (Def. square) 7. $GD = GF$, $KH = KJ$, $PL = PN$ (Def. square) 8. $GD = 2$, $KH = 5$, $PL = 9$ (Diff. in y-coord.) 9. Coord. of E, I, and M are (6, 0), (15, 0), (27, 0). (Def. square) 10. Coord. of F, J, and N are (6, 2), (15, 5), (27, 9). (Same as 10 and every pt. on a given line $\parallel$ y-axis has same x-coord.) 11. Slope of $\overline{FJ}$ is $\frac{1}{3}$, slope of $\overline{JN}$ is $\frac{1}{3}$. (Def. slope) 12. F, J, and N are collinear. (Fact: Three pt. A, B, and C are collinear if the slope of $\overline{AB}$ = slope of $\overline{BC}$.)

Mixed Review
1. 65

Lesson 12-3 Try This
1. $-\frac{5}{2}$ 2. slope of $\overline{RS} = -3$, slope of $\overline{TS} = \frac{1}{3}$
Since $(-\frac{1}{3})(3) = -1$, $\overline{RS} \perp \overline{TS}$, so $\angle S$ is a rt. $\angle$.

Exercise Set 12-3
1. $\overline{AB} \parallel \overline{CD}$ 3. neither   5. slope from (3, 9) to (7, 5) is -1; slope from (7, 5) to (3, -3) is 2; slope from (3, -3) to (-1, 1) is -1; slope from (-1, 1) to (3, 9) is 2; opp. sides are $\parallel$ so the fig. is a $\square$.   7. Slope from (-3, -3) to (-1, 2) is $\frac{5}{2}$; slope from (-1, -2) to (1, -6) is -2; slope from (1, -6) to (-1, -7) is $\frac{1}{2}$; slope from (-1, -7) to (-3, -3) is -2; consecutive sides are $\perp$, so fig. is rect.   9. $y = -3$
11. $-\frac{4}{3}$ 13. slope of $\overline{RS} = 1$, of $\overline{ST} = -1$, of $\overline{RT} = -5$
15. (0, 3) or (0, -3)   17. $y = \frac{1}{3}$ 19. $b = -8$
21. $(\frac{12}{5}, 0)$ 23. (1, -1)   25. Slope of $\overline{AB} = 0$; of $\overline{BC} = \frac{e-b}{d}$; of $\overline{CD} = 0$; of $\overline{DA} = \frac{e-b}{d}$; opp. sides are $\parallel$, so $ABCD$ is a $\square$.   27. $-\frac{c}{d}$

Algebra Review
1. -4 3. 24   5. 41   7. -8 9. 18

Lesson 12-4 Try This
1. $y = -2x - 3$ 2. $\frac{5}{2}$, -5 3. $y + 5 = \frac{4}{3}(x - 2)$

4. $y = -\frac{6}{5}x + 4$
$y - 4 = -\frac{6}{5}x$ or
$y + 2 = -\frac{6}{5}(x - 5)$

Exercise Set 12-4
1. $y = 2x + 3$ 3. $y = -\frac{3}{4}x - \frac{1}{2}$ 5. $y = -2$
7. 1, 4   9. $-\frac{3}{2}$, 3   11. 0, -1

13. $-\frac{1}{2}$, 2   15. $-\frac{3}{2}$, $\frac{5}{2}$

17. $y = \frac{2}{3}x$ 19. $y = -3$ 21. $y - 4 = -\frac{5}{2}x$
23. $y = -2x$ 25. $y = \frac{3}{4}x$ or $y - 3 = \frac{3}{4}(x - 4)$ 27. $y = x$ or $y + 3 = x + 3$ 29. $y - 3 = x - 1$ or $y + 2 = x + 4$ 31. $y - 4 = 2(x - 2)$ or $y + 4 = 2(x + 2)$
33. $y = 0$ 35. a. 0.1 b. $5.50   37. $\frac{1}{2}$ 39. $-\frac{3}{2}$
41. $y - 2 = \frac{1}{2}(x - 4)$ 43. $y = -3x$ 45. (4, 1)   47. $\frac{25}{2}$
49. $\overline{AC}$: $y + 4 = -2(x - 6)$ or $y - 2 = -2(x - 3)$; $\overline{BD}$: $y - 2 = 2(x - 6)$ or $y + 4 = 2(x - 3)$ 51. $x = \frac{13}{4}$
53. $y + 7 = -\frac{1}{2}(x - 8)$ and $y + 7 = -3(x - 8)$
55. (5.4, 1.8)   57. Answers may vary.

Algebra Review
1. $4\sqrt{3}$ 3. $9\sqrt{3}$

Lesson 12-5 Try This
1. $\sqrt{145}$ 2. isos.

Exercise Set 12-5
1. 10   3. $7\sqrt{2}$ 5. $2\sqrt{13}$ 7. $\sqrt{74}$ 9. isos.   11. isos.
13. yes   15. slope, less multiplication with smaller numbers   17. no   19.

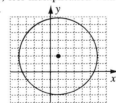

21. $3\sqrt{5}$ 23. 4   25. $\sqrt{130}$ 27. 20   29. $70\sqrt{17}$ ft
31. 65 yd   33. (2, 4)   35. $\frac{11}{5}\sqrt{5}$ 37. Answers may vary. Greatest % of error is $\approx 5.7\%$.

Mixed Review
1. 80   3. 70

Lesson 12-6 Try This
1. $(x - 4)^2 + (y + 1)^2 = 16$ 2. (-3, 7), $5\sqrt{2}$

Exercise Set 12-6
1. $x^2 + y^2 = 25$ 3. $(x + 5)^2 + y^2 = 16$ 5. $(x + 3)^2 + (y + 4)^2 = 16$ 7. $(x + 1)^2 + (y - 3)^2 = 12$

9. $(x - a)^2 + (y - b)^2 = c^2$ 11. $(0, 0), 2\sqrt{5}$
13. $(-6, 0), 3\sqrt{5}$ 15. $(a, b), 6$
17.

19. $(x + 4)^2 + y^2 = 16$ 21. $(x - 4)^2 + (y + 2)^2 = 65$
23. $(x + 1)^2 + y^2 = 9$ 25. $(x + 1)^2 + (y - 6)^2 = 16$
27. $y + 3 = -\frac{5}{9}(x - 5)$ or $y - 2 = -\frac{5}{9}(x + 4)$,
$5x + 9y + 2 = 0$ 29. $(x + 4)^2 + (y - 3)^2 = 16$
31. neither 33. secant 35. secant 37. neither
39. $(x - 4)^2 + y^2 = 16$, $(x + 4)^2 + y^2 = 16$,
$x^2 + (y - 4)^2 = 16$, $x^2 + (y + 4)^2 = 16$ 41. 11π
43. $(x - 1)^2 + (y - 7)^2 = 10$ 45. $x^2 + y^2 + z^2 = 48$
47. Ellipses; effect is to stretch or contract axis corresponding to term with coefficient. Given $ax^2 + by^2 = 16$, if $a = 1$ and $b = 1$, the eq. is of a circle, but as a gets larger, the circle is compressed along x-axis. Similarly, as b gets larger, fig. is compressed along y-axis. Resulting fig. are ellipses.

Mixed Review

1. 7900 sq yd

Lesson 12-7 Try This

1. $(\frac{a}{2}, \frac{a\sqrt{3}}{2})$ 2.

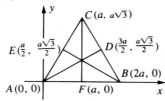

Exercise Set 12-7

1. $C(p + m, n)$
3.

5.

7.

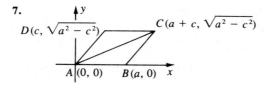

9. $C(0, \sqrt{3}a)$ 11. $E(\frac{a + b}{2}, c)$
13. $GF = \sqrt{(b + e - (a + b))^2 + (c + f - c)^2} = \sqrt{(e - a)^2 + f^2}$ $HE = \sqrt{(e - a)^2 + (f - 0)^2} = \sqrt{(e - a)^2 + f^2}$ so $GE = HE$;
$HG = \sqrt{(b + e - e)^2 + (c + f - f)^2} = \sqrt{b^2 + c^2}$
$EF = \sqrt{(a + b - a)^2 + (c - 0)^2} = \sqrt{b^2 + c^2}$ so
$HG = EF$. $EFGH$ is $\square$, because opp. sides of $EFGH$ are $\cong$.
15. $B(\frac{a}{2}, \frac{\sqrt{3}a}{2})$; $D(-a, 0)$; $E(-\frac{a}{2}, -\frac{\sqrt{3}a}{2})$; slope of $\overline{AB} = \frac{\frac{a\sqrt{3}}{2}}{\frac{a}{2} - a} = -\sqrt{3}$, slope of $\overline{DE} = \frac{-\frac{\sqrt{3}a}{2}}{-\frac{a}{2} + a} = -\sqrt{3}$

Algebra Review

1. $\frac{3}{4a^4}$ 3. $-3ab$

Exercise Set 12-8

1. 1. $\triangle RST$ with coord. $R(0, 0)$, $S(a, 0)$, $T(b, c)$ (Given)
2. M is midpt. of $\overline{RT}$; N is midpt. of $\overline{ST}$. (Given) 3. M has coord. $(\frac{b}{2}, \frac{c}{2})$; N has coord. $(\frac{a + b}{2}, \frac{c}{2})$. (Midpt. Th.)
4. $MN = \sqrt{(\frac{a + b}{2} - \frac{b}{2})^2 + (\frac{c}{2} - \frac{c}{2})^2} = \frac{a}{2}$, $RS = \sqrt{(a - 0)^2 + (0 - 0)^2} = a$ (Dist. Form.) 5. $\frac{1}{2}RS = \frac{a}{2}$ (Mult. Prop.) 6. $MN = \frac{1}{2}RS$ (Trans. Prop.) 3. 1. isos. trap. $ABCD$ (Given) 2. $AC = \sqrt{(a - b)^2 + c^2}$; $BD = \sqrt{(b - a)^2 + c^2}$ (Dist. Form.) 3. $(a - b)^2 = (b - a)^2$ (Prop. of Real No.)
4. $\sqrt{(a - b)^2 + c^2} = \sqrt{(b - a)^2 + c^2}$ (Subst.)
5. $AC = BD$ (Trans. Prop.)
5.

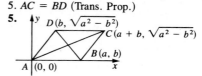

1. rhom. $ABCD$ with coord. $A(0, 0)$, $B(a, 0)$, $C(a + b, \sqrt{a^2 - b^2})$, $D(b, \sqrt{a^2 - b^2})$ (Given) 2. slope of $\overline{AC} = \frac{\sqrt{a^2 - b^2}}{a + b}$; slope of $\overline{BD} = -\frac{\sqrt{a^2 - b^2}}{a - b}$ (Def. slope) 3. (slope of $\overline{AC}$)(slope of $\overline{BD}$) = $\frac{\sqrt{a^2 - b^2} \cdot -\sqrt{a^2 - b^2}}{(a + b)(a - b)}$ (Subst.)
4. $\frac{\sqrt{a^2 - b^2} \cdot -\sqrt{a^2 - b^2}}{(a + b)(a - b)} = \frac{-(a^2 - b^2)}{a^2 - b^2}$ (Prop. of Real No.)
5. (slope of $\overline{AC}$)(slope of $\overline{BD}$) = -1 (Trans. Prop.)
6. $\overline{AC} \perp \overline{BD}$ (2 nonvert. lines are $\perp$ if product of their slopes is -1.)
7.

1. trap. $ABCD$ with coord. $A(0, 0)$, $B(a, 0)$, $C(d, c)$ $D(b, c)$ and $\overline{EF}$ median (Given) 2. E is midpt. of $\overline{AD}$. F is midpt. of $\overline{BC}$. (Def. median) 3. E has coord. $(\frac{b}{2}, \frac{c}{2})$ (Midpt. Th.) 4. $AB = \sqrt{a^2 + 0^2} = a$; $DC = \sqrt{(d - b)^2 + (c - c)^2} = d - b$; $EF = \sqrt{(\frac{a + d}{2} - \frac{b}{2})^2 + (\frac{c}{2} - \frac{c}{2})^2} = \frac{a + d - b}{2}$ (Dist. Form.)
5. $\frac{a + d - b}{2} = \frac{1}{2}[a + (d - b)]$ (Prop. of Real No.)
6. $EF = \frac{1}{2}(AB + DC)$ (Subst.)

9.

1. $\square ABCD$ with coordinates $A(0, 0)$, $B(a, b)$, $C(a + c, b + d)$, $D(c, d)$; $\overline{AC} \cong \overline{BD}$ (Given) 2. $AC = \sqrt{(a + c)^2 + (b + d)^2}$; $BD = \sqrt{(a - c)^2 + (b - d)^2}$ (Dist. Form.) 3. $\sqrt{(a + c)^2 + (b + d)^2} = \sqrt{(a - c)^2 + (b - d)^2}$ (Subst.) 4. $(a + c)^2 + (b + d)^2 = (a - c)^2 + (b - d)^2$ (Prop. of Real No.) 5. $(a + c)^2 - (a - c)^2 = (b - d)^2 - (b + d)^2$ (Add. Prop.) 6. $(2a)(2c) = 2b(-2d)$ (Prop. of Real No.) 7. $-1 = \frac{b}{a} \cdot \frac{d}{c}$ (Mult. Prop) 8. slope of $\overline{AB} = \frac{b}{a}$, slope of $\overline{AD} = \frac{d}{c}$ (Def. slope) 9. (slope of $\overline{AB}$)(slope of $\overline{AD}$) $= -1$ (Subst.) 10. $\overline{AB} \perp \overline{AD}$ (2 nonvert. lines are $\perp$ if product of slopes is -1.) 11. $ABCD$ is a rect. (If 2 sides of a $\square$ are $\perp$, the $\square$ is a rect.)

11.

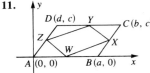

1. Quad. $ABCD$ with midpt. W, X, Y, and Z, and coord. $A(0, 0)$, $B(a, 0)$, $C(b, c)$, $D(d, c)$ (Given) 2. W has coord. $(\frac{a}{2}, 0)$; X has coord. $(\frac{a + b}{2}, \frac{c}{2})$; Y has coord. $(\frac{b + d}{2}, \frac{c + e}{2})$; Z has coord. $(\frac{d}{2}, \frac{e}{2})$ (Midpt. Th.) 3. slope of $\overline{WX} = \frac{\frac{c + e}{2} - \frac{c}{2}}{\frac{a + b}{2} - \frac{a}{2}} = \frac{c}{b}$, slope of $\overline{XY} = \frac{\frac{c + e}{2} - \frac{c}{2}}{\frac{b + d}{2} - \frac{a + b}{2}} = \frac{e}{d - a}$; slope of $\overline{YZ} = \frac{\frac{c + e}{2} - \frac{e}{2}}{\frac{b + d}{2} - \frac{d}{2}} = \frac{c}{b}$; slope of $\overline{ZW} = \frac{\frac{e}{2}}{\frac{d}{2} - \frac{a}{2}} = \frac{e}{d - a}$ (Def. slope) 4. $\overline{WX} \parallel \overline{YZ}$, $\overline{XY} \parallel \overline{ZW}$ (2 lines with same slope are $\parallel$). 5. $WXYZ$ is a $\square$. (Def. $\square$) **13.** If O is at the origin, $\overline{OD}$ on x-axis, $\overline{OC}$ on y-axis, and $\overline{OE}$ on z-axis; coord. of vert. of cube of side length a are: $O(0, 0, 0)$, $D(a, 0, 0)$, $C(0, a, 0)$, $E(0, 0, a)$, $A(a, a, 0)$, $B(0, a, a)$.
$OA = \sqrt{(a - 0)^2 + (a - 0)^2 + (0 - 0)^2} = a\sqrt{2}$;
$OB = \sqrt{(0 - 0)^2 + (a - 0)^2 + (0 - a)^2} = a\sqrt{2}$;
$AB = \sqrt{(a - 0)^2 + (a - a)^2 + (0 - a)^2} = a\sqrt{2}$ so $\triangle OAB$ is equilat. **15.** Answers may vary. Coordinate method uses simple algebra but has several variables. Method using $\triangle$s formed by diag. does not need many steps.

Mixed Review

1. 96 cm², 64 cm²

Chapter Review

1.–4.

5. $(-4, 3)$ **6.** $(-10, 13)$ **7.** $-\frac{3}{5}$ **8.** 0 **9.** -3 **10.** 7 **11.** $\perp$ **12.** $\parallel$ **13.** $-\frac{1}{4}$
14. $-\frac{3}{2}$, 5 **15.** 0, -2

16. $-\frac{3}{4}$, 9

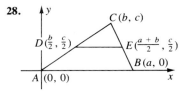

17. $y = \frac{1}{6}x + \frac{9}{2}$ **18.** $y = 3x - 9$ **19.** 4 **20.** $5\sqrt{2}$
21. isos., $AB = BC$ **22.** $C(-2, 4)$, $r = 4$ **23.** $C(1, 0)$, $r = 2\sqrt{5}$ **24.** $(x + 3)^2 + (y - 2)^2 = 81$ **25.** $(x - 4)^2 + (y - 7)^2 = 20$ **26.** A$(0, k)$, B$(h, 0)$
27.

28.

1. $\triangle ABC$ with coord. $A(0, 0)$, $B(a, 0)$, $C(b, c)$ (Given) 2. D is midpt. of $\overline{AC}$, E is midpt. of $\overline{CB}$. (Given) 3. D has coord. $(\frac{b}{2}, \frac{c}{2})$; E has coord. $(\frac{a + b}{2}, \frac{c}{2})$. (Midpt. Th.) 4. slope of $\overline{DE} = 0$, slope of $\overline{AB} = 0$ (Def. slope) 5. $\overline{DE} \parallel \overline{AB}$ (2 nonvert. lines are $\parallel$ if slopes are =.)

29.

1. $ABCD$ is isos. trap. with coord. $A(0, 0)$, $B(a, 0)$, $C(a - b, c)$, $D(b, c)$ and diag. $\overline{AC}$ and $\overline{BD}$. (Given)
2. $AC = \sqrt{(a - b)^2 + c^2}$, $BD = \sqrt{(b - a)^2 + c^2}$ (Dist. Form.) 3. $(a - b)^2 = (b - a)^2$ (Prop. of Real No.)
4. $\sqrt{(a - b)^2 + c^2} = \sqrt{(b - a)^2 + c^2}$ (Subst.)
5. $AC = BD$ (Subst. Prop.) 6. $\overline{AC} \cong \overline{BD}$ (Def. $\cong$ seg.)

Lesson 13-1 Try This

1. a. U' **b.** V **c.** $\overline{T'W}$ **2.** in x-axis $(1, 1)$; in y-axis $(-1, -1)$ **3. a.** **b.**

Exercise Set 13-1

1. H **3.** $\overline{CB}$ **5.** $\overline{XW}$ **7.** $\overline{TS}$ **9.** $(-1, 2)$ **11.** $(-2, -1)$
13. $(-3, 1), (-4, 2)$
15.   **17.**   **19.** no lines of symmetry

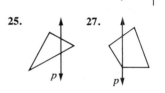

21.   **23.**

25.   **27.**

29. Answers may vary. **31.** $(2, 4)$ **33.** $(1, 1)$ **35.** $(-1, -1)$ **37. 1.** L' is reflection image of L in line p. (Given) **2.** line p is $\perp$ bis. of $\overline{LL'}$. (Def. reflection image) **3.** M is on line p. (Given) **4.** $\overline{LM} \cong \overline{L'M}$ (Pt. on $\perp$ bis. of seg. are equidist. from endpt.) **39.** $y = -x$ **41.** Reflect 1 city about line formed by river. Draw line connecting reflection image to other city. Bridge should be built where line intersects river. **43.** Reflect I about south shoreline and reflect that reflection image about north shoreline. Draw line connecting A to new reflection image. Intersection of line with north shoreline is point B. Draw line connecting B to original reflection image of I. Intersection of line with south shoreline is C. **45.** If $A'B'C'D'$ is a rhombus, then $ABCD$ is a $\square$. Converse is true. Original implication is not.

Mixed Review

1. true **3.** false **5.** false

Lesson 13-2 Try This

1. $\overline{FD}$ and $\triangle FDE$ **2. a.** $(2, 9)$ **b.** $(9, -2)$ **3.** E or G

Exercise Set 13-2

1. point Y **3.** point H **5.** $\overline{HI}$ **7.** $\triangle XYZ$ **9.** $(5, 3)$
11. $(7, 0)$ **13.** $(8, y + 2)$ **15.** $(-3, -1)$ **17.** $(-1, 2)$
19. A, D; A, F; D, F; B, G; C, E **21.** $(-1, 8)$ **23.** $(1, 1)$
25. line with slope $\frac{3}{2}$ **27.** If A' is on $\overleftrightarrow{AB}$; then, since $\overrightarrow{BB}'$ is in same direction as $\overrightarrow{AA}'$, B is also on $\overleftrightarrow{AB}$. If A' is not on $\overleftrightarrow{AB}$; then, since $\overrightarrow{BB}'$ is in same direction and of same length as $\overrightarrow{AA}'$, $\overline{AA}' \parallel \overline{BB}'$ and $\overline{AA}' \cong \overline{BB}'$, and by Theorem 5.5 $ABB'A'$ is a $\square$. **29.** 6 **31.** $P(p_1, p_2)$, $Q(q_1, q_2)$,

$P'(p_1 + a, p_2 + b)$, $Q'(q_1 + a, q_2 + b)$ $PQ = \sqrt{(p_1 - q_1)^2 + (p_2 - q_2)^2} = P'Q'$ **33.** As original key is slid along guide, it is "translated" to copy. **35.** Slope of translation image of line is same as slope of the line.

Mixed Review

1. 252 **3.** $\frac{32}{3}\pi$ **5.** 30π

Lesson 13-3 Try This

1. a. B **b.** G **c.** E **2. a.** $(3, 2)$ **b.** $(3, -1)$

Exercise Set 13-3

1. A' **3.** $\overline{A'B'}$ **5.** B **7.** B **9.** E **11.** $\overline{CD}$ **13.** $\overline{DH}$
15. G **17.** rectangle $GHCD$ **19.** Square $LIJK$
21. $(-1, 2)$ **23.** $(-2, -1)$ **25.** $(-3, -4)$ **27.** true
29. true **31.** yes **33.** yes **35.** yes **37.** no **39.** no
41. approx. $120°$ **43.** $(-y, x)$ **45. a.** $(-4, -3)$ **b.** $(2, -3)$
c. $(-x, -y)$ **47.** $90°$ clockwise about O ($45°$ counterclockwise about F) **49.** The rotation images of line ℓ intersect to form a sq. centered about O. $\overline{OA} \cong \overline{OA'} \cong \overline{OA''} \cong \overline{OA'''}$, and $\overline{AA''}$ and $\overline{A'A'''}$ are bis. of each other, intersecting at O.
51. The diag. of a $\square$ are bis. of each other, so $\overline{AO} \cong \overline{OC}$ and $\overline{BO} \cong \overline{OD}$. Since $m\angle AOC = m\angle BOD = 180$; it follows that C is the half-turn image of A about O, D is the half-turn image of B about O, A is the half-turn image of C about O, B is the half-turn image of D about O.
53. Find $\perp$ bis. of $\overline{XX'}$ and $\overline{YY'}$. These lines either intersect or are identical. If they intersect, center of rotation is at their intersection pt. If they are identical, then draw $\overleftrightarrow{XY}$ and $\overleftrightarrow{X'Y'}$. These lines will intersect at center of rotation which will be on the common $\perp$ bis. of $\overline{XX'}$ and $\overline{YY'}$. **55.** A, B, C, D, or F **57.** From Th. 10.9, arc length equals $\frac{2\pi rm}{360}$. For both arcs, $m(\angle$ of rotation) is the same, but r is different, so arc lengths are different. **59.** Figure has n sides, and 1 side may be rotated to any of the $n - 1$ other sides in exactly 1 way.

Algebra Review

1. $\parallel$ **3.** $\parallel$ **5.** $\parallel$

Lesson 13-4 Try This

1. J, K **2.** DH **3.** $H, \overline{FG}$

Exercise Set 13-4

1. $135°$ clockwise, O **3.** $90°$ clockwise **5.** D, A **7.** H, A **9.** I **11.** K **13.** L **15.** C **17.** C **19.** M **21.** D
23. C **25.** B **27.** $(6, 1)$ **29.** $(7, -1)$ **31.** $(3, 4)$
33. $(2, 9)$ **35.**

37. O lies on q and q is the $\perp$ bis. of $\overline{PP'}$. (Def. reflection in q) So $\overline{OP} \cong \overline{OP'}$ because pt. on $\perp$ bis. of seg. are equidist. from endpt. of seg. **39.** $\overline{AA'} \perp p$, $\overline{A'A''} \perp q$ (Def. reflection) Two distinct lines $\perp$ to $\parallel$ lines are $\parallel$. $\overline{A'A''}$ is not $\parallel \overline{AA'}$ because they share point A'. Therefore, the 2 lines must not be distinct, that is A' is on $\overleftrightarrow{AA''}$, so $\overline{AA''} \perp p$. **41.** Many $180°$ rotations about O' are possible. Only some of these rotate 1 cube to other. **43.** infinitely many

Algebra Review

1. $x < -1$ **3.** $n < 3$ **5.** $x \geq 0$

Lesson 13-5   Try This

1. a. $C'D' = 6$ **b.** $A'B' = 8$ **2. a.** $IJ = 5$ **b.** $KM = 13$
3. *HGFEO* is reflection image of *ABCDO*. Since a line reflection is an isometry, the pentagons are $\cong$.

Exercise Set 13-5

1. 7   **3.** 4   **5.** 7   **7.** Distance between points is preserved under isometries.   **9.** *C*   **11.** 8   **13.** 8   **15.** 3   **17.** Answers may vary. Diag. are $\cong$ and bisect each other by reflection.
19. reflection in *p*   **21.** *FABCX* is reflection of *AFEDX* in line *q*. Since line reflection is an isometry, *AFEDX* and *FABCX* are $\cong$.   **23.** $\overline{AB} \cong \overline{A'B'}$, $\overline{AC} \cong \overline{A'C'}$, and $\overline{BC} \cong \overline{B'C'}$ because isometries preserve distances. So $\triangle ABC \cong \triangle A'B'C'$ by SSS.   **25.** below ℓ **27.** on ℓ
29. Fig. in quad. I is reflection image of fig. in quad. II in line *q*. Fig. in quad. II is the reflection image of fig. in quad. III in line *p*. Therefore, fig. in quad. I is image of fig. in quad. III under reflection in line *p* followed by reflection in line *q*. Since composition of reflections is an isometry, fig. in quad. I is $\cong$ to fig. in quad. III.   **31.** Corr. parts of the fig. are $\cong$ since they are mapped to each other by an isometry. Corr. perimeters, circumferences, etc. are $=$.

Mixed Review

1. 72   **3.** 28   **5.** 8

Lesson 13-6   Try This

1.a. 1.5   **b.** 0.5   **2.a.** (1, 3)   **b.** (−0.5, 0.75)

Exercise Set 13-6

7. *EFGH*   **9.** *L*   **11.** *IJKL*   **13.** $\overleftrightarrow{(-4.2)}$ **15.** (2, 1.4)
17. (1.5, 2.5)   **19.** If *O* is on $\overleftrightarrow{BC}$, then since $kOB = OB'$ and $kOC = OC'$ (i) if *O* is between *B* and *C*, $B'C' = B'O + OC' = kBO + kCO = k(BO + CO) = kBC$; (ii) if *B* is between *O* and *C*, then *B'* is between *O* and *C'* and $B'C' = OC' - OB' = kOC - kOB = k(OC - OB) = kBC$; (iii) if *C* is between *O* and *B*, then *C'* is between *O* and *B'* and $B'C' = OB' - OC' = kOB - kOC = k(OB - OC) = kBC$. If *O* is not on *BC*, then since $OB' = kOB$, $OC' = kOC$, $\frac{OB'}{OB} = \frac{OC'}{OC}$. And since $\angle BOC \cong \angle B'OC'$, $\triangle BCO$ is $\sim$ to $\triangle B'C'O$ by the SAS $\sim$ Th., so $\frac{B'C'}{BC} = \frac{OB'}{OB} = k$, i.e. $B'C' = kBC$, so $BC = \frac{1}{k}B'C'$.   **21.** 64
23. Dilation image of (1, 5) is (2, 10). Dilation image of (3, 2) is (6, 4). slope of $\ell = \frac{5-2}{1-3} = \frac{-3}{2}$, slope of $\ell' = \frac{10-4}{2-6} = \frac{-3}{2}$, $\ell \parallel \ell'$ **25.** *A'* is (−2, 4), *B'* is (4, 8), *C'* is (10, 4). Area of $\triangle ABC = \frac{1}{2}(6 \times 2) = 6$, area of $\triangle A'B'C' = \frac{1}{2}(12 \times 4) = 24$, area of $\triangle A'B'C' = 4 \times$ area of $\triangle ABC$ **27.** $A'(-1, 1\frac{2}{3})$, $B'(1, 2)$, $C'\left(1\frac{2}{3}, \frac{-2}{3}\right)$ **29.** *SA*: 4 to 1, vol.: 8 to 1

Mixed Review

1. center (0, 0), radius 8   **3.** center (−4, 5), radius $\sqrt{10}$
5. $x^2 + y^2 = 36$ **7.** $(x - 1)^2 + y^2 = 5$

Lesson 13-7   Try This

1. a. 16   **b.** 4   **c.** *AF*   **2.** Translation *AT* followed by dilation with center *T* and scale factor 2 maps *ABCDEF* to *TUVWXY*.

Exercise Set 13-7

1. 8   **3.** 6   **5.** $18\frac{1}{3}$ **7.** $13\frac{1}{3}$ **9.** 120   **11.** $3\frac{1}{2}$ **13.** *AC*
15. Rotate *ABFGE* − 90° about *B*. Follow this with dilation of scale factor 2 and center *B*.   **17.** 24   **19.** 8   **21.** By Th. 13.10, dilations take $\triangle$s to $\sim$ $\triangle$s. So $\triangle ACD \sim \triangle A'C'D'$, hence $\angle CDA \cong \angle C'D'A'$. Since $\overline{CD}$ is an alt. of $\triangle ABC$, $\angle CDA$ is a rt. $\angle$, so $\angle C'D'A'$ is a rt. $\angle$, so $\overline{C'D'}$ is an alt. of $\triangle A'B'C'$.   **23.** 486   **25.** 9 to 1, 27 to 1   **27. a.** Not $\sim$; no isometry composed with a dilation will map one to the other.   **b.** Not $\sim$; no isometry composed with a dilation will map one to the other.   **29. a.** line of reflection   **b.** center of rotation   **c.** none   **d.** center of dilation   **e.** common center

Algebra Review

1. −10, 3   **3.** ±7   **5.** $\frac{1}{2}$, 3

Chapter Review

1. *E*   **2.** *F*   **3.** $\overline{CD}$ **4.** $\overline{EF}$ **5.** 2   **6.** (8, 7)   **7.** (4, 0)
8. $(x + 4, y + 1)$ **9.** *E*   **10.** *K*   **11.** $\overline{IJ}$ **12.** *EFGH*
13. *M*   **14.** $\overline{QL}$ **15.** no   **16.** yes   **17.** true   **18.** false
19. false   **20.** 6   **21.** 12   **22.** yes   **23.** (50, −25)
24. *X*   **25.** *I*   **26.** 3   **27.** 90° clockwise rotation about *B* followed by dilation with scale factor 2 and center *B* maps *AEBF* to *GCBD*.

ACKNOWLEDGEMENTS

page	credit	page	credit
2	Craig Aurness/Woodfin Camp & Associates	300 B	Pete Saloutos/The Stock Market
3	Wayland Lee*/Addison-Wesley Publishing Company	300 T	Bill Gallery/Stock, Boston
5	Gary Withey/Bruce Coleman Inc.	303	Rob Nelson/Stock, Boston
6 B	Janice Sheldon*	319	Brownie Harris/The Stock Market
6 T	Wayland Lee*/Addison-Wesley Publishing Company	323	Brian Parker/Tom Stack & Associates
11	Janice Sheldon*	325	Bob Straus/Woodfin Camp & Associates
13	Wayland Lee*/Addison-Wesley Publishing Company	333	Roy Morsch/The Stock Market
17	Wayland Lee*/Addison-Wesley Publishing Company	339	Billy Stickland/Allsport USA
18	Wayland Lee*/Addison-Wesley Publishing Company	340	Jose Azel/Contact Press/Woodfin Camp & Associates
19	Greg Vaughn/Tom Stack & Associates	350	Greg Davis/Black Star
25	Peter Tenzer/Wheeler Pictures	351	Wayland Lee*/Addison-Wesley Publishing Company
26	Dan McCoy/Rainbow	360	Wayland Lee*/Addison-Wesley Publishing Company
29	Eric Carle/Stock, Boston	361	Wayland Lee*/Addison-Wesley Publishing Company
30	Janice Sheldon*	390	Michael C. Radigan /The Stock Market
35	Janice Sheldon*	391	G. Contorakes/The Stock Market
51 BR	Wayland Lee*/Addison-Wesley Publishing Company	400	Janice Sheldon*
51 TL	Patrick Vielcanet/Allsport-USA/Vandystadt	415	Claudia Parks/The Stock Market
56	Gary Milburn/Tom Stack & Associates	418 B, C	Wayland Lee*/Addison-Wesley Publishing Company
58	Janice Sheldon*	418 T	Alan Schwartz/Allsport USA
62	The Bettman Archive, Inc.	420	Greg Vaughn/Tom Stack & Associates
63	David Madison/Bruce Coleman Inc.	423	Wayland Lee*/Addison-Wesley Publishing Company
78	Greg Vaughn/Tom Stack & Associates	428 B	Budd Symes/Allsport USA
82	Janice Sheldon*	428 T	Janice Sheldon*
92	Ann Duncan/Tom Stack & Associates	433 B	James Sugar/Black Star
96	Scott Blackman/Tom Stack & Associates	433 T	Janice Sheldon*
104	Craig Aurness/Woodfin Camp & Associates	436	David Madison/Bruce Coleman Inc.
105	Cameron Davidson/Bruce Coleman Inc.	437	William Waterfall/The Stock Market
109	Stephen Frisch*	442	The Bettmann Archive, Inc.
110	Wayland Lee*/Addison-Wesley Publishing Company	447	David Austen/Stock, Boston
122	Rick Stewart/Allsport-USA	451	John Flannery/Bruce Coleman Inc.
135	Wayland Lee*/Addison-Wesley Publishing Company	460 BL	Keith Gunnar/Bruce Coleman Inc.
139 B, C, T	Wayland Lee*/Addison-Wesley Publishing Company	460 BR	Wendy Neefus/Earth Scenes
141	Bob Winsett/Tom Stack & Associates	460 T	Joan Saxe/Bruce Coleman Inc.
145	Wayland Lee*/Addison-Wesley Publishing Company	467	Doug Wechsler/Earth Scenes
148	Harald Sund	473	George Gardner/Stock, Boston
149	Leif Skoogfors/Woodfin Camp & Associates	484	Frank E. Pedrick/Light Images
159	Janice Sheldon*	490	E. R. Degginger/Earth Scenes
164	Paul Solomon/Wheeler Pictures	491	C. Benjamin/Tom Stack & Associates
166	R. S. Uzzell/Woodfin Camp & Associates	498	Janice Sheldon*
183	Declan Haun/Black Star	499	Christopher Morris/Black Star
200	Chuck O'Rear/Woodfin Camp & Associates	506	Wayland Lee*/Addison-Wesley Publishing Company
210	Wayland Lee*/Addison-Wesley Publishing Company	510	Dan McCoy/Rainbow
222	Peter L. Cole/Bruce Coleman Inc.	517	Stephen Frisch*
227	Cary Wolinsky/Stock, Boston	522	Charles Feil/Stock, Boston
229 C	Collection Haags Gemeentemuseum - The Hague M. C. Escher, Drawing (frogs)	525	Robert Essel/The Stock Market
229 L	Collection Haag Gemeentemuseum - The Hague M. C. Escher, 1946 (horsemen)	525	Wayland Lee*/Addison-Wesley Publishing Company
		532	Chris Sorensen/The Stock Market
229 R	Timothy Egan/Woodfin Camp & Associates	537	The Bettmann Archive, Inc.
235	Janice Sheldon*	538 C	Tom Stack/Tom Stack & Associates
239	Janice Sheldon*	538 L	Donald Dietz/Stock, Boston
254	Janice Sheldon*	538 R	Janice Sheldon*
260	Wayland Lee*/Addison-Wesley Publishing Company	540	Matt Bradley/Tom Stack & Associates
261 B	Kevin Schafer/Tom Stack & Associates	557	Wayland Lee*/Addison-Wesley Publishing Company
261 R	Art Resource/Scala	575	Harald Sund
261 T	Judy Canty/Stock, Boston	583	Dick Durrance/Woodfin Camp & Associates
262	Janice Sheldon*	586	Janice Sheldon*
265	Janice Sheldon*	588 L	Thomas Braise/The Stock Market
273	Wayland Lee*/Addison-Wesley Publishing Company	588 R	Charles Gupton/Stock, Boston
274	Wayland Lee*/Addison-Wesley Publishing Company	589	Dan McCoy/Rainbow
285	Janice Sheldon*	605	George Dritsas/Light Images
294	Hal Clasun/Tom Stack & Associates	Cover:	Chris Collins/The Stock Market

*Photographs provided expressly for the publisher

Index

186   224   245

36 ×2.5